PREFACE

The design of modern engineering structures and components relies heavily on implementing stress and vibration analysis methods. These analytical, computational and experimental analysis methods have been constantly changing to cater for the increasing demands for better accuracy and efficiency.

This book contains the edited proceedings of the Fourth International Conference on Modern Practice in Stress and Vibration Analysis, held at the University of Nottingham from 5 to 7 September 2000. This is the fourth in a series of successful international conferences organised by the Stress and Vibration Group of the UK Institute of Physics. Previous conferences in this series have been held in Liverpool (1989), Sheffield (1993) and Dublin (1997), and have been successful in attracting contributions from engineers and scientists from academia and industry. The purpose of this international conference is to encourage the exchange of information and knowledge in the fields of stress and vibration analysis, and bring together researchers from various disciplines in industrial organisations and academic institutions.

I am grateful to the members of the Scientific Committee for their contribution to the success of this conference and for reviewing the papers presented in the proceedings. I would also like to thank the members of the Organising Committee; Dr. J.M. Barton, Prof. M.P. Cartmell, Dr. M.D. Gilchrist and Dr. A.J. McMillan, for their help in organising this conference.

A.A.Becker
June 2000

The Fourth International Conference on Modern Practice in Stress and Vibration Analysis, 5-7 September 2000 , Nottingham, UK

Co-sponsored by
- *The Institute of Physics (Stress and Vibration Group)*
- *The Institution of Mechanical Engineers* (Materials and Mechanics of Solids Group)
- *British Society for Strain Measurement*

ORGANISING COMMITTEE

Dr. A.A. Becker (Chair), University of Nottingham
Dr. J.M. Barton, University of Southampton
Prof. M.P. Cartmell, University of Glasgow
Dr. M.D. Gilchrist, University College Dublin
Dr. A.J. McMillan, Rolls-Royce Aerospace

SCIENTIFIC COMMITTEE

Dr. J.M. Barton, University of Southampton, UK
Prof. G. Beer, Technical University Graz, AUSTRIA
Prof. J. F. Bratt, Norwegian Univ. of Sci & Tech, NORWAY
Dr. R. Brooks, University of Nottingham, UK
Dr. E.P. Busso, Imperial College, UK
Prof. M.P. Cartmell, University of Glasgow, UK
Dr. J.D. Clark, Bespak Ltd, UK
Dr. A. El-Zafrany, Cranfield Institute of Technology, UK
Dr. M. Friswell, University of Wales Swansea, UK
Prof. L Fryba, Inst.Theo. & App. Mech., CZECH REPUBLIC
Dr. U. Gallietti, Politecico de Bari, ITALY
Dr. M.D. Gilchrist, University College Dublin, IRELAND
Prof. J.L. Guyader, INSA Lyon, FRANCE
Dr. J. K. Hepworth, Powergen, UK
Dr. M. Imregun, Imperial College, UK
Prof. A.W. Lees, University of Wales Swansea, UK
Dr. D. Manley, UK
Dr. A.J. McMillan, Rolls-Royce Aerospace, UK
Dr D. Nowell, University of Oxford, UK
Prof. R. Ohayon, Conservat. Natl Arts & Metiers, FRANCE
Prof. F. Paris, Universidad de Seville, SPAIN
Dr. E. Remzi, CEDAR Ltd, UK
Prof. J.S. Sirkis, University of Maryland, USA
Prof P. Stanley, University of Manchester, UK
Prof. V. Tvergaard, Tech. Univ. of Denmark, DENMARK
Dr. K. Warden, University of Sheffield, UK
Dr. E.J. Williams, University of Nottingham, UK

Proceedings of the The Fourth International Conference on Modern Practice in Stress and Vibration Analysis Nottingham, UK, 5-7 September 2000

Modern Practice in Stress and Vibration Analysis

Edited by

A.A. Becker

University of Nottingham, UK

EMAS Limited, West Midlands

ENGINEERING MATERIALS ADVISORY SERVICES LTD.
19, Ashleigh Road, Solihull, West Midlands, B91 1AE, UK.
Tel : 44(0)121 705 1228. Fax: 44(0)121 705 4890.
E-mail: sales@emas.co.uk   Web Site: http://www.emas.co.uk

ISBN 1 901537 21 8 (2000)

PRINTED BY THE CHAMELEON PRESS LTD. LONDON, UNITED KINGDOM

TABLE OF CONTENTS

v

1. ANALYTICAL AND NUMERICAL TECHNIQUES

CLIFFORD ALGEBRA, CL₂, IN THE ANALYSIS OF PASSIVE PERIODIC STRUCTURES

S.D. Garvey*, M.I. Friswell† and U. Prells†

This paper considers structures which are periodic in one direction. When forces may only be applied at the ends of such structures, it is well known that their vibration at any given frequency can be described compactly in terms of a small number of characteristic wave shapes and associated propagation constants. This paper extends some work recently published on the use of Clifford Algebra, Cl_2, in connection with generally-damped structural dynamic systems to the determination of the characteristic vibrations of periodic structures at a given temporal frequency. These characteristics are shown to be embodied in a system of self-adjoint second-order difference equations. The central point of the paper is that a particular canonical form is proposed for such systems of equations and when this is written using Cl_2, the symmetry in the system is evident. A related form of the equations provides a highly efficient and stable solution route for the characteristic vectors and the squares of the roots.

INTRODUCTION

Figure 1 depicts a periodic structure comprising individual "bays" indexed by the letter i. The periodic structure is "assembled" from unconnected bays each of which has M displacement degrees held in a vector q_i. We are not concerned how many bays there may be in the structure. The relationship between the vector of forces, Q_i, acting on unconnected "bay" i, and its vector of displacments, q_i, is encapsulated (for any given temporal frequency, ω (rad/s)) by the (M x M) dynamic stiffness matrix $D(\omega)$. Assume, initially that $D(\omega)$ is strictly real (i.e. the structure is undamped). Since this paper is concerned only with the computation of characteristic behaviour at a single frequency, we will choose to omit the explicit dependence of D on (ω) for brevity and we therefore write the following equation describing a single unconnected "bay".

$$Q_i = D q_i \tag{1}$$

The connection of adjacent bays to form the connected periodic structure can be accomplished through an equation of constraint in the case of rigid connections. It is possible to consider the bays to be connected via some interface having finite

* School of Mechanical, Materials, Manufacturing Engineering and Management
  University of Nottingham, University Park, NG7 2RD
†Dept. of Mech. Engineering, University of Wales Swansea, Singleton Park, Swansea SA2 8PP

flexibility and since the computational penalty for this extension is nil and the marginal algebra is small, we embrace this extension. Define a vector, t_i, of N interface displacement coordinates between bays i and $i+1$. This vector is related to vectors q_i, and q_{i+1} as follows :

$$t_i = A q_i + B q_{i+1} = \begin{bmatrix} A & B \end{bmatrix} \begin{bmatrix} q_i \\ q_{i+1} \end{bmatrix} \qquad (2)$$

Each (i^{th}) system of interface connections is itself characterised by the same static stiffness matrix, K_t, which relates the vector T_i of interface forces (acting on the interface) to the vector of interface displacements as follows :

$$T_i = K_t \, t_i \qquad (3)$$

In the case of rigid connections, K_t approaches infinity. In the absence of external forces on the bays, the force vectors Q_i and Q_{i+1} must be comprised as follows :

$$Q_i = -\begin{bmatrix} B^T & A^T \end{bmatrix} \begin{bmatrix} T_{i-1} \\ T_i \end{bmatrix} , \qquad Q_{i+1} = -\begin{bmatrix} B^T & A^T \end{bmatrix} \begin{bmatrix} T_i \\ T_{i+1} \end{bmatrix} \qquad (4)$$

Combining (1) - (4) leads to this system of second order difference equations

$$\left(AD^{-1}B^T \right) T_{i-1} + \left(AD^{-1}A^T + BD^{-1}B^T + K_t^{-1} \right) T_i + \left(BD^{-1}A^T \right) T_{i+1} = 0 \qquad (5)$$

We are specifically interested in the case where both D and K_t are symmetrical. With suitable obvious definitions for matrices E and F, equation (5) becomes

$$E^T T_{i-1} + FT_i + ET_{i+1} = 0 \qquad (6)$$

Equation (6) has characteristic solutions in the form

$$T_i = u_k \, \alpha_k^i \qquad (7)$$

Each scalar, α_k, determines the spatial frequency of a wave propagating along the structure. These scalars are related to *propagation constants*, γ_k, in the literature (for example, Mead [1],[2] and Ouyang et al [3]), by $\gamma_k = j \ln(\alpha_k)$. Propagation constants are sometimes real, sometimes purely imaginary and sometimes generally complex.

Because $F = F^T$, equation (6) is self-adjoint and for every *right* solution $\{u_k, \alpha_k\}$

$$E^T u_k \alpha_k^{-1} + F u_k + E u_k \alpha_k = 0 \qquad (9)$$

there is a corresponding *left* solution pair $\{u_k, \alpha_k^{-1}\}$ satisfying

$$\alpha_k u_k^T E^T + u_k^T F + \alpha_k^{-1} u_k^T E = 0 \qquad (10)$$

This follows logically from (9) by simple transposition. Thus, we see that the characteristic roots occur in reciprocal pairs, $\{\alpha_k, \alpha_k^{-1}\}$. The *right* characteristic vector associated with α_k^{-1} will be denoted v_k. Thus in summary, we expect to find a set of *right* characteristic solutions to (6) comprising $(\{u_k, \alpha_k\}, \{v_k, \alpha_k^{-1}\})$ for $1 \leq k \leq N$ and a set of *left* characteristic solutions to (6) comprising $(\{u_k, \alpha_k^{-1}\}, \{v_k, \alpha_k\})$ for $1 \leq k \leq N$.

The above approach to computing characteristic wave vectors is not standard practice in the periodic structures literature – although a near-equivalent appears in [1]. It is more usual to establish a "bay transfer matrix" relating forces and deflections at one side of the bay to those at the other and to solve the eigenvalue problem for a symplectic ($2N \times 2N$) matrix derived from that. Symplectic matrices have special properties which can be useful in developing efficient solution methods for the eigenvalue problem ([2], Williams *et al* [4]). In the present paper, we expose a method for regarding periodic structures which may offer both computational advantage and simplicity and insight into the dynamics of this fascinating class of systems.

Determining the characteristic roots (and hence the propagation constants) of the system at any given frequency is by no means the only aspect of periodic structures of interest. Computing the natural frequencies and associated mode-shapes of a complete periodic structure is also of importance (Garvey & Penny [5],[6], Williams et al [7]). So too is the examination of energy flow through periodic structures and the effects of slight disruptions of periodicity. In all of the above, the characteristic properties of the periodic structure at a fixed frequency play or can play an extremely important role.

COMPUTING THE CHARACTERISTIC SOLUTIONS

Figure 1 was deliberately drawn such that the individual bays are not symmetrical. If they are symmetrical, it is found that $\mathbf{E} = \mathbf{E}^T$ and the determination of characteristic solutions is a relatively simple matter of solving the eigenvalue problem

$$\mathbf{E}\mathbf{v}(\alpha^{-1} + \alpha) + \mathbf{F}\mathbf{v} = 0 \tag{11}$$

In the general case, a more involved procedure is needed. The standard method for computing characteristic solutions for systems of difference or differential equations is to "reduce" them to an equivalent first-order system of equations and solve for the characteristic solutions using standard eigenvalue-eigenvector procedures. In the present case, equation (9) would normally be written equivalently as :

$$\begin{bmatrix} 0 & I \\ E^T & F \end{bmatrix} \begin{bmatrix} w_k \\ u_k \end{bmatrix} = \begin{bmatrix} I & 0 \\ 0 & -E \end{bmatrix} \begin{bmatrix} w_k \\ u_k \end{bmatrix} \alpha_j \tag{12}$$

The first block row of (12) ensures that for every solution-set found $\{\alpha_k, u_k, w_k\}$, the following relationship exists

$$\mathbf{w}_j = \mathbf{u}_j \alpha_j^{-1} \qquad (13)$$

The second block row of (12) then represents the original equation (9). Equation (12) is not the only equivalent form. In this paper, we prefer to use this form :

$$\begin{bmatrix} \mathbf{E}^T & \mathbf{0} \\ \mathbf{E}^T & \mathbf{F} \end{bmatrix} \begin{bmatrix} \mathbf{w}_k \\ \mathbf{u}_k \end{bmatrix} = - \begin{bmatrix} \mathbf{F} & \mathbf{E} \\ \mathbf{0} & \mathbf{E} \end{bmatrix} \begin{bmatrix} \mathbf{w}_k \\ \mathbf{u}_k \end{bmatrix} \alpha_j \qquad (14)$$

It is clear that if (13) is satisfied, both block rows of (14) represent the original equation. The enforcement of (13) is less direct in the case of (14) than it is with (12).

Notwithstanding this, it is not difficult to derive (13) for any given solution set $\{\alpha_k, \mathbf{u}_k, \mathbf{w}_k\}$, of (14) provided that $\mathbf{F}$ is non-singular. The exceptional cases where $\mathbf{F}$ is singular do merit some consideration but we defer that for brevity here.

The solution sets, $\{\alpha_k, \mathbf{u}_k, \mathbf{w}_k\}$, can be grouped into two distinct groups and the $(N \times N)$ matrices $\mathbf{U}_1, \mathbf{W}_1, \mathbf{S}_1, \mathbf{U}_2, \mathbf{W}_2, \mathbf{S}_2$ can be formed by obvious means obeying

$$\begin{bmatrix} \mathbf{E}^T & \mathbf{0} \\ \mathbf{E}^T & \mathbf{F} \end{bmatrix} \begin{bmatrix} \mathbf{W}_1 & \mathbf{W}_2 \\ \mathbf{U}_1 & \mathbf{U}_2 \end{bmatrix} = \begin{bmatrix} \mathbf{F} & \mathbf{E} \\ \mathbf{0} & \mathbf{E} \end{bmatrix} \begin{bmatrix} \mathbf{W}_1 & \mathbf{W}_2 \\ \mathbf{U}_1 & \mathbf{U}_2 \end{bmatrix} \begin{bmatrix} \mathbf{S}_1 & \mathbf{0} \\ \mathbf{0} & \mathbf{S}_2 \end{bmatrix} \qquad (15)$$

We shall invariably choose to arrange roots (the negatives of α_j) in $\mathbf{S}_1, \mathbf{S}_2$ so that

$$\mathbf{S}_1 \mathbf{S}_2 = \mathbf{I} \qquad (16)$$

Equation (15) has considerable symmetry in that the *system* matrices are related by an operation which comprises transposing each $(N \times N)$ block in situ and then swapping block rows and columns. We shall modify transform (15) to produce what we shall claim as a canonical form for equations of the form of (9).

Before this, however, we note that we will not use (15) directly to compute the characteristic solutions. Instead, observe that (9) can be applied directly to four successive vectors, $\mathbf{T}_{(i-1)}, \mathbf{T}_i, \mathbf{T}_{(i+1)}, \mathbf{T}_{(i+2)}$ as follows :

$$\begin{bmatrix} \mathbf{E}^T & \mathbf{F} \\ \mathbf{0} & \mathbf{E}^T \end{bmatrix} \begin{bmatrix} \mathbf{T}_{(i-1)} \\ \mathbf{T}_{(i)} \end{bmatrix} + \begin{bmatrix} \mathbf{E} & \mathbf{0} \\ \mathbf{F} & \mathbf{E} \end{bmatrix} \begin{bmatrix} \mathbf{T}_{(i+1)} \\ \mathbf{T}_{(i+2)} \end{bmatrix} = 0 \qquad (17)$$

Evidently, applying (7) again results in an eigenvalue problem which will return the squares of the characteristic values of interest. In this case, the eigenvalue problem has a more obvious symmetry to it (recall that $\mathbf{F} = \mathbf{F}^T$) and methods for exploiting this symmetry are straightforward. The set of eigenvectors computed based on (17) can be identical to that produced from (15) given appropriate scaling.

It is logical to attack the eigenvalue problem involving the two $(2N \times 2N)$ matrices in (17) in stages beginning with this eigenvalue-eigenvector decomposition

$$\begin{bmatrix} \left(\mathbf{E}^T + \mathbf{E}\right) & \mathbf{F} \\ \mathbf{F} & \left(\mathbf{E}^T + \mathbf{E}\right) \end{bmatrix} = \frac{1}{2} \begin{bmatrix} \mathbf{U}_{EpF} & -\mathbf{U}_{EmF} \\ \mathbf{U}_{EpF} & \mathbf{U}_{EmF} \end{bmatrix} \begin{bmatrix} \Lambda_{EpF} & 0 \\ 0 & \Lambda_{EmF} \end{bmatrix} \begin{bmatrix} \mathbf{U}_{EpF} & -\mathbf{U}_{EmF} \\ \mathbf{U}_{EpF} & \mathbf{U}_{EmF} \end{bmatrix}^T$$

$$(18)$$

$$\text{where } \begin{cases} \left(\mathbf{E}^T + \mathbf{E} + \mathbf{F}\right) = \mathbf{U}_{EpF} \Lambda_{EpF} \mathbf{U}_{EpF}{}^T & , & \mathbf{U}_{EpF} \mathbf{U}_{EpF}{}^T = \mathbf{I}_N \\ \left(\mathbf{E}^T + \mathbf{E} - \mathbf{F}\right) = \mathbf{U}_{EmF} \Lambda_{EmF} \mathbf{U}_{EmF}{}^T & , & \mathbf{U}_{EmF} \mathbf{U}_{EmF}{}^T = \mathbf{I}_N \end{cases}$$

Then a skew-symmetric ($2N$ x $2N$) matrix can be formed whose eigenvalues are of direct use in determining the characteristic roots. Our interest, here, is primarily in finding the following simultaneous decompositions :

$$\begin{bmatrix} \mathbf{E}^T & \mathbf{F} \\ 0 & \mathbf{E}^T \end{bmatrix} = \begin{bmatrix} \mathbf{W} & \mathbf{X} \\ \mathbf{Y} & \mathbf{Z} \end{bmatrix} \begin{bmatrix} \Lambda_W & \Lambda_X \\ \Lambda_Y & \Lambda_Z \end{bmatrix} \begin{bmatrix} \mathbf{W} & \mathbf{X} \\ \mathbf{Y} & \mathbf{Z} \end{bmatrix}^T$$

and hence $$(19)$$

$$\begin{bmatrix} \mathbf{E} & 0 \\ \mathbf{F} & \mathbf{E} \end{bmatrix} = \begin{bmatrix} \mathbf{W} & \mathbf{X} \\ \mathbf{Y} & \mathbf{Z} \end{bmatrix} \begin{bmatrix} \Lambda_W & \Lambda_Y \\ \Lambda_X & \Lambda_Z \end{bmatrix} \begin{bmatrix} \mathbf{W} & \mathbf{X} \\ \mathbf{Y} & \mathbf{Z} \end{bmatrix}^T$$

In (19), Λ_W, Λ_X, Λ_Y and Λ_Z are diagonal. Ideally, we would have only real matrices involved in (19). This is often possible – but not always. If we are fortunate to be able to produce real Λ_X, Λ_Y, Λ_Z, $\mathbf{W}$, $\mathbf{X}$, $\mathbf{Y}$ and $\mathbf{Z}$ we shall have followed an extremely efficient path to determining the (equivalent of the) characteristic roots.

DISPENSING WITH COMPLEX NUMBERS

In the previous section, we outlined an attractive computational route to determining the characteristic solutions for (6). Set this method aside for the present, together with the possibility of repeated characteristic roots as a special case to be considered in a separate paper. Instead, consider that we have solved the problem of (14) directly to find $2N$ solution sets $\{\alpha_k, \mathbf{u}_k, \mathbf{w}_k\}$. Some of the characteristic roots, α_j, may be real and the remainder must be complex. In these cases, the roots will occur in complex-conjugate pairs. Let P be the number of pairs of complex roots and let $2Q$ be the number of real roots. The vectors associated with the real roots can always be ordered and scaled such that those in the first group $\{\mathbf{U}_1, \mathbf{W}_1\}$ have no imaginary parts and those in the second group $\{\mathbf{U}_2, \mathbf{W}_2\}$ are purely imaginary. Obviously,

$$P + Q = N \qquad (20)$$

Define matrix $\mathbf{J}$ as follows (using the symbol j here as the square root of (-1))

$$\mathbf{J} = \begin{bmatrix} \frac{1}{\sqrt{2}}\mathbf{I}_P & 0 & \frac{-j}{\sqrt{2}}\mathbf{I}_P & 0 \\ 0 & \mathbf{I}_Q & 0 & 0 \\ \frac{1}{\sqrt{2}}\mathbf{I}_P & 0 & \frac{j}{\sqrt{2}}\mathbf{I}_P & 0 \\ 0 & 0 & 0 & j\mathbf{I}_Q \end{bmatrix} \qquad (21)$$

where $\mathbf{I}_P$ is the $(P \times P)$ identity matrix and $\mathbf{I}_Q$ is the $(Q \times Q)$ identity matrix.

$$\mathbf{J}^T \mathbf{J} = \begin{bmatrix} \mathbf{I}_N & \mathbf{0} \\ \mathbf{0} & -\mathbf{I}_N \end{bmatrix} \quad , \quad \mathbf{J}\mathbf{J}^T = \begin{bmatrix} \mathbf{0} & \mathbf{I}_N \\ \mathbf{I}_N & \mathbf{0} \end{bmatrix} \tag{22}$$

where $\mathbf{I}_N$ is the $(N \times N)$ identity matrix. Postmultiply (15) by $\mathbf{J}$ and insert the identity matrix factorised as the term $(\mathbf{J}\mathbf{J}^T\mathbf{J}\,\mathbf{J}^T)$ into the right hand side to obtain

$$\begin{bmatrix} \mathbf{E}^T & \mathbf{0} \\ \mathbf{E}^T & \mathbf{F} \end{bmatrix}\begin{bmatrix} \mathbf{W} & \mathbf{X} \\ \mathbf{Y} & \mathbf{Z} \end{bmatrix} = \begin{bmatrix} \mathbf{F} & \mathbf{E} \\ \mathbf{0} & \mathbf{E} \end{bmatrix}\begin{bmatrix} \mathbf{W} & \mathbf{X} \\ \mathbf{Y} & \mathbf{Z} \end{bmatrix}\begin{bmatrix} \Theta & -\Gamma \\ \Gamma & \Psi \end{bmatrix} \tag{23}$$

When the modulus of each one of the complex roots is unity, all of the matrices in (23) are real. It is illustrated in the example that at times, complex roots can appear in sets of four in which none of the roots in the set has unity modulus. We will discuss the existence of such cases in the concluding remarks. Up to that point, we shall implicitly assume that $\{\mathbf{W}, \mathbf{X}, \mathbf{Y}, \mathbf{Z}, \Theta, \Gamma$ and $\Psi\}$ are real. Matrices Θ, Γ and Ψ are also diagonal. Note that the determinant of the $(2N \times 2N)$ matrix containing $\{\Theta, \Gamma$ and $\Psi\}$ is unity and that moreover, each (2×2) sub-matrix comprising $\{\Theta(j,j), \Gamma(j,j)$ and $\Psi(j,j)\}$ has determinant 1. Note also that $\mathbf{W}$, $\mathbf{X}$, $\mathbf{Y}$ and $\mathbf{Z}$ have the same meanings here as they had in (19).

We assert that (23) provides a natural canonical form for (9). We found this assertion on the fact that if $\mathbf{E}$ and $\mathbf{F}$ are each diagonal matrices, solutions to (23) can be determined to produce real and diagonal matrices $\mathbf{W}$, $\mathbf{X}$, $\mathbf{Y}$ and $\mathbf{Z}$. If we now consider that we have found matrices $\mathbf{W}$, $\mathbf{X}$, $\mathbf{Y}$ and $\mathbf{Z}$ using the method outlined through (17),(18) and (19), it is clear that Θ, Γ and Ψ can be determined readily.

There is considerable symmetry present in (23) and although there are difficulties in exploiting this directly for computational purposes (we have no need for this anyway, given (18) and (19)), we can potentially gain some useful insight through it. To do this, we adopt a different representation for all $(2N \times 2N)$ matrices.

CLIFFORD ALGEBRA, CL_2

Clifford Algebra dates back to 1872 when Professor William Kingdon Clifford presented a structure for a family of algebras to the London Mathematical Society. Each of these algebras is founded on a vector space of finite dimension. In the general case where a vector space of dimension n is used, the algebra is called Cl_n and it is comprised of numbers having 2^n parts. The algebras have a very attractive geometric quality and they are distinguished from previous attempts at algebras for vector spaces by the existence of an inverse. The importance of Clifford Algebra is continually being uncovered and there is substantial evidence to suggest that this algebra may supplant a host of other mathematical devices (Hestenes [8], Doran [9]).

Most of these applications emerge as a direct result of the geometric properties of the algebra. The reader should note that the present proposed application is founded only on the algebraic behaviour and does not exploit the considerable geometric prowess available.

Each number in the Clifford Algebra, Cl_2, has four components just as each Complex Number has two. The basis elements are ordinarily denoted $\{1, e_1, e_2, e_1e_2\}$. Because we wish to use subscripts to implicitly pair coefficients with the basis components, we deliberately use the notation $\underline{1}, \underline{i}, \underline{j}, \underline{k}$ instead. In this paper, we are not interested in any Clifford Algebra other than Cl_2 and whenever the term *Clifford Number* arises, it will invariably mean a Clifford Number from Cl_2 though we shall not state this explicitly. The general Clifford Number, $\underline{x}$, is written as

$$\underline{x} = x_1\underline{1} + x_i\,\underline{i} + x_j\,\underline{j} + x_k\,\underline{k} \tag{24}$$

We can say that Cl_2, is *isomorphic* to Mat_{2x2} – the algebra of (2 x 2) matrices over the field of real numbers – and that a bijective mapping, Φ, maps from Cl_2 to Mat_{2x2} as follows

$$\Phi(\underline{x}) = x_1\begin{bmatrix} 1 & 0 \\ 0 & 1 \end{bmatrix} + x_i\begin{bmatrix} 0 & 1 \\ 1 & 0 \end{bmatrix} + x_j\begin{bmatrix} 1 & 0 \\ 0 & -1 \end{bmatrix} + x_k\begin{bmatrix} 0 & -1 \\ 1 & 0 \end{bmatrix} \tag{25}$$

The inverse map, Φ^{-1}, maps from Mat_{2x2} to Cl_2

$$\Phi^{-1}(\mathbf{X}) = \frac{\left(X_{(1,1)} + X_{(2,2)}\right)\underline{1} + \left(X_{(2,1)} + X_{(1,2)}\right)\underline{i} + \left(X_{(1,1)} - X_{(2,2)}\right)\underline{j} + \left(X_{(2,1)} - X_{(1,2)}\right)\underline{k}}{2} \tag{26}$$

The rules of multiplication for Cl_2 are readily deduced using the mapping, Φ. We can easily extend the mapping to deal with matrices of Clifford Numbers. Thus, for any real $(2N \times 2M)$ matrix comprising four $(N \times M)$ blocks, $\mathbf{W}, \mathbf{X}, \mathbf{Y}, \mathbf{Z}$, we can obtain

$$\Phi^{-1}\left(\begin{bmatrix} \mathbf{W} & \mathbf{X} \\ \mathbf{Y} & \mathbf{Z} \end{bmatrix}\right) = \frac{1}{2}\left[(\mathbf{W} + \mathbf{Z})\underline{1} + (\mathbf{Y} + \mathbf{X})\underline{i} + (\mathbf{W} - \mathbf{Z})\underline{j} + (\mathbf{Y} - \mathbf{X})\underline{k}\right] \tag{27}$$

Because the rules of multiplication for Clifford Numbers are based on matrix multiplication, we will automatically find that for any matrices $\mathbf{P}$ and $\mathbf{Q}$, the Clifford representation, $\underline{\mathbf{PQ}}$, of the product $\mathbf{PQ}$ is the equal to $\underline{\mathbf{P}}$ multiplied by $\underline{\mathbf{Q}}$.

The concept of a *conjugate* is important with the Clifford Numbers in this context. Indeed, it is the sole motivation for using Clifford Numbers here. It is possible to define several different conjugates for the Clifford Numbers but we shall be interested primarily in one. Letting $\underline{\mathbf{X}} = \mathbf{X}_1\underline{1} + \mathbf{X}_i\,\underline{i} + \mathbf{X}_j\,\underline{j} + \mathbf{X}_k\,\underline{k}$, then

$$conj\_jk(\underline{\mathbf{X}}) = \mathbf{X}_1\underline{1} + \mathbf{X}_i\underline{i} - \mathbf{X}_j\underline{j} - \mathbf{X}_k\underline{k} \tag{28}$$

9

In the context of solving self-adjoint systems of second order differential equations, the Garvey *et al* [10],[11] have made extensive use of two different conjugates and we have had recourse to define conjugate transposes but we do not require this here.

It is instructive to see the effects of this conjugate on the (2*N* x 2*N*) matrices. In this equation, we use Φ^{-1} to map from an original (2*N* x 2*N*) matrix, **X**, to a (*N* x *N*) matrix, of Clifford Numbers, we compute *conj_jk*(.) of this matrix and then map back again.

$$\Phi\left(conj\_jk\left(\Phi^{-1}\left(\begin{bmatrix} \mathbf{X}_{11} & \mathbf{X}_{12} \\ \mathbf{X}_{21} & \mathbf{X}_{22} \end{bmatrix} \right) \right) \right) = \begin{bmatrix} \mathbf{X}_{22} & \mathbf{X}_{21} \\ \mathbf{X}_{12} & \mathbf{X}_{11} \end{bmatrix} \tag{29}$$

Recognising the effects shown above, we can rewrite (23) in Clifford notation in the following very compact form

$$\underline{\mathbf{G}}\,\underline{\mathbf{U}} = conj\_jk\left(\underline{\mathbf{G}}^T\right)\underline{\mathbf{U}}\,\underline{\Theta} \tag{30}$$

Note that

$$conj\_jk(\underline{\Theta})\,\underline{\Theta} = \underline{\mathbf{I}} \tag{31}$$

Before proceeding further, observe the behaviour of the conjugate of a product. Using the bijective mapping Φ, it is straightforward to show that

$$conj\_jk(\underline{\mathbf{X}}\,\underline{\mathbf{Y}}) = conj\_jk(\underline{\mathbf{X}})\,conj\_jk(\underline{\mathbf{Y}}) \tag{32}$$

In words, *the "jk-conjugate" of a product is identical to the product of the "jk-conjugates" in the same order.* Now, we can begin to develop some intuitive faith in the "Clifford formulation". Take the *conj_jk*(.) of both sides of (30) and post-multiply both sides of by $\underline{\Theta}$ to find

$$\underline{\mathbf{G}}^T\,conj\_jk(\underline{\mathbf{U}}) = conj\_jk(\underline{\mathbf{G}})\,conj\_jk(\underline{\mathbf{U}})\,\underline{\Theta} \tag{33}$$

Note what has happened. $\underline{\mathbf{G}}^T$ has replaced $\underline{\mathbf{G}}$ and vice-versa. Also *conj_jk*($\underline{\mathbf{U}}$) has replaced $\underline{\mathbf{U}}$ and (31) has been invoked. In order that (33) can be compared most easily with (30), the sides of (33) have been juxtaposed. Swapping $\underline{\mathbf{G}}^T$ for $\underline{\mathbf{G}}$ turned the original system into the adjoint system which has the same roots. Replacing $\underline{\mathbf{U}}$ by *conj_jk*($\underline{\mathbf{U}}$) has the effect of swapping over the sets of vectors originally associated with the two different sets of roots.

Utilizing Clifford Algebra in the present context is motivated by reasons based on both computational efficiency and ability to comprehend. Having given some glimmer of why casting (23) in Cl_2 may provide some enlightenment, we now consider how it affects computation. Revisit equation (18). If the (2*N* x 2*N*) matrix in (18) containing ($\mathbf{E}^T + \mathbf{E}$) and **F** is represented as a (*N* x *N*) matrix of Cl_2 numbers, it is found to be symmetrical and to have zero j and k components. A decomposition

10

equivalent to (18) can be carried out completely in Cl_1 – a sub-algebra of Cl_2. The gain associated with using Clifford algebra here is in compactness of algorithm only. An evaluation of the effects further on in the computation requires analysis which could not fit in this paper.

EXAMPLE

We have prepared an example primarily to show what solutions look like in the field of Clifford Numbers. The periodic structure of interest is identical to that shown in Fig. 1. Each bay comprises a flat steel plate comprising 5 identical squares allowed to oscillate in its own plane. The thickness of the plate was 20mm and the side-length for the squares was 100mm. Each square is represented by an 8-node quadrilateral plate element and the right-hand end of bay #i is rigidly attached to the left-hand end of bay #(i+1) through the three coincident nodes (6 degrees of freedom). Hence $N=6$ in this case. Fig. 2 shows the first 4 non-rigid-body modes of a free bay. Fig. 3 shows a root locus for (some of) the characteristic roots, α_j as the angular frequency, ω, is swept from 1000 rad/s to 10000 rad/s. Fig. 4-6 show the $\underline{1}$, $\underline{i}$ and $\underline{k}$ components of the diagonal of the Θ as ω varies (the $\underline{j}$ component is always zero). They are not displayed between 7138 and 9238 rad/s since we cannot represent the system using real Θ, Γ and Ψ over this range of frequencies.

Several points are marked on Fig.s 3 to 6. One pair of roots begins (at $\omega=1000$ rad/s) at point A and proceeds leftwards about the unit circle to G. A second pair begins at B, proceeds leftwards until it hits the real axis again at D ($\omega =3754$rad/s) where it becomes a pair of real roots. The real roots extend out from D to points E and F ($\omega =3856$rad/s) and they turn back, become a complex pair at G ($\omega =3963$rad/s) again and proceed rightwards along the unit circle. At point H, two pairs of complex roots collide (at $\omega=7139$ rad/s) on the unit circle and all four roots involved depart from that circle. They return to the unit circle at I ($\omega=9238$ rad/s). Of most interest in Fig.s 4-6 are the frequencies corresponding to points D, (E,F), G, H and I.

CONCLUSIONS

We began by showing how to derive a system of self-adjoint second-order difference equations governing the characteristic vibrations of any arbitrary periodic system. This formalism allows for the inclusion of flexibility at the interfaces and it makes the self-adjoint-ness of the system quite evident. We showed two different new ways in which this system of equations can be represented in a "reduced" form. One of these is a good candidate for a canonical form for such systems while the other provides for efficient determination of characteristic solutions. The Clifford Algebra, Cl_2, was then introduced and we showed that the proposed canonical form appears very compactly in Cl_2. We cannot yet argue that there is a significant computational advantage to using Cl_2 in the determination of the characteristic vibrations but it was through considering the system using Cl_2 that an efficient new method was generated.

A significant counter-argument against the use of Cl_2 in the present context is that we must allow some of the coefficients of the "Clifford roots" (the characteristic roots in Clifford format) to become complex in certain circumstances. These circumstances occur precisely when there are complex roots present with non-unity modulus. In the example given, this occurs in the range (7139 rad/s < ω < 9238 rad/s). Work is ongoing to determine whether it may be possible to conduct this analysis entirely without complex numbers.

REFERENCES

[1]   Mead D.J. 'Wave propagation and natural modes in periodic systems: II. Multi-coupled systems, with and without damping'. *Journal of Sound & Vibration*, vol.40, no.1, 8 May 1975, pp.19-39. UK.

[2]   Mead D.J. 'Wave propagation in continuous periodic structures: research contributions from Southampton, 1964-1995'. *Journal of Sound & Vibration*, vol.190, no.3, 29 Feb. 1996, pp.495-524.

[3]   Williams FW. Zhong W. Bennett PN. 'Computation of the eigenvalues of wave propagation in periodic substructural systems'. *Journal of Vibration & Acoustics-Transactions of the ASME*, vol.115, no.4, Oct. 1993, pp.422-6

[4]   Ouyang H. Williams FW. Kennedy D. 'A general method for analyzing wave propagation along longitudinally periodic structures'. *Journal of Sound & Vibration*, vol.177, no.2, 20 Oct. 1994, pp.277-81. UK.

[5]   Williams FW. 'Natural Frequencies of Repetitive Structures'. *Quarterly Journal of Mechanics and Applied Mathematics*, vol 24, no. 3, 1971, pp285-310

[6]   Garvey S.D., Penny J.E.T. 'Representing periodic structures efficiently as substructures'. *Journal of Sound & Vibration*, vol.178, no.1, 17 Nov. 1994, pp.79-94. UK.

[7]   Garvey S.D., Penny J.E.T., 'Computing the Resonances of Finite Periodic Structures'. *IOP Conf on Modern Practice in Stress & Vibration Analysis, Sheffield.* (1993) April, p469-481, Sheffield Academic Press.

[8]   Hestenes D *Space Time Algebra,* Gordon & Breach, New York, 1966.

[9]   Doran C. 'A Complete Lecture Course in Geometric Algebra'. Published as 16 distinct ".pdf" files at www.mrao.cam.ac.uk/~clifford/ptIIIcourse/course99/

[10]   Garvey S.D., Friswell M.I., Penny J.E.T. 'Some Further Insight into Second Order Systems' *Journal of Vibration and Control*, vol 5., 1998, pp 237-252.

[11]   Garvey SD., Friswell MI, Penny JET. 'A Clifford Algebraic Perspective on Second Order Linear Systems'. *AIAA Journal of Guidance, Control and Dynamics.* To appear. 2000.

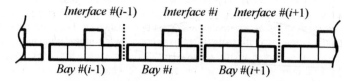

FIGURE 1   Illustration of a Periodic Structure.

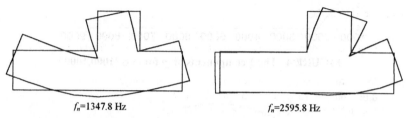

f_n=1347.8 Hz f_n=2595.8 Hz

FIGURE 2   **Two lowest non-rigid-body modes of the bay used for example.**

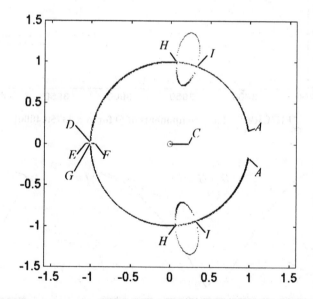

FIGURE 3   **Locus of complex characteristic roots for $\omega \in$ [1000,10000]**

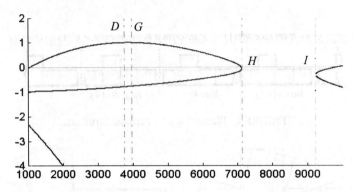

FIGURE 4 The $\underline{1}$ components of $\underline{\Theta}$ for $\omega \in [1000,10000]$

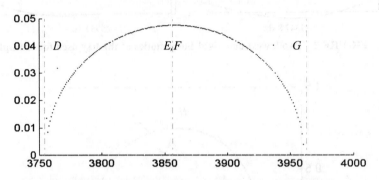

FIGURE 5 The $\underline{j}$ components of $\underline{\Theta}$ for $\omega \in [3750,4000]$

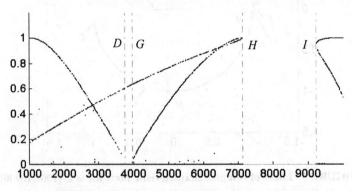

FIGURE 6 The $\underline{k}$ components of $\underline{\Theta}$ for $\omega \in [1000,10000]$

14

AXI-SYMMETRIC MODES OF VIBRATION OF A FLUID-FILLED

SHELL: A MODEL OF THE HUMAN HEAD

P.G Young*

The free vibration of homogeneous, isotropic shells filled with inviscid fluid is studied using three dimensional linear elasticity equations. A parametric study is presented for the natural frequency of the first ovalling (n = 2 spheroidal) mode of vibration. It is shown that for a remarkably wide range of geometric and material parameters, which encompasses values typical for the human head, the fluid-filled shell behaves like a membrane filled with incompressible fluid and a simple closed form expression is derived which closely approximates the natural frequencies obtained using the exact three dimensional equations.

1. INTRODUCTION

The free vibrations of solid and hollow spheres has been the subject of a number of studies [1-7] with the work, in many cases, motivated by an interest in modelling oscillations of the Earth. The free vibration of fluid filled spherical shells has been treated by a number of authors: Engin [8] developed a model of the human head consisting of a spherical shell filled with inviscid fluid using a thin shell theory; Advani and Lee [9] investigated the vibration of a fluid filled shell using higher order shell theory including transverse shear and rotational inertia; and Misra and Chakravarty [10] explored the problem of the free vibration of a multi-layer fluid-filled sphere, again as a model of the human head, taking into account both the dissipative behaviour of the brain and the mechanical influence of the scalp.

In previous work on the free vibration of fluid filled shells, frequency spectra or tabulated results were only presented for at most a few select cases. In the present study, numerical results are presented for a very wide range of material parameters (e.g. Young's modulus of shell, Bulk modulus of fluid...) and geometric parameters (thickness of shell, radius of fluid). However, rather than present results for a large range of modes for each case the emphasis has been placed on the behaviour of the first ovalling (n = 2) mode of spheroidal oscillation as we vary material and geometric parameters. The motivation for focusing our attention on this mode is a

*School of Engineering and Computer Science, University of Exeter, Exeter, EX4 4QF

recent parametric study (Young and Morfey [11]) on the response of a fluid-filled shell to a radially applied force, which has shown that both the onset of dynamic pressure effects in the brain and the magnitude of the observed pressures can be very accurately predicted by the ratio of the impact duration to the period of oscillation of the first ovalling mode. Numerical results obtained using the full three dimensional elasticity equations are compared with results obtained using simpler membrane and bending shell theories to explore the range of applicability of these theories.

2. THEORY

2.1 Formulation of frequency equations for a fluid-filled sphere.

The equations of motion, in spherical coordinates, for an isotropic, homogeneous, elastic medium are given by Sâto and Usami [4] and may be written

$$
\begin{aligned}
u_1 &= -A_{mn}U_1(n, h, r, z)Sph_1, \\
v_1 &= -A_{mn}V_1(n, h, r, z)Sph_2, \\
w_1 &= mA_{mn}W_1(n, h, r, z)Sph_3,
\end{aligned}
\tag{1}
$$

$$
\begin{aligned}
u_2 &= 0, \\
v_2 &= mB_{mn}V_2(n, k, r, z)Sph_4, \\
w_2 &= -B_{mn}W_2(n, k, r, z)Sph_5,
\end{aligned}
\tag{2}
$$

$$
\begin{aligned}
u_3 &= -C_{mn}U_3(n, k, r, z)Sph_1, \\
v_3 &= -C_{mn}V_3(n, k, r, z)Sph_2 \\
w_3 &= mC_{mn}W_3(n, k, r, z)Sph_3
\end{aligned}
\tag{3}
$$

where

$$
U_1 = \frac{1}{h^2}\frac{d}{dr}\left(\frac{Z_{n+1/2}(hr)}{r^{1/2}}\right),
$$

$$
V_1 = \frac{1}{h^2}\frac{Z_{n+1/2}(hr)}{r^{3/2}},
$$

$$
W_1 = V_1,
$$

16

$$V_2 = \frac{1}{n(n+1)}\frac{Z_{n+1/2}(kr)}{r^{1/2}},$$

$$W_2 = V_2,$$

$$U_3 = \frac{n(n+1)}{k^2}\frac{Z_{n+1/2}(kr)}{r^{3/2}},$$

$$V_3 = \frac{1}{k^2}\frac{1}{r}\frac{d}{dr}\left[r^{1/2}Z_{n+1/2}(kr)\right],$$

$$W_3 = V_3,$$

$$Sph_1 = P_n^m(\cos\theta)^{\cos}_{\sin}m\phi\exp(i\omega t),$$

$$Sph_2 = \frac{d}{d\theta}P_n^m(\cos\theta)^{\cos}_{\sin}m\phi\exp(i\omega t),$$

$$Sph_3 = \frac{P_n^m(\cos\theta)}{\sin\theta}^{\sin}_{-\cos}m\phi\exp(i\omega t),$$

$$Sph_4 = \frac{P_n^m(\cos\theta)}{\sin\theta}^{\cos}_{\sin}m\phi\exp(i\omega t),$$

$$Sph_5 = \frac{d}{d\theta}P_n^m(\cos\theta)^{\sin}_{-\cos}m\phi\exp(i\omega t),$$

u_i, v_i, $w_i (i = 1, 2, 3)$ are the radial, colatitudinal and azimuthal components of displacement respectively, and $Z_{n+1/2}$ are linear combinations of spherical Bessel functions of the first $(j_{n+1/2})$ and second kind $(y_{n+1/2})$, respectively. $P_n^m(\cos\theta)$ are associated Legendre functions, n is the harmonic number, $h = \omega / c_p, k = \omega / c_s$, in which ω is the radian natural frequency, $c_p = \left[(\lambda+2\mu)/\rho\right]^{1/2}$ is the speed of a longitudinal wave, $c_s = (\mu/\rho)^{1/2}$ is the speed of a shear wave, and ρ is the material density. The Lamé parameters λ and μ are given by $\lambda = v E /\left[(1-2v)(1+v)\right]$ and $\mu = E /\left[2(1+v)\right]$, where v is the Poisson ratio and E is Young's modulus of elasticity, and the quantities A_{mn}, B_{mn} and C_{mn} are constant coefficients.

The stress components of interest in this work may be written,

$$rr_1 = A_{mn}Rr_1(n, h, r, z, \mu)Sph_1,$$

$$r\theta_1 = -A_{mn}R\theta_1(n, h, r, z, \mu)Sph_2, \tag{4}$$

$$r\phi_1 = mA_{mn}R\phi_1(n, h, r, z, \mu)Sph_3,$$

$$rr_2 = 0,$$

$$r\theta_2 = mB_{mn}R\theta_2(n, k, r, z, \mu)Sph_4,$$

$$r\phi_2 = -B_{mn}R\phi_2(n, k, r, z, \mu)Sph_5,$$

(5)

$$rr_3 = -C_{mn}Rr_3(n, k, r, z, \mu)Sph_1,$$

$$r\theta_3 = -C_{mn}R\theta_3(n, k, r, z, \mu)Sph_2,$$

$$r\phi_3 = mC_{mn}R\phi_3(n, k, r, z, \mu)Sph_3$$

(6)

where

$$Rr_1 = (\lambda + 2\mu)\frac{Z_{n+1/2}(hr)}{r^{1/2}} + \frac{2\mu}{h^2}\left(\frac{2}{r}\frac{d}{dr}\left(\frac{Z_{n+1/2}(hr)}{r^{1/2}}\right)\right) - n(n+1)\frac{Z_{n+1/2}(hr)}{r^{5/2}},$$

$$R\theta_1 = \frac{2\mu}{h^2}\frac{d}{dr}\frac{Z_{n+1/2}(hr)}{r^{3/2}},$$

$$R\phi_1 = R\theta_1,$$

$$R\theta_2 = \frac{\mu}{n(n+1)}\left(\frac{d}{dr}\left(\frac{Z_{n+1/2}(kr)}{r^{1/2}}\right) - \frac{Z_{n+1/2}(kr)}{r^{3/2}}\right),$$

$$R\phi_2 = R\theta_2,$$

$$Rr_3 = \frac{2\mu n(n+1)}{k^2}\frac{d}{dr}\left(\frac{Z_{n+1/2}(kr)}{r^{3/2}}\right),$$

$$R\theta_3 = \frac{\mu}{k^2}\left(\frac{d^2}{dr^2}\left(\frac{Z_{n+1/2}(kr)}{r^{1/2}}\right) + (n(n+1)-2)\frac{Z_{n+1/2}(kr)}{r^{5/2}}\right),$$

$$R\phi_3 = R\theta_3.$$

For the free vibration of a fluid-filled shell, the stress components will vanish on the outer surface of the shell at r_o giving

$$rr^{(o)}(r_o) = 0, \qquad r\theta^{(o)}(r_o) = 0, \qquad r\phi^{(o)}(r_o) = 0.$$

At the interface between the shell and the fluid layer r_i there is continuity of the radial displacement and stress components, and the azimuthal and colatitudinal components of stress on the shell vanish, giving

$$rr^{i}(r_{i}) = rr^{o}(r_{i}), \quad u^{i}(r_{i}) = u^{o}(r_{i}), \quad r\theta^{o}(r_{i}) = 0, \quad r\phi^{o}(r_{i}) = 0,$$

where r_i is the inside radius of the shell (outside radius of the fluid), and the superscript o refers to the shell and the superscript i to the fluid.

Upon substitution of equations (1) to (6) into the above boundary and continuity conditions, two uncoupled sets of equations are obtained, one governing the toroidal or first class vibrations, which results from the use of expressions (2) and (5), and the other governing spheroidal or second class vibrations, which results from the use of equations (1), (3), (4) and (6). The toroidal modes of a shell filled with an inviscid fluid will be the same as those for the equivalent shell in vacuo. We will therefore only consider the spheroidal modes in the present study.

3. NUMERICAL RESULTS AND DISCUSSION

Numerical results were computed for fluid filled spheres consisting of a single homogeneous isotropic outer shell with an inviscid perfect liquid core. Results are presented in terms of the non-dimensional frequency parameter $\Omega = \sqrt{(\text{mass/hE})}$ which is, a priori, a function of the following four non-dimensional parameters: the ratio of Young's modulus of the shell to the Bulk modulus of the fluid (E/B); the ratio of the density of the fluid to the density of the shell (ρ_f/ρ_s), the Poisson's ratio of the shell material ν; and the ratio of the thickness of the shell to outer radius of the fluid (h/r_i). Because of the primary interest in head injury modelling, the non-dimensional geometric and material ratios are also given in the tables in terms of the values used by Engin [8], that is $(\rho_f/\rho_s)_{Engin} = 1000 \text{ kg/m}^3 / 2140 \text{ kg/m}^3$, $(E/B)_{Engin} = 13.79 \text{ MPa} / 2.18 \text{ MPa}$, and $(h/r_i)_{Engin} = (0.00381 \text{ m} / 0.0762 \text{ m}) = 1/20$.

Non-dimensional frequency parameters Ω are given in Table 1 for the first n = 2 spheroidal mode of vibration for $(\rho_f/\rho_s) = 1000/2140$ $((\rho_f/\rho_s)_{Engin} \times 1)$ and for a Poisson ratio equal to 0.25 as used by Engin [8]. Results were computed for a wide range of compressibility ratios E/B and thickness ratios h/ri. The percentage error in the non-dimensional frequency parameter obtained using membrane theory for a membrane filled with a compressible fluid and with an incompressible fluid, using bending theory again for a shell filled with a compressible and an incompressible fluid and finally for a compressible fluid in a rigid spherical cavity (acoustic modes) is also presented in Table 1.

Table 1 $\Omega = \sqrt{(\text{mass}/hE)}$ for fluid filled shells for $\rho_f/\rho_s = 1000/2140$.

(h/r$_i$)$_{EnginX}$	h/r$_i$	(E/B) $_{Engin\,X}$ E/B =	1/100 0.06	1/4 1.58	1/2 3.16	1 6.33	2 12.7	4 25.3	8 50.6	16 101	32 202	64 405
1/100	0.0005	3D	2.528	2.528	2.528	2.526	2.526	2.526	2.524	2.519	2.513	2.499
		Membrane	0%	0%	0%	0%	0%	0%	0%	0%	0%	0%
		Bending	0%	0%	0%	0%	0%	0%	0%	0%	0%	0%
		M incomp	0%	0%	0%	0%	0%	0%	0%	0%	1%	1%
½	0.025	3D	2.542	2.538	2.532	2.524	2.509	2.476	2.413	2.296	2.094	1.791
		Membrane	0%	0%	0%	0%	0%	0%	0%	0%	0%	0%
		Bending	0%	0%	0%	0%	0%	0%	0%	0%	0%	0%
		M. incomp	0%	0%	0%	1%	1%	3%	5%	11%	22%	42%
1	0.05	3D	2.556	2.550	2.544	2.532	2.505	2.454	2.356	2.178	1.891	1.523
		Membrane	0%	0%	0%	0%	0%	0%	0%	0%	0%	0%
		Bending	0%	0%	0%	0%	0%	0%	0%	0%	0%	0%
		Acoustic	-	-	-	-452%	-294%	-185%	-110%	-60%	-31%	-15%
		M. incomp	0%	0%	1%	1%	2%	4%	9%	18%	35%	68%
2	0.1	3D	2.587	2.579	2.571	2.554	2.519	2.452	2.315	2.067	1.699	1.304
		Membrane	0%	0%	0%	-1%	-1%	-1%	-1%	-1%	-1%	-1%
		Bending	0%	0%	0%	0%	0%	0%	0%	0%	-1%	-1%
		Acoustic	-	-	-	-337%	-213%	-128%	-71%	-35%	-16%	-7%
		M. incomp	0%	0%	0%	1%	2%	5%	11%	25%	52%	98%
4	0.2	3D	2.663	2.655	2.644	2.628	2.591	2.513	2.345	2.020	1.582	1.169
		Membrane	-3%	-3%	-3%	-3%	-3%	-3%	-4%	-4%	-4%	-4%
		Bending	1%	1%	1%	0%	0%	-1%	-2%	-3%	-3%	-3%
		Acoustic	-	-	-	-267%	-164%	-92%	-46%	-19%	-8%	-3%
		M. incomp	-3%	-2%	-2%	-1%	0%	3%	11%	28%	64%	122%
8	0.4	3D	2.837	2.831	2.822	2.810	2.781	2.710	2.526	2.106	1.529	1.148
		Membrane	-8%	-8%	-8%	-8%	-9%	-10%	-11%	-12%	-8%	-11%
		Bending	2%	2%	1%	1%	0%	-2%	-6%	-9%	-7%	-10%
		Acoustic	-	-	-	-231%	-136%	-71%	-30%	-10%	-7%	-1%
		M. incomp	-8%	-8%	-7%	-7%	-6%	-3%	4%	24%	71%	128%
16	0.8	3D	3.150	3.148	3.144	3.138	3.121	3.080	2.931	2.415	1.772	1.267
		Membrane	-16%	-16%	-16%	-17%	-17%	-19%	-23%	-25%	-24%	-24%
		Bending	6%	6%	6%	5%	3%	-2%	-14%	-22%	-23%	-23%
		Acoustic	-	-	-	-224%	-130%	-65%	-23%	-5%	-1%	0%
		M. incomp	-16%	-16%	-16%	-16%	-15%	-14%	-10%	10%	49%	109%
32	1.6	3D	3.506	3.506	3.504	3.500	3.498	3.490	3.451	3.095	2.266	1.613
		FE	3.508	3.508	3.506	3.504	3.500	3.490	3.447	2.982	2.161	1.537
		Acoustic	-	-	-	-268%	-161%	-85%	-32%	-4%	-1%	0%

It can clearly be seen that for h/r$_i$≤0.2, the results obtained for a membrane filled with compressible fluid are within 5% of the three dimensional results for the whole range of E/B values studied here. The results obtained using combined membrane and bending theory are accurate over a larger range of thickness ratios than results obtained using the membrane only theory as might be expected but the range is not dramatically increased by the introduction of bending action. The non-dimensional natural frequency parameters as obtained using the formula for a membrane filled with incompressible fluid are remarkably good over a wide range of values. This mode can be shown to be very accurately approximated by the following closed form expression (which is exact for a fluid-filled shell filled with incompressible fluid and with ρ_f/ρ_s tending to infinity):

$$\Omega = \sqrt{(8/(5+v))} \qquad (7)$$

4. CONCLUSIONS

Results of a parametric study on the fundamental spheroidal mode of a fluid filled shell have been presented and some interesting conclusions can be drawn from this study. The sensitivity of the frequency of the first $n = 2$ spheroidal mode of oscillation to changes in material and geometric parameters was explored and it was shown that for this mode of vibration:

(1) Fluid-filled spherical shells can be modelled as membranes filled with compressible fluid for shell thickness ratios up to at least 0.2 with at most a 5% error in the predicted natural frequencies. For an average head radius of approximately 8 cm, this is equivalent to a skull thickness of up to 1.6 cm. An interesting consequence of this predominantly membrane behaviour, is that the three layer sandwich structure of the skull will not have a stiffening effect on this mode compared with a single homogeneous layer with equivalent membrane stiffness

(2) For a surprisingly wide range of values of the compressibilty ratio E/B and the thickness ratio h/r_i, which encompasses values typical for the human head, results obtained using membrane theory for a shell filled with an incompressible fluid are very accurate. Furthermore, the non-dimensional frequency parameter can be very closely approximated by a very simple expression (equation (7)). Obtaining such a closed form expression for predicting the period of oscillation of the $n = 2$ mode of a fluid-filled shell over a very wide range of parameter values is very useful as it has previously been shown that both the onset of dynamic pressure effects in the fluid and the magnitude of the observed pressures in the fluid for a shell subjected to an applied force-time history can be very accurately predicted by the ratio of the impact duration to the period of oscillation of this mode.

ACKNOWLEDGEMENTS

The author wishes to thank Ms. Jenny Hayward for helping to put together the manuscript.

REFERENCES

(1) Lamb, H., *Proc London Math Soc*, Vol. 13, 1882, pp. 189-212.

(2) Chree, C., *Trans Cambridge Philos Soc*, Vol. 14, 1889, pp. 250-269.

(3) Sâto, Y. and Usami, T., *Geophys Mag*, Vol. 31, 1962, pp. 15-24.

(4) Sâto, Y. and Usami, T., *Geophys Mag*, Vol. 31, 1962, pp. 25-47.

(5) Shah, A. H., Ramkrishnan, C. V. and Datta, S. K., *Trans ASME J Appl Mech*, Vol. 36, 1969, pp. 431-439.

(6) Shah, A. H., Ramkrishnan, C. V. and Datta, S. K., *Trans ASME J Appl Mech*, Vol. 36, 1969, pp. 440-444.

(7) Lapwood, E. R. and Usami, T., *Free Oscillations of The Earth*. Cambridge: Cambridge University Press, 1981.

(8) Engin, A.E., *J. Biomech*, Vol. 2, 1969, pp. 325-341.

(9) Advani, S.H. and Lee, Y.C., *J Sound Vib*, Vol. 12, 1970, pp.453-461.

(10) Misra, J.C. and Chakravarty S., Vol.15, No. 9, pp. 635-645.

(11) Young, P.G. and Morfey, C.L., *Proc 1998 IRCOBI Conf Biomech Imp*, pp.391-403.

ANALYTICAL MODEL OF A THREE DIMENSIONAL BOX STRUCTURE UNDERGOING COMBINED TRANSLATIONAL AND ROTATIONAL MOTIONS

D.I.M. Forehand*, M.P. Cartmell*, A.A.B. MacLean[†] and R. Khanin[‡]

Modelling of three dimensional structures is normally the province of Finite Element codes because of their extremely wide capabilities and their application-independent numerical internals, thus rendering them particularly useful for analysing the dynamics of complicated shapes. Full nonlinear analysis capabilities are prevalent and bench-marked functionality is generally assured. On this basis there seems little reason to look elsewhere for modelling tools, however one of the weaknesses of Finite Elements, when applied to engineering dynamics, is the inherent black-box nature of the programs and the fact that the physical links between the excitations that cause the responses and the responses themselves can be lost within the internal numerical calculations. This paper offers an analytical model of a simplified three dimensional box-like structure, as an alternative approach.

1 INTRODUCTION

The problem of deriving a reasonably tractable analytical model of the vibrational behaviour of a three dimensional open box structure is addressed within this paper. The applications area relates to the design of offshore oil and gas platform modules, in particular the sort of accommodation and service modules that are supplied to the oil and gas majors by the industry's engineering support sector. These structures are all different in detail but comprise a common configuration in the form of a multi-storied box with rigid vertical corner beams, massive floors, and cross bracing of the walls to provide the requisite stiffness in bending and torsion. The number of stories, and the aspect ratio of the three overall dimensions of these structures, each depend on the specific application, and conventionally such structures are modelled for both static and dynamic performance using finite element analysis. The FEA is necessarily based on an appropriate meshing scheme in order to achieve the desired level of predictive accuracy without incurring prohibitive computational overheads. This requires considerable skill, judgement, and product knowledge on the part of the structural engineer. It also assumes, as do all finite element analyses, that the internal 'pre-solution' calculations are of little practical relevance.

*Department of Mechanical Engineering, University of Glasgow, Glasgow, Scotland, UK
[†]W.S. Atkins Ltd., Aberdeen, Scotland, UK
[‡]DAMTP, University of Cambridge, Cambridge, England, UK

This is, in many ways, true because finite element algorithms do not generally lend themselves to consistent physical transparency during the analysis, and instead provide a final numerical solution which can be graphically interpreted in the context of a graphic of the original problem. Modern finite element routines contain sufficient error checking and minimisation features to ensure that their inherently 'black-box' calculations do indeed reach meaningful solutions, however the build-up to such solutions is rarely obvious at any stage, particularly in the case of nonlinear dynamical phenomena [1]. A significant body of nonlinear effects is now routinely accommodated in most industrial vibration studies, particularly those arising from material interactions and geometrical configurations. Despite this limitation in insight the power and scalability of finite element analysis is usually considered to be more than sufficient to warrant its adoption as the first, if not the only, choice when modelling complex engineering problems.

The alternative route is to model such problems analytically, using a Newtonian or Lagrangian formulation from which systems of PDEs and/or ODEs are constructed. However, this approach is invariably immediately rejected because of perceived difficulties in deriving suitable equations of motion for complicated structures, and in most cases this can seem to be the right decision given the power and ease of use of modern FEA packages. It is obviously better to have an accurate numerical result, albeit based upon hidden internal calculations along the way, than a fully transparent analytical model of poor accuracy due to the need to keep it small, simplistic, and tractable. However, if the need for algebraic tractability can be offset to some extent by the judicious use of high power symbolic computing then it is possible to consider the provision of medium, or even large-scale, analytical models of complicated problems in engineering dynamics.

To date most computerised modeller-solvers have been intrinsically numerical, although some have offered considerable symbolic 'feel' [2,3]. On the basis that fully symbolic systems can perhaps now be made to compete computationally with symbolic-numerical approaches then the move to fully analytical modelling, and solution, can appear to be rather more attractive. Not least because it potentially gives the engineer the scope not only to obtain useful response information but also a deep insight into the physical routes necessary to get this information. This is highly relevant when it comes to interpreting nonlinear and parametric vibration effects in complicated structures, and the vast body of literature devoted to this sort of interpretation within even the simplest of structures underpins the huge range of problems where such effects pre-dominate. It is well known that nonlinearities can massively modify the vibrational response characteristics of structures and that relatively minor design changes can have very major qualitative effects on the structure of the solutions. It is this sort of interpreting power that has motivated the research reported within this paper [4,5].

The present paper considers a fundamental box-like system and discusses the derivation of an analytical model of the system in modal space. The structure has been pared down to its basic essentials in an attempt to model the principal features. A literature search has revealed little in the way of analytical models

24

for systems of this sort and so a preliminary attempt at modelling an open box structure is proposed in this paper. The model is based on the kinematics of bent and twisted beams attached to the four corners of identical plates, top and bottom, these being representative of a floor and a ceiling, and thus constituting the most basic box shape. The governing equations of motion are stated in terms of generalised modal co-ordinates representing translational and rotational motions of the top plate in certain modes. This simplifies the scale of the model, whilst retaining much of the more important information contained within the coupled lower modes. The modal ODEs can be nondimensionalised and ordered as necessary, prior to their solution by the perturbation method of multiple scales. This perturbation method is commonly use in Structural Engineering and other areas of science to study nonlinear vibrations. The multiple scales method has been encoded in a semi-automatic symbolic solver written in Mathematica and running on a high speed multi-processor computer [4,5]. Preparation of the equations of motion for solution using the analytical solver, and then generation and interpretation of specific symbolic output will be discussed in future publications, but a general discussion is offered in subsequent sections of this paper.

2 THE OPEN BOX STRUCTURE

On considering the open box structure shown in Figure 1(a) it can be seen that it consists of two square plates joined by four initially vertical light uniform bars of circular cross-section and length l. These bars are clamped to the corners of both plates. The mass of the top plate is m_o. Now, if the structure is loaded such that it is under combined bending and torsion, as depicted in Figure 1(b), it can be seen that there is bending, u, in the x-direction and v in the y-direction, combined with torsion ϕ. This bending and torsion causes a vertical drop, w. All four quantities, u, v, ϕ, and w are functions of z and t, noting that the torsion $\phi(z,t)$ is the torsion in the bars and that this is assumed to be the same for each bar. In this paper u, v, and ϕ (and consequently w) assumed to be small. The centre of mass (COM) of the top plate is displaced by distances u_o, v_o, and $-w_o$ in the x, y, and z directions, respectively. Also, the twist angle at the top plate is ϕ_o. Therefore,

$$u_o(t) = u(l,t), \quad v_o(t) = v(l,t), \quad \phi_o(t) = \phi(l,t) \quad \text{and} \quad w_o(t) = w(l,t). \quad (1)$$

Note that in this analysis we assume that the top plate stays horizontal. This assumption seems reasonable, provided that the ratio R/l is not too small (where R is the radius of separation of the COM from the bars). This assumption is also supported by experimental observation.

Next, suppose that we take two modes of vibration in bending, in both the x and the y directions, and one mode of torsional vibration, for example, then application of the Galerkin formulation gives

$$u(z,t) = f_1(z)u_1(t) + f_2(z)u_2(t), \quad (2)$$

$$v(z,t) = f_1(z)v_1(t) + f_2(z)v_2(t) \tag{3}$$

and

$$\phi(z,t) = g_1(z)\phi_1(t). \tag{4}$$

Therefore, by using equations (2), (3) and (4), equations (1a), (1b) and (1c) become, respectively,

$$u_o(t) = f_1(l)u_1(t) + f_2(l)u_2(t), \tag{5}$$

$$v_o(t) = f_1(l)v_1(t) + f_2(l)v_2(t) \tag{6}$$

and

$$\phi_o(t) = g_1(l)\phi_1(t). \tag{7}$$

2.1 Potential Energy

On considering the potential energy of the system, U, first of all, it is evident that this must comprise three parts: the strain energy in the bars due to their bending, U_b, the strain energy in the bars due to their torsion, U_t, and the gravitational potential energy of the top plate, U_g. That is

$$U = U_b + U_t + U_g. \tag{8}$$

2.1.1 Strain Energy due to Bending

The pure bending case is taken firstly. In this particular case all the bars bend in exactly the same way as the imaginary "centre" curve shown in Figure 1(b). The equation of this curve is

$$\boldsymbol{r} = (u(z,t), v(z,t), z). \tag{9}$$

Now, since u and v are small we can regard the arc length, s, up the curve and z as interchangeable. Therefore the tangent $\boldsymbol{t}$ to the curve at height z is given by

$$\boldsymbol{t} = (u', v', 1), \tag{10}$$

where $'$ denotes differentiation with respect to z. Furthermore, the curvature, κ, of this curve is given by

$$\kappa = \|\boldsymbol{t}'\| = \sqrt{(u'')^2 + (v'')^2}. \tag{11}$$

In obtaining equation (11) the Serret-Frenet formulas of differential geometry [6] have been used. Consequently, the total strain energy in the four bars due to bending, in the pure bending case, is

$$
\begin{aligned}
U_b &= 4\left(\frac{1}{2}\int_0^l EI\,\kappa^2\,dz\right) \\
&= 4\left(\frac{1}{2}\int_0^l EI\left((u'')^2 + (v'')^2\right)\,dz\right),
\end{aligned}
\tag{12}
$$

where EI is the flexural rigidity of the bars. Using equations (2) and (3), equation (12) becomes

$$
U_b = 2EI\left(\zeta_{11}u_1^2 + 2\zeta_{12}u_1u_2 + \zeta_{22}u_2^2 + \zeta_{11}v_1^2 + 2\zeta_{12}v_1v_2 + \zeta_{22}v_2^2\right),
\tag{13}
$$

where ζ_{ij} is defined in Appendix A.

Next we consider the pure torsion case, as shown in Figure 2. As can be seen from the Figure we assume that on looking down from above (along the negative z axis) the bars appear as straight lines. Also from Figure 2 it can be shown that the distance, d, that each corner moves horizontally and the angle α are given by

$$
d = 2R\sin\frac{\phi_o}{2}
\tag{14}
$$

and

$$
\alpha = \frac{\pi}{4} - \frac{\phi_o}{2}.
\tag{15}
$$

Since ϕ_o is small $\sin(\phi_o/2)\approx \phi_o/2$ and equation (14) becomes

$$
d \approx R\phi_o.
\tag{16}
$$

Table 1 shows the x and y displacements of corners 1, 2, 3 and 4 of the top plate. In the table

$$
d_c = d\cos\alpha
\tag{17}
$$

and

$$
d_s = d\sin\alpha.
\tag{18}
$$

For the bending due to torsion shown in Figure 2(b) we assume that it is proportional to the first bending mode, which leads to

$$
q(z,t) = \frac{d(t)}{f_1(l)}f_1(z).
\tag{19}
$$

27

Corner	x-displacement	y-displacement
1	$-d_c$	d_s
2	$-d_s$	$-d_c$
3	d_c	$-d_s$
4	d_s	d_c

Table 1: The x and y displacements of the corners of the top plate due to torsion.

As a result of this the total strain energy in the four bars due to bending in the pure torsion case is given by

$$U_b = 4\left(\frac{1}{2}\int_0^l EI(q'')^2\,dz\right)$$
$$= 2EI\,\beta\,\zeta_{11}\,\phi_1^2, \tag{20}$$

where β is defined in Appendix A. It is important to note that in obtaining equation (20) we have used equations (19), (16) and (7).

Finally, the combined bending and torsion case is considered. Again we assume that the bending due to torsion is proportional to the first bending mode. In order to calculate the strain energy due to bending we follow the method used to obtain equation (12).

Consider the bending of bar 1 in the x-direction. By reference to Table 1 it can be seen that this is given by

$$u(z,t) - \frac{d_c}{f_1(l)}f_1(z)$$
$$= f_1(z)u_1(t) + f_2(z)u_2(t) - \frac{d_c}{f_1(l)}f_1(z)$$
$$= \left(u_1(t) - \frac{d_c}{f_1(l)}\right)f_1(z) + u_2(t)f_2(z), \tag{21}$$

where we have used equation (2). Also, by using Table 1, the bending of bar 3 in the x-direction is given by

$$u(z,t) + \frac{d_c}{f_1(l)}f_1(z)$$
$$= f_1(z)u_1(t) + f_2(z)u_2(t) + \frac{d_c}{f_1(l)}f_1(z)$$
$$= \left(u_1(t) + \frac{d_c}{f_1(l)}\right)f_1(z) + u_2(t)f_2(z), \tag{22}$$

where again we have used equation (2). Differentiating expressions (21) and (22) twice with respect to z, and then squaring and adding them yields

$$2\left(u_1^2(t) + \frac{d_c^2}{f_1^2(l)}\right)(f_1''(z))^2 + 4u_1(t)u_2(t)f_1''(z)f_2''(z) + 2u_2^2(t)\left(f_2''(z)\right)^2. \tag{23}$$

28

By applying a similar analysis to the bending of bars 2 and 4 in the x-direction we obtain

$$2 \left(u_1^2(t) + \frac{d_s^2}{f_1^2(l)} \right) (f_1''(z))^2 + 4u_1(t)u_2(t)f_1''(z)f_2''(z) + 2u_2^2(t) (f_2''(z))^2. \quad (24)$$

Adding expressions (23) and (24) together, and noting that $d_c^2 + d_s^2 = d^2$, gives

$$4 \left((f_1''(z))^2 u_1^2(t) + 2f_1''(z)f_2''(z)u_1(t)u_2(t) + (f_2''(z))^2 u_2^2(t) \right) + 2\frac{d^2}{f_1^2(l)} (f_1''(z))^2. \quad (25)$$

Exactly the same analysis can be applied to the bending of bars 1, 2, 3, and 4 in the y-direction, yielding

$$4 \left((f_1''(z))^2 v_1^2(t) + 2f_1''(z)f_2''(z)v_1(t)v_2(t) + (f_2''(z))^2 v_2^2(t) \right) + 2\frac{d^2}{f_1^2(l)} (f_1''(z))^2. \quad (26)$$

To conclude, expressions (25) and (26) are added together, multiplied by EI, integrated from $z = 0$ to $z = l$ and then divided by 2. This gives the total strain energy in the four bars due to bending in the combined bending and torsion case

$$U_b = 2EI \left(\zeta_{11}u_1^2 + 2\zeta_{12}u_1u_2 + \zeta_{22}u_2^2 + \zeta_{11}v_1^2 + 2\zeta_{12}v_1v_2 + \zeta_{22}v_2^2 + \beta\zeta_{11}\phi_1^2 \right), \quad (27)$$

where we have used equations (16) and (7). It is interesting to note that, under the assumptions in this analysis, the strain energy due to bending in the combined bending and torsion case (equation (27)) is just the sum of the strain energy due to bending in the pure bending case (equation (13)) and the strain energy due to bending in the pure torsion case (equation (20)).

2.1.2 Strain Energy due to Torsion

The total strain energy in the four bars due to their torsion, U_t, is given by

$$\begin{aligned} U_t &= 4 \left(\frac{1}{2} \int_0^l GJ (\phi')^2 \, dz \right) \\ &= 2GJ \, \gamma_{11} \, \phi_1^2, \end{aligned} \quad (28)$$

in which we have used equation (4). Also, it should be noted that GJ is the torsional rigidity of the bars and γ_{11} is defined in Appendix A.

2.1.3 Gravitational Potential Energy of the Top Plate

The gravitational potential energy of the top plate is given by

$$U_g = -m_o \, g \, w_o, \quad (29)$$

where w_o is the vertical drop of the top plate due to combined bending and torsion.

We initially consider the pure bending case, in which all the bars bend in exactly the same way as the imaginary "centre" curve shown in Figure 1(b). Therefore, since u and v are small, a very good approximation to the drop of the top plate is given by

$$w_o = \frac{1}{2} \int_0^l (u')^2 + (v')^2 \, dz. \tag{30}$$

Equation (30) is a 2 dimensional version of an equation derived by Timoshenko [7]. By recourse to equations (2) and (3) equation (30) becomes

$$w_o = \frac{1}{2} \left(\eta_{11} u_1^2 + 2\eta_{12} u_1 u_2 + \eta_{22} u_2^2 + \eta_{11} v_1^2 + 2\eta_{12} v_1 v_2 + \eta_{22} v_2^2 \right), \tag{31}$$

where η_{ij} is defined in Appendix A.

We then move on to consider the pure torsion case and note that from Figure 2 and Timoshenko [7] the drop of the top plate, w_o, is given by

$$
\begin{aligned}
w_o &= \frac{1}{2} \int_0^l (q')^2 \, dz \\
&= \frac{1}{2} \beta \, \eta_{11} \, \phi_1^2, \tag{32}
\end{aligned}
$$

for which we have used equations (19), (16) and (7).

Finally, the combined bending and torsion case can be constructed and for this we assume that the drop of the top plate is the average drop of the tops of the four bars. In order to calculate the drop of the top plate we follow the method used to obtain equation (30). To do this we consider the bending of bar 1 in the x-direction, this being given by expression (21), and the bending of bar 3 in the x-direction, as defined by expression (22). Differentiating expressions (21) and (22) with respect to z and then squaring and adding them yields

$$2 \left(u_1^2(t) + \frac{d_c^2}{f_1^2(l)} \right) (f_1'(z))^2 + 4u_1(t)u_2(t)f_1'(z)f_2'(z) + 2u_2^2(t)(f_2'(z))^2. \tag{33}$$

By applying a similar analysis to the bending of bars 1 and 3 in the y-direction we obtain

$$2 \left(v_1^2(t) + \frac{d_s^2}{f_1^2(l)} \right) (f_1'(z))^2 + 4v_1(t)v_2(t)f_1'(z)f_2'(z) + 2v_2^2(t)(f_2'(z))^2. \tag{34}$$

Adding expressions (33) and (34) together, and using the fact that $d_c^2 + d_s^2 = d^2$, gives

$$
\begin{aligned}
&2 \left((f_1'(z))^2 u_1^2(t) + 2f_1'(z)f_2'(z)u_1(t)u_2(t) + (f_2'(z))^2 u_2^2(t) \right) \\
&+ 2 \left((f_1'(z))^2 v_1^2(t) + 2f_1'(z)f_2'(z)v_1(t)v_2(t) + (f_2'(z))^2 v_2^2(t) \right) \\
&+ 2 \frac{d^2}{f_1^2(l)} (f_1'(z))^2. \tag{35}
\end{aligned}
$$

To conclude, expression (35) is integrated from $z = 0$ to $z = l$ and then divided by 4. This gives the average drop of the top of bar 1 and the top of bar 3 as

$$\frac{1}{2}\left(\eta_{11}u_1^2 + 2\eta_{12}u_1u_2 + \eta_{22}u_2^2 + \eta_{11}v_1^2 + 2\eta_{12}v_1v_2 + \eta_{22}v_2^2 + \beta\eta_{11}\phi_1^2\right). \qquad (36)$$

Exactly the same result is obtained if we calculate the average drop of the top of bar 2 and the top of bar 4. This is a pleasing result because it means that, under the assumptions of this analysis, the tops of the four bars remain coplanar, as they should.

Consequently, the drop of the top plate in combined bending and torsion, w_o, is given by

$$w_o = \frac{1}{2}\left(\eta_{11}u_1^2 + 2\eta_{12}u_1u_2 + \eta_{22}u_2^2 + \eta_{11}v_1^2 + 2\eta_{12}v_1v_2 + \eta_{22}v_2^2 + \beta\eta_{11}\phi_1^2\right). \qquad (37)$$

It is interesting to note that, under the assumptions in this analysis, the drop of the top plate in the combined bending and torsion case (equation (37)) is just equal to the sum of the drop of the top plate in the pure bending case (equation (31)) and the drop of the top plate in the pure torsion case (equation (32)).

2.1.4 Summary of Section 2.1

The potential energy of the system, U, is given by

$$U = U_b + U_t + m_o g(Z(t) - w_o), \qquad (38)$$

where we have now introduced excitation by vertically displacing the base by $Z(t)$. The total strain energy in the four bars due to bending in the combined bending and torsion case, U_b, can be obtained from equation (27). The total strain energy in the four bars due to their torsion in the combined bending and torsion case, U_t, can be obtained from equation (28). Lastly, the vertical drop of the top plate, relative to the base, in the combined bending and torsion case, w_o, can be obtained from equation (37).

2.2 Kinetic Energy

Suppose we excite the base by displacing it by $(X(t), Y(t), Z(t))$ and then rotating it by $\Phi(t)$ about its centre. Figure 3 shows a plan view of the open box structure without its bars drawn in.

From Figure 3 the x-position of the COM of the top plate is

$$X + u_o\cos\Phi - v_o\sin\Phi \qquad (39)$$

and the y-position of the COM of the top plate is

$$Y + u_o\sin\Phi + v_o\cos\Phi. \qquad (40)$$

Consequently, the x-component of velocity of the COM of the top plate is

$$\dot{X} + \dot{u}_o \cos \Phi - u_o \dot{\Phi} \sin \Phi - \dot{v}_o \sin \Phi - v_o \dot{\Phi} \cos \Phi \qquad (41)$$

and the y-component of velocity of the COM of the top plate is

$$\dot{Y} + \dot{u}_o \sin \Phi + u_o \dot{\Phi} \cos \Phi + \dot{v}_o \cos \Phi - v_o \dot{\Phi} \sin \Phi, \qquad (42)$$

where the dot denotes differentiation with respect to t. Therefore, the kinetic energy, T, of the system is

$$\begin{aligned}
T = \frac{1}{2} m_o \Bigg[&\left(\dot{X} + \dot{u}_o \cos \Phi - u_o \dot{\Phi} \sin \Phi - \dot{v}_o \sin \Phi - v_o \dot{\Phi} \cos \Phi \right)^2 \\
&+ \left(\dot{Y} + \dot{u}_o \sin \Phi + u_o \dot{\Phi} \cos \Phi + \dot{v}_o \cos \Phi - v_o \dot{\Phi} \sin \Phi \right)^2 \\
&+ \left(\dot{Z} - \dot{w}_o \right)^2 \Bigg] + \frac{1}{2} I_o \left(\dot{\Phi} + \dot{\phi}_o \right)^2,
\end{aligned} \qquad (43)$$

where I_o is the moment of inertia of the top plate about a vertical axis through its COM.

Expanding the first two terms inside the square brackets in equation (43) and then simplifying gives

$$\begin{aligned}
T = \frac{1}{2} m_o \Bigg[&\dot{u}_o^2 + \dot{v}_o^2 + 2 \left(u_o \dot{v}_o - v_o \dot{u}_o \right) \dot{\Phi} + \left(u_o^2 + v_o^2 \right) \dot{\Phi}^2 + \dot{X}^2 + \dot{Y}^2 \\
&+ 2 \dot{X} \left(\dot{u}_o \cos \Phi - u_o \dot{\Phi} \sin \Phi - \dot{v}_o \sin \Phi - v_o \dot{\Phi} \cos \Phi \right) \\
&+ 2 \dot{Y} \left(\dot{u}_o \sin \Phi + u_o \dot{\Phi} \cos \Phi + \dot{v}_o \cos \Phi - v_o \dot{\Phi} \sin \Phi \right) \\
&+ \left(\dot{Z} - \dot{w}_o \right)^2 \Bigg] + \frac{1}{2} I_o \left(\dot{\Phi} + \dot{\phi}_o \right)^2.
\end{aligned} \qquad (44)$$

Finally, equation (44) can be written in terms of the modal coordinates (u_1, u_2, v_1, v_2 & ϕ_1) and their time derivatives by using equations (5) and (6), and the time derivatives of equations (5), (6), (7) and (37). For brevity this is not shown here.

3   THE EQUATIONS OF MOTION

Having obtained the potential energy of the system, U, and the kinetic energy of the system, T, (in terms of the five modal coordinates) the equations of motion can be obtained from Lagrange's equations. For this problem Lagrange's equations take the form

$$\frac{\mathrm{d}}{\mathrm{d}t} \left(\frac{\partial T}{\partial \dot{\mu}_i} \right) - \frac{\partial T}{\partial \mu_i} + \frac{\partial U}{\partial \mu_i} = 0, \qquad (45)$$

where the μ_i are the generalised (modal) coordinates and may be specified as u_1, u_2, v_1, v_2 and ϕ_1. Taking μ_i as u_1 we obtain the following ("u_1") equation of motion

$$m_o f_1(l)\big(f_1(l)\ddot{u}_1 + f_2(l)\ddot{u}_2\big) + \big(4EI\zeta_{11} - m_o g\eta_{11}\big)u_1 + \big(4EI\zeta_{12} - m_o g\eta_{12}\big)u_2$$

$$+ m_o\big(\eta_{11}u_1 + \eta_{12}u_2\big)\Big[\eta_{11}\Big(\dot{u}_1^2 + u_1\ddot{u}_1 + \dot{v}_1^2 + v_1\ddot{v}_1 + \beta\dot{\phi}_1^2 + \beta\phi_1\ddot{\phi}_1\Big)$$

$$+ \eta_{12}\Big(u_1\ddot{u}_2 + 2\dot{u}_1\dot{u}_2 + \ddot{u}_1 u_2 + v_1\ddot{v}_2 + 2\dot{v}_1\dot{v}_2 + \ddot{v}_1 v_2\Big)$$

$$+ \eta_{22}\Big(\dot{u}_2^2 + u_2\ddot{u}_2 + \dot{v}_2^2 + v_2\ddot{v}_2\Big)\Big]$$

$$= m_o f_1(l)\Big[-\ddot{X}\cos\Phi - \ddot{Y}\sin\Phi + \ddot{\Phi}\big(f_1(l)v_1 + f_2(l)v_2\big) + \dot{\Phi}^2\big(f_1(l)u_1 + f_2(l)u_2\big)$$

$$+ 2\dot{\Phi}\big(f_1(l)\dot{v}_1 + f_2(l)\dot{v}_2\big)\Big]$$

$$+ m_o\ddot{Z}\big(\eta_{11}u_1 + \eta_{12}u_2\big).$$

$$(46)$$

On the left hand side of equation (46) there are recognisable linear inertia terms, linear stiffness terms and nonlinear inertia terms, the latter being in the form of the cubic product combinations that are so typical of this type of structural problem. In future publications it will be shown that, because of orthogonality of the bending modes ($f_1(z)$ & $f_2(z)$), it is possible to replace the linear inertia terms, $m_o f_1^2(l)\ddot{u}_1 + m_o f_1(l)f_2(l)\ddot{u}_2$, with just $m_o\ddot{u}_1$. On the right hand side of equation (46) there are conventional forced excitation terms and linear parametric excitation terms. Cross-coupling between all five generalised coordinates is evident and it is clear that the presence of these forced and parametric excitation terms will have profound consequences for the resonant behaviour of the structure.

Taking μ_i as u_2 we obtain the "u_2" equation of motion, which is exactly the same as equation (46), except that the subscripts 1 and 2 are exchanged. In exchanging these subscripts it is important to note that ζ_{ij} and η_{ij} are symmetric, that is $\zeta_{ji} = \zeta_{ij}$ and $\eta_{ji} = \eta_{ij}$.

Due to the symmetry of the structure, the "v_1" and "v_2" equations of motion are identical to the "u_1" and "u_2" equations of motion, respectively (with the u's and v's exchanged).

Taking μ_i as ϕ_1 we obtain the "ϕ_1" equation of motion

$$I_o g_1^2(l)\ddot{\phi}_1 + \left(4GJ\gamma_{11} + 4EI\beta\zeta_{11} - m_o g\beta\eta_{11}\right)\phi_1$$
$$+ m_o\beta\eta_{11}\phi_1\left[\eta_{11}\left(\dot{u}_1^2 + u_1\ddot{u}_1 + \dot{v}_1^2 + v_1\ddot{v}_1 + \beta\dot{\phi}_1^2 + \beta\phi_1\ddot{\phi}_1\right)\right.$$
$$+ \eta_{12}\left(u_1\ddot{u}_2 + 2\dot{u}_1\dot{u}_2 + \ddot{u}_1 u_2 + v_1\ddot{v}_2 + 2\dot{v}_1\dot{v}_2 + \ddot{v}_1 v_2\right)$$
$$\left. + \eta_{22}\left(\dot{u}_2^2 + u_2\ddot{u}_2 + \dot{v}_2^2 + v_2\ddot{v}_2\right)\right]$$
$$= -I_o g_1(l)\ddot{\Phi} + m_o\beta\eta_{11}\ddot{Z}\phi_1.$$

$$(47)$$

Equation (47) defines the torsional motion of the structure. As with the other four equations of motion, the "ϕ_1" equation of motion has linear inertia terms, linear stiffness terms and nonlinear inertia terms on the left hand side, and forced and parametric excitation terms on the right hand side.

4 CONCLUSIONS

This paper has taken the problem of a three dimensional open box structure, for which little analysis has been found from the literature, and has proposed an analytical model for the vibrations of the structure when subjected to various configurations of base excitation. The model is based upon the kinematics of bent and twisted beams applied to a pair of parallel massive plates separated vertically by four identical, corner attached, circular section beams. The governing equations of motion are derived by means of a Galerkin formulation involving a limited number of modes from which kinetic and potential energy expressions are obtained, leading to five ordinary differential equations in terms of generalised modal coordinates. This is on the understanding that the number of modes taken for both bending and torsional motions could be extended, in principle, to as many as are required. The motivation for this analysis was to show that interesting and physically relevant phenomena can be observed within such a system, in particular the resonant phenomena due to combined forced-parametric excitations. Such excitations are very commonly encountered in the heave-surge motions experienced by offshore structures, for which this model is a somewhat idealised representation. The system of governing equations is in a form that can be readily solved by means of suitably approximate analysis, such as the perturbation method of multiple scales, for example. The differential equations contain linear inertia and stiffness terms, nonlinear inertia terms, and a range of forced and parametric excitation terms, and all equations exhibit precisely the sort of inter-coordinate cross-coupling typical of structural systems based upon beam kinematics. Solutions of these equations are not presented in this paper, for space reasons, but will form the subject of further publications in the very near future.

ACKNOWLEDGEMENTS

The authors would like to acknowledge the EPSRC grant, GR/L30749, which enabled this research to go ahead, permissions granted by Consafe Engineering (UK) Ltd for the use of original case study data, conversations between D.I.M.F. and S.W. Ziegler on certain issues relating to Mathematica, experimental work carried out by M.A. Kleschinski, and the use of facilities in the Department of Mechanical Engineering at the University of Glasgow and the Department of Mathematics and Statistics in the University of Edinburgh.

APPENDIX A

The quantities η_{ij}, ζ_{ij}, γ_{ij} and β are defined as follows:

$$\eta_{ij} = \int_0^l f_i'(z) f_j'(z) \, \mathrm{d}z,$$

$$\zeta_{ij} = \int_0^l f_i''(z) f_j''(z) \, \mathrm{d}z,$$

$$\gamma_{ij} = \int_0^l g_i'(z) g_j'(z) \, \mathrm{d}z,$$

$$\beta = \frac{R^2 g_1^2(l)}{f_1^2(l)}.$$

REFERENCES

(1) Sharpe, R.S., *Proceedings of the I.Mech.E.*, Vol. **208**, D05292, 1994, pp. 55–61.

(2) Schiehlen, W., *Multi-body Systems Handbook*, Springer Verlag, Berlin, 1990.

(3) Rosenthal, D.E., and Sherman, M.A., Symbolic Multi-body Equations via Kane's Method, *AAS/AIAA Astrodynamics Specialist Conference*, paper 83-803, Lake Placid, New York, 1983.

(4) Khanin., R, and Cartmell, M.P., *Mathematica in Education and Research*, Vol. **8**, No. 2, 1999, pp 19–26.

(5) Khanin., R, Cartmell, M.P. and Gilbert, A.D., *Computers and Structures*, to appear in 2000.

(6) Carmo., M.D., *Differential Geometry of Curves and Surfaces*, Prentice Hill, 1976.

(7) Timoshenko, S., *Theory of Elastic Stability*, McGraw-Hill, New York, 1936.

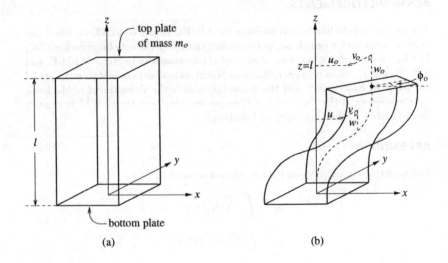

Figure 1: (a) the open box structure, (b) the structure under combined bending and torsion.

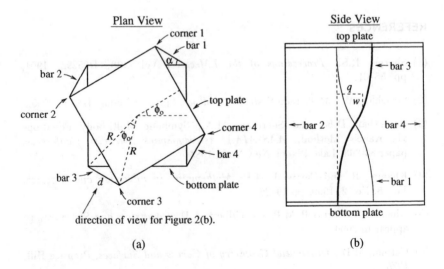

Figure 2: The open box structure under pure torsion.

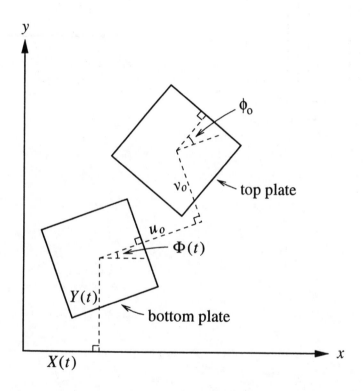

Figure 3: Plan view of the open box structure when the base is excited.

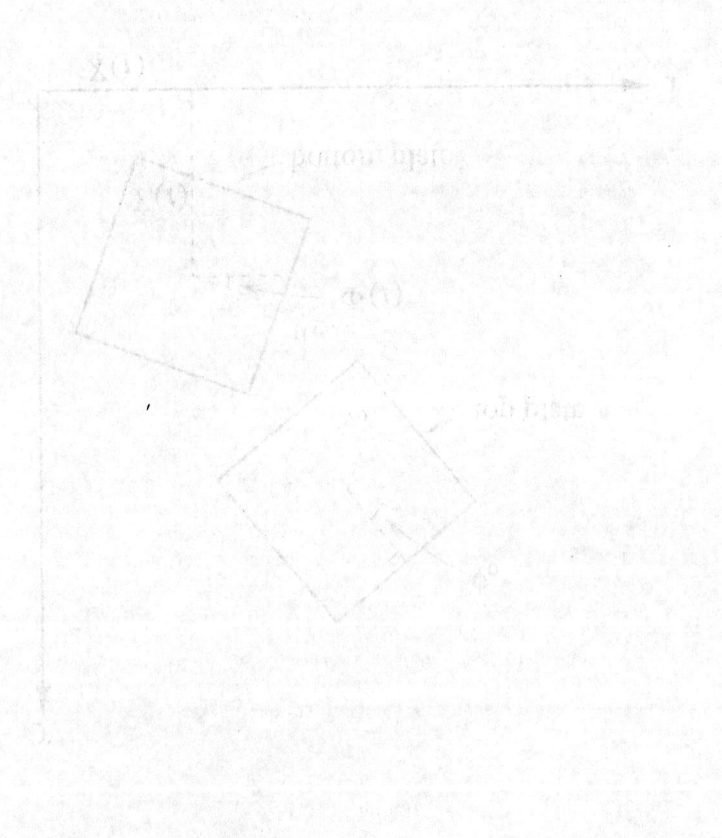

A NEW CRITERION OF STABILITY FOR THE VISCOUS SOLIDS: DISPLACEMENT FIELD APPROACH

F. Abed-Meraim*

This study deals with the stability problems encountered in the strain-rate-dependent solids and structures. The absence of equilibrium state in these viscous solids leads us to study the stability of their quasi-static evolutions. This concept of stability in the sense of trajectories thus generalises the stability of an equilibrium state but leads to more complex problems because of the non-autonomous (time-dependent) character. Once the problem of evolution is set in the form of a non-autonomous differential equation, the method of linearisation will be used to obtain results concerning the stability. The criterion of stability thus obtained is equivalent to studying the sign of the eigenvalues of a certain time-dependent operator. Note that the approach presented here consists of eliminating the internal variables to write the problem of evolution as a differential equation in the displacement field. This approach in displacement will be compared with that in internal variables recently proposed by the same author.

INTRODUCTION

It is historically well known that the studies of stability and bifurcation are the subjects of great interest in mechanics, both for their theoretical importance as well as for their practical aspects. Those studies try, in general, to answer fundamental questions for the engineer: critical buckling loads of certain thin-walled structures, forming limit curves for sheet metals related to the problems of necking, life times of structures before their failure by creep instabilities, etc.

For the reasons mentioned above, the theory of stability and bifurcation of solids has been an important pole of interest for researchers, engineers and manufacturers since more than one century. Many previous works can be found in the literature. In the elastic or elasto-plastic case, energy criteria of stability as well as conditions for uniqueness (i.e., non-bifurcation) were formulated and programmed in computer codes. Without giving an exhaustive list of references, one can quote most outstanding works (Koiter [1], Budiansky [2], Timoshenko and Gere [3] and Thompson and Hunt [4]) for the elastic case, and (Hill [5], Hutchinson [6], Nguyen [7] and Petryk [8]) in plasticity. It is also recalled that the distinction between the

* L.M.T. Cachan
E.N.S. de Cachan/C.N.R.S./Université Paris VI
61, avenue du Président Wilson, 94235 Cachan, France

concept of stability and that of bifurcation was first made by Shanley [9] in plasticity. For these time-independent materials, the concept of stability is understood in the sense of Lyapunov [10] and is characterised by the capacity of the system to remain in the vicinity of the equilibrium state under weak perturbations. The bifurcation is defined by the loss of uniqueness of the problem of evolution under consideration.

On the contrary to the preceding case of time-independent materials, the bifurcation does not occur at realistic stress levels for viscous solids without geometrical imperfections, because it is entirely governed by elasticity. Moreover, the equilibrium states do not exist for those materials because of the viscosity. Thus, the study of stability of viscous solids is more difficult and was less frequently investigated in the literature.

Our approach aims to explain the instabilities observed in experiments in these strain-rate-dependent solids, without using the concept of the bifurcation theory or that of the stability of an equilibrium. The absence of equilibrium state in viscous solids leads us to study the stability of their quasi-static evolutions. This concept of stability in the sense of trajectories is less common in mechanics than that of equilibrium states, and it leads to non-autonomous problems. The main difficulty encountered in the stability study of viscous structures comes from the non-autonomous character of their linearised differential equations system.

The proposed analysis of stability uses the method of linearisation which is composed of the following stages:

- The choice of the basic variable used for the writing of the problem of quasi-static evolution.

- The setting of this problem of evolution in the form of a differential equation which is a function of the basic variable selected and the parameter of loading.

- The linearisation of this differential equation around the non-stationary quasi-static evolution of which the stability is studied.

- The application of the results of stability [11, 12] to the non-autonomous differential equation obtained by this linearisation.

The originality of our approach lies in its capacity to address the problem of stability of the original non-linear system and not only that of the linearised one. Moreover, it takes into account the non-autonomous character of the problem and it allows for the establishment of the link with the usual mathematical procedures of linearisation of the non-linear differential equations.

40

FORMAL STUDY

To explain our approach, we will carry out the formal study of a general mechanical system, characterised by a total potential energy $\mathbb{W}(u, \alpha, \lambda)$ and a total dual potential of dissipation $\Omega(A)$. The quasi-static evolution of such a viscous solid is governed by the system of equations:

$$\begin{cases} \text{Equilibrium:} & \mathbb{W}_{,u}(u, \alpha, \lambda) \cdot \delta u = 0 \quad \forall \, \delta u \\ \text{State equation:} & A = -\mathbb{W}_{,\alpha}(u, \alpha, \lambda) \\ \text{Complementary law:} & \dot{\alpha} = \Omega_{,A}(A) \\ \text{Initial value:} & \alpha(0) = \alpha_0 \end{cases} \tag{1}$$

In addition to these equations of evolution, this mechanical system satisfies the incremental form of the equilibrium equation (i.e., rate problem) given by:

$$\delta u \cdot \left[\mathbb{W}_{,uu} \cdot \dot{u} + \mathbb{W}_{,u\alpha} \cdot \dot{\alpha} + \mathbb{W}_{,u\lambda} . \dot{\lambda} \right] = 0 \quad \forall \, \delta u \tag{2}$$

In this quasi-static evolution, the variables (u, α), representing the displacement and the internal variable (i.e., visco-plastic strain), are not independent and they are linked by the equilibrium equation. One can thus use one or the other of these variables for the writing of the differential equation governing the quasi-static evolution. For example, the elimination of u from the equilibrium equation enables us to write $u = u(\alpha, \lambda)$, and to consider equation (1) as a differential equation in the variable α only. One obtains thus:

$$\dot{\alpha} = g(\alpha, \lambda) \tag{3}$$

where:

$$g(\alpha, \lambda) = \Omega_{,A}(A(u(\alpha, \lambda), \alpha)) \tag{4}$$

In an earlier study, this choice of the variable α provided us with sufficient conditions of stability (Abed-Meraim [11, 12]). In the present paper, we will present the other alternative called the field of displacement approach. It consists of retaining for basic variable the kinematic field u. Indeed, the equilibrium allows the extraction of the relation $\alpha = \alpha(u, \lambda)$. Substituting this expression of α and of its flow, given by the complementary law, in the incremental form of the equilibrium equation (2), one obtains:

$$\dot{u} = f(u, \lambda, \dot{\lambda}) \tag{5}$$

where:

$$f(u, \lambda, \dot{\lambda}) = -\mathbb{W}_{,uu}^{-1} \cdot \left(\mathbb{W}_{,u\alpha} \cdot \Omega_{,A}(A) + \mathbb{W}_{,u\lambda} . \dot{\lambda} \right) \tag{6}$$

41

In the above expressions of $W_{,uu}$, $W_{,u\alpha}$, $W_{,u\lambda}$ and A, we have replaced α by its expression $\alpha(u, \lambda)$. Note that the operator $W_{,uu}$ is invertible since one will remain at the levels of loadings below the critical load of elastic loss of stability. For a given initial condition $u(0) = u_0$, the resolution of the differential equation (5) provides us with a fundamental solution $u^0(t)$. The application of the method of linearisation to the differential equation (5) will enable us, in the sequel, to deduce results concerning the stability of this fundamental evolution $u^0(t)$.

VISCOUS SOLID IN FINITE TRANSFORMATION

We consider here the general case of a three-dimensional viscous solid occupying in its initial configuration, not deformed, a volume V of boundary ∂V. This solid is subject to specified body forces $F(\lambda)$, to surface tractions $T(\lambda)$ on a part ∂V_T of its boundary and to prescribed displacements $u_d(\lambda)$ on the complementary part. The scalar λ represents a parameter of loading.

A total Lagrangian description will be adopted: the configuration of reference will be the initial configuration of the solid. Also, we consider the context of generalised standard materials (cf. Halphen and Nguyen [13]). The method of the two potentials (cf. Germain [14]), potential of free energy and that of dissipation, will enable us to write the equilibrium and evolution equations in a systematic way.

Quasi-static evolution

In this section, we will write the equations governing the quasi-static evolution of the solid subject to a loading path and we will formulate the associated rate problem. They are equations (1) and (2) previously written in a global form.

If one denotes by $w(e, \alpha)$ the free energy density of the solid, then the state equations are written:

$$\pi = w_{,e} \tag{7}$$
$$A = -w_{,\alpha} \tag{8}$$

In these relations, A is the thermodynamic force associated to the internal variable α. This latter variable represents the visco-elastic strain e^v or visco-plastic strain e^p. The variable π represents the second Piola-Kirchhoff stress tensor and appears as the thermodynamic force associated to the variable e. This non-linear Green-Lagrange strain tensor is obtained from the Lagrangian gradient of displacement ∇u by the relation:

$$e = \frac{1}{2} \left(\nabla u + \nabla^T u + \nabla^T u . \nabla u \right) \tag{9}$$

The equilibrium of the solid under the loading effect parameterised by $\lambda(t)$, $\lambda \in [0, \lambda_M]$, is given by the principle of virtual work:

$$\int_V \boldsymbol{\pi} : \delta e \ dv = \int_V \boldsymbol{F}(\lambda).\delta \boldsymbol{u} \ dv + \int_{\partial V_T} \boldsymbol{T}(\lambda).\delta \boldsymbol{u} \ ds \qquad \forall \delta \boldsymbol{u} \quad \text{C.A.} \qquad (10)$$

Using the first Piola-Kirchhoff stress tensor b, given by:

$$b = w_{,\nabla u} = \boldsymbol{F}.\boldsymbol{\pi} \qquad , \qquad \boldsymbol{F} = \nabla \boldsymbol{u} + \boldsymbol{I} \qquad (11)$$

the equilibrium equation can be set in the equivalent form:

$$\int_V b : \nabla \delta \boldsymbol{u} \ dv = \int_V \boldsymbol{F}(\lambda).\delta \boldsymbol{u} \ dv + \int_{\partial V_T} \boldsymbol{T}(\lambda).\delta \boldsymbol{u} \ ds \qquad \forall \delta \boldsymbol{u} \quad \text{C.A.} \qquad (12)$$

One can also write the equilibrium equations (10) or (12) in the global form (1) by using total potential energy $\mathbb{W}(\boldsymbol{u}, \boldsymbol{\alpha}, \lambda)$, given by:

$$\left\{ \begin{array}{c} \mathbb{W}(\nabla \boldsymbol{u}, \boldsymbol{\alpha}, \lambda) = W(\nabla \boldsymbol{u}, \boldsymbol{\alpha}) - W_{ext}(\boldsymbol{u}, \lambda) \\[2mm] W(\nabla \boldsymbol{u}, \boldsymbol{\alpha}) = \int_V w(\nabla \boldsymbol{u}, \boldsymbol{\alpha}) \ dv \\[2mm] W_{ext}(\boldsymbol{u}, \lambda) = \int_V \boldsymbol{F}(\lambda) \cdot \boldsymbol{u} \ dv + \int_{\partial V_T} \boldsymbol{T}(\lambda) \cdot \boldsymbol{u} \ ds \end{array} \right. \qquad (13)$$

In the above expression of total potential energy, $W(\nabla \boldsymbol{u}, \boldsymbol{\alpha})$ and $W_{ext}(\boldsymbol{u}, \lambda)$ denote respectively the global potential of free energy and the potential of the external efforts. By derivation of the equilibrium equation which is written from now on in a condensed form, as follows:

$$\mathbb{W}_{,u}(\boldsymbol{u}, \boldsymbol{\alpha}, \lambda) \cdot \delta \boldsymbol{u} = 0 \qquad \forall \delta \boldsymbol{u} \qquad (14)$$

one obtains the global incremental equation describing the rate problem:

$$\delta \boldsymbol{u} \cdot \left[\mathbb{W}_{,uu} \cdot \dot{\boldsymbol{u}} + \mathbb{W}_{,u\alpha} \cdot \dot{\boldsymbol{\alpha}} + \mathbb{W}_{,u\lambda}.\dot{\lambda} \right] = 0 \qquad \forall \delta \boldsymbol{u} \qquad (15)$$

This equation, denoting the rate problem, is written more explicitly as:

$$\int_V \nabla \delta \boldsymbol{u} : (w_{,\nabla u \nabla u} : \nabla \dot{\boldsymbol{u}} + w_{,\nabla u \alpha} : \dot{\boldsymbol{\alpha}}) \ dv = \int_V \dot{\boldsymbol{F}}(\lambda).\delta \boldsymbol{u} \ dv + \int_{\partial V_T} \dot{\boldsymbol{T}}(\lambda).\delta \boldsymbol{u} \ ds \quad (16)$$

To completely define the quasi-static evolution of the solid, we should give the law of evolution of its irreversible variables $\boldsymbol{\alpha}$. This can be done by means of the dual potential of dissipation $\Omega(\boldsymbol{A})$. This complementary relation is written then:

$$\dot{\boldsymbol{\alpha}} = \Omega_{,A}(\boldsymbol{A}) \qquad (17)$$

By replacing the expression of the flow of α in the incremental form of the equilibrium equation (15), we can see that this approach of stability in the basic variable u amounts to studying jointly the two following equations:

$$\begin{cases} \mathbb{W}_{,u}(u, \alpha, \lambda) \cdot \delta u = 0 \\ \delta u \cdot \left[\mathbb{W}_{,uu} \cdot \dot{u} + \mathbb{W}_{,u\alpha} \cdot \Omega_{,A} + \mathbb{W}_{,u\lambda} \cdot \dot{\lambda} \right] = 0 \end{cases} \qquad \forall \, \delta u \qquad (18)$$

The linearisation of these equations around the fundamental solution will be made in the following section to study its stability. Before proceeding to this stage of linearisation, one proposes to clarify the incremental form of the equilibrium equation for a given free energy density. For a viscous solid with kinematic hardening modulus h and with isotropic elasticity, one takes a free energy density of the form:

$$w(e, \alpha) = \frac{1}{2}(e - \alpha) : E : (e - \alpha) + \frac{1}{2}\alpha : h : \alpha \qquad (19)$$

The fourth-order tensor of the moduli of elasticity: $w_{,ee} = E$ satisfies the classical symmetries:

$$E_{ijkl} = E_{jikl} = E_{klij} \qquad (20)$$

Under these conditions, the equilibrium equation is set under one or the other of the equivalent forms (10) or (12), with the following expressions of the state relations:

$$\begin{cases} \pi = w_{,e} = E : (e - \alpha) \\ A = -w_{,\alpha} = E : (e - \alpha) - h : \alpha \end{cases} \qquad (21)$$

While the rate problem (15) or (16) can be set in the form:

$$\int_V \nabla \delta u : (L_e : \nabla^T \dot{u} + L_1 : \dot{\alpha}) \, dv = \int_V \dot{F}(\lambda).\delta u \, dv + \int_{\partial V_T} \dot{T}(\lambda).\delta u \, ds \qquad (22)$$

with:

$$\begin{cases} L_e = (\nabla u + I).E.(I + \nabla^T u) + R \\ L_1 = -(\nabla u + I).E \end{cases} \qquad (23)$$

In the expression of the modulus L_e, the fourth-order tensor R is defined by:

$$R_{ijkl} = \pi_{jk}\delta_{il} \qquad (24)$$

Let us recall that in the analyses of elastic bifurcation, it is this modulus L_e which controls the possibility of buckling. It comes from the terms of elasticity and change of geometry.

Linearisation

For a given loading path and a given initial condition, the resolution of the equation of evolution (1) provides us with a quasi-static evolution $(u(t), \alpha(t))$. In the sequel, one will denote by $(u^0(t), \alpha^0(t))$ the fundamental solution of which one seeks to study the stability. This quasi-static evolution is solution of the differential equation formed by the system:

$$\begin{cases} \mathbb{W}_{,u}(u, \alpha, \lambda) \cdot \delta u = 0 \\ \delta u \cdot \left[\mathbb{W}_{,uu} \cdot \dot{u} + \mathbb{W}_{,u\alpha} \cdot \Omega_{,A} + \mathbb{W}_{,u\lambda} \cdot \dot{\lambda} \right] = 0 \qquad \forall \, \delta u \\ u(0) = u_0 \end{cases} \tag{25}$$

To obtain a differential equation of variable u only, it is necessary to extract from the first equilibrium equation the relation $\alpha = \alpha(u, \lambda)$ that we replace then into the second equation translating the incremental form of the equilibrium equation.

This fundamental solution $(u^0(t), \alpha^0(t))$ will be disturbed at an arbitrary time t_0 by the introduction of a small disturbance: $(u^*(t_0), \alpha^*(t_0))$. In the sequel, one will denote by $(u^*(t), \alpha^*(t)) = (u(t) - u^0(t), \alpha(t) - \alpha^0(t))$, $t \geq t_0$, the time evolution of this disturbance of the fundamental solution.

The linearisation of the differential equation in u formed by the above system (25), around the fundamental solution, is obtained by the simultaneous linearisation of the equilibrium equation and the rate problem, respectively.

The linearisation of the equilibrium equation gives:

$$\int_V \nabla \delta u : (w_{,\nabla u \nabla u} : \nabla u^* + w_{,\nabla u \alpha} : \alpha^*) \, dv = 0 \tag{26}$$

This linearised equation can be written more clearly as:

$$\int_V \nabla \delta u : (L_e : \nabla^T u^* + L_1 : \alpha^*) \, dv = 0 \tag{27}$$

where:

$$\begin{cases} L_e = (\nabla u^0 + I) \cdot E \cdot (I + \nabla^T u^0) + R^0 \\ L_1 = -(\nabla u^0 + I) \cdot E \end{cases} \tag{28}$$

Finally, the incremental form of the equilibrium equation combined with that giving the evolution of the dissipative parameters gives after linearisation:

$$\int_V \nabla \delta u : (L_e : \nabla^T \dot{u}^* + L_2 : \nabla^T u^* + L_3 : \alpha^*) \, dv = 0 \tag{29}$$

with:

$$\begin{cases} L_2 = \left(\nabla u^0 + I\right).E.\nabla^T \dot{u}^0 + \nabla \dot{u}^0.E.\left(I + \nabla^T u^0\right) + \dot{R}^0 - \\ \qquad \left(\nabla u^0 + I\right).E : \Omega_{,AA}^0 : E.\left(I + \nabla^T u^0\right) \\ L_3 = \left(\nabla u^0 + I\right).E : \Omega_{,AA}^0 : (E + h) - \nabla \dot{u}^0.E \end{cases} \qquad (30)$$

Stability analysis

In this approach of stability where the displacement field u is taken as basic variable, the implicit differential equation to linearise is:

$$\dot{u} = f(u, \lambda, \dot{\lambda}) \qquad (31)$$

where:

$$f(u, \lambda, \dot{\lambda}) = -W_{,uu}^{-1} \cdot \left(W_{,u\alpha} \cdot \Omega_{,A}(A) + W_{,u\lambda}.\dot{\lambda}\right) \qquad (32)$$

In the above function f, we have replaced α by its expression $\alpha(u, \lambda)$, given implicitly by the equilibrium equation. By linearisation of this differential equation around the fundamental solution $u^0(t)$, one obtains formally:

$$\dot{u}^* = L(t) \cdot u^* \qquad (33)$$

where:

$$L(t) = \frac{\partial f}{\partial u}\left(u^0(t), \lambda(t), \dot{\lambda}(t)\right) \qquad (34)$$

At this stage, one can apply the results of [11, 12] concerning the stability of the non-autonomous differential systems. The negative-definite character of the symmetrical part L^S of the operator L, at every point of the evolution, provides a sufficient condition of uniform and asymptotic stability of this evolution.

An explicit expression of the operator L cannot be calculated in the general case, it is preferable to carry out this analysis of eigenvalues in an equivalent way on the following system:

$$\begin{cases} \int_V \nabla \delta u : \left(L_e : \nabla^T u^* + L_1 : \alpha^*\right) \, dv = 0 \\ \int_V \nabla \delta u : \left(L_e : \nabla^T \dot{u}^* + L_2 : \nabla^T u^* + L_3 : \alpha^*\right) \, dv = 0 \end{cases} \qquad (35)$$

46

with :

$$
\begin{cases}
L_e = \left(\nabla u^0 + I\right).E.\left(I + \nabla^T u^0\right) + R^0 \\[2mm]
L_1 = -\left(\nabla u^0 + I\right).E \\[2mm]
L_2 = \left(\nabla u^0 + I\right).E.\nabla^T \dot{u}^0 + \nabla \dot{u}^0.E.\left(I + \nabla^T u^0\right) + \dot{R}^0 - \\[2mm]
\qquad \left(\nabla u^0 + I\right).E : \Omega_{,AA}^0 : E.\left(I + \nabla^T u^0\right) \\[2mm]
L_3 = \left(\nabla u^0 + I\right).E : \Omega_{,AA}^0 : (E + h) - \nabla \dot{u}^0.E
\end{cases} \tag{36}
$$

Such an analysis of eigenvalues is carried out in general by a recourse to the numerical means. A classical approach by finite elements consists in discretising the structure then calculating the various rigidities, generated by the fourth-order tensors L_i, along the fundamental solution. Under these conditions, the system (35) is set in the following matrix form:

$$
\begin{cases}
\mathcal{L}_e \cdot u^* + \mathcal{L}_1 \cdot \alpha^* = 0 \\[2mm]
\mathcal{L}_e \cdot \dot{u}^* + \mathcal{L}_2 \cdot u^* + \mathcal{L}_3 \cdot \alpha^* = 0
\end{cases} \tag{37}
$$

By combining the equations of system (37), one arrives at a relation expressing the evolution of the time disturbance and relating $\dot{u}^*$ to u^* by:

$$
\dot{u}^* = \mathcal{L} \cdot u^* \tag{38}
$$

If one denotes by $\mathcal{L}^S$ the symmetrical part of $\mathcal{L}$, then a sufficient condition of uniform and asymptotic stability of the evolution is that the maximum eigenvalue of the operator $\mathcal{L}^S$ is upper bounded by a strictly negative constant throughout this evolution.

Case of an infinitesimal fundamental solution

In the case where the fundamental solution $u^0(t)$ satisfies: $\|\nabla u^0\| \ll 1$, one can operate some simplifications in the above operators, and the eigenvalues analysis previously described must be carried out on the following system:

$$
\begin{cases}
\displaystyle\int_V \nabla \delta u : \left(H_e : \nabla u^* + H_1 : \alpha^*\right) \, dv = 0 \\[4mm]
\displaystyle\int_V \nabla \delta u : \left(H_e : \nabla \dot{u}^* + H_2 : \nabla^T u^* + H_3 : \alpha^*\right) \, dv = 0
\end{cases} \tag{39}
$$

with :

$$
\begin{cases}
H_e = E + S^0 \\[2mm]
H_1 = -E \\[2mm]
H_2 = E.\nabla^T \dot{u}^0 + \nabla \dot{u}^0.E + \dot{R}^0 - E : \Omega_{,AA}^0 : E \\[2mm]
H_3 = E : \Omega_{,AA}^0 : (E + h) - \nabla \dot{u}^0.E
\end{cases} \tag{40}
$$

47

In the term $\boldsymbol{H}_e$ coming from elasticity, the fourth-order tensor $\boldsymbol{S}^0$ giving geometrical rigidity is defined by:

$$S^0_{ijkl} = R^0_{ijlk} = \pi^0_{jl}\delta_{ik} \tag{41}$$

Note that within this framework of the assumptions of small displacements, one can confuse the configurations V and V_t, the stress tensors $\boldsymbol{\pi}$ and $\boldsymbol{\sigma}$ as well as the Lagrangian and Eulerian gradients.

In the same spirit as previously, this system leads to a relation between $\dot{\boldsymbol{u}}^*$ and $\boldsymbol{u}^*$ of the form:

$$\dot{\boldsymbol{u}}^* = \mathcal{H} \cdot \boldsymbol{u}^* \tag{42}$$

where the operator $\mathcal{H}$, not necessarily symmetrical, is obtained by combination of the equations of the system given in (39).

The strict negative-definite character of the symmetrical part $\mathcal{H}^S$ of the operator $\mathcal{H}$ provides a sufficient condition of uniform and asymptotic stability of the evolution.

CONCLUSION

A new criterion of stability of the quasi-static evolution of the viscous solids was proposed in this paper. The method used consists in setting the problem of evolution in the form of a differential equation in variable u only, after having eliminated the internal variable α from the equilibrium. The criterion of stability thus obtained was given for a general three-dimensional continuous medium.

This new approach of stability was also applied and validated on the example of the viscous Shanley's column [12]. The same results were obtained on this example with the two approaches of stability: the approach in internal variables [11] and the approach in displacement field presented here. Under the loading effect parameterised by $\lambda(t) \in [0, \lambda_M]$, one shows that the quasi-static evolution of the viscous column is uniformly and asymptotically stable as long as the load remains lower than λ_T. Otherwise, this column becomes unstable for $\lambda_M > \lambda_T$. Let us recall that λ_T, known as the critical load of the tangent modulus, corresponds to the first load of bifurcation of the column with elasto-plastic behaviour [5].

It is interesting to notice that the problem of the choice of the basic variables would not have been arisen if one of these approaches had led to a sufficient and necessary condition of stability. However, the stability conditions obtained in general are sufficient conditions, except for some simple cases. It is thus important to compare these approaches of stability (approach in u and approach in α) in the general case of a viscous solid. Indeed, if these two approaches could be reconciled on the example of the viscous Shanley's column, they can give critical loads however different for general three-dimensional continuous media.

REFERENCE LIST

(1) Koiter, W.T., On the thermodynamic background of elastic stability theory. In *Problems of hydrodynamics and continuum mechanics*, pp. 423–433, Philadelphia, 1967.

(2) Budiansky, B., Theory of buckling and post-buckling behavior of elastic structures. *Adv. Appl. Mech.*, Vol. 14, 1974, pp. 1–65.

(3) Timoshenko, S.P., and Gere, J.M., *Theory of elastic stability*, Mc Graw-Hill, New York, 1961.

(4) Thompson, J.M.T., and Hunt, G.M., *A general theory of elastic stability*, Wiley, London, 1973.

(5) Hill, R., A general theory of uniqueness and stability in elastic-plastic solids. *J. of Mech. Phys. Solids*, Vol. 6, 1958, pp. 236–249.

(6) Hutchinson, J.W., Plastic buckling. *Adv. Appl. Mech.*, Vol. 14, 1974, pp. 67–144.

(7) Nguyen, Q.S., Bifurcation and post-bifurcation analysis in plasticity and brittle fracture. *J. of Mech. Phys. Solids*, Vol. 35, No. 3, 1987, pp. 303–324.

(8) Petryk, H., Theory of bifurcation and instability in time-independent plasticity. In *Advanced Course on Bifurcation and Stability of Dissipative Systems*, C.I.S.M., Udine, Italie, 1991.

(9) Shanley, F.R., Inelastic column theory. *J. Aeronaut. Sci.*, Vol. 14, 1947, pp. 261–267.

(10) Lyapunov, A., *Stability of motion*, Engl. transl., New York, 1966.

(11) Abed-Meraim, F., Conditions suffisantes de stabilité pour les solides visqueux. *C. R. Acad. Sci., Paris*, t. 327, Série II b, No. 1, 1999, pp. 25–31.

(12) Abed-Meraim, F., *Quelques problèmes de stabilité et de bifurcation des solides visqueux*, Ph.D. Thesis, Ecole Polytechnique, France, 1999.

(13) Halphen, B., and Nguyen, Q.S., Sur les matériaux standard généralisés. *J. de Mécanique*, Vol. 14, No. 1, 1975, pp. 39–63.

(14) Germain, P., *Cours de mécanique des milieux continus*, Masson, Paris, 1973.

A NON-LINEAR ANALYTICAL MODEL FOR PRELOADED RUBBER CYLINDERS

L.Kari †

A materially and geometrically non-linear analytical model for statically preloaded cylindrical rubber isolators is presented, where influences of cylinder radius and height, material parameters and precompression are investigated. The rubber material is assumed to be incompressible with deviatoric response determined by a Rivlin type of Helmholtz free energy function. The analytical model is based on a semi-inverse method where material planes parallel to the bonded metal plate in the rubber cylinder are assumed to remain parallel throughout the pre-deformation range and where the traction free boundary condition on the rubber surface is approximately satisfied by collocation. Contrary to other semi-inverse models, this model coincides at vanishing preload with a well known linear formula used in engineering environment. The model extends, in addition, the applicable shape factor range to cover also small shape factors, typically used for vibration isolators.

1. INTRODUCTION

A vibration isolator basic attenuation principle is to provide a mechanical property mismatch between the source and receiving structure; the mismatch acting as a mirror, while reflecting the vibrations from the source backwards. As the source and receiving structure are usually stiff, a suitable isolator is accordingly soft; the softer the better the attenuation, with zero stiffness as the optimum, that is, replacing the isolators with an empty space. However, as isolators also carry the source, provide dynamic and static stability etc.; the attenuation optimization process has to be solved with strongly restricted design parameters - clearly, excluding the zero stiffness solution. This paper focuses on one of those parameters: the non-linear preload effects on the static stiffness of the most common commercially available resilient element; namely, the circular cylindrical vibration isolator with bonded end plates.

A direct approach to solve the problem is through a numerical method, such as a (non-linear) finite element method (FEM); Kari [1], or a (linear) boundary element method; Gaul [2]. Although FEM handles arbitrary geometry and difficult constitutive equations with great success, it is not ideal in an engineering environment, where they may be quite cumbersome in an iterative design process, while interpreting the results is usually difficult, as no closed form solution is

† MWL/Department of Vehicle Engineering, Kungliga Tekniska Högskolan, 100 44 Stockholm, Sweden.

obtained. An alternative approach is through a simple analytical method; such as Klingbeil and Shield [3] or Zdunek [4]. This paper enlarges the semi-inverse model in [3] and [4] to cover also small shape factors, typically used for vibration isolators. The derived model is also shown to coincide at vanishing preload with a well known linear formula used in engineering environment, Gent [5].

2. METHOD

2.1 Vibration isolator

The studied vibration isolator in Figure 1 consists of an L long vulcanized rubber cylinder with radius R, firmly bonded to two parallel metal plates. The metal parts facilitate installation and distribute the applied load over the rubber surfaces in a fail safe manner, while increasing the overall stiffness. The rubber carries the load and reflects, attenuates and transmits structure borne sound.

2.2 Kinematics and the model

Consider the vibration isolator, a simple body consisting of continuously distributed material occupying a reference configuration $\mathscr{B}$ in its natural state; stress-free and undeformed, and refer to $\mathscr{S}$ as an ambient space in which the evolution of the body takes place, where $\mathscr{B}$ and $\mathscr{S} \subset \mathbb{R}^3$ are sufficiently smooth, oriented open manifolds endowed with metrics I and i, respectively. A configuration space $\mathcal{C}$ is a set of all non-degenerated, admissible configurations; $\varphi : \mathscr{B} \to \mathscr{S}$. The isolator undergoes a regular motion; a curve in $\mathcal{C} : t \in \mathbb{R} \mapsto \varphi_t \in \mathcal{C}$ and $x = \varphi_t(X) = \varphi(X,t)$ where $\varphi_t^{-1} : \mathscr{S} \to \mathscr{B}$ exists, $X \in \mathscr{B}$ and $x \in \mathscr{S}$ are material and spatial points.

The rubber material is assumed to be isotropic, homogeneous and incompressible, the latter constraining the volume strain measure $J : \mathscr{B} \to \mathbb{R}$ into $J = 1$, where in positively oriented coordinates $J = \sqrt{\det(i)/\mathrm{DET}(I)}\, \partial(\varphi^1,\varphi^2,\varphi^3)/\partial(X^1,X^2,X^3)$, being the Jacobian of φ. This motion constraint results in a constitutively undetermined spherical stress, which depends - in a spatially non-local way - upon motion, as in fluid mechanics, and therefore, contradicts the basic postulate, Noll [6]. The remedy is to split the Cauchy stress on $\mathscr{S}$ into $\sigma = -p\,i + \mathrm{dev}[\sigma]$, where the deviatoric stress is constitutively determined while p an unknown pressure function; $\mathrm{tr}\,\sigma = i : \sigma = -3p$, where $\mathrm{dev}[\cdot] = [1 - \frac{1}{3}(i \otimes i)] : [\cdot]$ and the fourth order unit tensor $1 = \frac{1}{2}[(i \boxtimes i) + (i \square i)]$. The tensor products $\otimes$, $\boxtimes$ and $\square$ are defined by $(a \otimes b):c = (b:c)a$, $(a \boxtimes b):c = a\,c\,b^T$ and $(a \square b):c = a\,c^T b^T$ where a, b and c are arbitrary second order tensors, : and T denote double contraction and transpose, respectively. The pressure plays the role of a Lagrange multiplier in Hamiltonian systems with constraints or is determined from a compressible theory as the incompressible limit $p = \lim_{K \to 0} p_K$, provided $J = 1$, where p_K is a constitutive pressure function given by a compressible theory and K a compressibility, defined as $K = [\partial p_K / \partial \rho]^{-1}$. In order to state a problem where the body surface is deformed on which to impose the boundary conditions, it is convenient to apply a material description such as in [4], using the First Piola-Kirchhoffs stress. This two-point stress tensor T is related to Cauchy stress through a Piola transformation on the second index of σ; $T = J \sigma F^{-T}$. The First Piola-Kirchhoffs stress response tensor is derivable from a Helmholtz free energy $\Psi: \mathcal{B} \to \mathbb{R}$ per unit undeformed volume, Marsden and Hughes [7], as

$$T = -pF^{-T} + \frac{\partial \Psi}{\partial F}, \tag{1}$$

where the two-point tensor $F = T\varphi: T\mathcal{B} \to T\mathcal{b}$ is the usual deformation gradient to φ; which, after variable change, equals

$$T = -pF^{-T} + 2\left[\frac{\partial \Psi}{\partial I_1} + I_1 \frac{\partial \Psi}{\partial I_2}\right] F - 2\frac{\partial \Psi}{\partial I_2} bF, \tag{2}$$

where the Finger deformation tensor $b = F F^T: T\mathcal{b} \to T\mathcal{b}$; the principal invariants of b are: $I_1 = \operatorname{tr} b$, $I_2 = \operatorname{tr} [b^{-1}]$ and, trivially $I_3 = \det b = J^2 = 1$. The isochoric free energy function Ψ is assumed to be additively decomposible into

$$\Psi(I_1, I_2) = \sum_{n \in \mathbb{N}} \sum_{m \in \mathbb{N}} C_{nm}[I_1 - 3]^n [I_2 - 3]^m, \tag{3}$$

where $C_{nm} \in \mathbb{R}$, $C_{00} = 0$ and $\mu_\infty = 2[C_{10} + C_{01}]$ is the classical equilibrium shear modulus. In particular, the equilibrium stress is reduced to

$$T = -pF^{-T} + [\mu_\infty + 4C_{20}(I_1 - 3) + 6C_{30}(I_1 - 3)^2] F, \tag{4}$$

$$T = -pF^{-T} + [\mu_\infty + 2C_{01}(I_1 - 1)] F - 2C_{01} bF \tag{5}$$

and

$$T = -pF^{-T} + \mu_\infty F, \tag{6}$$

for Yeoh [8], Mooney-Rivlin and neo-Hookean materials, respectively. The latter having a sound basis in a simple statistical molecular theory, Treloar [9], Mooney-Rivlin extends it by assuming a linear response to simple shear, while Yeoh studies agree with carbon black filled rubber behavior.

Consider the isolator in Figure 2 undergoing an axisymmetric torsion-free motion from a cylinder length L to l; $L \geq l$. The imposed coordinate systems on $\mathcal{B}$ and $\mathcal{b}$ are $\{X^A\} = \{R, \Phi, Z\}$ and $\{x^a\} = \{r, \phi, z\}$, respectively; having parallel basis vectors and coinciding origins at the cylinder center. The motion reads $r = r(R, Z)$, $\phi = \Phi$ and $z = z(R, Z)$, subjected to the mixed boundary conditions

$$r = P \tag{7}$$

and

$$z = Z, \tag{8}$$

on $Z = \pm L/2$ and

$$TN = 0, \tag{9}$$

on the free rubber surface, where N is the unit outward normal to the surface on $\mathscr{B}$. The analytical model is based on a semi-inverse method where material planes parallel to the bonded metal plate in the rubber cylinder are assumed to remain parallel throughout the pre-deformation range, narrowing the motion down to

$$z = \zeta(Z), \tag{10}$$

where ζ is a function. The incompressibility condition reads

$$\frac{r}{R} \frac{\partial r}{\partial R} \frac{d\zeta}{dZ} = 1, \tag{11}$$

giving

$$r = R \sqrt{\frac{1}{\dfrac{d\zeta}{dZ}}}, \tag{12}$$

where the integration constant is set to zero as $r = 0$ on $R = 0$. The deformation gradient tensor components read

$$F(e^a, E_A) = F^a{}_A = \begin{bmatrix} \gamma & 0 & R\dfrac{d\gamma}{dZ} \\ 0 & 1 & 0 \\ 0 & 0 & \gamma^{-2} \end{bmatrix}, \tag{13}$$

the Finger deformation tensor components are

$$b(e^a, e_b) = FF^T(e^a, e_b) = b^a{}_b = \begin{bmatrix} \gamma^2 + [R\dfrac{d\gamma}{dZ}]^2 & 0 & R\dfrac{d\gamma}{dZ}\gamma^{-2} \\ 0 & \gamma^2 & 0 \\ R\dfrac{d\gamma}{dZ}\gamma^{-2} & 0 & \gamma^{-4} \end{bmatrix}, \tag{14}$$

having the inverses

$$F^{-1}(E^A, e_a) = F^{-1A}{}_a = \begin{bmatrix} \gamma^{-1} & 0 & -R\gamma\dfrac{d\gamma}{dZ} \\ 0 & 1 & 0 \\ 0 & 0 & \gamma^2 \end{bmatrix} \tag{15}$$

and

$$b^{-1}(e^a, e_b) = b^{-1a}{}_b = \begin{bmatrix} \gamma^{-2} & 0 & -R\dfrac{d\gamma}{dZ} \\ 0 & \gamma^{-2} & 0 \\ -R\dfrac{d\gamma}{dZ} & 0 & \gamma^4 + [R\gamma\dfrac{d\gamma}{dZ}]^2 \end{bmatrix}, \tag{16}$$

where the function $\gamma = [d\zeta/dZ]^{-\frac{1}{2}}$; E_A and e_a are base vectors on $\mathcal{B}$ and δ, respectively, while E^A and e^a are their reciprocals. The first principal invariant

$$I_1 = 2\gamma^2 + [R\dfrac{d\gamma}{dZ}]^2 + \gamma^{-4} \tag{17}$$

and the second

$$I_2 = \gamma^4 + [R\gamma\dfrac{d\gamma}{dZ}]^2 + 2\gamma^{-2}. \tag{18}$$

The (contravariant) First Piola-Kirchhoffs stress tensor components become

$$T(e^a, E^A) = T^{aA} = -p \begin{bmatrix} \gamma^{-1} & 0 & 0 \\ 0 & [R\gamma]^{-2} & 0 \\ -R\gamma\dfrac{d\gamma}{dZ} & 0 & \gamma^2 \end{bmatrix} +$$

$$+ \left[\mu_\infty + 4C_{20}(2\gamma^2 + [R\dfrac{d\gamma}{dZ}]^2 + \gamma^{-4} - 3) + 6C_{30}(2\gamma^2 + [R\dfrac{d\gamma}{dZ}]^2 + \gamma^{-4} - 3)^2 \right] \times$$

$$\times \begin{bmatrix} \gamma & 0 & R\dfrac{d\gamma}{dZ} \\ 0 & R^2 & 0 \\ 0 & 0 & \gamma^{-2} \end{bmatrix}; \tag{19}$$

$$T(e^a, E^A) = T^{aA} = -p \begin{bmatrix} \gamma^{-1} & 0 & 0 \\ 0 & [R\gamma]^{-2} & 0 \\ -R\gamma\dfrac{d\gamma}{dZ} & 0 & \gamma^2 \end{bmatrix} + [\mu_\infty + 2C_{01}(I_1 - 1)] \begin{bmatrix} \gamma & 0 & R\dfrac{d\gamma}{dZ} \\ 0 & R^{-2} & 0 \\ 0 & 0 & \gamma^{-2} \end{bmatrix} +$$

$$-2C_{01} \begin{bmatrix} \gamma^3 + \gamma[R\dfrac{d\gamma}{dZ}]^2 & 0 & R\gamma^2\dfrac{d\gamma}{dZ} + [R\dfrac{d\gamma}{dZ}]^3 + R\gamma^{-4}\dfrac{d\gamma}{dZ} \\ 0 & R^{-2}\gamma^2 & 0 \\ R\gamma^{-1}\dfrac{d\gamma}{dZ} & 0 & \gamma^{-6} + \gamma^{-2}[R\dfrac{d\gamma}{dZ}]^2 \end{bmatrix} \qquad (20)$$

and $\quad T(e^a, E^A) = T^{aA} = -p \begin{bmatrix} \gamma^{-1} & 0 & 0 \\ 0 & [R\gamma]^{-2} & 0 \\ -R\gamma\dfrac{d\gamma}{dZ} & 0 & \gamma^2 \end{bmatrix} + \mu_\infty \begin{bmatrix} \gamma & 0 & R\dfrac{d\gamma}{dZ} \\ 0 & R^{-2} & 0 \\ 0 & 0 & \gamma^{-2} \end{bmatrix}, \qquad (21)$

for the three models (4) to (6). Apparently, the First Piola-Kirchhoffs stress tensor is (in general) not symmetric. Instead, the local form of balance of moment of momentum on $\mathcal{B}$ reads $FT^T = TF^T$. The local form of balance of momentum on $\mathcal{B}$ in absence of body forces is $\mathrm{DIV}[T] = 0$, where $\mathrm{DIV}[\cdot] = I : \nabla[\cdot]$ and ∇ is (total) covariant derivative on $\mathcal{B}$. Its tensor component form is

$$\mathrm{DIV}[T]^a = \frac{\partial T^{aK}}{\partial X^K} + T^{aL}\Gamma_{LK}^K + T^{kK}\gamma_{kl}^a F_K^l = \begin{pmatrix} 0 \\ 0 \\ 0 \end{pmatrix} \qquad (22)$$

where summation of repeated indexes is enforced; Γ_{BC}^A and γ_{bc}^a are the Christoffel symbols [7] for I and i, respectively, which here is reduced to

$$\begin{bmatrix} \dfrac{\partial T^{rR}}{\partial R} + \dfrac{\partial T^{rZ}}{\partial Z} + \dfrac{T^{rR}}{R} - \gamma R T^{\phi\phi} \\ \dfrac{\partial T^{\phi\phi}}{\partial \Phi} \\ \dfrac{\partial T^{zR}}{\partial R} + \dfrac{\partial T^{zZ}}{\partial Z} + \dfrac{T^{zR}}{R} \end{bmatrix} = \begin{pmatrix} 0 \\ 0 \\ 0 \end{pmatrix} \qquad (23)$$

and - after applying the Neo-Hookean material model (21); being a sufficiently accurate model in this context - to

$$
\begin{bmatrix}
-\dfrac{\partial p}{\partial R} + \mu_\infty R\gamma \dfrac{d^2\gamma}{dZ^2} \\[2ex]
-\dfrac{\partial p}{\partial \Phi} \\[2ex]
-\dfrac{\partial p}{\partial Z} + \mu_\infty [R^2 \dfrac{d\gamma}{dZ}\dfrac{d^2\gamma}{dZ^2} - 2\gamma^{-5}\dfrac{d\gamma}{dZ}]
\end{bmatrix}
=
\begin{pmatrix} 0 \\ 0 \\ 0 \end{pmatrix}.
\tag{24}
$$

Elimination of pressure in (24) results in $d[(d^2\gamma/dZ^2)/\gamma]/dZ = 0$ and $d^2\gamma/dZ^2 + \alpha_1\gamma = 0$, giving

$$
p = \mu_\infty[\tfrac{1}{2}(\gamma^{-4} + \alpha_1 R^2\gamma^2) - \alpha_2],
\tag{25}
$$

where α_1 and α_2 are integration constants, and by (7) $\gamma = \lambda\cos[\alpha Z]$, where $\lambda = \gamma(0) \geq 1$ and $\alpha^2 = -\alpha_1$; related as $\lambda = 1/\cos[\alpha L/2]$, and, finally $\zeta = \tan[\alpha Z]/[\lambda^2\alpha]$. The relations

$$
\frac{l}{L} = \frac{\sin(\alpha L)}{\alpha L} = \frac{\sqrt{\lambda^2 - 1}}{\lambda^2\cos^{-1}(\lambda^{-1})},
\tag{26}
$$

are obtained by the boundary conditions (7) and (8). Thus, the motion becomes

$$
r = R\,\lambda\cos[\alpha Z],
\tag{27}
$$

$$
\phi = \Phi
\tag{28}
$$

and
$$
z = \tan[\alpha Z]/[\lambda^2\alpha].
\tag{29}
$$

The remaining unknown constant α_2 is determined by the boundary condition (9) on the free rubber surface. However, this condition cannot be completely fulfilled due to the approximations involved; mainly disclosed by the assumption (10). In [3] and [4] the stress free boundary condition is replaced by an approximate requirement of vanishing force and moment resultants on every portion of the free surface subtended by an arbitrary range of the polar angle ϕ. In this paper, the collocation method is applied; requiring vanishing surface traction on the circle $r = P\lambda$, $z = 0$ and $\phi = [0, 2\pi[$. This circle is a 'natural' choice: located on a symmetry plane of the isolator, displaying zero shear stresses; thus leaving the radial stress to be adjusted, by the constant, to zero. In addition, the force and moment resultants for the whole free rubber surface are zero. By inserting (25) in (21), the integration constant reads

$$
\alpha_2 = \tfrac{1}{2}[\lambda^{-4} - (\alpha P\lambda)^2] - \lambda^2.
\tag{30}
$$

The physical components of the Cauchy stress $\sigma^{<ab>}$, where $\sigma = T F^T$ - that is an inverse isochoric Piola transformation, become

$$\sigma^{<rr>} = \frac{\mu_\infty}{2}[\lambda^{-4} - (\alpha P\lambda)^2 - 2\lambda^2 + 2[\lambda\cos(\alpha Z)]^2 - [\lambda\cos(\alpha Z)]^{-4} +$$

$$+ (\alpha R\lambda)^2[1 + \sin^2(\alpha Z)]], \tag{31}$$

$$\sigma^{<\phi\phi>} = \frac{\mu_\infty}{2}[\lambda^{-4} - (\alpha P\lambda)^2 - 2\lambda^2 + 2[\lambda\cos(\alpha Z)]^2 - [\lambda\cos(\alpha Z)]^{-4} +$$

$$+ [\alpha R\lambda\cos(\alpha Z)]^2], \tag{32}$$

$$\sigma^{<zz>} = \frac{\mu_\infty}{2}[\lambda^{-4} - (\alpha P\lambda)^2 - 2\lambda^2 + [\lambda\cos(\alpha Z)]^{-4} + [\alpha R\lambda\cos(\alpha Z)]^2], \tag{33}$$

$$\sigma^{<rz>} = \sigma^{<rz>} = \mu_\infty \alpha R\tan(\alpha Z)[\lambda\cos(\alpha Z)]^{-1} \tag{34}$$

and
$$\sigma^{<r\phi>} = \sigma^{<\phi r>} = \sigma^{<\phi z>} = \sigma^{<z\phi>} = 0. \tag{35}$$

The axial tension force resultant at the bonded rubber surfaces is

$$F^{<z>} = \int_A \sigma^{<zz>} dA = \frac{\mu_\infty \pi P^2}{2}[\lambda^{-4} - (\alpha P\lambda)^2 - 2\lambda^2 + 1 + \tfrac{1}{2}[\alpha P]^2]. \tag{36}$$

2.3 Vanishing preload

In order to study the axial stiffness at the infitesimal strain $e = (l - L)/L$, the ascending series

$$\frac{l}{L} = \frac{\sin(\alpha L)}{\alpha L} = 1 - \tfrac{1}{6}(\alpha L)^2 + O((\alpha L)^4), \tag{37}$$

$$e = -\tfrac{1}{6}(\alpha L)^2 + O((\alpha L)^4), \tag{38}$$

$$\lambda = \frac{1}{\cos(\alpha L/2)} = 1 + \tfrac{1}{8}(\alpha L)^2 + O((\alpha L)^4), \tag{39}$$

$$\lambda^2 = 1 + \tfrac{1}{4}(\alpha L)^2 + O((\alpha L)^4) \tag{40}$$

and
$$\lambda^{-4} = 1 - \tfrac{1}{2}(\alpha L)^2 + O((\alpha L)^4), \tag{41}$$

are inserted in (36) giving

$$F^{<z>} = 3\mu_\infty \pi P^2 [1 + \tfrac{1}{2}[P/L]^2][e + O(e^2)] \tag{42}$$

and the linearised axial stiffness

$$k = \frac{EA}{L}[1 + 2S^2], \tag{43}$$

where the elasticity modulus $E = 3\,\mu_\infty$, area $A = \pi P^2$ and the shape factor $S = P/[2L]$. The axial stiffness result is identical to the classic formula; such as in Gent [5], whereas the result of [4] or [5] is not.

3. RESULTS

The formulas given above are implemented and results presented using MATLAB®. Three test objects are studied: $L = 100$, 50 and 25 mm long cylindrical isolators of radius $R = 50$ mm. Thus, the shape factors are $S = 0.25$, 0.50 and 1.00; the range covering the majority of commercially available isolators. The shear modulus $\mu_\infty = 4.50\,10^5\,\text{N/m}^2$ corresponds to a nominal hardness of 40° IRH.

The parameter α is determined from (26) by a one-point iteration method with full error control using the linear solution to (37) as initial value, Dahlquist and Björck [10]. The calculated compressional force versus displacement for $S = 0.5$ in Figure 3a closely follows a corresponding FEM solution, whereas the Klingbeil and Shield solution, [3] or [4], underestimates the force in the whole displacement range. The applied FEM [1] uses the same shear modulus and isolator geometry as here. The increasing deviations from the linear stiffness solution (43) – being the straight line in Figure 3 – as the isolator compresses are results from the non-linear preload effects. Also shown is the result from a simple non-linear model, Lindley [11], accounting for the increasing shape factor resulting from the decreasing length of the cylinder during compression. Although Lindley's model slightly underestimated the force, it nevertheless follows the FEM solution rather well; being more suitable than the Klingbeil and Shield solution.

The stiffness in Figure 3b is calculated from the analytical solution by numerical differentiation using repeated Richardson Extrapolation in order to reduce possible truncation errors [10]. The results for $S = 0.5$ are similar to those of Figure 3a: the present and Lindley models follow the FEM results closely, displaying minor deviations at large deformations, while the linear and Klingbeil and Shield solutions show large deviations.

The force and stiffness versus displacement in Figure 4 correspond to shape factors $S = 0.25$, 0.50 and 1.00. Clearly, the presented model follows the FEM solution rather closely; showing a slight underestimation at $S = 0.25$ and a slight overestimation at $S = 1.00$. Curiously, the Klingbeil and Shield solution underestimates the force at $S = 0.25$ and 0.50, while displaying a good agreement at $S = 1.00$. The good agreement at large shape factors $(2 \leq S \leq 8)$ is also noted by Klingbeil and Shield experiments. However, these large shape factors are not customary for isolators. In addition, the incompressibilty assumption is invalid for large shape factors; the non-vanishing dilatation resulting in a decrease of stiffness. The FEM applies a bulk modulus of order 3 000 times larger than the shear modulus; showing a slightly smaller force and stiffness than the presented model for $S = 1.0$.

Finally, the deformed isolator for $S = 0.5$ is shown in Figure 5 at compression ratios 0, 5, 10 and 20 %.

REFERENCE LIST

(1) Kari, L. The Audible Stiffness of Preloaded Vibration Isolators *Sixth International Congress on Sound and Vibration*. Edited by Finn Jacobsen, Copenhagen, Denmark, 1999.

(2) Gaul, L., *Mechanical Systems and Signal Processing*, **5**, 1991,13-24.

(3) Klingbeil, W. and Shield, R., *ZAMP*, **17**, 1966, 281-305.

(4) Zdunek, A., *Konstruktionsunderlag för dämpare* (in Swedish), Swedish Plastics and Rubber Institute, PGI-Rapport NR 8a, 1981.

(5) Gent, A., *Engineering with Rubber*, Carl Hansen Verlag, Munich, 1992.

(6) Noll, W., *Archive for Rational Mechanics and Analysis*, **2**, 1958, 197-226.

(7) Marsden, J. and Hughes, T., *Mathematical Foundations of Elasticity*. Dover Publications, New York, 1994.

(8) Yeoh, O., *Rubber Chemistry and Technology*, **63**, 1990, 792-805.

(9) Treloar, L., *The Physics of Rubber Elasticity*, Third Edition, Clarendon Press, Oxford, 1975.

(10) Dahlquist, G. and Björk, Å., *Numerical Methods*, Prentice Hall, New Jersey, 1974.

(11) Lindley, P., *J. Strain Anal.*, **1**, 1966, 190.

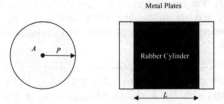

FIGURE 1   Cylindrical vibration isolator.

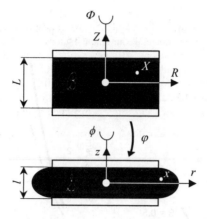

FIGURE 2   A configuration φ of the vibration isolator from the reference configuration $\mathcal{B}$ to the current in $\mathcal{S}$. Also shown are material and spatial points; X and x, respectively, together with imposed coordinate systems on $\mathcal{B}$ and $\mathcal{S}$, respectively.

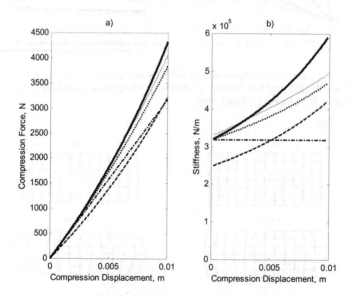

FIGURE 3   a) Compression force and b) stiffness versus displacement. Shape factor $S = 0.5$. Present (solid thick), Klingbeil & Shield [3] or [4] (dashed), FEM [1] (solid thin), Lindley [11] (dotted) and Linear model [5] (dash-dotted).

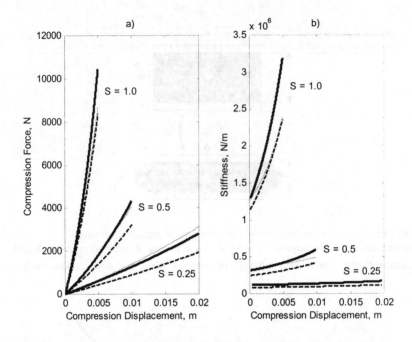

FIGURE 4   a) Compression force and b) stiffness versus displacement. Shape factors S = 0.25, 0.5 and 1.0. Present (solid thick), Klingbeil & Shield [3] or [4] (dashed) and FEM model [1] (solid thin).

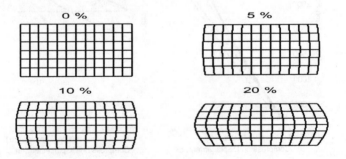

FIGURE 5   Deformed isolator. Shape factor S = 0.5. 0, 5, 10 and 20% deformation.

A STRAIN-BASED FAILURE CRITERION FOR NOTCHED BARS MADE FROM LOW DUCTILITY CAST ALUMINIUM ALLOY

R.S. Hack* and T.H. Hyde* and J.W. Taylor†

In this paper a strain-based failure criterion for predicting the failure loads of notched bar specimens, made from a low ductility aerospace grade cast aluminium alloy, is presented. It has been shown that the strain-based method can be used, in conjunction with either the finite element method or the approximate methods of Neuber and Glinka, to make good predictions of the failure loads in comparison to experimental failure loads of notched tensile specimens.

INTRODUCTION

Lightweight cast alloys are now widely used in the manufacture of a large number of complex components, due to their strength at a range of temperatures, enabling their use for high temperature applications such as aero-engine inter-casings and automobile engine blocks, Caceres et al [1]. However, uniaxial tensile test data indicates that some of these alloys have low ductilities, i.e. less than 3% failure strains, which may depend on any post-casting cooling, heating and quenching treatments. Components made from these materials are often subject to complex loading conditions. A common approach, used to model component behaviour, when subject to these complex loading conditions, is based on the finite element method. Depending on the complexity of the component geometry, the finite element analysis may not always be practical, due to the model size and time requirements which are associated with the execution of full elastoplastic analyses for these cases. In this paper alternative analytical methods proposed by Neuber [2] and Molski and Glinka [3] are employed, in conjunction with a strain based failure criterion, to predict the loads at which notched bars will fail. Glinka [4] suggests that the previously established method by Neuber [2] will make higher notch strain overestimation as the

* School of Mechanical, Materials, Manufacturing Engineering and Management, University of Nottingham, University Park, UK, NG7 2RD

† Rolls-Royce plc, Aerospace Group, Derby, UK, DE24 8BJ

K_σ is increased. It will be shown how to apply these methods to predict the failure loads for materials with low ductility.

NOTATION

A   notch depth

D   specimen nominal diameter

E   Young's Modulus

ε local strain

ε_n remote nominal strain

K   strength coefficient

K_t elastic stress concentration factor

K_ε elastic strain concentration factor

K_σ elastic-plastic stress concentration factor

L_c parallel length

L_o gauge length

r   transition radius

R   notch radius

S_o cross-sectional area

σ local peak stress

σ_f applied stress at failure

σ_n remote nominal stress

σ_y yield stress

EXPERIMENTAL METHOD

Four batches, designated B1, B2, B3 and B4, of a cast aluminium alloy, designated A356, were used for this experimental programme. The dimensions for the tensile test specimens were in accordance with the European Standard EN10002 part 1 [5], which specifies that,

$$L_o = 5.65\sqrt{S_o} \qquad\qquad (1)$$

where L_o is the gauge length and S_o is the nominal cross-sectional area, as shown in fig. (1).

The plain uniaxial test pieces were machined to the dimensions corresponding to a nominal diameter D=5.64 mm. From each of the batches a number of specimens with different notch types were also machined, as shown in fig. (2), with their dimensions given in table (1),

TABLE 1.   Notch dimensions

Notch type	R (mm)	A (mm)	D (mm)
N1	1.0	1.0	5.64
N2	0.5	1.0	5.64
N3	0.5	1.5	5.64

EXPERIMENTAL RESULTS

Plain specimens
Fig. (3) shows the experimental tensile stress strain curves for the four material batches (B1, B2, B3 and B4). From the stress strain curves in fig. (3) a Young's Modulus of 76 GPa has been obtained. Also, it can be seen that fracture occurs after yielding and a relatively small amount of plastic strain; from the failed specimens, it was clear that no necking had occured. It can also be seen from fig. (3), that there is significant batch to batch variation in the failure strains, with failure strains varying from 1.05% to 1.5%.

However the stresses at failure only varied by approximately 8%, ranging from 229 MPa to 248 MPa. Hence, it was concluded that a failure criterion based on fracture strain behaviour would be likely to more accurately account for the batch-to-batch variations in properties than a criterion based on the failure stress.

Notched specimens
Table (3) shows the experimentally obtained failure stresses for the notched specimens, as shown in fig. (2), obtained from specimens made from the four batches, B1, B2, B3 and B4.

TABLE 2.   Summary of uniaxial failure stresses and strains

	σ_f (MPa)	$\varepsilon\,\%$
B1	248	1.436
B2	229	1.045
B3	233	1.237
B4	230	1.498

FINITE ELEMENT ANALYSIS

The notched specimens were modelled using eight noded, axisymmetric, isoparametric finite elements. The RIKS algorithm within the ABAQUS [6] finite element commercial software package was used with the proof stress data shown in table (4).

FE Meshes
The axisymmetric finite element models of the notched bars in fig. (2), are shown in fig. (4). The models were constrained in the axial direction on the planes of symmetry for the notches and a uniform stress was incrementally applied to the remote end of the models, to match the failure loads, in table (3). The axisymmetric FE meshes for specimens 1, 2 and 3 consisted of 340, 528 and 528 elements, respectively, shown in fig. (4).

TABLE 3.   Summary of the remote stresses at failure for the notched
                 specimens

Notch Type Batch	Remote Stress at failure (MPa)		
	N1	N2	N3
B1		131.40	74.17
B2			78.77
B3	119.50	133.80	
B4	124.90	118.80	75.45

TABLE 4.   Summary of proof stress data used in the ABAQUS FE RIKS
analysis

	2 % (MPa)	4 % (MPa)	6 % (MPa)
B1	196	210.5	224
B2	199	213	225
B3	186	199	212
B4	185	198	209

FE Results

From the elastic finite element solutions, the stress concentration factors for the notch types 1,2 and 3 at the notch roots, were determined to be 1.53, 1.90 and 1.72, respectively. The same location was selected for the three notch types in order to ensure the comparability of the SCF results. Figs. (5) and (6) show the comparisons of the predicted failure loads for the notched specimens, based on limiting failure strains at the notch tip, with the experimental failure data. The predictions in fig. (5) used a failure strain of 1.05% and fig. (6) used a failure strain of 1.5%, these were the lowest and highest failure strains obtained from the uniaxial tensile tests, see table (2).

APPROXIMATE METHODS

The approximate methods established by H. Neuber [2] and K. Molski and G. Glinka [3] have also been selected to predict the failure loads.

Neuber's method

Neuber's method [2] relates the remotely applied loads to the local stress and strain behaviour via the elastic stress concentration factor, such that the elastic-plastic stress and strain concentration factors, K_σ and K_ε, are related to the elastic concentration factors K_t, as follows;

$$\sqrt{K_\sigma K_\varepsilon} = K_t \qquad (2)$$

where $K_\sigma = \dfrac{\sigma}{\sigma_n}$ and $K_\varepsilon = \dfrac{\varepsilon}{\varepsilon_n}$

This equation is more commonly written in the form of Neuber's rule, Sharpe [7],ie.,

$$\frac{(\sigma_n K_t)^2}{E} = \sigma\varepsilon \tag{3}$$

which can also be written as follows;

$$\varepsilon = \frac{K_t^2 \varepsilon_n \sigma_n}{\sigma} \tag{4}$$

where, $\varepsilon_n = \dfrac{\sigma_n}{E}$ and $\sigma \geq \sigma_y$

Fig. 7 shows that given that the elastic solution of point E is known, it is possible to project a parabolic curve of equation (4) from point E, and hence at the intersection of this curve obtain an approximate solution for the elastic-plastic stress-strain conditions at point P on the stress-strain curve.

Glinka's method

Molski and Glinka [3] proposed an alternative model to that of Neuber, to relate remotely applied loads to the local stress and strain behaviour. This model uses an energy-based method to determine local elastoplastic stresses and strains. From fig. (8), points E and P represent the stress and strain solutions, at the peak stress position, under elastic and elastic-plastic conditions. Molski and Glinka [3] state that the two solutions are related by having the same area under the stress-strain curves. Hence, if the elastic solution, point E is known, then the elastic-plastic solution for the same load, point P, can be determined by finding the position along the stress-strain curve where point P has the same area as that of the elastic solution.

Application of Approximate methods

The Neuber [2] and Glinka [4] methods are usually used to predict the elastic stresses and strains in the stress concentration regions of components subjected to a particular load level. For materials with low ductility such as the aluminium alloy used for the present investigation, the failure can be related to a limiting strain criterion. Hence, taking the limiting failure strain as a starting point (ie. point F in Fig. 9), the Neuber and Glinka methods can be used in reverse to predict the corresponding peak stress (ie. points N and G in Fig. 9 respectively). The associated remote nominal stresses, and hence the loads, to cause failure can then be easily determined from a knowledge of the elastic stress concentration factor. Using the inverse Neuber and Glinka methods with the four individual stress-strain curves, shown in Fig. 3, for each batch of the aluminium alloy material, two predictions of the remote applied stress at failure for the three notch types made from the four batches, as identified in table (3), were obtained. Figures (10) and (11), show the comparisons of the Neuber and Glinka predicted failure stresses based on the experimental stress strain curves with the actual experimental tensile test results for the notched specimens, as summarised in table (3). It can be seen that the Neuber method gives reasonably good overall correlation and that the Glinka method tends to overpredict the failure load.

DISCUSSION

From figures (5) and (6), it can be seen that the strain based failure criterion, used in conjunction with the finite element method produces conservative predictions of the failure loads for the three notch types. The FE predictions, using the lower strain limit were on average 27% lower than the experimental failure loads, while for the upper strain limit the FE predictions were on average 16% lower than the experimental failure loads. From figures (10) and (11), it can be seen that by applying the approximate methods, Neuber's method will predict failure loads on average 9.5% below the experimental failure stresses, while Glinka's method will predict failure loads on average 19% above the experimental failure stresses for this particular material type, ie. low ductility aluminium alloy A356.

CONCLUSIONS

A strain-based failure criterion has been presented on the basis of the experimental results, which suggested that when the strain at any given point of a component made from Aluminium alloy A356, fell between an upper and lower limit failure was imminent. Subsequently it has been shown that in comparison with experimental failure applied stresses of notched specimens, the finite element method in conjunction with the strain based failure criterion made conservative estimates of the failure load, ranging from 16% up to 27% lower than the experimental failure loads. While it has also been shown that the analytical methods of H. Neuber and G. Glinka also make estimates that range from 9.5% below and 19% above the experimental loads. The comparable correlation of the analytical methods, to the finite element analysis and the experimental data, imply that it should be possible to apply this approach to a more complex component made of the same material, without the need for a full finite element elastoplastic analysis to determine the load at which the loaded component initiates failure behaviour.

ACKNOWLEDGEMENTS

The authors are grateful for funding from the Engineering and Physical Sciences Research Council (EPSRC, Grant GR/L71285), and acknowledge the assistance of Mr. Keith Dinsdale for the tensile tests. The assistance of Mr. Nigel Twiggs and Mr. Paul Walton is also very appreciated.

REFERENCES

(1)   Caceres C.H., Djurdjevic M.B., Stockwell T.J. and Sokolowski J.H., *Scripta Materialia*, vol. 40, no. 5, 1999, pp 631-637

(2)   Neuber H., *Trans. ASME*, 1961, pp 544-550

(3)   Molski K. and Glinka G., *Matls. Sci. Eng.*, vol. 50, 1981, pp 93-100

(4)   Glinka G., *Eng. Frac. Mech.*, vol. 22, no. 3, 1985, pp 485-508

(5)   European Standard, *Metallic Materials-Tensile Testing-Part 1: Method of test (at ambient temperature)*, EN 10 002, part1, 1990

(6)   ABAQUS User's Manual (ver. 5.8), (HKS Inc., Pawtucket, USA), 1998

(7)   Sharpe W.N., *J. Eng. Matls. Tech.*, vol. 117, 1995, pp 1-7

(8)   FEMGV User Manual (ver. 4.2), (Femsys Ltd., Leicester, UK), 1997

(9)   Glinka G., *Eng. Frac. Mech.*, vol. 22, no. 5, 1985, pp 839-854

(10) Hoffman M. and Seeger T.,, *Trans. ASME*, vol. 107, 1985,pp 250-254

(11) Hoffman M. and Seeger T., *Trans. ASME*, vol. 107, 1985, pp 255-260

(12) Hyde T.H. and Marsden B.J., *J. Strain Analysis*, vol. 19, no. 3, 1984, pp 167-171

(13) Roark R.J. and Young W.C., *Formulas for stress and strain, 5th Ed.*, McGraw-Hill, London, 1975

(14) Rodd C., *Metals Databook*, The Institute Of Metals, London, 1987

(15) Sharpe W.N., Yang C.H. and Tregoning R.L., *Trans. ASME*, vol. 59, 1992, pp s50-s56

(16) Topper T.H., Wetzel R.M. and Morrow J., *J. Materials, JMLSA*, vol. 4, no. 1, 1969, pp 200-209

(17) Toribio J., *Eng. Frac. Mech.*, vol. 57, no. 4, 1997, pp 391-404

(18) Zhang K.S., *Eng. Frac. Mech.*, vol. 52, no. 3, 1995, pp 575-582

FIGURE 1.   Tensile test specimen

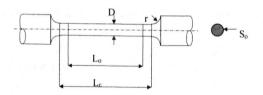

FIGURE 2.   Notch geometries

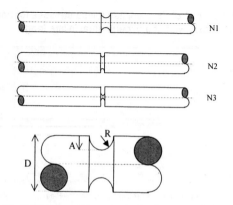

FIGURE 3.   Experimental stress strain curves of plane specimens

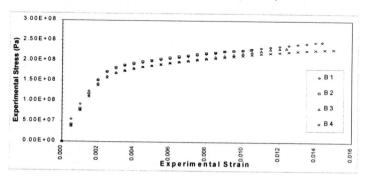

FIGURE 4.   FE meshes of the three notched specimens

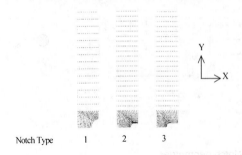

Notch Type   1   2   3

FIGURE 5.   Comparison of FE predicted failure stresses for notched specimens (using a strain limit of 1.05%) with the experimental failure loads

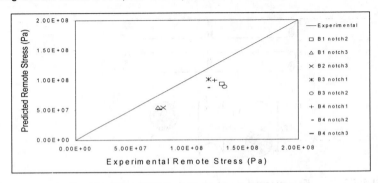

FIGURE 6.   Comparison of FE predicted failure stresses for notched specimens (using a strain limit of 1.5%) with the experimental failure loads

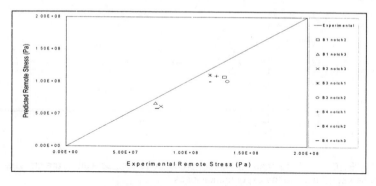

FIGURE 7.   Diagrammatic representation of the Neuber method

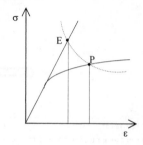

FIGURE 8.   Diagrammatic representation of the Glinka method

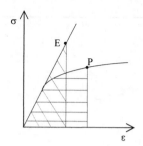

FIGURE 9.   Schematic diagram showing the inverse Neuber and Glinka
methods

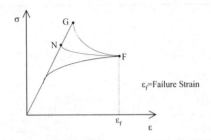

FIGURE 10.   Comparison of Neuber predicted remote applied failure stresses of
notched specimens to the experimental loads

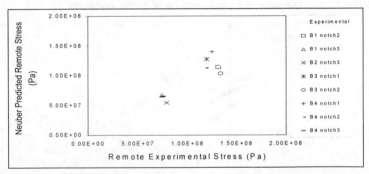

FIGURE 11.   Comparison of Glinka predicted remote applied failure stresses of
notched specimens to the experimental loads

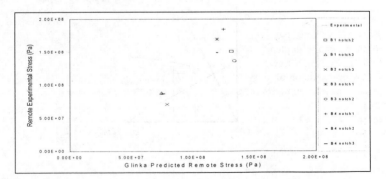

FRAMEWORK FOR OBJECT-ORIENTED BOUNDARY ELEMENT PROGRAMMING

D. Chen*, I. A. Jones* and A. A. Becker*

This paper reviews the concept of object-oriented software in the context of engineering computation and, in particular, boundary element analysis. The process of designing an object-oriented boundary element system is described, with particular reference to the use of Universal Modelling Language (UML) diagrams to represent the class hierarchy and the use of "CRC (class-responsibility-collaborators) cards" within a walkthrough of the draft design. The details of the design are described. The advantages and disadvantages of the object-oriented paradigm for a piece of engineering analysis software are discussed, and may be summarised as improved understanding of concepts and data structures which are traded for a loss of clarity in execution sequence. The accuracy of the resulting object-oriented boundary element system is demonstrated using a simple plane-strain pressurised cylinder example.

1. INTRODUCTION

Engineering analysis software has traditionally been written using procedural programming techniques, which view the software system primarily as a series of processes performed upon the numerical data. Data is organised in a way which is much more closely related to the tasks which the data undergoes rather than to the nature, meaning and associations of the data. Much engineering analysis software has its roots in legacy code written (typically) in FORTRAN 66 and modified with FORTRAN 77 enhancements. The progress from FORTRAN 66 to FORTRAN 77 reflects the partial implementation of so-called "structured programming" constructs (block-IF, IF-THEN-ELSE etc.) without the opportunities for proper structuring of data, or the provision of a complete set of structured programming constructs (case selection, WHILE and DO WHILE etc.). Such constructs, along with data structuring constructs (user-defined variable TYPEs or structs) have been available in languages such as Pascal, structured BASIC, C etc. for many years, and have now been incorporated into FORTRAN 90. Also incorporated are some features which loosely follow the object-oriented paradigm.

*School of Mechanical, Materials, Manufacturing Engineering and Management, University of Nottingham, University Park, Nottingham NG7 2RD

In contrast to procedural programming, object-oriented programming views the software system in terms of the real-world entities it models, and in terms of the relationships and interactions of those entities. The entities are modelled as "objects", which encapsulate both the attributes or data describing the entity and the methods which operate upon those attributes. Objects are said to interact by the passing of messages from one object to another, with a given message to an object invoking a particular method or member function of that object. An early object-oriented language, Smalltalk, adopted this paradigm in a rather pure form without (for example) the facility to have simple variables which were not objects. However, the object-oriented language which is (at present) the most commonly-used is C++, which builds upon the data structuring constructs in the C language (of which it is a superset) to permit a less purist implementation of object-oriented software engineering. Message-passing in C++ is implemented directly as the invocation of an object's member functions, and variables and functions are permitted which are not members of any particular object. Two important object-oriented features of C++, which are heavily used in this project, are the concepts of *inheritance* and *polymorphism*. The former permits base objects to be enhanced to form classes of derived objects with attributes and methods in addition to those inherited from the base class; the latter allows variants of the methods to be defined for each derived version of an object, whilst allowing the exact variant of the method to be selected at run-time (run-time binding). These features provide a powerful route to structuring an engineering analysis tool, where numerous variants on a particular analysis technique or analysis sub-feature (e.g. element type) may exist, and where all variants of a particular class of feature behave in a broadly similar way which differs only in detail.

Each software engineering paradigm and approach has its own notation, and indeed object oriented design has several. However, among the most commonly used are that associated with Object Modelling Technique (OMT) described by Rumbaugh et al [1] and its derivative Universal Modelling Language (UML) [2]. Some basic features of UML notation are illustrated in Figure 1.

Perhaps because of its roots in computer science and its strong ties (via C++) with the C language (traditionally less popular than FORTRAN and Pascal for numerical calculation), the object-oriented paradigm does not appear to have been greatly used in the coding of major items of engineering software. A limited number of examples of its use, each following the object-oriented paradigm with varying amounts of rigour, are reported in the literature and will be examined further. The present work presents a timely opportunity to review the relative merits of the paradigms, since it can be regarded as a case study of a significant item of engineering software which appears to be the first of its kind written in a relatively pure object-oriented manner.

The present project has arisen because of the need to integrate the BE method with automated digital photoelasticity, requiring the formulation of an inverse BE analysis approach and (preferably) the adoption of a single programming paradigm and language across the whole photoelasticity/BE system. From the photoelastic data obtained at various internal points distributed inside the solution domain, an inverse BE formulation is used to compute the displacements and tractions at all surface points. This enables all boundary conditions, including those of contact problems, to be accurately computed. This situation presented the opportunity to review the manner in which the BE method was implemented, and to start from scratch with an object-oriented implementation in the language C++. As a matter of terminology, objects are defined in C++ as classes, which are effectively compound variable types; individual objects are instances of these classes. In practice, the inverse BE procedures were tested first in a modified version of the existing (forward) BE program written in FORTRAN 77. However, present work is aimed at unifying the forward and reverse methods via the creation of a set of objects whose possible interactions permit either the forward or the inverse BE method to be followed without the introduction into the program of undue complexity.

2. A REVIEW OF OBJECT-ORIENTED FINITE ELEMENT AND BOUNDARY ELEMENT SOFTWARE

Very little literature exists on the object-oriented implementation of the BE method, whereas a moderate body of literature exists on the object-oriented finite element systems. Archer et al [3] identify the shortcomings of procedural finite element programming, and review the history of object-oriented finite element (OOFE) work. Archer et al then describe their own object-oriented FE implementation, which is based especially upon isolating the numerical objects and algorithms into an analysis object which is distinct from the model object consisting of the components of the finite element model. As will be seen, this approach has clear parallels in the present work. The other top-level objects in Archer's approach are a map object (which links the model to the analysis) and handlers for the matrices and the constraints and for reordering the unknowns. Load cases, elements, nodes, boundary conditions and constraints are all sub-classes of the model object. Mackie [4] presents an overlapping review, from which he concludes that the advantage of object-oriented methods is in handling the complexity of finite elements and in integrating FE with other systems. He also describes various FE equation solution techniques from an object-oriented viewpoint. Both Archer and Mackie trace object-oriented FE back to work by Forde et al [5], which makes some interesting claims on OOFE code size (64%) and development time (10%) compared with those for an equivalent procedural system. Besson et al [6] and Patzak and Bittnar [7] both consider the structure and object heirarchy of OOFE systems, while Kong [8] compares and contrasts the data structures used in C++ and FORTRAN FE implementations. Scholz [9], Lu et al [10] and Zeglinski et al [11] concentrate upon the matrix and vector classes suitable for use in object-oriented structural analysis and FE implementations. Other relevant papers include those of Zimmermann et al [12] who describe an integrated OOFE development environment with additional symbolic, graphical and knowledge-based capability.

The literature on object-oriented BE (OOBE) systems is sparse. Favela and Connor [13] introduce the object-oriented paradigm in some detail before presenting an overview of the class hierarchy of their OOBE system for 2D elastic bodies. Their basic approach is to separate the design object from the analysis object, with the former being used purely to define the boundary whilst having no involvement in the BE process itself. The objects are not described in detail so it is not possible to judge the degree to which the OO paradigm is used within their implementations. Lage [14] presents the design of a class library to support the development of BE software, with particular reference to the panel clustering method; the design of a complete OOBE system is not presented. No detailed description of an OOBE system's design and implementation therefore appears to be available.

3. THE OBJECT-ORIENTED BE DESIGN: EVOLUTION AND DETAILS

The present OOBE system has as its origin the procedural BEACON program written in FORTRAN 77, a version of which is presented in the book by Becker [15] along with the theory on which it is based. It is instructive to present an overview of the procedural FORTRAN BE algorithms which can divided into 6 main steps as follows:

Step 1: Data input and sorting of variables

Step 2: Matrix assembly and numerical Integration

Step 3: Application of the Boundary Conditions

Step 4 : Solution of the Algebraic Equations

Step 5 : Calculation of the Boundary Stresses

Step 6 : Calculation of Internal Variables

The starting point for the derivation of an object-oriented design is the identification of the objects and their methods. Objects typically represent real-world entities or nouns in a textual description of the problem to be solved; methods represent the actions they undergo or the verbs in a description of the problem. Given that the present problem is essentially an abstract one made up of mathematical rather than tangible entities, the identification of some objects (nodes, elements, materials etc.) was nonetheless straightforward. However, for other possible candidates such as kernels, arguments could be made for them to be objects, methods or neither (e.g. partitions of a matrix forming an attribute of some other object). The present design was finalised after some iteration (and some exploratory programming to test the usefulness of, for example, nested matrices and vectors) based upon a good understanding of the BE method and its possible variants. An important stage in finalising the design was the use of a walkthrough or simulated BE run using so-called CRC (class-responsibility-collaborators) cards. This took place under the leadership of one of the team members, with the other members identifying (and acting-out) all the significant stages in an analysis process. At each stage, the validity of the classes was questioned and their responsibilities and collaborators identified. Some classes were introduced and others renamed or eliminated. This walkthrough was performed twice: once for the conventional (forward) BE analysis, once for the inverse BE approach, with most of the classes being found to be common to both approaches. The output of this process was a list of classes, their responsibilities (most of which map onto the methods of the relevant objects) and their collaborators i.e. other classes with which they are linked, typically via aggregation or association.

The design finally chosen makes use of object-oriented methods to a very large degree. For example, stream objects have been used throughout for file handling in preference to C-style functions. Moreover, container classes have been used for representing and manipulating of arrays and matrices, with little use of C-style arrays.

A key feature of the present design is the separation of the BE model itself (and its sub-objects) from the representation of the model and its sub-objects within the input process. While this does apparently result in a certain amount of duplication of data, it has the benefit that a different derived version of the data input routines could be used, as described below.

At the highest level, the program may be regarded as consisting of three classes, one instance of each of which is created to form three objects: the *model builder*, the *model* and the *analysis*. It would also be quite feasible to have an overall *application* object whose purpose is to contain and control the three other main objects, but for the present purposes that object is implicit in the top-level program unit which creates instances of the three classes. This overall structure is illustrated in Figure 2. In practice, only one of these classes (CBemModel) is directly created as an instance; the others are *abstract classes* which merely provide a framework for the existence of different variants, each of which may differ in the details of its behaviour. For example, the abstract class CBemModelBuilder is the base class for the concrete derived class CBemModelBuilderReadModelFile, which sets up the nodes, elements etc. in the BE model using a conventional text input file similar to that used by BEACON. An alternative (not currently implemented) would be to have a model builder based upon a graphical user interface; its purpose would be identical but its method of operation would be totally different and its method of storing its internal data would probably be quite different. Such a class CBemModelBuilderGUI would also be derived from CBemModelBuilder.

The CBemModelBuilderReadModelFile class is effectively a driver and buffer for the input text file and the file containing the internal point coordinates. Its attributes include dynamic arrays to store the lists of nodes and their coordinate vectors, elements and their topology lists etc. but does not attempt any interpretation of this data other than the parsing of the input file. It inherits from the generic CBemModelBuilder class the ability to interact with the CBemModel, and its main task after reading the input files is to sort the lists of nodes, elements, constraints etc.

into order and call the methods in CBemModel to create the nodes etc. within the model.

The CBemModel class (Figure 3) is effectively a database to manage the many-to-many relationships between the various features in the model. Like the CBemModelBuilder class, it contains dynamic arrays (vectors) of the various features comprising the model (nodes, elements, constraints and internal points). However, the classes (CBemNode etc.) representing these objects also include the arrays of pointers needed to represent the many-to-many links between the various objects. The links between the node and element objects etc. are set up by the various methods contained within the CBemModelVerify class; this is little more than a collection of methods rather than an object in its own right. It also includes methods to loop through all the elements etc. in the CBemModel database and print them to an output file for checking.

The structure of data within each node object, element object etc. is worthy of comment. For each object a vector of *variable tables* is set up. Each variable table consists of a variable identifier (for stress, displacement etc.) and a dynamic matrix to contain the vectorial or tensorial value of that variable. Such variables are easily added as required during the analysis, and provide a flexible alternative to hard-coding the variables associated with each object. Variables for data specific to a class (for example, the array of node pointers representing an element's topology) is, of course, hard-coded into the class definition. It should also be noted that inheritance is used to avoid duplication of coding so that, for example, the CBemNode and CBemInternalPoint classes are both derived from the abstract class CBemPoint.

The CBemAnalysis class and its derived classes are the most complex objects in the application, with much of the complexity being due to the degree to which inheritance is used to apply a uniform approach to the different types of possible analysis. The inheritance hierarchy of the different analysis types is shown in Figure 4. For the purposes of the present discussion, however, the different variants of the analysis and its constituent objects will be ignored and the process will be discussed in terms of a generic static analysis, integrator etc.

The analysis object manages the solution process, including assembly of the equation set and the application of the boundary conditions. As shown in Figure 5, separate objects are used for kernel evaluation, integration of the kernels (using a separate object for Gaussian quadrature), equation solution and solution interpretation (i.e. keeping track of whether variables represent displacements or tractions). The equation solution object currently uses Gaussian elimination but could easily be rewritten to use the singular value decomposition (SVD) method [Press, 16] when the system is adapted for the solution of overdetermined inverse problems.

4. THICK CYLINDER EXAMPLE

In order to demonstrate the accuracy of the object-oriented BE program, an example involving a pressurised thick cylinder is presented. A thick-walled cylinder of internal radius R_1 and outer radius R_2 subjected to internal pressure P. The cylinder is assumed to be sufficiently long in the axial direction for plane strain conditions to be applicable. The numerical values used are R_1=3.0, R_2=6.0, P=1.0 with material properties E=1.0 and ν=0.3 (arbitrary consistent units). One quadrant of the cylinder is modelled, using 12 elements in total, so symmetry conditions are applied to the quadrant's straight boundaries (Figure 6(a)). 4 Gauss points per element were used in generating these results. In Figure 6(b), the results from the OOBE model are compared with those obtained from the classical (Lamé) solution. As expected, the results from the OOBE program closely match those obtained from the Lamé solution. They also agree to at least 5 significant figures with the equivalent results from the procedural boundary element program BEACON [15], for which the theoretical basis is identical.

5. DISCUSSION

The exercise described above clearly demonstrates the feasibility of structuring a BE program around object-oriented methods.. While this appears to be one of the first such BE programs (indeed, possibly the first truly OOBE program, depending upon the code's extent of object-orientation and upon one's definition), the approach is broadly similar to that used for at least some of the OOFE programs reviewed earlier. The program's accuracy and effectiveness are not in doubt, but the usefulness of this approach is worthy of debate. In particular, what advantages does the object-oriented implementation present compared with the procedural implementation, from the viewpoint of the developer (ease of understanding, maintenance etc.) and the analyst (speed of execution)?

5.1 The developer's perspective: code transparency and maintainability

One of the most commonly-quoted advantages of OO methods is the supposed ease with which such programs are extended and modified owing to the localised effect of changes and the intuitive structure of the program. These advantages will be tested in practice when the OO program is extended to cope with the inverse BE method required for the photoelastic work. In the meantime, however, a number of comparisons can be drawn between the procedural (FORTRAN) and OO (C++) programs. The most obvious contrast is the difference in code size, with the C++ source code being larger (in terms of numbers of lines) by a factor of approximately 4. The frequency of comment lines in the programs was approximately the same, although it should be noted that by convention, and as a matter of good practice, C++ code includes many lines containing only the block delimiters { and }. The

81

FORTRAN code is therefore much more terse, and this experience contrasts strongly with Forde's comparison of OO and procedural implementation [5].

Since the FORTRAN code was originally written to maximise compatibility even with older versions of FORTRAN, it does not exploit many of the features incorporated in practice into most FORTRAN77 implementations (free formatting, long symbolic names etc.). It is therefore difficult to perform a fair comparison of ease of understanding between the C++ and FORTRAN codes, and any judgements by those involved are inevitably subjective and biased. However, some general comments are that the program flow in the procedural implementation is generally more transparent than in the object-oriented implementation, since the sequence of processes is by definition the basis of the program structure. On the other hand, the meaning of the various items of data and their interrelationships are much less clear in the procedural implementation owing to the lack of data structuring facilities in FORTRAN77 and its precursors, and the fact that the data is primarily structured for ease of processing rather than ease of identification or understanding. It is probably a fair summary to say that the relationship between the data items in the program and the corresponding theoretical concepts is much more intuitive and clear in the OO implementation. The price paid is the difficulty of tracing (at least in hard copy) the stages within the analysis as one switches from object to object (and up and down inheritance hierarchies) to pursue the thread of program execution.

5.2 The user's perspective: efficiency and speed

Code transparency and maintainability are generally of little interest to the user, who is mainly interested in robustness, correctness and speed of execution. Once again, a completely fair comparison of the FORTRAN and C++ programs is not entirely achievable because of possible differences in the efficiency of the compilers used, but it is to be expected (and it is observed) that the OO implementation will be slower on account of the following:

- The additional complexity of the data structures being handled, especially when passing variables;

- The availability of different implementations of a given function, whose choice depends upon factors known at run-time, sometimes leads to the need for a decision-making process known as "run-time binding" which can slow execution. The need for run-time binding should, however, have been kept to a minimum in the present work.

- The fact that some of the data structures, especially the dynamic vectors, currently involve considerable copying and reallocation. There is some scope for streamlining of these processes.

It is planned that the CPU and disk usage etc. of the new code will be compared with those of the procedural BEACON code in order to identify and eliminate bottlenecks.

5.3 Scope for further work

Although the version of the program presented here illustrates the feasibility of an OOBE implementation and appears to be the first such detailed description presented, it is designed with enhancement in mind and indeed has specifically been written with the aim of being used for the solution of inverse BE problems such as that discussed in Section 1. It is intended that relatively few changes, primarily the overloading (redefinition) of certain functions in a derived version of the present CBemElastoStaticAnalysis2D class, will be required. As stated earlier, the ease with which such modifications can be achieved will be the first true test of the system's maintainability, especially as this will primarily be done by staff other than the original developer of the OOBE system owing to personnel changes.

The present version of the program only permits one 2D homogeneous region to be analysed, thus precluding (for example) 3D structures, assemblies of regions from different materials or (more especially) the analysis of contact. All of these have been implemented in various versions of the procedural BE program BEACON. It would be an interesting, albeit a labour-intensive one, to re-implement these in features within the OOBE system. However, whether such modifications are implemented is likely to be demand-led rather than curiosity-driven. A more likely immediate direction of development is the scope for developing a graphical user interface which is fully integrated with the CBemModelBuilder class. This would contrast with the usual form of pre/post processor for engineering analysis software which generally hides a conventional batch analysis process undertaken by a separate program. At the time of reporting this work, only rather basic text-based pre- and post-processing have been implemented, and ease-of-use comparisons have therefore not yet been undertaken.

6. CONCLUSIONS

As part of a more general project on the integration of boundary element analysis with photoelasticity, an object-oriented boundary element program has been designed and implemented in C++. Its accuracy for a representative test problem is demonstrated, and formal verification of its accuracy and robustness in a wide range of problems is underway. While the structure of the program is clearly more closely related to the conceptual objects (elements, nodes etc.) forming the engineering problem than is the corresponding FORTRAN program, program flow may appear to be harder to follow, at any rate on paper. The object-oriented paradigm's often-quoted benefits of improved understandability and maintainability are only partially demonstrated. However, these benefits will meet their true test when new personnel perform its extension to cope with inverse and (as a future possibility) multi-domain and non-linear problems. Comparisons of the efficiency, ease of use and maintainability will be undertaken within future work.

REFERENCES

(1)   Rumbaugh, J., Blaha, M., Premerlani, W., Eddy, F. and Lorensen, W., *Object-oriented modelling and design*. Prentice-Hall, New Jersey, 1991.

(2)   Bennett, S., McRobb, S. and Farmer, R., *Object-oriented systems analysis and design using UML*. McGraw-Hill, London, 1999.

(3)   Archer, G. C., Fenves G. and Thewalt, C., Computers and Structures, Vol. 70, 1999, pp. 63-75.

(4)   Mackie, R.I., in *Developments in Analysis and Design using Finite Elements*, B.H.V. Topping and B. Kumar (eds.), CIVIL-COMP Ltd, Edinburg, Scotland, 1999, pp 55-62.

(5)   Forde, B.W.R., Foschi, R.O. and Stiemer, S.F., Computers and Structures, Vol. 34, No. 3, 1990, pp. 355-374.

(6)   Besson, J. and Foerch, R., Comput. Methods Appl. Mech. Engrg., Vol. 142, 1997, pp. 165-187.

(7)   Patzak, B. and Bittnar, Z., in *Developments in Analysis and Design using Finite Elements*, B.H.V. Topping and B. Kumar (eds.), , CIVIL-COMP Ltd, Edinburg, Scotland, 1999, pp 41-45.

(8)   Kong, X-A., Computers and Structures, Vol. 61, 1996, pp. 503-513.

(9)   Scholz, S.-P., Computers and Structures, Vol. 43, 1992, pp. 517-529.

(10)   Lu, J., White, D.W., Cen, W.-F. and Dunsmore, H.E., Computers and Structures, Vol. 55, No. 1, 1995, pp. 95-111.

(11)   Zeglinski, G.W. and Han, R.P.S., Int. J. Num. Meth. Engng., Vol. 37, 1994, pp. 3921-3927.

(12)   Zimmermann, Th., Bomme, P., Eyheramendy, D., Vernier, L. and Commend, S., Computers and Structures, Vol. 68, 1998, pp. 1-16.

(13)   Favela, J. and Connor, J.J., Proc. 2nd Int. Conf. Computer Meth. In Water Resources, 1991, Marrakesh, Morrocco, pp. 103-117.

(14)   Lage, C., Comput. Methods Appl. Mech. Engrg., Vol. 157, 1998, pp. 205-213.

(15)   Becker, A.A., *The Boundary Element Method in Engineering*, Mc-Graw-Hill, London, 1992.

(16)   Press, W.H., Teukolsky, S.A., Vetterling, W.T. and Flannery, B.P., Numerical Recipes in FORTRAN 77, 2nd Edition, Cambridge University Press, UK, 1992.

Figure 1: Basic features of Universal Modelling Language (UML) notation

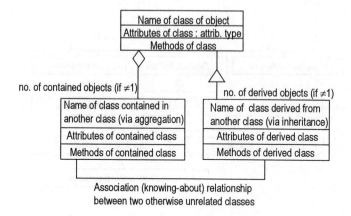

Figure 2: Overall structure of object-oriented boundary element system

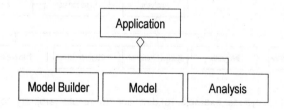

Figure 3: CBemModel class, formed by aggregation of other classes.

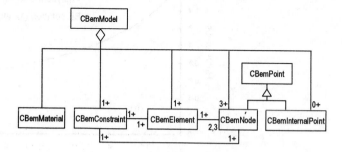

Figure 4: Inheritance hierarchy of different analysis types (those in italics represent possible future enhancements)

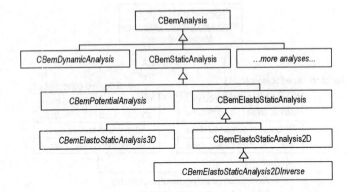

Figure 5: Analysis object and objects related by aggregation and association (simplified diagram)

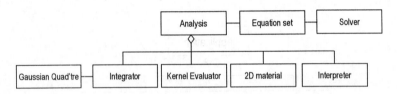

Figure 6: Thick cylinder example: (a) definition (b) results (arbitrary consistent units)

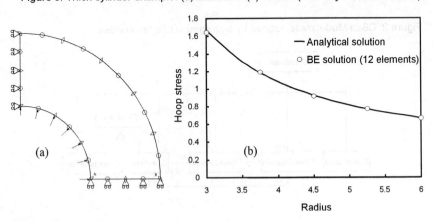

2. EXPERIMENTAL TECHNIQUES

DETERMINATION OF MECHANICAL PROPERTIES FROM INDENTATION TESTS

K. Tunvisut, N. P. O'Dowd and E. P. Busso

Indentation is a popular, non-destructive technique used to determine the mechanical properties of materials. In this work, expressions are derived to relate mechanical properties to load-indentation behaviour using dimensional analysis in conjunction with finite element simulations. Based on these expressions, a method is proposed to determine Young's modulus, yield strength and strain hardening properties of polycrystalline materials from indentation tests. The method is applicable to both homogeneous substrates and to thin coatings deposited on substrates of known mechanical properties.

1. INTRODUCTION

Indentation is a widely used technique to determine material hardness and other mechanical properties. For example, micro-indentation has become a popular method for studying the mechanical properties of thin films and coatings (e.g. Pharr *et al.* [1], Vlassak *et al.* [2]) where the properties of the coating may differ considerably from its nominal, bulk properties.

A variety of methods have been proposed to determine mechanical properties from indentation data of uncoated substrates, *e.g.* Doerner and Nix [3]; Oliver and Pharr [4]; Cheng and Cheng [5]). For example, in Cheng and Cheng [5] a method is proposed to determine values for the Young's modulus and yield strength from the peak load and the initial slope of the indentation load-displacement unloading curves. Giannakopoulos and Suresh [6] have recently proposed a method to determine Young's modulus, yield strength and strain hardening behaviour from the loading part of the indentation curve and the indentation depth after unloading. However, as discussed in Section 4, different materials can give rise to almost identical load-indentation curves and final indentation depths. Hence, it is not possible to identify uniquely the material properties from the indentation curve alone. For coated systems, indentation solutions, determined from finite element analysis in conjunction with dimensional analysis, have recently been presented in Tunvisut *et al.* [7].

In this work, relationships for conical indentation are presented for both uncoated substrates and coated systems. A method is proposed to determine material properties

Department of Mechanical Engineering, Imperial College of Science Technology and Medicine, Exhibition Road, London, SW7 2BX, UK.

using the indentation curve and the final indentation *area*, which is more sensitive to material properties than the indentation *depth*. This avoids problems of uniqueness, which arise from attempting to determine material properties from the indentation curve alone. The same method can be used for homogeneous substrates and coatings though different indentation solutions are used in each case.

2. DIMENSIONAL ANALYSIS OF THE INDENTATION PROCESS

2.1 Indentation of an uncoated substrate

A rigid, conical indenter with a half angle, θ, indenting into an elastic-plastic material, is considered. The material is characterised by a Young's modulus, E, Poisson's ratio, v, yield strength, σ_y, and strain hardening exponent n, with the post-yield tensile behaviour of coating is described by a power law relation, *viz.*,

$$\tilde{\varepsilon} = \frac{\sigma_y}{E}\left(\frac{\tilde{\sigma}}{\sigma_y}\right)^n,$$ (1)

where $\tilde{\varepsilon}$ and $\tilde{\sigma}$, are the equivalent von Mises strain and stress, respectively. It is assumed that there is no friction between the indenter and the coating surface, *i.e.*, the coating and indenter are both considered to be microscopically smooth.

A typical load-indentation curve is illustrated in Fig. 1, identifying the loading and unloading portions of the curve. The maximum indentation depth, h_m, the corresponding maximum load, F_{max}, and the indentation depth after unloading, h_f, are also shown. In what follows, dimensionless relationships to describe the indentation behaviour of a wide range of materials are derived.

During loading, the indentation force, F, depends on the elastic-plastic properties of the material, indentation depth, h, and the indenter angle. By applying the Buckingham PI Theorem (Barenblatt [8]), the following dimensionless relationship can be obtained:

$$\frac{F_{max}}{h^2 E} = \hat{\Pi}_\beta\left(\frac{\sigma_y}{E}, v, n, \theta\right).$$ (2)

During unloading, the unloading force, F, exhibits an additional dependence on the maximum indentation depth, h_m. Considering the initial slope, dF/dh, at the onset of unloading, dimensional analysis gives,

$$\frac{1}{h_m E}\frac{dF}{dh}\bigg|_{h=h_m} = \hat{\Pi}_\gamma\left(\frac{\sigma_y}{E}, v, n, \theta\right).$$ (3)

Dimensional relations for indentation have also been derived in [5] and [6], but these differ somewhat in form from those presented here and the resultant method used to extract material properties is also somewhat different.

2.2 Indentation of a thin elastic-plastic coating on an elastic substrate

Consider again a rigid, conical indenter with a half angle, θ. Here the indentation of an elastic-plastic coating of thickness, h_o, with Young's modulus, E_c, Poisson's ratio, v_c, yield strength, σ_{yc}, and strain hardening exponent, n_c, deposited on an elastic substrate with Young's modulus, E_s, and Poisson's ratio, v_s, is examined. The required dimensionless relationships are given below.

During loading,

$$\frac{F_{max}}{h_o^2 E_s} = \hat{\Pi}_\alpha \left(\frac{h}{h_o}, \frac{E_c}{E_s}, \frac{\sigma_{yc}}{E_s}, v_c, v_s, n_c, \theta \right), \tag{4}$$

and for unloading

$$\frac{1}{h_o E_s} \frac{dF}{dh} \bigg|_{h=h_m} = \hat{\Pi}_\delta \left(\frac{h_m}{h_o}, \frac{E_c}{E_s}, \frac{\sigma_{yc}}{E_s}, v_c, v_s, n_c, \theta \right). \tag{5}$$

3. FINITE ELEMENT MODEL

The functional forms of the dimensional scaling functions have been given in Section 2. The dependence of these functions on their non-dimensional arguments has been determined using the finite element method.

The assumption of a conical indenter allows the problem to be modelled numerically in two dimensions using axisymmetric elements, with the coating/substrate system modelled as a cylinder. A very fine mesh was used in the contact region to ensure a high degree of accuracy and a gradually coarser mesh was employed in the interior of the specimen. The loading and unloading curves were obtained directly from the finite element output of the normal reaction force on the rigid indenter, as a function of the vertical displacement of the node directly beneath the tip of the indenter. The finite element code ABAQUS [9] was used in all the simulations. Further details of the finite element analysis are provided in [7].

The indenter angle chosen in the analysis was $\theta = 70°$ which has been shown (Cheng and Cheng [10], COMPWERC [11]) to give indentation curves very similar to those using Berkovich and Vicker indenters.

4. RESULTS OF FINITE ELEMENT ANALYSIS

4.1 Indentation of a substrate

In this section, the indentation of an uncoated material is examined. The indentation simulations were undertaken on materials characterised by a range of yield strengths and Young's moduli, (i.e. σ_y/E). Materials with $n = 5$, 10 and ∞ (non-hardening) were considered.

The function, $\hat{\Pi}_y$ in Eq. 3 is first considered. Though not shown here, the finite element results indicate that the dimensionless initial unloading slope $(1/h_m E)(dF/dh)$ is almost independent of the hardening exponent, n. Figure 2 shows the dependence of initial unloading slope on normalised yield strength (σ_y/E). For low strength materials, $\sigma_y/E < 0.01$, the dependence is very strong, while for high strength materials, $\sigma_y/E \geq 0.01$, this dependence is weaker and $(1/h_m E)(dF/dh)$ can be assumed constant. For the latter case, we can then write,

$$\left(\frac{1}{h_m E}\frac{dF}{dh}\right) = 6.8 \pm 0.1, \qquad \text{for } h_f/h_m < 0.875. \qquad (6)$$

The range of applicability of Eq. 6 is given in terms of a directly measurable quantity, h_f/h_m, the ratio between unloaded and maximum depth, rather than the ratio σ_y/E, which is not known *a priori*. The material's Young's modulus can therefore be determined from the unloading slope and the maximum indentation depth, provided the above inequality is satisfied.

For the case where $h_f/h_m > 0.875$ (*i.e.* a low strength material), an alternative normalising parameter is introduced—the initial unloading slope is divided by $h_f E$ rather than $h_m E$. Figure 3 shows this normalised unloading slope plotted against normalised yield strength, σ_y/E. In contrast to Fig. 2, the dependence of the unloading slope on σ_y/E is weak for a low strength material, $\sigma_y/E < 0.01$ leading to the following expression,

$$\left(\frac{1}{h_f E}\frac{dF}{dh}\right) = 7.8 \pm 0.1 \qquad \text{for } h_f/h_m > 0.875. \qquad (7)$$

Equations 6 and 7 allow identification of the Young's modulus from the initial unloading slope of the indentation curve for a high and low strength material, respectively, if the final and maximum indentation depths are known.

In Fig. 4 the normalised maximum indentation loads as a function of normalised yield strength for three values of n are shown. It may be noted that a number of combinations of σ_y/E and n can give the same value of normalised maximum load. Therefore, an additional matching parameter is required in order to identify unique values of σ_y and n. It has been found that two materials, which have almost the same normalised indentation force, have different stress distributions in the contact area and different associated contact radii, [7]. Hence, the contact area after unloading, denoted A_f can be chosen as the additional matching parameter. A_f is calculated by:

$$A_f = \pi(r_{cf})^2, \qquad (8)$$

where r_{cf} is the corresponding contact radius, defined as the radial distance from the axis of symmetry to the point of last contact, [7].

Figure 5 displays the relationship between the normalised final area of contact, A_f/h_m^2, and normalised yield strength for different strain hardening exponents. Figure 4 in combination with Fig. 5 can then be used to evaluate unique values for the yield strength and strain hardening properties after the Young's modulus has been determined. For a known value of F_{max}, a range of possible values for the material yield strength and corresponding strain hardening exponent can be obtained from Fig. 4. Subsequently, Fig. 5 can be used to select the correct pair of yield strength and hardening exponent among those pre-predicted by Fig. 4. For example, consider the case with $F_{max}/h_m^2 E = 0.3$ and $A_f/h_m^2 = 1.92$. Figure 4 gives the following possible ratios of normalised yield stress: $\sigma_y/E = 1, 3, 5 \times 10^{-3}$ for $n = 5, 10$ and ∞ respectively. Figure 5 gives another three possible values of $\sigma_y/E = 1, 3, 5 \times 10^{-3}$ for $n = 5, 10$ and ∞ respectively. It may be deduced therefore, that the material's yield strength and hardening exponent are $\sigma_y/E = 1 \times 10^{-3}$ and $n = 5$, respectively.

As discussed earlier, two materials with different yield strength and hardening exponent having almost identical indentation curves have different areas of contact, A_f. The current approach can therefore overcome inaccuracies that may arise in the determination of mechanical properties using the final indentation depth, h_f, as proposed in [6].

4.2 Indentation of a coated substrate

We next examine indentation of coated substrates. All simulations of the coating/substrate systems were carried out to the same maximum indentation depth, namely 33% of the coating thickness, h_o. This choice of indentation depth minimises the possibility of yielding in the substrate and therefore justifies the assumption of elastic behaviour in the substrate. The simulations were undertaken for a variety of coating materials characterised by a range of yield strengths and Young's moduli, (i.e. ratios σ_{yc}/E_s and E_c/E_s). Results are presented for three typical Young's modulus ratios, $E_c/E_s = 0.1, 1$, and 10 and materials with $n_c = 5, 10$ and ∞ are again considered. In what follows it is assumed that the Young's modulus of the substrate, E_s, is known and the properties of the coating, σ_{yc}, E_c and n_c are unknown.

Finite element results, [7], show that, for given values of h_m and θ, the initial unloading slope of an elastic- plastic coating material is relatively insensitive to σ_{yc}/E_s and n_c, and is only a function of E_c/E_s. Therefore,

$$\left. \frac{1}{h_o E_s} \frac{dF}{dh} \right|_{h=h_m} = \hat{\Pi}_\delta \left(\frac{E_c}{E_s} \right). \tag{9}$$

The log-log plot of normalised unloading slope versus Young's modulus ratio given in Fig. 6 allows an immediate identification of the Young's modulus of the coating from the initial unloading slope of the indentation curve, if the coating thickness, h_o, and substrate Young's modulus, E_s, are known.

In Fig. 7, the normalised maximum indentation load, $F_{max}/h_o^2 E_s$, is given as a function of normalised coating yield strength, σ_{yc}/E_s, for $E_c/E_s = 0.1, 1$, and 10 with three values of n_c. (A smaller scale is needed to resolve differences between the curves for $E_c/E_s = 0.1$). As for the homogeneous case, it can be seen that, for a given value of E_c/E_s, a number of combinations of σ_{yc}/E_s and n_c can give the same maximum of normalised indentation load. To extract unique values of σ_{yc}/E_s and n_c from an indentation test, the final contact area after unloading, A_f, is again used.

Figure 8 shows the relationship between normalised final area of contact, A_f/h_o^2, and coating yield strength for different strain hardening exponents and two E_c/E_s ratios. Figure 7 in combination with Fig. 8 can then be used to evaluate the yield strength and strain-hardening properties of the coating material after the coating Young's modulus has been determined. For example, consider the case with $E_c/E_s = 10$, $F_{max}/h_o^2 E_s = 0.3$ and $A_f/h_o^2 = 1.92$. Figure 7 gives the following possible ratios of normalised yield stress: $\sigma_{yc}/E_s \approx 42$, 55 and 68×10^{-3} for $n_c = 5$, 10 and ∞, respectively. Figure 8 gives another three possible values of σ_{yc}/E_s, i.e. 24, 43 and 68×10^{-3} for $n_c = 5$, 10 and ∞ respectively. The value of the yield strength and the hardening exponent estimated from this approach are therefore $68\times10^{-3}E_s$ and ∞, respectively.

5. DISCUSSION AND CONCLUSIONS

Results from parametric studies have been presented here for the indentation of an elastic-plastic substrate or an elastic-plastic coating deposited on an elastic substrate. The following procedures are proposed. In each case the experimental indentation curve (load vs. displacement) during the loading and unloading process and the final contact area are required.

For an uncoated substrate:

1. Calculate h_f/h_m, $(dF/dh)_{h=h_m}$, $F_{max}/h_m^2 E$ and A_f/h_m^2

2. Depending on the value of h_f/h_m use Eq. 6 or 7 to determine E

3. Use the pre-determined E and Figs. 4 and 5 to determine σ_y and n

   The method relies on accurate measurement of the maximum load, the initial unloading slope and the final contact area. It should be pointed out that, in practice, accurate measurement of these quantities may be difficult, particularly the unloading slope. Our calculations indicate that a 5% error in measuring the unloading slope can lead to maximum errors of 5%, 30% and >50% in the predicted value of E, σ_y and n respectively. This emphasises the importance of precise measurement of the indentation parameters.

It has been found (Tunvisut, et. al. [12]) that the relatively shallow indentation ($h_m/h_o < 0.33$) of a relatively low strength coating ($\sigma_y/E \leq 0.001$) or elastically similar coating ($E_c/E_s \approx 1$) is unaffected by the presence of the underlying substrate. For these conditions, the substrate may be ignored and the above procedure may be used to extract the coating properties. Otherwise, the substrate strongly influences the indentation behaviour and the methodology below is required for an accurate determination of the coating mechanical properties.

1. Calculate $(1/h_o E_s) (dF/dh)_{h=h_m}$, $F_{max}/h_o^2 E_s$, and A_f/h_o^2

2. Determine E_c from Fig. 6.

3. Determine σ_{yc} and n_c from Fig. 7 and 8.

   The applicability of the method again depends strongly on the precision of the experimental data and a maximum error of 30%, 40% and >50% in the predicted values of E_c/E_s, σ_{yc}/E_s and n_c respectively may result from a 5% error in the unloading slope.

The current method relies on determining the material properties graphically from Figs. 4–8. Work is in progress to obtain accurate fits to these curves to allow determination of material properties directly. These results will be presented in future work.

6. ACKNOWLEDGMENT

Support for this work has been provided by the government of Thailand. Helpful discussions with the COMPWERC group (Brite Euram project, BE97-4283) are acknowledged.

REFERENCE LIST

(1) Pharr, G.M., Bolshakov, A., Tsui,T.Y., and Jack C. Hay, *J. Mat. Res*, 1995, pp. 100.

(2) Vlassak, J., Tsui, T.Y., and Nix , W.D., *J. Mat. Res.,* 14, No. 6, 1999, pp. 2196.

(3) Doerner, M.F. and Nix, W.D., *J. Mat. Res.*, 1, 1986, pp. 601.

(4) Oliver, W.C. and Pharr, G.M., *J. Mat. Res.*, 7, 1992, pp. 1564.

(5) Cheng, Y.T., and Cheng, C.M., *J. Appl. Phys.*, 84, No. 3, 1998, pp. 1284.

(6) Giannakopoulos, A.E. and Suresh, S., *Scripta Materiallia*, 40, No. 10, 1999, pp. 1191

(7) Tunvisut, K., O'Dowd, N.P., and Busso, E.P., To appear *in Int. J. Solids Structures*.

(8) Barenblatt, G.I., Scaling, self-similarity, and intermediate asymptotics, Cambridge University Press, 1996

(9) ABAQUS V. 5.7, Hibbitt, Karlsson and Sorensen Inc., Providence, RI, 1996

(10) Cheng, Y.T., and Cheng, C.M., *Phil. Mag. Lett.*, 78, No. 2, pp. 115.

(11) COMPWERC, Brite EuRam project, BE97-4283, 1999

(12) Tunvisut, K., O'Dowd, N.P., and Busso, E.P., Manuscript in preparation, 1999

FIGURE 1 Typical indentation curve

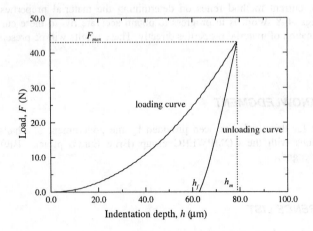

FIGURE 2 Normalised initial unloading slope against normalised yield strength

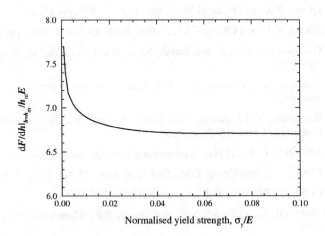

FIGURE 3 Normalised initial unloading slope against normalised yield strength.

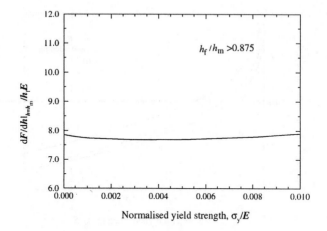

FIGURE 4 Normalised maximum indentation load against normalised yield strength.

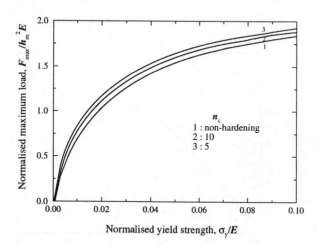

FIGURE 5 Normalised final area of contact against normalised yield strength.

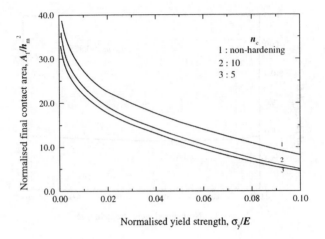

FIGURE 6 Normalised initial unloading slope against normalised coating Young's modulus on log-log scale.

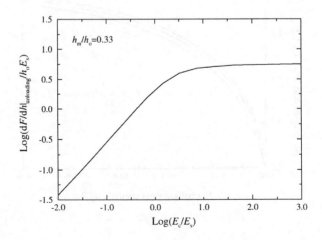

FIGURE 7 Normalised maximum indentation load against normalised coating yield strength.

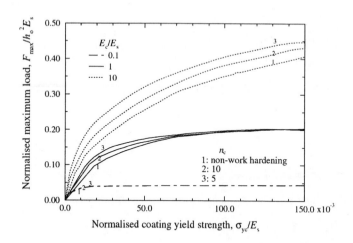

FIGURE 8 Normalised final area of contact against normalised coating yield strength.

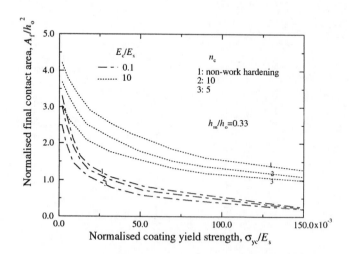

STRESS ANALYSIS OF AN AUTOMOTIVE COMPONENT USING THERMOELASTICITY

R.J. Greene*, S. Barone† and E.A. Patterson*

A thermoelastic stress analysis of a racecar wheel hub carrier is presented. The component was loaded to simulate in-service loads and thermoelastic data captured using both the SPATE and Deltatherm detectors. The analysis employs an iterative data smoothing technique to reduce noise in the thermoelastic signal. Results from this method identify possible failure sites on the component surface which correlate well with observed failures of in-service hub carriers, and suggestions for improvement in the design of the component are made. The performance of the two thermoelastic detectors is also compared for this analysis, and the quality of data output from the two systems quantified in terms of signal to noise ratio, repeatability of results and speed of data acquisition. The work concludes that the technique of thermoelastic stress analysis is a valuable tool for the analysis of complex components, that the technique correctly predicts initiation sites for fatigue crack growth, and that both SPATE and Deltatherm offer reliable and accurate data capture tools in this experimental situation.

INTRODUCTION

The experimental technique of thermoelastic stress analysis allows the direct measurement of the change in the sum of the principal stresses on the surface of a component which is experiencing a cyclic stress regime. An infrared detector is employed which generates a two-dimensional spatial record of the thermoelastic signal from the surface of an isotropic component which can be related to the surface stress by equation (1)

$$AS = \Delta(\sigma_1 + \sigma_2) \tag{1}$$

where A is a calibration constant, S is the thermoelastic signal and σ_1, σ_2 are the principal surface stresses[1].

The hub carrier to be analysed is a lightweight alloy casting from the racecar industry which has been experiencing fatigue failure in service. The casting is hollow and in operation is oil-filled to permit lubrication of the axle. The complex internal

*Department of Mechanical Engineering, University of Sheffield

†Dipartimento di Construzioni Mecaniche e Nucleari, Università degli Studi di Pisa, Italy

and external geometry makes the development of a finite element model unattractive, and suggests the use of an experimental technique to obtain information about the surface stresses developed under service loads.

Two thermoelastic detectors were employed sequentially in these experiments. SPATE (Stress Pattern Analysis by Thermal Emission)[2] uses a pair of mirrors to build a two-dimensional raster scan of a surface, bringing a single detector to bear on each point of the scan, whereas Deltatherm[3] uses a staring array of detectors which are read continuously at the framing rate of the camera. These experiments have been used as an opportunity to compare the performance of the two systems and the data which they are each able to generate.

In order to validate the data from Deltatherm, an initial analysis was performed on a tensile plate specimen. This allowed the quantification of noise and acquisition repeatability of the instrument before considering the more complex component.

EXPERIMENTAL METHOD

Specimen preparation and loading

The hub carriers supplied for testing contained small surface imperfections resulting from the manufacturing process which were removed with light abrasion. This was considered acceptable as the resulting macroscopic stress field on the component surface would experience only minor change with an associated improvement in thermoelastic data acquisition from the surface.

A thin coating of matt black paint was applied to both the flat plate specimen and the hub carrier to ensure a uniform emissivity in the infrared region, and the same paint was applied to the loading frame of the hub carrier to reduce reflection effects and problems associated with signal overload of the thermoelastic detectors. A strain gauge rosette was applied to both specimens in a region of moderate surface stress and low stress gradient to allow the calibration of each material for thermoelastic response. The components are presented in figures (1) and (2).

DATA COLLECTION

All tests were performed in a servohydraulic loading frame, from which a reference signal was taken to allow the thermoelastic signal to be correctly phased in with the load cycle. Loading for both specimens was applied with a frequency of 10 Hz to ensure that the materials being analyzed were operating under adiabatic conditions.

SPATE

The spot size of the detector on the component surface is determined by the distance between the SPATE head and the component, which in turn defines the effective limit of resolution of the scan. If the centre-to-centre distance between analysis points is smaller than the spot diameter, the only result is 'over-sampling' of the data field. Therefore the primary limit on the resolution of scans of small area is the spot size, and on scans of large area is the time taken to execute the scan.

The raw data from the SPATE 4000 detector contains comparatively low noise – typically a local variation of ±5% for these experimental conditions – because the two dimensional data map is built up by the progression of a pair of mirrors through a raster scan, always using the same photoelastic detector. This produces images with inherently low spatial noise because the same detector is used to assess each data point.

DeltaTherm

The focal plane array used by Deltatherm gives the potential of high resolution scans of small area, as well as a very considerable reduction in data acquisition time. The array of 320x256 is sampled at 64 Hz, which in practice allows repeatable scans to be captured in 30 seconds. Alternatively, an array of 128x128 can be selected, allowing a frame rate of 204 Hz and corresponding reduction in capture time.

The raw data from Deltatherm is comparatively noisy as the detector chip is built up from 81920 individual detectors, each of which has a slightly differing thermoelastic response. This leads to local variations which are typically ±12% in areas of moderate signal strength. Although calibration of the offset of each detector is simple, calibration of gain is not currently available within the camera system.

ANALYSIS

Background removal

The background was removed from the raw data images using a routine which searches for a large step in signal value along either the horizontal or vertical direction, as selected by the user. Modification of the magnitude of the step allows the correct identification of background areas and sets the signal value of pixels in these areas to zero.

A second routine is used to identify bad pixels in the raw Deltatherm data. In any detector array there exist a small number of individual detectors which function incorrectly and return either near full scale or near zero readings. These are identified using a combined high and low threshold filter, and the values at the selected pixels then extrapolated from neighbouring pixels using a three by three median mask.

Smoothing algorithm

The noise inherent in thermoelastic data can be reduced by several post-processing techniques, but with an associated cost of degradation of true features in the thermoelastic scan. However, some form of data smoothing is often desirable when measuring weak thermoelastic signals in order to improve the signal to noise ratio of the data[4].

The Laplace differential equation, which defines the compatibility condition for an elastic body experiencing a constant body force, can be expressed as

$$\frac{\partial^2 S}{\partial x^2} + \frac{\partial^2 S}{\partial y^2} = 0 \tag{2}$$

where
$$S = \sigma_1 + \sigma_2 \tag{3}$$

Although it is not possible to solve equation (2) analytically for most data, the use of an iterative numerical solution produces an acceptable approximation to the surface stress harmonic function[5]. A numerical solution can be generated from the general formula expressed in equation (4) relating the value of the stress function to be improved S_0 to the values at surrounding points a,b,c and d

$$\left(\frac{1}{ac} + \frac{1}{bd}\right)S_0 = \frac{1}{a(a+c)}S_a + \frac{1}{b(b+d)}S_b + \frac{1}{c(c+a)}S_c + \frac{1}{d(d+b)}S_d \tag{4}$$

For the special case of an equally spaced grid of data, with the point of interest $S_{i,j}$ being surrounded by four equidistant points, equation (4) reduces to Liebmann's formula

$$S_{i,j} = \frac{S_{i+1,j} + S_{i,j+1} + S_{i-1,j} + S_{i,j-1}}{4} \tag{5}$$

As the map produced in a thermoelastic analysis is the inverse of the above problem, equation (5) can be applied iteratively in order to achieve an approximation to the harmonic function which describes the surface stresses[6].

One or two instances of this smoothing algorithm have been applied to the raw thermoelastic data, improving the signal to noise ratio whilst retaining local features in the data map.

Tensile plate

Data from SPATE and Deltatherm were smoothed as described above, the results of which appear as figures (3a) and (3b), as maps of 95 by 94 pixels and 255 by 255 pixels respectively. The stress data has been normalized by the remote stress, σ_0, and the distance from the hole has been normalized by the radius of the hole, a. Calibration of the scans was made by strain gauge rosette applied midway between the scan area shown and the mounting grips. Figure (3a) was produced over $2^1/_2$ hours using the optimum SPATE spot size without oversampling, and shows characteristic low spatial noise but poor edge definition due to the spot size. Figure (3b) was captured in 30 seconds with a 25 mm lens and no motion compensation, and shows comparatively high spatial noise but good edge definition.

Figures (4a) and (4b) allow comparison between the two images by the selection of a horizontal line of data which passes through the centre of the hole. The theoretical solution[7] is shown together with the smoothed experimental data for comparison. Each data set has been scaled to account for the different magnification of each scan.

Hub carrier

Figures (5a) and (5b) show the SPATE and Deltatherm scans of the hub carrier after two instances of Liebmann smoothing have been applied. The images show considerable specimen motion in the direction of loading due to the flexibility of the loading jig, which precluded the capture of data at a higher magnification in regions of particular interest.

The design of the loading jig and method of application of load to the hub carrier permitted the application of approximately 20% of the magnitude of loading which is seen in service. This inevitably means that the sum of principal stresses exhibited on the specimen surface generates a thermoelastic signal which is greatly influenced by background noise and leads to the capture of data of low quality.

DISCUSSION AND CONCLUSIONS

The thermoelastic data presented allow both the detailed analysis of the hub carrier and a comparison to be made between the two thermoelastic detectors used in this work.

Data from the tensile plate specimen presented in figures (3) and (4) show that both thermoelastic detectors are capable of capturing accurate surface scans in a geometrically simple situation. The comparison of the data with the theoretical result shows the value of a smoothing routine to reduce signal to noise ratio, and allow the application of both systems to more complex components to be made with confidence.

Both thermoelastic scans of the hub carrier show regions of larger than expected surface stress in several key areas. The most obvious feature is the asymmetry of the thermoelastic pattern on the component surface which is itself geometrically symmetrical. This arises from the simulation of in-service loads by the loading jig by bolting a plate to the side of the hub carrier with the aim of reproducing loading conditions which would occur from the axle. The plate is secured with six bolts which leaves a statically indeterminate loading condition, and has resulted in one bolt bearing a greater load than the other in the region of interest.

The scans also show an area of stress concentration, indicated in figure (5), which coincides with the site of initiation of fatigue cracks on failed components. Once initiation has occurred, the cracks propagate towards the loading point in the centre of the hub carrier, leading to fast fracture of the casting. Assuming plane-stress conditions are present on the component surface the data maps can readily be processed to separate the individual stresses by calibration and the measurement of appropriate boundary values. The correlation between the experimental data and the failure mode of the component confirms that the technique of thermoelastic stress analysis is an appropriate tool in this situation for the determination of weak areas in the design of a complex component.

ACKNOWLEDGEMENTS

The authors would like to thank the UK Engineering and Physical Sciences Research Council for the provision of equipment and financial support, and Bradley Boyce of Stress Photonics Inc., Wisconsin, for extensive technical assistance.

REFERENCE LIST

(1) Dulieu-Barton, J.M., *Strain*, Vol. **35**, No. 2, 1999, pp. 35-39.

(2) *SPATE 4000 Manual*, Ometron Ltd, Chiselhurst, Kent.

(3) Boyce, B.R. and Lesniak, J.R., *Proc. BSSM Conf.*, Sheffield, 1995, pp. 31-33.

(4) Barone, S., *Strain*, Vol. **33**, No. 1, 1997, pp. 9–13.

(5) Frocht, M.M., *Photoelasticity*, Vol. 2, John Wiley and Sons, New York, 1948.

(6) Barone, S., Patterson, E.A, *Jnl Strain Anal.*, Vol. **33**, No. 6, 1998, pp. 437–447.

(7) Savin, G.N., *Stress Concentration Around Holes*, Pergamon, London, England, 1961.

Figure 1 – Schematic of the aluminium tensile specimen (w=120mm, a=10mm).

Figure 2 – Photograph of the hub carrier, with dotted area showing analysis region.

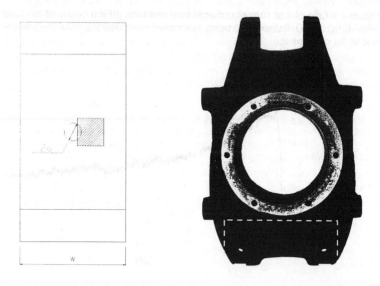

Figure 3 – Interpolated contour plots of the normalized sum of principal stresses obtained by SPATE (a) and Deltatherm (b) from the aluminium hole in plate specimen, with one application of Liebmann smoothing.

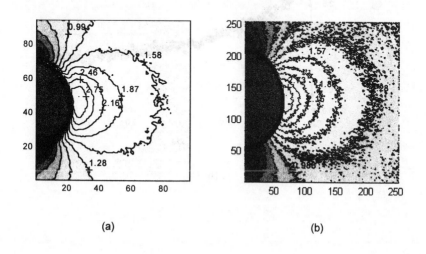

(a)   (b)

Figure 4 – Line plot of sum of principal stresses through the centre of the hole, for SPATE (a) and Deltatherm (b) using smoothed thermoelastic data (theoretical result shown for comparison)

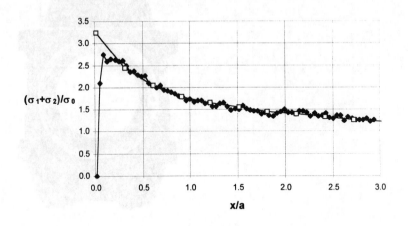

(a)

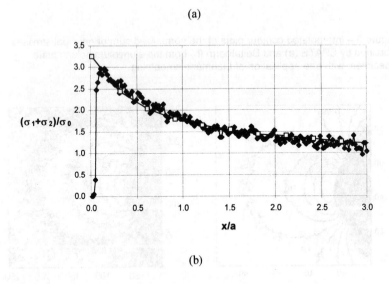

(b)

Figure 5 – Interpolated contour plots of sum of principal stresses of the hub carrier measured with SPATE (a) and Deltatherm (b), with two applications of Liebmann smoothing (uncalibrated signal, axes showing pixel number)

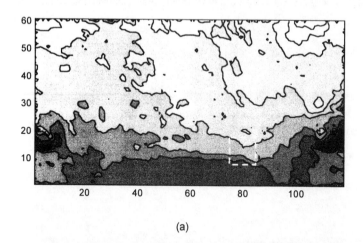

(a)

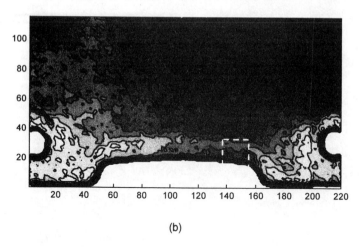

(b)

STRATEGIES FOR APPLYING PHASE-STEPPING TO THREE-COLOUR DIGITAL IMAGING PHOTOELASTICITY

A. Triplow*, I.A. Jones* and D. Chen*

This paper examines several approaches to the gathering of isoclinic and isochromatic data in digital imaging photoelasticity. The literature on phase-stepping and three-colour (RGB) photoelasticity is briefly reviewed. The use of phase angles of light variation over a sequence of images in order to calculate (for example) the isoclinic parameter (principal stress orientations) is described. Three strategies are then investigated for the determination of the isochromatic parameter, based upon Tardy and Sénarmont compensation and upon polarimetry techniques. The polarimetry-based technique is also demonstrated experimentally using a 3CCD analogue video camera. Good results are obtained except in the region of low fringe order where it is difficult to determine the isoclinic parameter accurately.

INTRODUCTION

Digital imaging techniques, in a variety of forms, have breathed new life into photoelasticity as a technique for experimental stress analysis, yet of the numerous approaches developed over the last 20 years or so, no single ideal approach appears to have been identified. This paper aims to explore the overlap between two such approaches, namely phase-stepping and RGB (three-colour) photoelasticity.

Early approaches to digital imaging photoelasticity (Seguchi *et al* [1], Müller and Saackel [2], Voloshin and Burger [3] and Ramesh *et al* [4]) produced integral or fractional fringe order positions rather than a full field of continuous values. Umezaki *et al* [5] used Fourier analysis to extract isoclinic data. More recent work on automated photoelasticity has followed three slightly overlapping routes. Phase-stepping [6] forms the basis of the systems built by Patterson and his co-workers [7] who also review the many papers on this approach [8]. Their system gathers the images via a monochromatic charge-coupled device- (CCD-) based camera. Six different configurations of the analyser and its quarter-wave plate (QWP) are used to find the relative retardation and the isoclinic angle. Further developments of this system have involved unwrapping algorithms to resolve fractional fringe orders [9], simultaneous observation of fringe-stepped images [8] and integration with spectral contents analysis [10] (see below). Buckberry and Towers [11] describe an imaging photoelasticity system with a different unwrapping algorithm.

*School of Mechanical, Materials, Manufacturing Engineering and Management, University of Nottingham, University Park, Nottingham NG7 2RD

Spectral content analysis has been used point-by-point for photoelasticity by Voloshin and Redner [12] and Haake and Patterson [13]. A full-field variant of this is RGB [14] or three-fringe [15] photoelasticity, which identifies isochromatic fringes by their unique combinations of red, green and blue (RGB) components of colour camera output. This technique is typically limited to 3 or 4 fringe orders, alone it cannot recover the isoclinic parameter, and its accuracy is limited by inaccuracies in the optical retarders (QWPs) and by the finite bandwidths of the filters in the camera.

Few papers can be found which combine RGB with phase-stepping. Nurse [16] has used a least-squares approach to fit phase-stepped RGB intensities to the isochromatic value. Ramesh and Deshmukh [17] encountered problems with RGB phase-stepping because their camera had very broad filter bandwidths.

BACKGROUND AND AIMS

Most of the techniques based upon phase-stepping use very similar strategies based upon exact fitting of both isoclinic and isochromatic data directly to a small number of observations, rather than least-squared fitting of the two sets of parameters (separately or sequentially) to one or more overdetermined sets of experimental data. It was considered beneficial here to examine a number of alternative phase-stepping strategies to take advantage of the colour imaging hardware now available. The following issues therefore need to be addressed by such a strategy.

- It is impractical to use directly any strategy (e.g. conventional Tardy or Sénarmont compensation) which requires alignment of the polariscope with the principal stress directions, since these directions vary over the specimen.

- While conclusive measurements have not yet been obtained, it is likely that the prismatic beam-splitter used in all 3CCD cameras results in some polarisation sensitivity of the camera. Rotation of a polarising element (i.e. the analyser) adjacent to the camera would result in the measured output varying with a periodicity covering 180° of analyser rotation. The phase stepping strategy should therefore either avoid analyser movement completely within a given sequence of images, or enable that order of variation to be ignored.

- The use of three colours (R, G and B, each detected by one of the camera's three CCD detectors) presents the opportunity to measure the isoclinic angle at almost all positions since an integral non-zero fringe will not normally be encountered for all three colours simultaneously (although the first-order fringe comes close to this). However, the QWPs in the polariscope can be well matched to, at best, only one of the colours unless achromatic waveplates are used. Sufficiently large, accurate and achromatic QWPs are proving difficult or impossible to source.

- RGB photoelasticity is limited to low fringe orders since the variations in colour between the different fringes become too weak to be distinguished by the filters (of finite bandwidth) used in colour cameras. Furthermore, the use of practical model materials (e.g. epoxy) of varying colour are likely to skew the values of any spectral content measurement. However, the possibility of detecting unique combinations of (say) fractional fringe order seems more promising.

- In digital imaging photoelasticity, the resolution for each colour is normally eight bits (256 values), out of which the three least significant bits may be corrupted by noise [16]. The phase angle of a varying signal over an image sequence is less likely to be corrupted by noise and quantisation error than its absolute values. Similarly, nonlinearity in camera response (including saturation) would not affect phase angle measurements. Initial strategies therefore used phase angle detection, but these were later identified as special cases of a least-squares fitting process.

OPTICAL THEORY

The derivations made use of the Stokes vector definition of polarized light [18,19]:

$$
\begin{Bmatrix} S_0 \\ S_1 \\ S_2 \\ S_3 \end{Bmatrix} = \begin{Bmatrix} \text{intensity of light} \\ \text{preference for horizontal polarization} \\ \text{preference for polarization at } 45° \\ \text{preference for RH circular polarization} \end{Bmatrix} \tag{1}
$$

so that (for instance) the Stokes vector for unpolarized light is $\{1, 0, 0, 0\}^T$. The effects upon polarized light of optical elements such as polarizers and retarders were modelled using the so-called *Mueller matrix approach* described by Aben [18].

A graphical representation of the Stokes vector of polarised light is as a point on the Poincaré sphere (Figure 1), whose radius corresponds to light intensity. Points around the equator of the sphere represent plane polarised light whose azimuth θ varies from 0 to π radians. The poles of the sphere represent right-handed and left-handed circularly polarised light, while intermediate points on a given great circle through the poles gives light of a given azimuth but varying ellipticity. A given point on the sphere with spherical polar coordinates $(2\theta, 2\psi)$ may be reached by passing unpolarised light through a polarizer with azimuth $\theta-\psi$ followed by a QWP of azimuth θ. Aben [18] presents a thorough discussion of the Poincaré sphere.

INVESTIGATION OF PHASE-STEPPING STRATEGIES

Fundamental strategy: phase angle detection e.g. for isoclinic measurement

This is presented as an illustration and no novelty is claimed, although few examples of its use have been reported (e.g. [5]). The light intensity is assumed to vary sinusoidally with harmonic order n over a given sequence of N images:

$$I_i = A + B\sin\frac{2n\pi(i-1)}{N} + C\cos\frac{2n\pi(i-1)}{N} = A + \sqrt{B^2 + C^2}\sin\left(\frac{2n\pi(i-1)}{N} + \psi\right)$$

$$= A + \sqrt{B^2 + C^2}\left(\sin\frac{2n\pi(i-1)}{N}\cos\psi + \cos\frac{2n\pi(i-1)}{N}\sin\psi\right) \qquad (2)$$

where A, B and C are constants and ψ is the phase angle. A, B and C are found by solving the following overdetermined set of equations, expressed in matrix form:

$$\begin{bmatrix} 1 & \sin 0 & \cos 0 \\ 1 & \sin\dfrac{2\pi n}{N} & \cos\dfrac{2\pi n}{N} \\ \vdots & \vdots & \vdots \\ 1 & \sin\dfrac{2\pi n(N-1)}{N} & \cos\dfrac{2\pi n(N-1)}{N} \end{bmatrix} \begin{Bmatrix} A \\ B \\ C \end{Bmatrix} = \begin{Bmatrix} I_1 \\ I_2 \\ \vdots \\ I_N \end{Bmatrix} \qquad \text{or}: \quad [\mathbf{B}]\{\mathbf{A}\} = \{\mathbf{I}\} \quad (3)$$

The least-squared solution to this set of equations is

$$\{\mathbf{A}\} = \left([\mathbf{B}]^{\mathrm{T}}[\mathbf{B}]\right)^{-1}[\mathbf{B}]^{\mathrm{T}}\{\mathbf{I}\} \qquad (4)$$

When the points in this simple sinusoidally-varying sequence are evenly spaced, as in the present situation, $[\mathbf{B}]^{\mathrm{T}}[\mathbf{B}]$ is a diagonal matrix so that the solution becomes:

$$\begin{Bmatrix} A \\ B \\ C \end{Bmatrix} = \begin{Bmatrix} \dfrac{1}{N}\sum I_i \\ \dfrac{2}{N}\sum_{i=1}^{N}\sin\dfrac{2n\pi(i-1)}{N}I_i \\ \dfrac{2}{N}\sum_{i=1}^{N}\cos\dfrac{2n\pi(i-1)}{N}I_i \end{Bmatrix} \qquad (5)$$

which is equivalent to the first and the imaginary and real parts of the $n+1$'th terms of the discrete Fourier transform of the sequence. The phase angle is then easily calculated from:

$$\tan\psi = \frac{C}{B} \qquad (6)$$

The most straightforward application of this approach is in the determination of the isoclinic angle. It is standard bookwork to demonstrate that the intensity of light emerging from a crossed plane polariscope exhibits one cycle of harmonic variation as the polariscope's polariser (with orientation θ) and analyser (with orientation $\theta + \pi/2$ radians) rotate through $\pi/2$ radians relative to a model of fixed orientation ϕ:

$$I = \frac{I_0}{4}\sin^2 2(\theta - \phi)(1 - \cos\Delta) = \frac{I_0}{8}[1 - \cos 4(\theta - \phi)](1 - \cos\Delta)$$

$$= \frac{I_0}{8}\left[1 + \sin 4\left(\theta - \frac{\pi}{8} - \phi\right)\right](1 - \cos\Delta) \tag{7}$$

so that the isoclinic angle is easily calculated in terms of the phase angle ψ:

$$\phi = -\frac{\pi}{8} - \frac{\psi}{4} \tag{8}$$

Any polarisation sensitivity of the camera could be ignored by capturing a sequence of images covering two adjacent quadrants of polariscope orientation (i.e. a polariscope rotation of π radians), and applying equation (5) to the extraction of the sine and cosine components for $n=2$ (variation over $\pi/2$ radians) thus ignoring the spurious ($n=1$) component varying over π radians . This is equivalent to averaging the light intensities for corresponding positions within the two adjacent quadrants. An alternative (or additional) strategy would be the use of an additional QWP to convert the plane polarised light leaving the polariscope into (approximately) circularly polarized light, reducing or eliminating any interaction with the camera.

Less straightforward than the foregoing application of phase angle variation is the investigation into whether it can be applied directly or otherwise to the determination of the isochromatic parameter in the full-field situation.

Strategy 1: reversed, non-aligned analogue of Tardy compensation

In conventional Tardy compensation [19], fractional fringe order is measured by aligning the polariser and analyser of a dark field circular polariscope with the principal stress directions then rotating the analyser until extinction occurs. The fraction of π physical radians rotated by the analyser is equal to the fractional fringe order (the sign of that fractional part requiring further work to identify). The present discussion explores whether the alignment step can successfully be omitted, with the isoclinic angle being taken into account in processing the results. Furthermore, it is desirable to avoid rotation of the analyser during the image sequence to avoid interactions with the camera, especially as the light variations due to such interactions are of the same angular periodicity as those arising from the Tardy compensation process. Accordingly, the entire polariscope assembly is reversed, so that the polariser rotates while the analyser remains stationary during a given image sequence. It is assumed here that the polariser orientation is θ (stepped through the range 0 to π radians), the first and second wave plates (with relative retardations of equal value ρ) are orientated at $\pi/4$ and $-\pi/4$ radians respectively and the specimen (of relative retardation Δ) is orientated at ϕ, all measured with respect to the fixed orientation 0 radians of the analyser. For a light source of intensity I_0 the output intensity is:

$$I = \frac{I_0}{4}\left\{1+\left[\left(\cos^2 2\phi+\sin^2 2\phi\cos\Delta\right)\cos^2\rho+\cos\Delta\sin^2\rho\right]\cos 2\theta\atop +\left[\sin 2\phi\left(1-\cos\Delta\right)\cos\rho-\sin\Delta\sin\rho\right]\cos 2\phi\sin 2\theta\right\} \qquad (9)$$

which can be expressed in the form:

$$I = \frac{I_0}{4}\left\{1+A\sin\left(2\theta+\psi\right)\right\} = \frac{I_0}{4}\left\{1+A\sin 2\theta\cos\psi+A\cos 2\theta\sin\psi\right\} \qquad (10)$$

where ψ is calculated as follows:

$$\tan\psi = \frac{\left(\cos^2 2\phi+\sin^2 2\phi\cos\Delta\right)\cos^2\rho+\cos\Delta\sin^2\rho}{\left[\sin 2\phi\left(1-\cos\Delta\right)\cos\rho-\sin\Delta\sin\rho\right]\cos 2\phi} \qquad (11)$$

In the ideal case, where the relative retardation of both waveplates is exactly a quarter of a wave (i.e. $\rho = \pi/2$ radians), equation (11) can be simplified and rearranged:

$$\tan\Delta = -\frac{\cot\psi}{\cos 2\phi} = \frac{1}{\cos 2\phi}\tan\left(\psi-\frac{\pi}{2}\right) \qquad (12)$$

In theory at least, it becomes relatively straightforward to calculate the phase angle ψ of the light variation at each pixel over the image sequence then to calculate Δ knowing the isoclinic angle ϕ of the specimen.

Strategy 2: reversed, non-aligned analogue of Sénarmont compensation

Conventional Sénarmont compensation [19] is another manual method of fractional fringe order measurement superficially quite similar to Tardy compensation. Its benefit is that it requires only one QWP (just before the analyser). In conventional Sénarmont compensation, the model is orientated at $\pi/4$ to the polariser and the second quarter-wave plate, and the analyser is rotated through the an angle of π radians. Once again, the fraction of π radians of analyser rotation required to cause extinction is equal to the fractional fringe order.

A broadly similar approach to the adaptation of Tardy compensation was followed here for Sénarmont compensation, where alignment with the principal stresses is no longer feasible. However, with this adaptation the equations became rather more complex with multiple solutions. Experience of using this method even for simulated data suggests that the problems in identifying the correct solution make it impractical as an approach to digital imaging photoelasticity.

Strategy 3: method based upon polarimetry

The approach underlying this method appears to have had little attention within the mainstream literature on photoelasticity although it can be used to generalise most of the strategies discussed in this paper. In general, polarimetry is used to characterise the polarisation of a given ray of light (for instance, in astronomy) in terms of its Stokes vector, and its usual implementation involves passing this ray of light through a QWP followed by a polarising element. This is of course an identical arrangement to the analyser/QWP combination used in Tardy or Sénarmont compensation (which may be regarded as special cases of polarimetry). Here, however, the polarising element and its associated QWP both step through a given sequence of pairs of orientations, and a reading of light intensity is taken for each setting. The Stokes vector can then be obtained by solving the simultaneous equations for the various light readings.

In the present implementation, the sequence of optical elements is reversed so that the polariser and its associated QWP rotate. The analyser and its associated QWP may be assumed for the present to be fixed in the same configuration (0 radians and $-\pi/4$ radians respectively) as for the reversed Tardy compensation strategy. The rotating optical elements (the polariser and its quarter-wave plate) form a generator of polarisation states, which may be considered as points on the Poincaré sphere.

In conventional polarimetry (rotating analyser and associated QWP), Ambirajan and Look [20] optimised the four settings of analyser and QWP used for an exactly-determined solution to the Stokes vector, and showed that the optimum angles are those which maximise the volume of the tetrahedron joining the resulting four points on a Poincaré-like sphere, thus making that tetrahedron regular. The present work extends these concepts to generate over-determined equations for characterising the photoelastic model, involving many more points (e.g. 20) and a least-squared solution. The isoclinic angle of the specimen is assumed to be available from a separate phase angle experiment as described earlier rather than being found as part of the least-squared solution exercise or (as in the case of Patterson et al [7] and numerous other authors) by exact fits to a selection of the present points. The 20 points on the Poincaré sphere used in demonstrating this strategy are the vertices of a regular dodecahedron (12-faced solid, Figure 2(a)). A simpler shape, the regular octahedron (Figure 2(b)) actually defines the six polariscope settings used by Patterson et al [7] and other researchers.

It can be demonstrated that if the orientation of the polariser is θ, that of the first quarter-wave plate is γ, the relative retardations of both quarter-wave plates are accurately $\pi/2$, the orientation and relative retardation of the model are respectively ϕ and Δ and the orientations of the second quarter-wave plate and the analyser are respectively $-\pi/4$ and 0 radians, then the light intensity I observed is given by:

$$I = \tfrac{1}{4}I_0\left[1 + \sin\Delta\cos 2(\theta - \gamma)\sin 2(\phi - \gamma) + \cos\Delta\sin(\theta - \gamma)\right] = a_0 + ba_1 + ca_2 \quad (13)$$

where $a_0 = 1/4I_0$, $a_1 = 1/4I_0 \sin\Delta$, $a_2 = 1/4I_0 \cos\Delta$, $b = \cos 2(\theta - \gamma) \sin 2(\phi - \gamma)$, and $c = -\sin 2(\theta - \gamma)$. For a set of N measurements at different polariscope settings an overdetermined set of equations can be written in a_0, a_1 and a_2:

$$\begin{bmatrix} 1 & b_1 & c_1 \\ 1 & b_2 & c_2 \\ \vdots & \vdots & \vdots \\ 1 & b_N & c_N \end{bmatrix} \begin{Bmatrix} a_0 \\ a_1 \\ a_2 \end{Bmatrix} = \begin{Bmatrix} I_1 \\ I_2 \\ \vdots \\ I_N \end{Bmatrix} \tag{14}$$

which is of similar form to equation (3) and can similarly be solved least-squares:

$$\begin{Bmatrix} a_0 \\ a_1 \\ a_2 \end{Bmatrix} = \begin{bmatrix} N & \sum_{i=1}^{N} b_i & \sum_{i=1}^{N} c_i \\ \sum_{i=1}^{N} b_i & \sum_{i=1}^{N} b_i^2 & \sum_{i=1}^{N} b_i c_i \\ \sum_{i=1}^{N} c_i & \sum_{i=1}^{N} b_i c_i & \sum_{i=1}^{N} c_i^2 \end{bmatrix}^{-1} \begin{Bmatrix} \sum_{i=1}^{N} I_i \\ \sum_{i=1}^{N} b_i I_i \\ \sum_{i=1}^{N} c_i I_i \end{Bmatrix} \tag{15}$$

The relative retardation may then be found:

$$\tan \Delta = \frac{a_1}{a_2} \tag{16}$$

A simulation was used to determine the errors in estimated relative retardation arising from inaccuracies in the QWPs or the assumed isoclinic angle. Figures 3 and 4 respectively show that an error of 10% in the quarter-wave plate retardation and an error of $10°$ in the assumed orientation of the specimen lead to errors of up to 0.025 and 0.005 fringes respectively in the estimates of relative retardation. A further strategy, additionally involving rotation of the other two elements, will be reported elsewhere; this appears to lead to improved results but may interact with the camera.

APPLICATION OF STRATEGIES: RESULTS AND DISCSSION

As part of the process of selecting the digital imaging hardware, a simple specimen was examined using some of the above strategies. This consisted of a short beam of annealed polycarbonate sheet ($150\times50\times3$mm) subjected to an approximately uniform bending moment with a small amount of shear superimposed. The beam was held approximately vertically in a polariscope with a 75mm diameter field of view, fitted with plastic optical elements. An additional QWP was placed at $\pi/4$ radians to the analyser to reduce interactions with the camera.

Two types of RGB camera were evaluated: a 3CCD analogue camera (JAI CV-M90), and a single CCD megapixel digital camera (Basler A113C). Only the results from the former are presented here. The following image sequences were captured:

- 16 images with the apparatus configured as a crossed plane polariscope, with all elements stepped simultaneously through $\pi/2$ radians to collect isoclinic data.

- 16 images each with the apparatus configured for Tardy compensation, orientated respectively for a specimen with its principal axes at 0 and at $\pi/4$ radians.

- 20 images with the polariser and first QWP configured so as to create polarisation states forming vertices of a dodecahedron on the Poincaré sphere.

A further sequence of 16 images was also captured in an attempt to understand the polarisation sensitivity of the cameras, but no conclusive results were obtained. Space does not permit the reproduction of all the results, but a brief summary is presented here. The isoclinic angle was consistently estimated where relative retardation was high, but estimates became irregular in the region of the first-order fringe where all three intensities are low. Three strategies for overcoming this problem were tried: to use the mean of the intensities for the isoclinic measurements, to use the root mean square (RMS) of the intensities, and a voting/averaging approach for the angles. The mean and RMS methods gave the most consistent results and agreed very closely, but some irregularities and suspected inaccuracies remained.

The inaccuracies in the isoclinic angle in the region of unity fringe order would contribute to, but are insufficient to explain, significant errors in evaluating the isochromatic parameter leading to blurring of the sharp "wraparound" across the unity fringe. Results elsewhere were encouraging; those from the polarimetry method are presented in Figure 5. Where possible, the measured relative retardations were "unwrapped" manually, although where the wraparound became indistinct the results have been omitted. The plots mostly remain reasonably distinct and well-behaved at high relative retardations (cf. the 3- or 4-fringe limit of conventional RGB photoelasticity). It seems likely that the confusion in the region of unity fringe order is mainly due to the camera being unable to distinguish properly between the broadly similar intensity variations in the RGB components in this region. An unexplained feature, possibly due to the polycarbonate's optical behaviour, is that at high relative retardations the graphs of measured fringe order for red and green light run parallel instead of asymptotically approaching diverging straight lines. In general, the results for the red light were the best-behaved, and those for the blue light the least regular. This trend was stronger for the single-CCD camera. The results presented here are those of initial experiments on pilot apparatus; future work will include addressing the problems encountered in the unity fringe order region as well as the construction of a polariscope with improved optical elements and positioning accuracy. Calibration issues will also be addressed, and benchmarking undertaken.

CONCLUSIONS

Several strategies for the unification of RGB and phase-stepping in photoelasticity have been presented. Preliminary results are generally encouraging, with surprisingly high fringe orders being estimated in a well-behaved manner. However, problems remain with the accuracy of the isoclinic angle especially in regions of near-unity relative retardation, contributing to inaccuracies in the isochromatic measurements.

ACKNOWLEDGEMENTS

This research forms part of a project funded by EPSRC (GR/M40684). The authors gratefully acknowledge this support along with the assistance of the staff of Vortex Vision Ltd and Dr T.P. Pridmore in the tests during which the experimental results were generated. Preliminary work by R. Aldridge, J. Tearle, I. Bottomley and S. Crook, including development of the pilot apparatus, is also gratefully acknowledged.

REFERENCE LIST

(1) Seguchi, Y., Tomita, Y. and Watanabe, M., *Exp. Mech.*, Oct. 1979, pp. 362-370.

(2) Müller, R.K. and Saackel, L. R., *Exp. Mech.*, Vol. 19, No. 7, 1979, pp. 245-251.

(3) Voloshin, A. S. and Burger, C. P., *Exp. Mech.*, Vol. 23, Sept. 1983, pp. 304-313.

(4) Ramesh, K., Ganesan, V.R and Mullick., S.K. *Exp. Tech.*, Sept/Oct. 1991, pp. 41-46.

(5) Umezaki, E., Tamaki, T., Shimamoto, A. and Takahashi, S., In T. H. Hyde and E. Ollerton (eds.,) *Applied Stress Analysis*, Elsevier, 1990, pp. 526-535.

(6) Hecker, F.W. and Morsche, B., In Weiringa, H (ed.), *Experimental Stress Analysis*, Nijhoff, The Netherlands, 1986, pp. 532-542.

(7) Patterson, E.A. and Wang Z.F., *Strain*, May 1991, pp. 49-53.

(8) Patterson, E.A. and Wang, Z.F., *J. Strain Analysis*, Vol. 33, No. 1, 1998, pp.1-15.

(9) Wang, Z.F. and Patterson, E.A., *Opt. Lasers in Eng.*, Vol. 22, 1995, pp. 91-104.

(10) Carazo-Alvarez, J., Haake, S.J. and Patterson, E.A., *Opt. Lasers in Eng.*, Vol. 21, 1994, pp. 133-149.

(11) Buckberry, C. and Towers, D., *Meas. Sci. and Tech.*, Vol.6, 1995, pp.1227-1235.

(12) Voloshin, A. S. and Redner, A. S., *Exp. Mech.*, Vol. 29, No. 3, 1989, pp.252-257.

(13) Haake, S. J. and Patterson, E.A., *Exp. Mech.*, Vol. 32, No. 3, 1992, pp. 266-272.

(14) Ajovalasit, A., Barone, S. and Petrucci, G., *Exp. Mech.*, Vol. 35, No. 3, 1995, pp. 193-200.

(15) Ramesh, K. and Deshmukh, S.S. *Strain*, Vol. 32, 1996, pp. 79-86.

(16) Nurse, A. D., *Applied Optics*, Vol. 36, No.23, 1997, pp. 5781-5786.

(17) Ramesh K. and Deshmukh, S.S., *Opt. and Lasers in Eng.*, Vol. 28, 1997, pp. 47-60.

(18) Aben, H., *Integrated Photoelasticity*. New York: McGraw-Hill, 1979.

(19) Cloud, G., *Optical Methods in Engineering Analysis.* Cambridge, UK: Cambridge University Press, 1998.

(20) Ambirajan, A. and Look, D.C., *Opt. Eng.*, **34**(6), 1995, pp.1656-1658

Figure 1. The Poincaré sphere, showing states of polarisation obtained using a polariser of azimuth $\theta-\psi$ followed by a QWP of azimuth θ (after Aben [18]).

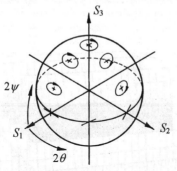

Figure 2. Regular polyhedra whose vertices lie on a Poincaré sphere (a) 20 points defining vertices of a dodecahedron (b) 6 points defining vertices of an octahedron.

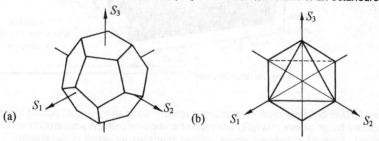

Figure 3. Simulated errors in relative retardation (in wavelengths or fringe orders) estimated using polarimetry approach, due to 10% error in QWP retardation.

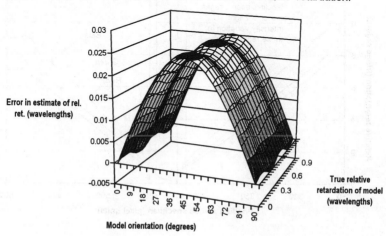

Figure 4. Simulated errors in relative retardation (in wavelengths or fringe orders) estimated using polarimetry approach, due to 10° error in assumed isoclinic angle.

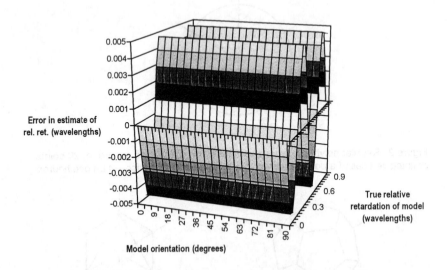

Figure 5: Distribution of relative retardation (measured as fringe order) across beam specimen; fringe orders manually unwrapped and omitted where wraparound was indistinct. Regions are shown where isoclinic scans are too weak to be reliable.

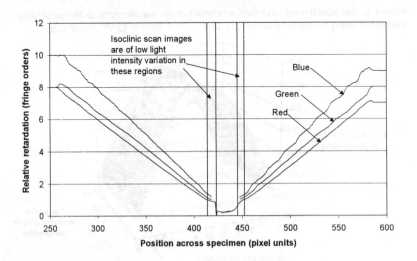

COMPONENT ANALYSIS USING A NEW GENERATION OF LASER OPTICAL 3D-ESPI STRAIN/STRESS SENSOR: MICROSTAR

R. Wegner*, A. Ettemeyer*, L. Yang*

This paper presents the principle and application of a new miniaturized laser optical sensor combining contour and deformation measurement for the first time. A module for contouring was developed and integrated into a single interferometer.

1. INTRODUCTION

Today's industry demands high-performance components meeting toughest mechanical features and ultimate safety standards. Especially in automotive and machine industry the development focuses on tailor-made design and solutions according to customer specifications. Many companies are looking for new advanced strain/stress analysis techniques to improve cost efficiency and limitations of classical methods. Detection of weak points and fatigue tests are carried out mainly with strain gauges which need careful application and experience. ESPI allows a rapid, full field and 3D-measurement without contact.

Highly interesting opportunities for strain/stress analysis on components are offered by ESPI (Electronic Speckle-Pattern Interferometry) as a full field and non contact measuring technique [1]. However basic restrictions are known of standard ESPI-setups resulting from relatively large rigid body movement of components under test, harsh environmental conditions and a complex shape of the analyzed component, especially in the most interesting areas. These application problems have lead to a new laseroptical measuring technique and device for quantitative strain/stress measurement on nearly any component in the industry test area. This concept of radical miniaturization of 3D-ESPI technique [2] as well as the combination of shape with deformation measurement provides all necessary data for quantitative 3D strain analysis.

This new 'mini-ESPI sensor' is based on a compact design and new glassfiber concepts, so it's application in material testing has already achieved an interesting level of acceptance during its development in research and industry [3]. Commercial systems are used to detect small deformations with a resolution below 100nm leading to new application of component analysis in the case of elastic or plastic deformations, pressure loads, shear forces or vibrations with complex industry

* Dr. Ettemeyer GmbH & Co., Heinz-Ruehmann-Str. 207, D-89231 Neu-Ulm, Germany

products like car bodies, gear boxes, engines, suspensions and many other mechanical devices. Relevant in ESPI measurements is not only the correct scaling of interferometric signals (phase distribution) according to the set-up of the object and reference beam (Fig. 1) but also the geometry of the object under investigation [4].

During the design phase of high performance components in automotive or aircraft industry the actual load has to be determined experimentally. Equipped with dozens of strain gauges in critical areas the component is loaded in special single or multi axis loading devices. Preparation time for mounting, connecting and calibrating the strain gauges is time consuming, producing delay in the product validation process and increasing costs. Furthermore, the location of the strain gauge position is only defined by theoretical calculations or personal experience of the test engineer. Therefore, engineers have been searching for faster and easy to use measuring equipment for load quantification of components. Goal of the presented invention was the design of a new optical measuring tool, which could overcome these problems.

2. ESPI MEASURING PRINCIPLE

Due to the possibility of measuring deformation, form and surface conditions within a large variety of objects and surfaces interferometry has been found in industrial measuring techniques. Laser Speckle Interferometry (ESPI) allows the full field and three-dimensional measurement of deformations and strains on complex surfaces. The basic setup is simple (Fig. 1): the surface to be measured is illuminated by laser light from different directions and the speckle images are recorded by a CCD-camera.

The fundamental principle lies in the reconstruction of the specimen's contour by recording amplitude and phase of the wavefront reflected by the object [5]. Together with the elementary experimental set-ups, e.g. Michelson-Morley interferometer, new measuring systems have been developed. Generally in optical interferomtry the detectable signal of the light intensity together with it's spatial or temporal alteration is the consequence of a coherent superposition of two or more wavefronts.

$$I = I_0 \left(1 + \gamma \cos\left(\phi + \phi_{stat}\right)\right) \tag{1}$$

The intensity distribution I of the interference pattern is given by (1). γ specifies the modulation of contrast and I_0 the intensity of the interferogram signal. The contour phase ϕ is directly proportional to the optical path difference between the reference- and the measurement path of the ESPI setup. ϕ_{stat} is an additional phase term which occurs in speckle-interferometry due to the influence of the surface microstructure and varies stochastically within the interferogram. To guarantee a sufficient contrast and resolution of the requirements within the physical setup has to be taken into account: a narrow spectral bandwidth of the used laser light source, a definite polarization-state of the beams and a correct definition of the used form of the reference beam's wavefront [5]. By use of polarized monomode glassfibers both frequency and polarization of the mostly employed diode lasers can be preserved.

Hence, laser speckle interferometry allows by means of definite guided beams a full field and three-dimensional measurement of deformations Δδ and strains ε on complex surfaces. All technical surfaces show the so called 'speckle-effect' (appearing as a fingerprint of the illuminated area) by which the microstructure of the object's surface can be analyzed.

The resulting speckle pattern is stored as a digital reference image on a personal computer. Since the specific speckle pattern is changing when the surface is deformed correlation fringes ΔΦ representing the displacement Δδ of the object will be visible (2).

$$\Delta\Phi = \frac{2\pi}{\lambda}\Delta\delta \quad with: \quad \vec{S}_{Displacement} \cdot \Delta\vec{d}_{Object} = \Delta\delta \tag{2}$$

Appropriate image comparison or correlation techniques allow the detection of three-dimensional movements of any point in the measuring area with submicrometer accuracy. Depending on the specific sensor beam geometry $\vec{S}$ or direction of laser illumination the obtained fringes ΔΦ correspond to out-of plane or in-plane displacements. For deformation and contour measurement so far two different ESPI sensor modules have been used. The contouring module's fringe pattern δ (z) can be described as a scalar product (3) of the specific sensor beam geometry $\vec{S}$ and the vector of beam-shift $\vec{t}$ (i.e. movement of the illumination beam by a specific distance).

$$\vec{S}_{Contour} \cdot \vec{t}_{Beam} = \delta(z) \tag{3}$$

The unique feature of the new mini-ESPI sensor is the combined illumination setup (4) of deformation and contour recording. Therefore the two sensitivity vectors are identically:

$$\vec{S}_{Contour} = \vec{S}_{Displacement} \tag{4}$$

Strain components (5) and also the flexible components at each position of the measuring area can be calculated from the complete 3D-deformation field according to the standard mechanical equations.

$$\varepsilon_x = \frac{\partial u}{\partial x}, \varepsilon_y = \frac{\partial v}{\partial y}, \gamma_{xy} = \frac{\partial u}{\partial y} + \frac{\partial v}{\partial x} \tag{5}$$

$$\varepsilon_{xb} = -\frac{t}{2}\frac{\partial^2 w}{\partial x^2}, \quad \varepsilon_{yb} = -\frac{t}{2}\frac{\partial^2 w}{\partial y^2}, \quad \gamma_{xyb} = -t\frac{\partial^2 w}{\partial x \partial y}$$

3. CLASSICAL STRAIN MEASUREMENT METHODS

A characterization of the tested component only by strains and stresses at the surface in tangential directions is not sufficient. Additionally shear and bending strains (5), principal strains/stresses and different failure criteria, e.g. maximum shear strain energy criterion, etc. have to be detected giving a complete description of the specimen. One important demand can be seen from industrial applications: the measurement of an error free deformation field can only be done by attaching some detectors at the specimen itself.

For this purpose strain gauges are commonly used. Main types are metallic and semiconductor strain gauges in a vast amount of special forms and designs. Often the user has just a vague impression of the object to be examined. Selecting a strain gauge means to predict the behavior of the component beforehand and a small collection of approximately twenty kinds of strain gauges solve only half the measuring tasks. A further point is the preparation of the surface. On the one hand it must not be altered or damaged. On the other hand a transmission of the strains onto the strain gauge has to work without loss.

Detection of weak points on the component's design is quite limited with classical measuring techniques. The strain gauge is glued directly to the surface of the component and records the integrated elongation of the material underneath it's length. Very careful application is important for good and reliable measuring results. The surface has to be smoothed and cleaned carefully, the electrical cables have to be soldered and the strain gauge has to be calibrated. Strain gauges solely output strain components in the direction of the strain gauge and at only one position. Since critical areas often show high strain gradients, strain levels quickly reduce at a distance of few millimeters from the hot spot , to levels which are too low to be accurately measured.

4. RAPID STRAIN ANALYSIS BY MINIATURIZATION OF ESPI

The measurement and analysis of components has always been a challenging approach to speckle measuring systems . Hence, the development of a new miniaturized integrated 3D-ESPI sensor, forthcoming product name 'MicroStar' will offer new possibilities to obtain full field and non contact deformation and strain analysis of materials and components. Fig. 2 shows the new compact ESPI-device which was developed for component testing. The small sensor head is positioned onto the surface of the component over the area to be inspected. The system measures the deformations and strains over an area of about 20x30 mm² while the load is applied equivalent to as many as 250.000 individual strain gauges over that area. An interesting feature of the new system is the complete detection of all the components of the surface strains and stresses, as e.g. principal strains and the direction of principal strain, shear strains, etc. So it is possible to receive simultaneously the information about position, dimension and direction of the maximum load in the test area. The inspection result is displayed as a color graphic on a computer within a few seconds.

The new ESPI sensor reduces the inspection time for complex components significantly. Preparation time for measurements is just a fraction required for conventional measurement but it additionally offers a complete and very much more detailed information about local strains and stresses.

Principally, the new ESPI sensor can be applied to any components which are optically accessible. It can also be applied to notches and edges as long as they are not too narrow and allow enough space above for the sensor head. After fixation of the sensor to the object or material under test the MicroStar head records the shape of the object in the measuring field [6][7]. Following, the deformations are recorded when any load is applied. It is preferable to apply the load in steps and store the measured data at each load step. This can be done automatically and allows the display of the strain-load curve for any measuring point.

5. APPLICATIONS

Measuring strain gradients in the example of a Compact Tension specimen demonstrates the application of the new ESPI sensor. The CT sample is loaded with a vertical force to spread the notch. The graphic show the in-plane fringe pattern (here: y-deformation) and the z-deformation (out-of-plane contraction) in colors. From the 3D deformation data the strain field is calculated. As example Fig. 3 shows the ε_{yy} strain field. Additionally the strain was measured by a strain gauge at the tip of the notch.

As an example for a validation measurement a comparable measurement between the new ESPI sensor and strain gauge was carried out. The result shows that local strain gradients even in the length of the relatively short strain gauge at the notch (Fig. 3, ca. 3 mm) can be resolved. Fig. 4 shows also the result of an tensile test measurement with a deviation of just few percent. Other comparable tests confirm these results.

A complete strain and stress analysis and application of the new ESPI sensor can be demonstrated on a truck engine. Fig. 5 shows the sensor clamped to the side wall of the engine by the use of magnetic bases. The load is applied via oil pressure above the cylinders onto the crankshaft which affects the mechanical strength and property of the engine wall.

The measuring field is limited by some holes where the stress distribution at different loading conditions is to be analyzed. In the hydraulic test stand the 3D deformation was recorded at combined loads of internal pressure (oil pressure), torsion and 3 tension loads. All required strain and stress components can be calculated. In Fig. 5 as an example the principal stress and the shear stress are

127

displayed. Especially the shear stresses show increased values at the locations of plastifications and material fatigue. Additionally, the knowledge of the out-of-plane component of the deformation (z-component) allows the calculation of the curvature, which gives an indication on the flexible strain of the component. The lines indicate the positions where the component showed cracks in life cycle tests. They correspond to the locations of maximum stresses.

A triform T-branch is analyzed (Fig. 6). The 3D-ESPI system first provides deformation data in x-, y- and z-coordinates of the sensor head. To achieve quantitative surface strain values from the 3D-displacement values the data have to be transformed to the object's coordinate system. In the present case a cylindrical coordinate system was chosen with a circumferential direction t_1, axial direction t_2 (according to y-direction of sensor) and a normal direction n of the main pipe (Fig. 6, top right). The result of the transformation is the displacement field in t_1, t_2 and n direction. From these data the circumferential and axial strain fields can be calculated. At certain positions the strain field was additionally measured with strain gauges (Fig. 6, bottom). The comparison is carried out at a center line through the measuring area and shows good agreement.

New composite and fiber reinforced materials gain importance since their properties can be arbitrarily manipulated by individual alignment of fibers within the layers according to the components requirements. Different manufacturing techniques are used like weaving or knitting. Especially the strongly inhomogeneous material properties call for measuring systems which work full field and detect local strain gradients. Suchlike materials do not show any homogeneous deformation fields and the value of E-modulus depends on lateral position. Due to their alignment single fiber bundles directly influence the strength and fatigue locally within the component. Fig. 7 shows an application at a helicopter rotor blade which experiences combined loads of bending and torsion. The amplitude of rigid body movement of the blade is in the range of several centimeters and the testing bench is vibrating caused by the hydraulic load cylinders. Since the ESPI sensor head can be attached directly to the blade only local strains are detected without superposition of deformations due to the rugged testing conditions.

Fig. 8 shows the result of a fatigue measurement at a glassfiber reinforced plastic tube which was loaded with inner pressure. On the left side of the color graphic cracks are visible by high values of principle strain ε_{h1} in vertical direction. Since the surface of the tube is very frayed due to the fragile glass filaments it is necessary to measure without contact. The mismatch of weldings is an interesting phenomena, too, which can preferably investigated with ESPI methods [3]. The evaluation of welded configurations is generally difficult with conventional methods since weldings show areas of very inhomogeneous texture. Only by the additional contour measurement option of the ESPI sensor a correct representation of the strain fields according to the coordinate system of the welded region is possible.

6. CONCLUSION

The new miniaturized ESPI system allows a full field and fast strain and stress analysis on components and working materials. Rapid application and measurement of all strain and stress components reduces experimental analysis time significantly. The sensor can advantageously be used to inspect critical areas before life cycle tests are carried out and to determine the exact positions for strain gauges during the following dynamic tests. Validation measurements in comparison with strain gauges have produced proof of the accuracy and performance of the new ESPI system.

REFERENCE LIST

(1) R. Jones, C. Wykes, "Holographic and Speckle Interferometry", ch.3-5, Cambridge University Press, Cambridge, New York, New Rochelle, Melbourne, Sidney, 1989

(2) A. Ettemeyer, "Non contact and whole field strain analysis with a laseroptical strain sensor", VIII International Congress on Experimental Mechanics, June, 10-13, 1996, Nashville, Tennessee

(3) A. Ettemeyer, Z. Wang, T. Walz, "Applications of speckle interferometry to material testing", presentation at KSME conference, Nov., 1st, 1996, Seoul, Korea

(4) T. Pfeifer, H. Mischo, S. Koch, J. Evertz, "Coded Speckle-Interferometrical Formtesting", in: W. Jüptner, W. Osten, Fringe '97 - Automatic Processing of Fringe Patterns, Vol. 3, pp. 171-178, Akademie Verlag, Berlin, 1997

(5) M. Born & E. Wolf, "Principles of Optics".-Pergamon Press, Oxford, 1970

(6) D. Kerr, R. Rodriguez-Vera, "Surface contouring using electronic speckle pattern interferometry", Proc. SPIE, 1554 A, pp. 668-680, 1991

(7) T. Pfeifer, H. Mischo, A. Ettemeyer, Z. Wang, R. Wegner, "Stress/Strain Measurement using Electronic Speckle Pattern Interferometry", Proc. SPIE,-Three-Dimensional Imaging, Optical Metrology and Inspection IV, Vol. 3520, pp. 262-271, Boston, Massachusetts, 1998

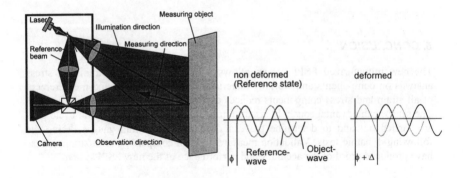

Fig. 1: ESPI interferometer with reference and measuring beam of a out-of plane setup (single illumination technique)

Fig. 2: New miniaturized 3D-ESPI sensor for rapid strain and stress analysis

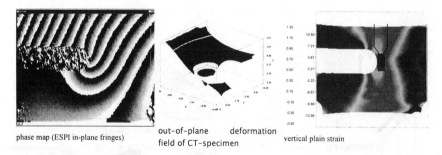

phase map (ESPI in-plane fringes)   out-of-plane   deformation field of CT-specimen   vertical plain strain

Fig. 3: Strain field ε_{yy} (right) at a CT-specimen with position of the strain gauge

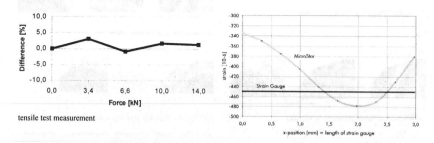

tensile test measurement

Fig. 4: Comparison of ESPI measurement with strain gauge results

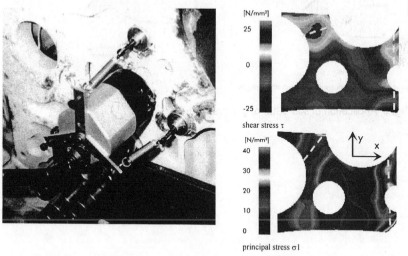

Fig. 5: Application of ESPI sensor on the wall of a truck engine and strain results.

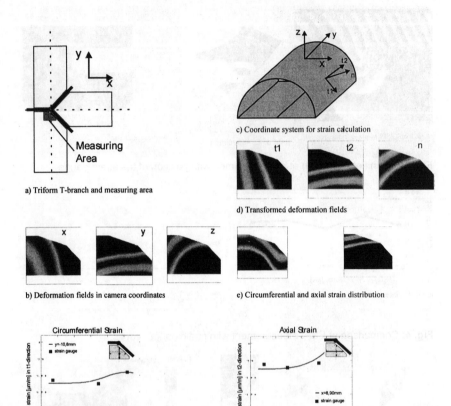

a) Triform T-branch and measuring area

c) Coordinate system for strain calculation

d) Transformed deformation fields

b) Deformation fields in camera coordinates

e) Circumferential and axial strain distribution

f) Comparison of strain distribution with strain gauges

Fig. 6: Application of MicroStar at a T-branch tube

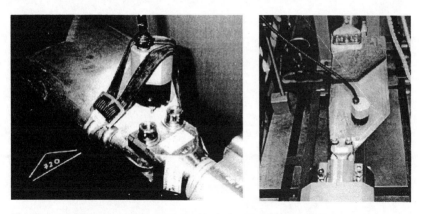

Fig. 7: Application at a helicopter rotor blade (composite material).

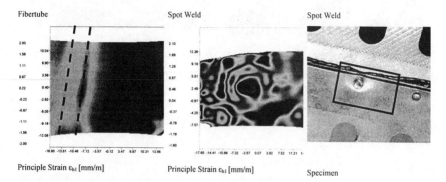

Fig. 9: Areas of high strains at fatigue test of composite material and welded steel

Acknowledgement: The authors wish to thank MPA Staatliche Materialprüfanstalt Stuttgart, MAN Nutzfahrzeuge AG Nürnberg, and Eurocopter Deutschland GmbH for the friendly support.

133

3. DESIGN APPLICATIONS

APPLICATIONS OF STRESS ANALYSIS TO PROBLEMS IN LARGE INDUSTRIAL GAS TURBINES

J K Hepworth* and A Morris*

This paper describes a number of examples where stress analysis methods have been used to contribute to the solution of problems with gas turbine power generation plant. These include life management of turbine blading, compressor rotor cracking problems and smaller components, such as combustion liners and inspection cones.

1. INTRODUCTION

Modern gas turbine combined cycle power generation plant operates in an environment of increasing competition and regulatory control. It is therefore vital for the operator to minimize costs wherever possible. In general, the only scope for cost reduction lies in operation and maintenance. Thus particular attention has to be paid to components that require regular inspections, with the attendant costly shutdowns and to components with a known history of problems in similar plant. Beyond this, there is a considerable incentive to extend the life and replacement intervals of expensive components, such as turbine blading.

This paper describes a number of case studies where stress analysis methods have been used to improve understanding of the behaviour of a range of different components. In one case, this was to support work to redesign a problem component. In further instances the aim was to provide the understanding which would allow critical evaluation of a detailed root cause analysis being carried out by the original equipment manufacturer, OEM, and any modifications they might propose. Other examples were to underwrite the feasibility of extending component life or extending inspection intervals.

The manufacturer's design data is not normally available and geometry information usually has to be obtained by measuring components. Analysis can provide valuable insights into component behaviour, which in conjunction with other information, such as materials data and plant inspection results, will allow cost-effective decisions to be made about the plant. Because of the complex geometries

* Powergen plc, Power Technology Centre, Ratcliffe-on-Soar, Nottingham NG11 0EE

involved the stress analysis uses the finite element method. Pre and post processing was carried out using MSC/Patran[1] and Abaqus[2] was used as the analysis program.

2. COMBUSTION LINERS

A class of large gas turbines with can combustors suffers from problems of deformation and cracking in the combustion liners, illustrated in figure 1. In essence the liner has the burners at one end and the other end supplies the hot gases to the power turbine via a transition piece. The internal hot gases are at a temperature above 1000°C and to keep the liner material, Hastelloy X, to a reasonable temperature, it is cooled on the outside by air from the compressor and coated internally with a thermal barrier coating. In spite of these precautions, the liners bulge and cracks may be generated, which in extreme cases can result in a portion of the liner becoming detached and passing into the turbine leading to serious damage to the blading.

In order to establish the likely cause of the problems an analysis of the liner was carried out. The liner was modeled using 8 noded shell elements and the outer surface ribs were represented by beam elements, which shared nodes with the shells, but were offset by the appropriate distance. The function of the ribs is to increase the external heat transfer rather that to stiffen the structure, but they were included in the structural model. Initially the vibration mode shapes were computed to see if the stress maxima for any of the modes correlated with the observed cracking patterns. The combustion noise could potentially excite vibrations in the can, particularly under transient conditions. As no correlation was found, the effects of temperature gradients in the liner were next considered. A limited amount of temperature data was available from an instrumented liner. The data for the most severe condition was extrapolated to provide a plausible temperature distribution for the liner. The analysis indicated severe thermal stresses, well in excess of the yield stress at the temperature of the liner in the local hot spots. Thus the source of the problem could be identified as the hot spots generated in certain phases of the start up procedure. The results are being used to contribute to an understanding of the behaviour of the liners, which will allow any design or operating modifications put forward by the OEM to be assessed and evaluated.

3. MIXING CHAMBERS

On a gas turbine with twin silo combustors mounted vertically, the mixing chambers convey the hot gases from the combustor to the turbine inlet. They are essentially ducts, about 1.5m in diameter, with a 90° bend, made from the nickel based alloy, IN617. There were concerns about the ultimate life of these components and whether

---

[1] MSC/Patran is a registered trade mark of MSC Software
[2] Abaqus is a registered trade mark of HKS

replacement was really necessary once the design life was expired. The mixing chambers are subjected to considerable vibration and buffeting from the combustion process and cracks are regularly repaired during overhauls. The main issue was whether long term degradation, such as creep damage, would limit the serviceability and reparability of the chambers. The chamber was modelled using shell elements and the boundary conditions are relatively cool compressor discharge air on the outer surface and hot combustion gases on the inner surface. The results of the analysis show modest stresses in the chamber, see figure 2, leading to the conclusion that creep life exhaustion should not be a problem.

4. INSPECTION CONES

The mixing chambers described above have an access hole, which is also used for viewing the flames. Part of this viewing system is the cone shown in figure 3, which is held in place by clamping forces on the closure flange holding the lugs against their support blocks. The upper flange on the cone fits in the hole in the mixing chamber with a gap of a few millimetres. Persistent problems have been encountered with these cones with the cracking of the lugs or their attachment to the cones. Under the worst scenario, broken fragments may enter the turbine where they can cause considerable damage. The problem is contained by a programme of regular inspection and careful fitting of the cones. In view of the costs associated with this and the risks to the machine a more permanent solution to the problem was needed. The first step was to analyse the behaviour of the existing cone design and compare the results with the limited amount of data available from an instrumented cone. The initial analysis assumed no slip between the lugs and the guide blocks. The base of the cone and the lugs are at the compressor discharge temperature of around 300°C and as the outer casing is a ferritic carbon manganese steel and the cone is an austenitic stainless steel it is necessary to allow for differential thermal expansion. A displacement load applied to the base of the cone represented the clamping forces. The combined effect of the thermal and displacement loads was to induce very high static stresses in the lugs. A number of analyses were carried out to investigate the dependence of these stresses on how the displacement load was applied. For instance, biasing it towards the short lug side, by removing material from the cone base near the long lug, reduces the stresses in that lug, which is particularly prone to failure.

Examination of the reaction forces at the guide blocks showed clearly that the assumption of no slip could not be valid as it would require much too high a coefficient of friction. The analysis was repeated using contact to represent the boundary condition on the lugs in the guide blocks. The guide blocks were assumed to be rigid and a coefficient of friction was chosen at the upper end of the range given in the literature for metal to metal contact, namely $v=1.0$. While this reduced the stresses, the peak values were still around the yield stress of the material.

While the static stresses on the cone were high, they were not sufficient of themselves to cause failure. Examination of fracture surfaces on damaged cones had indicated that a fatigue mechanism was responsible and the high static loading would make the cone more susceptible to fatigue loading. There appeared to be two main possible sources of fatigue loading. Firstly, vibrations induced by noise in the combustion processes and secondly, movements in the mixing chamber causing impact on the top flange of the cone. Data from the, albeit short lived, strain gauges on the instrumented cone, indicated that coupling with the combustor noise was very weak. This is consistent with the observed lives of the cones as significant loads at the relevant frequencies would have led to much earlier failure than has been observed. Attention was therefore concentrated on the loads that could be produced by impact from the mixing chamber. Unfortunately, no data were available on the movement of the chamber for either the magnitude or the rate of displacement. However, the chamber is massive in comparison with the cone, so the loading was represented by an imposed displacement at the top of the cone. This showed that for modest displacement of the top of the cone, the stresses at the top of the weld joining the long lug to the cone were well in excess of yield. Clearly without a knowledge of the loading it was not possible to predict life and the results were used to evaluate the relative performance of modified designs, with either strengthened lugs to resist the applied loads or with the highly stressed lugs eliminated altogether.

5. BLADE LIFE MANAGEMENT

The aim of this work was to calculate crack initiation and growth in the turbine blades. The motivation for this is the very high cost of replacing blades, particularly the first stage, which require relatively frequent replacement and may or may not be fit for refurbishment. It is beyond the scope of this paper to describe this work in detail, but more information can be found in [1]. The intention here is to highlight the role of stress analysis techniques. The behaviour of a blade will depend on its service history in terms of temperature, stresses and its environment. The machines under consideration operate in a relatively benign environment, being fired on natural gas, which is very low in sulphur. Thus the only environmental consideration is oxidation, which is a function of temperature. In order to calculate blade metal temperatures, a good knowledge of the external and internal gas temperatures are needed, together with the corresponding heat transfer coefficients. These were obtained from an aerothermal analysis of the machine [2] to obtain gas temperatures, pressures and mass flow rates, followed by a boundary layer calculation to give heat transfer calculations. A further set of calculations was required to provide the coolant conditions on the inner surfaces. Using these boundary conditions, a finite element thermal analysis gives the steady state on load temperature distribution in the blade. The finite element model was constructed from geometry data, determined firstly by measuring the external shape with a coordinate measuring machine. The inner geometry was obtained by digitising cut sections on an image analyser and fitting the sections to the external profile. The resulting geometry model was then meshed with 20 noded hexahedra with a few wedge elements in the top cover of the blade. The temperature results were then used to calculate the stress distribution using the same mesh. Initially this was done for the elastic stresses, but subsequently it became clear that a creep run was needed to understand blade behaviour. For much of the blade, the stress is dominated by the thermal component, induced by the through wall temperature gradient in the cooled blade, see figures 4 and 5. At operating temperature these stresses will redistribute, relaxing the compressive thermal stress on the outer surface, where the temperature is greatest. The role of thermal transients, such as the chilling which accompanies a trip from full load, was investigated. It was expected from experience with other plant components that these transients would be important, so a simplified model, effectively representing the blade wall as a plate, was used to rapidly study a wide range of transients. This indicated that, within the plausible range of transients, no increase in stress was generated, because the chilling in a trip acts to remove the pre-existing temperature gradient. Heating transients are much slower and do not generate significant stresses for that reason. The conclusion was checked for a particular transient on the three dimensional model. Of course, it is important to recognise that this conclusion only applies to cooled blades.

In order to make crack growth estimates, knowledge of fracture mechanics parameters is required. In this work, it was all based on the stress intensity factor, K, from which C* was derived using reference stress methods. Some calculations of K were made using finite elements on a two dimensional model of a section of the blade in generalised plane strain. It was found that the values obtained were in good agreement with those obtained using the stress distribution in the uncracked blade, so in the majority of cases this procedure was adopted. The effects of oxidation on cracking were incorporated using the methods of [3]. Oxide spalling was considered using the approach of [4].

6. COMPRESSOR ROTOR ANALYSIS

The overall objective of the analysis is to develop analytical models of the compressor rotor to gain greater understanding of the machines operational characteristics, and to provide a means of assessing the merits of any modifications proposed by the OEM. The compressor rotor, about 4m long, is made up of a series of discs which are held together by a number of tie-bolts, forming a disc stack-up. The tie-bolts clamp the disc stack-up to a central rotating forging. This central forging also forms the last stage of the compressor rotor and separates the relatively cool compressor from the hot turbine rotor. The turbine rotor is bolted to the opposite end of the central forging. The OEM has acknowledged that there have been problems with cracking in the captive nut retaining slot in the central forging. The gas turbine unit is exposed to a number of operational transients. The current trend is for greater flexibility in power generation, resulting in a higher frequency of operational transient. Figure 6 shows a schematic of the last four stages of the compressor, up to and including a portion of the central forging. Cooling air is bled off the main compressor air flow to cool the first stage turbine blades, this flows around the last stage of the compressor, through several holes in the central forging, eventually reaching the internal passages of the first stage turbine blade.

It is of particular interest to study the response characteristics in the fillet region of the captive nut retaining slot. This involves detailed examination of a small region of a very large structure, so submodelling techniques were employed. To gain confidence in the results structured sensitivity analyses were used.

6.1 Details of Analysis

A global 'coarse' compressor model has been constructed, which extends from the compressor end bearing through to a locating flange in the central forging. Figure 7 represents a side view of the 'coarse' 3D segment model. The regions where detailed information is needed are represented by submodels, for example Figure 8 illustrates the extent of the fillet region submodel. The decision to terminate the submodel boundary as depicted in Figure 8 was based upon a comparison of the response of a much larger submodel. Although the stress in the larger submodel correlated better with the full model at the submodel boundary, the difference in stress at the fillet radius between the submodels was only 2%. The larger submodel took considerably longer to run; hence the submodel depicted in Figure 8 is preferred. The finite element models are discretized with 20-noded brick elements. The finite element model simplifies the disc stack-up assembly by assuming that the radial contact planes are tied, thereby simulating a solid rotor. This assumption does not significantly affect the response at the fillet radius in the captive nut retaining slot. The interface between the underside of the tie-bolt head and the mating face of the end compressor stage is modelled as a master-slave contact pair. The models have symmetry constraints applied to the radial boundaries. The radial boundary plane at the flange in the central forging is constrained in the axial direction, and radial motion is constrained along the centreline of the compressor end bearing. The load history is defined as a linear elastic thermal stress analysis. The load steps are defined in general terms as follows;

Apply tie-bolt preload.

Apply centrifugal loads

Apply thermal loads from a thermal model – this thermal model is based upon the geometry illustrated in figure 6, with a modelling extension which includes the first stage turbine disc. This is required to make use of the available on-line thermal data.

Typical CPU times are 80 minutes for the 4900 element global model and 60 minutes for the 2750 element submodel.

Figure 9 illustrates typical results in the vicinity of the captive nut retaining slot, the displaced shape plots clearly show the end stage bending about the fillet radius at the base of the retaining slot. The stress contour plots give an indication on the magnitudes of stress in the fillet region for a linear elastic analysis.

6.2 Sensitivity Analyses

The aim of these analyses is to provide some insight into the response characteristics of the compressor rotor. This will aid further development of the model for use in subsequent transient analyses. The sensitivity of response has been assessed by a series of finite element models, based on a full factorial design. The variables selected represent the source of the greatest uncertainty, or have the greatest potential effect on the response in the fillet region. This experimental design necessitates the definition of 2 levels for each variable (high and low). The sensitivity analyses have been defined in a 2^4 array for the assessment of the effect of the variation of the heat transfer coefficient and cooling air temperatures either side of the end compressor stage. In addition a 2^3 experimental array has been used to assess the significance of varying the coefficient of friction between the bolt head and mating face of the end compressor stage, the tie-bolt preload and the coefficient of expansion of the disc material. The levels for each variable were defined based on an assessment of their potential variation.

The sensitivity study was based on steady state analyses, and the response variable was the peak stress in the fillet region. The main conclusions are;

- The variation of the coefficient of friction between 0.25-1.0 is not significant. The definition of a tied contact would be pessimistic and will result in significantly reduced analysis times.

- In terms of these steady state analyses the centrifugal loads are the most significant component.

- Practical variations in the tie-bolt preload are not significant.

- Variations in the coefficient of expansion of the disc material of 10% are not significant.

- Three of the local thermal boundary conditions are significant, hence their variation down the face of the end compressor stage should be modelled in subsequent transient analyses.

The benefits of the submodelling techniques are that detailed results can be obtained in large-scale complex structures whilst minimising the analysis time. The use of structured sensitivity analyses can give further insight into the significance of certain parameters and if a significant interaction exists between them. Further analysis of the operational transients is anticipated, along with additional submodels to investigate the elastic-plastic response in the fillet region and an assessment of alternative designs offered by the OEM.

7. CONCLUSIONS

The paper has given an overview of some of the techniques being used at Power Technology to gain further insight into the behaviour of several gas turbine components. Clearly, these techniques could be used in the assessment of a wide variety of components or assemblies in a range of plant.

The immediate benefits have been the successful redesign of a problematic component and the extension of operating life of other items. It is anticipated that the understanding gained of other components will lead to better control of costs.

REFERENCES

[1] J K Hepworth, J E Fackrell, L W Pínder & J D Wilson, 'A Modelling Approach to Gas Turbine Blade Life Assessment', *Conference on Life Assessment of Hot Section Gas Turbine Components, Edinburgh*, October 1999, IOM Communications.

[2] J D Denton, 'The Calculation of Three-Dimensional Viscous Flow through Multistage Turbomachines', *ASME Journal of Turbomachinery*, 1992, **114**, 18-26.

[3] L Remy, 'Fatigue Damage and Lifetime Prediction in Alloys for Gas Turbine Components submitted to Thermal Transients', *Behaviour of Defects at High Temperatures, ESIS 15*, MEP, London, 1993, 167-187.

[4] K S Chan, 'A Mechanics-Based Approach to Cyclic Oxidation', *Met. Mat. Transactions A*, 1997, **28A**, 411.

Figure 1: Combustion Liner

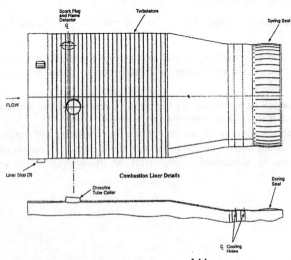

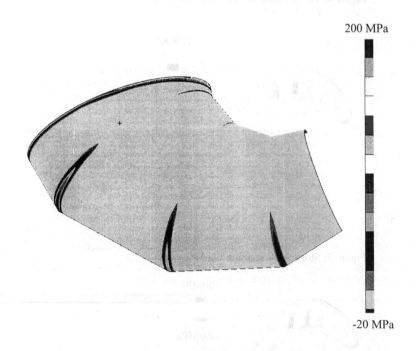

Figure 2: Maximum Principal Stress in Mixing Chamber after 40000 hours

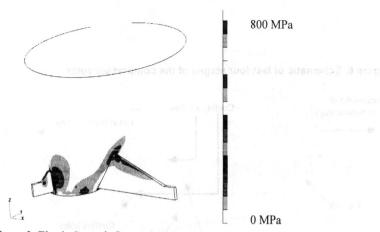

Figure 3: Elastic Stress in Inspection Cone

Figure 4: Temperature in First Stage Blade

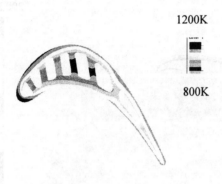

1200K

800K

Figure 5: Stress in First Stage Blade

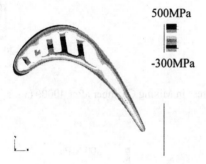

500MPa

-300MPa

Figure 6. Schematic of last four stages of the compressor rotor

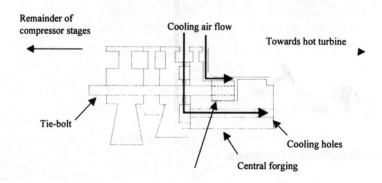

Figure 7. Side view on coarse 3D segment model of compressor

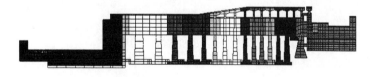

Figure 8. Submodel (a) End stage fillet region & tie-bolt, (b) End stage fillet region.

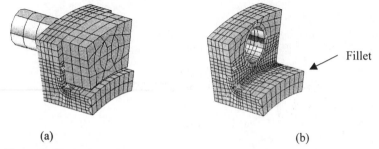

(a)   (b)

Figure 9. Typical results (a) Displaced shape (preload and centrifugal loads), (b) Von Mises stress (preload and centrifugal loads)

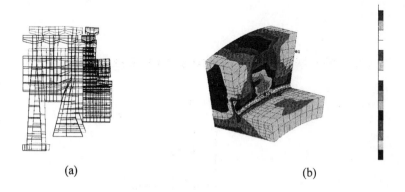

(a)   (b)

IMPROVED CROWN SPECIFICATION FOR CORRUGATOR ROLLS

S.J. Evans* and J.R. Wright**

The majority of sheet production processes rely on a roll crown to achieve uniform pressure as the material passes through the roll nip. In the production of paper, the rolls are treated as simple beams, and the crown calculated using a linear assumption. If the resultant crown is incorrect, the rolls are reground based on a simple correction formula. In the corrugating process, the rolls cannot be reground after production for a number of reasons. The study shows that the beam-based method does not take into account the three-dimensional roll behavior and the non-linear contact effect between rolls. A single roll experimental analysis shows that the three-dimensional roll deflection is considerably different from that given by the beam theory. A full three-dimensional contact finite element model, using a commercial FE code, is given. A parametric approximate model is developed and validated against the three-dimensional model. This model shows that the beam-based method can be improved in calculating roll crown. A genetic algorithm, in conjunction with the approximate FE model, is proposed as a method of improving on the crown specification for corrugator rolls.

INTRODUCTION

The rolling process is used in many industries for the production of sheet material such as steel, plastic and paper. The material passes through a series of 'nip' points where two or more rolls are pressed together. This formation pressure has many functions depending upon the material being rolled. In the majority of applications, it is important that the pressure is constant along the width of the sheet to ensure uniform sheet properties.

In the paper production and related industries, there are numerous distinct rolling operations. The formation of paper relies on the de-watering section (to remove excess moisture) and the calendering section (to change the surface finish) amongst others. The manufacture of corrugated cardboard (known as corrugating) is performed by the singlefacer machine. This process utilizes a series of fluted rolls, which mesh in a similar manner to gear teeth. The paper is corrugated as it passes through these fluted nip points.

In all of these processes the load is applied though the bearing housings at the ends of the rolls. This applied moment causes the load to be concentrated at the outer edges of the sheet. In order to achieve uniform formation pressure, a roll crown is used. This

*Department of Mechanical Engineering, University of Manchester, Manchester M13 9PL

is a machined contour on the outer surface of the roll, which gives a gradual increase in diameter from the end of the roll towards the centre. This increase in diameter is used to compensate for the roll deflection due to external deflection and body forces and results in a parallel gap at the nip and hence uniform pressure (figure 1).

In certain applications the need for a predefined roll crown has been negated by the use of various different forms of loading mechanisms. The crown-compensating roll utilizes a series of hydraulic cells or chambers located within the roll body (Smook, [1]). The thickness of the paper sheet is measured as it leaves the roll nip. A control system is used to vary the load at discrete points within the roll to ensure uniform formation pressure at all times. Obviously, these methods require a fundamental change in the design of the formation rolls. In certain high volume industries, such as the production of newsprint, there has been considerable investment to allow a shift over to these forms of load application. However, in many sectors of the paper industry, where the economic constraints are more pronounced, this has not been possible. These methods are still very much reliant on roll crown.

Traditional Crown Specification

The approximate method used to determine roll crown is well known throughout the paper industry. It relies on the assumption that each roll in the stack behaves as a simple beam, and its deflection given by a well-known beam theory approximation (Timoshenko, [2]). By treating each beam individually, its deflection due to the external loads can be calculated. Each roll will deflect up or down depending on its position in the roll stack. The resulting crown required for uniform pressure distribution is calculated from the amount of 'overlap' that one roll will exhibit when compared with the adjacent rolls (figure 2). The method can be seen as a subtraction of roll material to ensure a parallel nip gap, and will therefore be known as the Crown Subtraction Method (CS method). There has been various work in the literature on the development of the CS method and its effect on paper production (Smith [3], Stone & Liebert [4]).

The deflection of a simply-supported beam under the action of an UDL and end moment (due to the load application offset distance) can be described, using the principle of superposition, as: -

$$y = \frac{q\,x}{24\,E\,I}\left(L^3 - 2Lx^2 + x^3\right) + \frac{M\,x}{2\,E\,I}\left(L - x\right) \qquad (1)$$

where y = deflection at distance along roll, x, q = distributed load magnitude, E = modulus of elasticity, I = moment of inertia of roll, L = roll face length, x = distance along roll, and M = moment arm length (load offset distance).

The CS method roll crown is given by the relative deflections of adjacent rolls. Thus the crown required for two adjacent rolls can be expressed as: -

$$Cr = y_1 + y_2 \qquad (2)$$

where Cr = radial crown magnitude, y_1 = roll 1 deflection and y_2 = roll 2 deflection.

Although the method is shown in its simplest form, both equation (1) and (2) can be developed to include shear deflection, non-uniform weight distributions, compound beam effects and stack position to improve accuracy.

The major assumption that the rolls behave as simple beams can have a significant effect on the effectiveness of the crown. The three-dimensional nature of the roll can result in ovalisation ('tin canning') under load. This, along with non-linear contact, changes in roll stiffness due to variation in cross-section and non-uniform body forces can often invalidate the CS method (TAPPI [5]). There is no closed form solution that can be used to combine all these factors. However, in traditional pressing and drying, the problems associated with the beam theory assumption can be eliminated, often based on practical experience.

Once a roll crown has been specified, its effectiveness in the press can be measured using simple pressure tests (using pressure sensitive paper) to determine the pressure 'footprint' and resultant load distribution across the nip length. A crown correction formula, which relates the pressure footprint to the roll diameter, can then be used to show how the roll crown distribution should be amended (TAPPI [6]). The roll is then removed from the press for regrinding. In a typical press it is often the smaller rolls that are crowned as it is far easier to remove them should the crown need to be changed.

Crown Specification for Corrugator Rolls

In the calculation of corrugator roll crown, the process of using the CS method, followed by the crown correction formula and roll regrinding would be inappropriate. This is for three main reasons: -

- The cost of the flute grinding process, followed by hardening and coating, would mean that re-machining due to poor crown is not an economically viable option.

- The crown correction formula cannot be applied to corrugated rolls due to the fluted nip. Any pressure measurements would not be continuous and could not be used to determine the footprint, and subsequent crown correction.

- The traditional paper nip often uses a polymer felt between the rolls. This 'soft' nip process is far more able to spread non-uniform load due to inappropriate crown. Consequently, a 'hard' nip, as seen in the corrugator, is far more sensitive to non-uniform loading [1].

Given these factors, the OEM singlefacer manufacturer can often develop the optimum crown for their particular machine set-up based on an iterative procedure of trial and error. As the loading and roll construction will be well known, any particular load distribution problems due to crown magnitude and profile can be removed. However, for a new machine design or for the independent roll manufacturer, who design and manufacture for a range of different machines, the crown specification method must be far better understood. Similarly, it is often the case that a board producer will specify a roll design, without knowing the loading that will be used in the singlefacer. The main purpose of this study is therefore to analyse how appropriate the CS method is in specifying crown in the singlefacer.

Analysis of Roll Behavior

The assumption that the roll behaves as a simple beam was analyzed using experimental and computational means. The profile of the beam deflection (including both bending and shear terms) was compared with a typical roll experimental set-up, along with a three-dimensional finite element model. The results showed how much the three-dimensional effects would invalidate the CS beam-based method.

Experimental Method

An experimental test rig to measure static roll deflection was designed, manufactured and commissioned (figure 3). The experiment consisted of a single roll that sat on an I-beam. The ends of the roll were supported by machined end blocks, to give the simply supported boundary conditions as experienced in the single facer.

A plane ground singlefacer roll (chrome molybdenum steel, OD=395mm, Face Length=2830mm and Bearing Distance=2970mm) was loaded using 20 hydraulic cylinders from a central pressure source. This gave an approximate uniformly distributed load as would be experienced in a typical singlefacer. The load per cylinder was calibrated using a load cell and related to the hydraulic fluid pressure via a pressure sensor. The load was applied through the hydraulic cylinders and was reacted by restraining bolts at the end blocks. The roll was deflected about the end blocks.

The supporting I-beam had a machined top surface which allowed accurate positioning of the hydraulic cylinders and deflection measuring transducers. The deflection was measured by a non-contact LED transducer (accurate to 0.01mm) and a LVDT transducer (accurate to 0.005mm). The LED measured deflection at the centre of the roll and acted as a control. The LVDT was used to measure the deflection at various points along the roll length. Accuracy was maintained by checking the central LED deflection each time the LVDT was moved. This process gave both the deflected magnitude and profile of the roll at a range of loads. Both the load and deflection data was collected using a PC connected via a Sclumberger data-logger.

The transducers sat on the upper surface of the I-beam during loading. This provided a measurement datum. However, the I-beam itself experienced some deflection due the reaction forces at the end blocks and the supports on the ground. In order to determine the net deflection of the roll, the deflection of the I-beam was determined, again using the LVDT transducer (connected from ground using a remote arm support). The net deflection of the I-beam was subtracted from the gross deflection of the rig, to determine the actual roll deflection. The experimental procedure was repeated to remove the effects of systematic errors.

FE Analysis

A linear finite element model consisting of three-dimensional second order continuum elements was constructed to represent both the roll and the supporting I-beam. Patran™ v8.5 was used to pre- and post-process the model, with Abaqus™ v5.8 used to solve it. The appropriate boundary conditions to represent the experimental test rig were included. A mesh dependency study was performed to ensure the optimum mesh density. The load was applied to the roll as a series of point loads to emulate the hydraulic cylinders. The net deflection of the roll was determined and compared with that of the experimental data. The applied load on both the experimental and FE models was substantially greater than would be experienced in a typical singlefacer. This increased load was used to minimize measurement errors. However, the deflections were small and were therefore considered linear.

The results of the experiment showed that the three-dimensional experimental roll behavior (validated by the FE model) was around 15% greater than that given by the beam-based model (figure 4). The experimental and FE data matched very well, given the magnitude of deflection being measured. This gave confidence in both the experimental and FE modelling procedure. The difference in the deflected magnitudes would imply that the crown derived by the CS beam-based method would be consistently too low, given the 'extra' deflection of the roll nip surface from three-dimensional effects. The effects of this on the load distribution would be difficult to determine from a single roll analysis and would require a full non-linear contact solution.

Non-Linear Analysis of Contact Behavior

The full effect of the three-dimensional roll behavior on the crown determination could only be seen using a non-linear representation of the system. The load/crown relationship meant that the contact area changed as load was applied. A full non-linear FE model was required to give the appropriate change in contact boundary condition. In order to simplify the pre-processing stage and keep the model to a reasonable size, the outer surface of the roll was considered plane. The flute geometry was ignored, but it was later seen that contact area was less than the typical flute tip radius.

Again using Abaqus, a surface to surface based contact boundary condition was used, along with a non-linear solution to allow the change in contact behavior as the load was increased. A plane strain two-dimensional model was created to validate the contact behavior against the known pressure distribution for Hertzian contact between cylinders (Johnson [7]). The mesh distribution was optimized to show the full contact behavior, whilst using the minimum amount of elements.

A data transfer problem between Patran and Abaqus meant that it was only possible to model the contact between two rolls (the majority of singlefacers utilize three rolls in a stack). The curvature required to model the plane strain contact surfaces resulted in a very small node spacing. When writing the FE input file from Patran, a rounding-off operation of the node geometry caused the curve to become a stepped set of straight lines. Thus the curve geometry was lost, unless the contact surface started on the y=0mm plane (figure 6). Hence, only one nip (two rolls) could be modeled.

A full three-dimensional contact model was developed from the plane strain model. The pre-processing stage required to give the full crown definition was laborious given the complex geometry and mesh required for the contact behavior. The combined effects of non-uniform roll cross section, body forces and the presence of paper were developed to give a full representation of the system. The initial model consisted of a circular arc to represent the crown. A series of pressure distributions at different loads were obtained using this simple arc.

The CS beam-based model yielded a crown profile made up of a fourth order polynomial. Given the complex geometry and mesh distribution, it was difficult to incorporate the full crown representation into the model. It became apparent that the full three-dimensional FE method would be impractical from a design viewpoint. The full model consisted of a very large number of elements, which took some considerable time to solve. This has been experienced in other studies involving this kind of modeling procedure (Mayrhofer et al [8], Deger [9]). Thus in order to analyze the CS beam-based method, a procedure to develop a parametric reduced order model would be required.

Parametric Model Order Reduction Process

Given that the three-dimensional contact model was insufficient in modelling the full three-roll stack and crown efficiently, an order reduction process was used. A parametric model that allowed any crown magnitude and profile to be analyzed would be far more useful than the three-dimensional model.

A series of pseudo-three-dimensional models were developed to give an approximate representation of the three-dimensional system. The continuum elements of the full model were replaced by a model made up of a series of beam and spring elements, along with a series of gap elements to give the non-linear contact condition (figure 5). The beam element properties were given by the geometry of the three-dimensional roll. The ovalising behavior of the roll was determined by the two-dimensional plane strain analysis. By defining the roll sectional geometry in this manner, the contact behavior under load could be determined. The approximate stiffness of a plane strain 'spring' segment could be calculated from the applied load and the corresponding deflection. A non-dimensional study of many different roll cross sectional parameters was performed to give the approximate spring stiffness for a range of roll types.

The pseudo-3D model was written in Abaqus text input file format. The line load distributed output was validated against the contact pressure from the three-dimensional models. The contact pressure (N/mm^2) was converted into line load (N/mm) by integrating about the plane section of each portion of the roll. The simple crown arc 3D models correlated well with the equivalent pseudo-3D models. The nature of the pseudo-3D model meant that the limit on the number of nips modeled could be eliminated. As there was no longer a plane strain curve (due to the spring and gap element representation), the full three-roll stack could be modeled.

Once the pseudo-3D models had been validated, the FE input files were written in parametric format. A series of Matlab^{TM} v5.1 scripts were written to generate the FE input files for any geometry specified by the user. This procedure determined the node and element positions, along with the element definitions (including beam parameters, spring stiffness and gap element closure directions). The parabolic beam-based crown profile could be determined from the central magnitude and the roll geometry. Thus the crowns given by the beam-based model could now be analyzed using a full approximate three-dimensional non-linear representation of the roll stack.

A second set of Matlab scripts were written to extract the load distributions from the FE output files. This eliminated the need for a post-processor in the analysis procedure. The development of the pseudo-3D models in parametric form reduced the model creation and analysis time drastically. The full 3D models required over 6 hours solution time using a parallel processor without including pre- and post-processing time. The approximate model meant that a crown could be analyzed for any stack configuration in a matter of minutes.

Analysis of Beam-Based Crown Specification Method

A number of typical two- and three-roll stack geometries and load cases were used to test the effectiveness of the linear assumption. The parametric pseudo-3D models allowed the geometry to be set. The respective crown magnitudes and profiles (as derived in a version of equation (1) and (2)) were read into the model. In all cases, the predicted crown was consistently too low. This resulted in a line load distribution that caused excessive load at the roll ends and reduced load at the centre (figure 6). This was consistent with the single roll analysis that showed that the three-dimensional roll would exhibit greater deflection than given by the beam-based method.

In the case of the two-roll stack, the crown magnitude could be increased manually to give the desired line load distribution. However, in the three-roll models, changing the magnitude of one crown may improve the line load distribution in one nip, but would adversely effect the distribution in the other. It became apparent that the load distribution in both nips was very sensitive to both crown magnitude and profile.

The excessive load at the roll ends was consistent with a phenomenon that is often experienced with poorly designed crown. Many singlefacer rolls show signs of fatigue damage to the flute tips at the ends of the roll. This often causes the tip to fracture and render the roll useless. If the beam-based model were used, then the load distribution would be too great at the roll ends. It is rare that a roll will fail due to flute fatigue in the centre.

The manually adjustment of crown in the parametric models was lengthy given the sensitivity of the problem. The three-roll models were very difficult to optimize in this manner. Manual optimization was clearly impractical from a design perspective. The non-uniform load distribution could not be related to the crown change required for even load. Given that the analysis procedure of the pseudo-3D models was already in parametric form, an automated optimization procedure was used.

Automated Optimization using Genetic Algorithm

A genetic algorithm (G.A.) is an iterative search procedure that can be used to find the optimum output of a system based on a series of predefined inputs. In the case of crown specification, the inputs were defined as the crown parameters, with the uniformity of the resultant load distribution defined as the system output. Thus for a roll stack the optimum crown parameters would result in a perfect uniform load distribution.

Given that the problem was of a multi-parameter nature (namely crown magnitudes and profiles, in their simplest forms) the G.A. was by far the most efficient method available. Unfortunately, the commercially available optimization routines based on G.A.s are focussed on closed-loop functions. Thus a series of G.A. programs had to be written which used the pseudo-3D FE model as the 'function'. The parametric nature of the FE models was necessary to allow the crowns to be specified and the subsequent load to be analyzed. A G.A. consisting of roulette-wheel reproduction, multi-point crossover and mutation was used (Goldberg [10]).

The efficiency of the G.A. search procedure is dependent upon the number of parameters being analyzed and the bounds set in which the search can take place. The ability to find the optimum state depends on how well the optimum crown can be defined. If the bounds are set too tightly, the optimum crown may be missed. Likewise if the bounds are set too widely, then the process will be inefficient in finding the optimum.

A number of methods were used to define the crown profiles. These ranged from individual node positions to polynomial and spline functions. However, the most efficient crown definition was a trigonometric function. This gave the most flexible definition whilst keeping the number of parameters to a minimum. The function is given as: -

$$y = \frac{Cr}{1 - Cos(\theta)} \left(Cos\left(\theta - \frac{2x}{L}\theta \right) - Cos(\theta) \right) \tag{3}$$

where, y = crown magnitude at x, Cr = crown magnitude at roll centre, θ = crown angle, x = distance along roll and L = roll face length

Thus any crown could be specified by defining the crown magnitude at the roll centre and the crown angle. The G.A. selects a value for these parameters at random, and proceeds in an iterative manner to find the optimum system output.

The automated optimization procedure was very effective in finding the optimum crown parameters for any roll stack configuration. The search procedure was honed to give a solution time of less than two hours. Given that the initial non-linear roll stack models took over six hours to solve for an arbitrary crown, the optimization procedure was far more efficient in a design sense.

The parametric FE model and the experimental data showed the inaccuracies of using the beam-based method to derive the crowns in the singlefacer roll stack. The FE model combined with the G.A. optimization procedure showed that the load distribution at both nip points could be significantly improved as a multi-parameter process based on a multi-crown magnitude and profile (figure 6).

Summary

The conclusions made in this study are numerous and can be summarized as: -
- *Effectiveness of beam-based crown calculation*
The assumption that the rolls in the singlefacer stack behave as simple beams was analyzed against an experimental roll and a finite element model. Both the experimental roll and the model showed approximately 15% more deflection at the load point than given by the beam method. This would imply that crown derived in this manner would be consistently too low. A full non-linear contact model of the stack was developed to show that this was the case.
- *Sensitivity of crown magnitude and profile*
The parametric finite element model showed that the load distribution at the nip is extremely sensitive to crown magnitude and profile, especially at the roll ends. The construction of the rolls can have a large influence on the load distribution. A trigonometric crown profile was considered the most effective in achieving the optimum load distribution.
- *Effect of three rolls in stack*

The presence of three rolls and two nip points gives rise to a complex problem. Changes in one crown can have a large impact in the load distribution of load in the other nip. The sensitivity of the load/crown relationship gives rise to a difficult problem in achieving uniform load at both nips.

- *Optimization routine to better predict crown magnitude and profile*

The complexity of the multi parameter problem had to be tackled using a genetic algorithm optimization procedure. This showed that the optimum crown was only subtly different from the CS method crowns, but resulted in a significant improvement in load distribution.

In summary, the study led to a far better understanding of the crown specification for any singlefacer in any operating condition. The optimization routine was a powerful technique in calculating crown for any stack. It is hoped that the better crown specification for corrugator rolls will lead to better paper quality, enhanced roll life and reduced overhead for the paper producer.

ACKNOWLEDGEMENTS

This work is supported by the Engineering and Physical Sciences Research Council (EPSRC) and Flute and Coating Technologies Ltd (FACT). The author gratefully acknowledges this support.

REFERENCES

(1) Smook, G.A., *Handbook for Pulp and Paper Technologists* (2nd.Ed.), Angus Wilde, Vancouver (1997)

(2) Timoshenko, S.P. & Goodier, J.N., *Theory of Elasticity* (3rd Ed.), McGraw-Hill, Tokyo (1970)

(3) Smith, S.F., 'The Calculation and Camber of Paper Machine Rolls', *Proc. Tech. Section of Paper Makers Association of Great Britain*, 1936

(4) Stone, M.D. & Liebert, A.T., 'Crown Control of Paper Calenders', *TAPPI Journal*, 44(5): 308-315 (1961)

(5) TAPPI Technical Information Paper 0420-06, 'Roll Crown Specifications and Definitions', (withdrawn 2/17/97) (www.tappi.org)

(6) TAPPI Technical Information Paper 0404-06, 'Techniques for Nip Impressions' (www.tappi.org)

(7) Johnson, K.L., *Contact Mechanics*, Cambridge University Press, Cambridge (1985)

(8) Mayrhofer, K., Finstermann, G. & Gruber, R., 'Contact Pressure Analysis of a Roll Stack', *1998 Abaqus Users' Conference Proceedings*, HKS Ltd. P.535-551 (www.hks.com)

(9) Deger, Y., 'FE Simulation of Paper Calendering', *1999 Abaqus Users' Conference Proceedings*, HKS Ltd. P.175-190 (www.hks.com)

(10) Goldberg, D.E., *Genetic Algorithms in Search, Optimisation and Machine Learning*, Reading, Mass.; Wokingham : Addison-Wesley (1989)

FIGURES

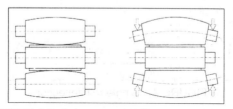

FIGURE 1 Roll crown and deflection mechanism

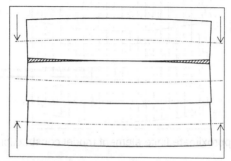

FIGURE 2 – Roll overlap to determine linear crown

FIGURE 3 – Experimental single roll test rig

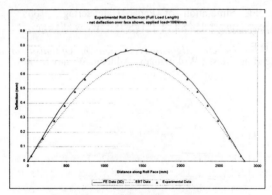

FIGURE 4 – Single roll deflection

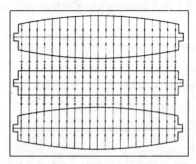

FIGURE 5 – Approximate finite element model construction (simplified)

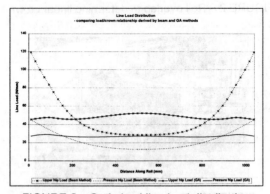

FIGURE 6 – Optimised line load distribution

AUDIO ACOUSTIC PLANT CONDITION MONITORING

B Blakeley* , B Lewis** and A Lees [†]

Plant Condition Monitoring (PCM) is widely used by a variety of industries as part of a condition based maintenance program. This replaces the previous 'schedule' based maintenance program, in which individual components of a machine are replaced at specified intervals. With PCM the condition of the individual components are monitored, and are only replaced when their performance is deemed unsatisfactory.

PCM monitoring techniques are often capital and/or labour intensive, and their use limited to critical machines only. The objective of this research is to investigate the possibility of using sound as a basic indicator of machine health. Machines critical to plant would continue to be monitored using vibration analysis; sound would only be used on ancillary equipment that is not vital to the operation of the plant. When this 'audio PCM' technique indicates that a machine is in poor condition, the results from sound would be verified by standard vibration monitoring before maintenance work is undertaken.

INTRODUCTION

PCM techniques include vibration monitoring, motor current monitoring, thermal imaging and oil analysis; these techniques are often capital and/or labour intensive. The prohibitive cost of these techniques often limits their use to critical machines within the plant. Less critical machines continue to be maintained under the schedule based maintenance program.

The objective of this research is to create a system capable of screening a large number of rotating machines in an industrial environment such as the hot rolling mill of a steel plant. The system must be able to identify malfunctioning machinery with the minimum use of transducers. These transducers may include accelerometers and microphones.

* EngD Centre, Welsh Technology Centre, Port Talbot, Wales.
** Corus Research Development and Technology, Port Talbot, Wales.
† University of Wales - Swansea, Mechanical Engineering Dept, Singleton Park, Swansea.

The purpose of this system is to screen less critical machines for faults, and to provide an early warning system for failures. Maintenance engineers often find that the first indication of a machine's declining condition is a change of sound and vibration. However, as greater efficiency is demanded from plant, the number of experienced personnel in the plant will decrease; because of this, there is rarely an operative within the vicinity to hear and recognise the abnormal sound. It is believed that a study of the noise produced from failing machines will provide the information necessary to develop the screening system.

The study included the following:

1. The building of a test-rig, consisting of a motor, gearbox and load. Faults were introduced into the gearbox and their effect on sound and vibration noted. These experiments were conducted in a relatively quite workshop.
2. The test-rig experiments were then repeated in a descaling fluid pump house, located on Corus' Port Talbot plant. The background noise level was in excess of 98 dB.
3. Analysis of the background noise, produced by the descaling pumps.

To date the following faults have been investigated in the relatively quiet workshop:-

1. Baseline and manufacturing errors.
2. Dismantling and reassembling the gearbox.
3. Misalignment of the brake motor coupling.
4. Removal of an input shaft gear tooth.
5. Evenly worn teeth.
6. Lubrication starvation of teeth.
7. Lubrication starvation of bearings.
8. Roller and cage damage of bearings.
9. Rotor rub.
10. Drive motor faults.

The experiment to investigate the removal of a tooth was also carried out in the descaling pump house. This paper concentrates on the results of this experiment, and the analysis of background noise.

THE TEST-RIG

The test-rig consists of an electric motor, gearbox and load. Faults were deliberately added to the gearbox and their effects on sound and vibration noted. A schematic of the test-rig is shown in Figure 1. The gearbox is of a right angled spiral bevel type with two output shafts and a reduction ratio of 2:1. The input shaft gear has twelve teeth, while the output shaft has twenty four.

The test-rig is driven by a 370 W three-phase induction motor and phase-inverter over a range of speeds from 300 to 2400 RPM. The load is a permanent magnet DC motor with a regenerative absorption drive, capable of placing a 0 to 4 Nm braking torque on the gearbox's output shaft. A 1000 pulse per revolution shaft encoder was attached to the end of the flywheel shaft for precise determination of the output shaft speed. The shafts were connected using flexible couplings.

The accelerometers used in these experiments were manufactured by Brüel and Kjær (B&K) and D.J. Birchall (DJB). The microphone used was of the measuring capacitance type, again manufactured by B&K.

METHODOLOGY

The sound and vibration characteristics of a broken tooth was conducted in the following manner:

A newly purchased gearbox was fitted to the test-rig and a baseline of sound and vibration was taken. The vibration was recorded in the axial, vertical and horizontal directions over a range of motor speeds from 10 to 40 cps. For the vertical signal the shaft encoder 'z pulse' was also recorded on the second channel of the data logger. This z pulses produces a pulse at the beginning of each revolution of the output shaft; this pulse is used during the signal processing for time domain averaging (Futter [1], Futter [2] and McFadden [3]). Sound was recorded by suspending the B&K microphone 0.3 metres above the gearbox. The z pulse was also recorded.

The input shaft of the gearbox was then removed, and a small angle grinder used to remove most of one tooth. The gearbox was then reassembled and the readings of sound and vibration were repeated in an identical manner for comparison.

RESULTS

The following results were taken in the descaling fluid pump house.

Waterfall Plots of Vibration

A waterfall plot (Middleton and Rumble [4]) of vibration indicates that the test-rig exhibits a vertical resonance between 250 and 600 Hz. This acts as a 'sounding board' for the microphone suspended over the gearbox [3]. Other 'sounding boards' on the rig include electrical cabinet surfaces. These cabinets resonate below 200 Hz, and are only lightly damped, making analysis of sound below 200 Hz difficult.

Time Domain Averaging

Time domain averaging (TDA) [1,2,3] of the sound and vibration signal was conducted by splitting the signal into lengths; each length corresponding to exactly one revolution of the output shaft by way of the z pulse. The rotational speed of the shaft varies slightly from one revolution to the next. These small fluctuations in speed result in the individual signals being slightly different in length. Each of the lengths were resampled to ensure that they were all the same length, and contained the same number of samples. The equally sized samples were then added to one another and an average taken. Figures 2 and 3 show the results of TDA vibration and sound respectively. Each time domain plot is for one revolution of the output shaft.

The gearbox has a 2:1 reduction ratio, and the tooth has been removed from the input shaft. Two distinct events can be seen in the time domain, corresponding to the broken tooth passing through the gear mesh twice per revolution of the output shaft. Figures 4 and 5 show fast Fourier transforms (FFTs) of the same TDA signals of vibration and sound with the tooth passing frequencies (TPF) indicated. Inter modulation of the TPFs and the input shaft are clearly visible in both plots, as predicted by theory (Randal [5]). The momentary loss of tooth contact and subsequent impact of the teeth as they regain contact, causes a large number of sidebands to be generated over a relatively large frequency range around the TPF and harmonics.

Analysis of Background Noise

The test-rig was located in a descaling fluid pump house. This pump house contains three pumps which supply the hot mill with descaling fluid, used to remove oxides from the steel slabs before rolling. The sound pressure level produced by these pumps, measured at the test-rig, varies between 95 to 98 dB. Figure 6 is a diagram of one such pump.

A ten second sound signal of the background noise, generated by these pumps, was recorded via the B&K microphone and data logger. Figure 7 is a Cepstrum of this sound signal [5]. Peaks A1 to A9 are rhamonics spaced 40.603 ms apart, corresponding with a shaft speed of 24.629 cps. This is consistent with the running speed of a four pole motor. Figure 8 is an FFT of the sound signal. The shaft speed of 24.629 cps, indicated by the Cepstrum, was used to identify peaks within the spectrum. The TPF and second harmonic have been indicated. A zoom of this plot shows that the 1 x shaft order is also present. The 3,4,6,7 and 8 x are present, but the 1 x is the largest peak in the spectrum. A high 1 x shaft order and harmonics of the TPF are often associated with misalignment within the gearbox. Corus' PCM department is investigating this possible fault.

CONCLUSION

Two methods for using a microphone as a PCM tool have been presented in this paper. The first technique made use of a shaft encoder to average out the background noise of the descaling pumps, so that a broken tooth in a small gearbox could be investigated. The time domain averaging (TDA) technique [1,2,3] dramatically improves the signal to noise ratio, and makes it possible to diagnose faults, by sound, of a small component whose sound power would normally be to small to distinguish amongst the background noise. The disadvantage of TDA is that a shaft encoder or 'once per rev' signal is not always available.

The second technique is far less complex. A simple sound sample of the descaling fluid pumps was recorded, and a Cepstrum [5] employed to reveal any sideband patterns. If these sideband patterns are evident a shaft speed can be determined, and subsequent shaft orders and passing frequencies identified within the spectrum. Unfortunately, this simpler technique can only be used when the sound power generated by the fault is large enough not to require TDA..

FUTURE WORK

An FEA vibration model of the test-rig is underway. The purpose of this model is to increase the understanding of the vibrations caused by the faults. To date only the broken tooth has been investigated outside of the quiet workshop. The remaining faults will be investigated. The use of directional microphones and microphone probes may be investigated, to reduce the effect of reflections and background noise [Heng and Mohd Nor [6], [4]) if time allows.

ACKNOWLEDGMENTS

The author would like to thank Dr. B.J. Hewitt, Director, R&D - Programmes and Mr. E.F. Walker, Manager, Technical Co-ordination, Welsh Technology Centre, Corus Group for permission to publish this paper.

REFERENCE LIST

(1) Futter, D.N., *G.B. Noise & Vib. Diagnostics*, 1995.
(2) Futter, D.N., *G.B. Cond. Mon.*, Vol 37, No 8, August 1995, pp. 591-589.
(3) McFadden, P.D., *NDT Int.*, Vol. 18, No. 5, October 1985, pp. 279-282.
(4) Middleton, A., and Rumble, A., *Noise and Vib. Worldwide*, Nov. 1991, pp. 11-14.
(5) Randal, R.B., *Maint. Manage. Int.* 3, 1982/1983, pp. 183-208.
(6) Heng, R., Mohd Nor, M., *Profitable Con. Mon.*, 1996, pp. 145-157.

FIGURE 1   The Test-rig

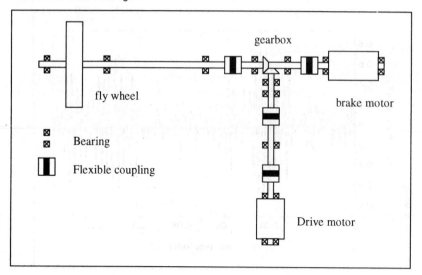

FIGURE 2   Time Domain Plot of TDA Vibration of Broken Tooth

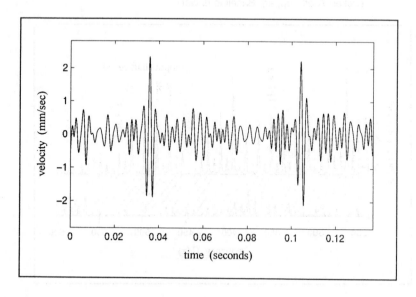

FIGURE 3   Time Domain Plot of TDA Sound of Broken Tooth

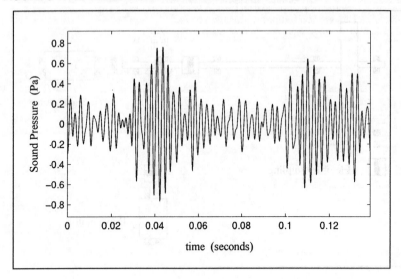

FIGURE 4   Frequency Domain Plot of TDA Vibration of Broken Tooth
            Broken Tooth (upper) Baseline (lower)

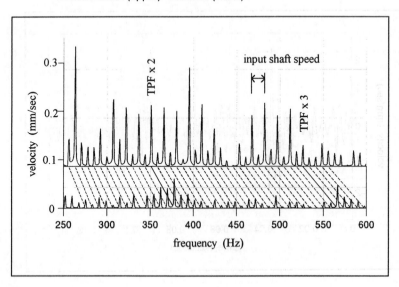

FIGURE 5   Frequency Domain Plot of TDA Sound of Broken Tooth
Broken Tooth (upper) Baseline (lower)

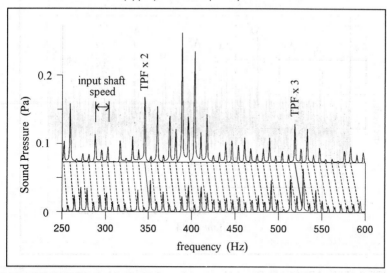

FIGURE 6   Diagram of Descaling Fluid Pump

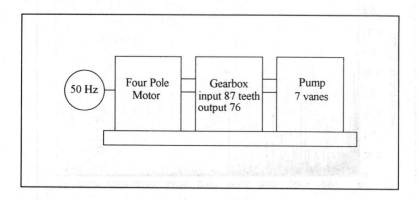

FIGURE 7   Cepstrum of Descaling Pump Noise

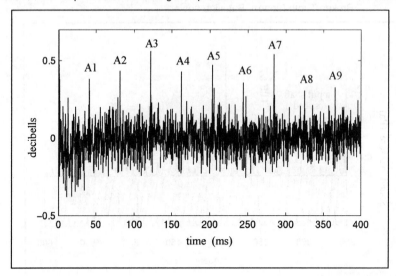

FIGURE 8   FFT of Descaling Pump Noise

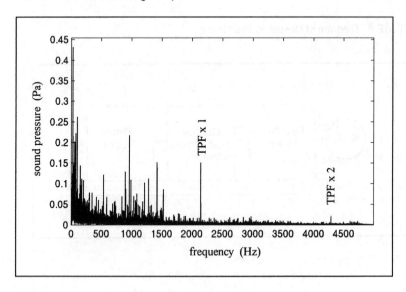

BLAST FURNACE HEARTH JACKET MONITORING & DESIGN

O. Milling* and G. Everson*

Corus' R,D&T, Teesside Technology Centre has developed considerable experience monitoring and modelling blast furnace hearth jackets. The purpose of this paper is to look at methods developed for the monitoring of hearth jackets during furnace operation, from the 1960s to the present, and trends in the data collected. It is demonstrated that this monitoring is an invaluable aid to safe furnace operation and design to maximise furnace life. Observations are compared to hypothetical mechanisms describing hearth behaviour and finite element models. These models provide good estimates of hearth stress during normal operation. Changes in stress patterns over the past twenty years are reviewed and reasons for the changes hypothesised. Finally the influence of hearth jacket monitoring on furnace operation is considered.

INTRODUCTION

Failure of the hearth jacket of a blast furnace may have catastrophic consequences, causing damage to plant, and compromising safety. This paper describes a strategy for the monitoring of blast furnace hearth jackets developed by Corus R,D&T, Teesside Technology Centre.

Comprehensive measurements from a number of furnaces are compared to hypothesised mechanisms that describe increased stress in the furnace hearth and to finite element models used to predict hearth behaviour. The influence of furnace design on hearth jacket stress and the roles played by monitoring and modelling in furnace operation and design are reviewed.

HEARTH JACKET FUNCTION

The blast furnace hearth jacket is designed to contain the refractory walls forming the furnace, preventing molten material from 'breaking out'. The jacket must have sufficient strength to contain the refractory walls without rupture. If the construction is too rigid then it will not deform under pressure as the refractory bricks in the wall expand when heated, increasing the stresses in the refractory, initiating their cracking and eventual failure.

*Corus R,D&T, Teesside Technology Centre, PO Box 11, Grangetown, Middlesbrough, TS6 6UB, United Kingdom.

Any cracking in the refractory produces small gaps, reducing its conductivity. This impedes the conduction of heat away from the furnace, causing localised heating of the wall and furnace shell. This in turn increases the stresses in the refractory and furnace shell inducing further cracking in the refractory and potentially damaging the shell.

Molten material may enter cracks in the refractory and track towards the furnace shell. As the furnace is cooled by conduction through the furnace walls, by stave or spray cooling, the advancing hot material may be stopped by freezing before it reaches the shell. If molten material reaches the steel shell then it will quickly penetrate the steel jacket and 'break out' will occur.

The highest stresses in a furnace hearth occur during 'blow in'. The stresses in the shell rise steadily as the furnace is put back on blast, reaching a peak after some days, and then relax to a lower level [1]. This lower level remains relatively constant during normal furnace operation with some fluctuations as iron demand and blast pressure change.

The stresses in the jacket are generally higher after a furnace stop than when a new or relined furnace is blown in.

HEARTH JACKET STRESS MECHANISMS AND FAILURE

Freezing of the iron salamander

The pool of molten iron in the bottom of the furnace, known as the salamander, freezes when the furnace is stopped. The salamander shrinks away from the walls of the furnace as it cools, leaving a void. Hypothesis suggests that this void becomes filled with debris, as the furnace is filled, and with mortar from any remedial lining work. Iron reduced at first blow in may also enter this void and solidify [1]. As the furnace heats up the salamander expands pushing directly against the furnace wall as the shrinkage void left when it cooled is now filled. This increases the stresses in the furnace lining and hearth jacket above those encountered when the furnace was first started. As the salamander melts the force that it exerts on the furnace wall relaxes and the stresses in the furnace hearth jacket decrease.

To reduce the additional stresses caused by the expanding salamander it is common practice to drill through the furnace hearth and tap off the iron whilst it is still molten [1], preventing the formation of a solid deposit. This is usually only done for longer furnace stops, is not always practical, and may cause long term damage by creating a weakness in the hearth material.

On furnaces with a spray cooled hearth jacket the cooling water may be heated to 60 °C for the first two to three weeks of operation after a stop [1]. This expands the hearth jacket slightly allowing increased expansion of the refractory, thus reducing the stress in the shell. When the stresses in the shell relax to their equilibrium level the water heating is removed and the stresses increase slightly as the shell cools. The peak stress in the shell is thus reduced, decreasing the chance of hearth jacket failure.

Relaxation of the furnace lining

When a new or relined furnace is blown in there is no salamander present in the bottom of the furnace to explain any relaxation in stresses observed. This relaxation has been attributed to the bedding in of the furnace lining as the refractory blocks heat up. In a modern furnace the bricking and grouting is very tight so this effect should be minimal.

When a furnace is lit or reheated the hot face of the refractory is quickly heated. The resulting temperature gradient and induced stress gradient is thus very large towards the hot face of the lining. This temperature gradient reduces with time until an even temperature gradient is maintained through the furnace wall [2]. The stresses in the refractory blocks relax as the thermal expansion through the thickness becomes more even.

Heating a furnace more gradually may reduce the effect by maintaining a more even thermal gradient through the brickwork. A more even thermal gradient will also reduce cracking and spalling on the hot face of the refractory [2]. This is not always practical or even possible due to the nature of the environment within the furnace.

Brittle fracture

Japanese studies have identified brittle fracture [3] in blast furnace shells. This was shown to be caused by thermal cycling of the shell and embrittlement on the inside face of the material at hot spots. No evidence of stress corrosion cracking in the shell was found. Recommendations show that high toughness, low alloy steels can be used to reduce these effects. This type of brittle failure is only normally found in the stack shell and not the hearth jacket. Typically little deterioration in the hearth jacket material is seen even after a furnace has been relined several times. Reference to brittle fracture of a hearth jacket could not be found by the author.

Fatigue failure of the shell at welds and cut outs

Significant cracking of a furnace hearth jacket around tuyere coolers, slag/iron notches and at weld intersections was observed at Kuznetsk Iron and Steel Combine, USSR, in the late 1970s (4). Measurements using strain gauges on the furnace shell showed cyclic variation in shell stress as the furnace was taken on and off blast between casts. The small pressure variations during stove changes did not produce significant cyclic stresses. Fatigue calculations estimated furnace shell life to be of the order of 12 years. In practice the furnaces had been in operation for 15 to 17 years when cracking occurred. These cracks were reported to be between 0.5 and 12.0 metres long. It was noted that most crack growth occurred in the winter months when shell temperature was 25 to 30 °C and ambient air temperature was -20 to −30 °C. The effects of this cumulative fatigue damage are an essential consideration when designing a furnace. Consideration should also be given to the environment in which the furnace will operate as shell material may become brittle at very low temperatures.

MEASUREMENT OF HEARTH JACKET STRESS

The first reported measurements of the stresses in furnace shells were carried out at United Steel Companies, Scunthorpe[†] in the 1960s [6,7]. Several experiments were made using electrical resistance gauges on strain links attached to the furnace shell from 1962 to 1966. One experiment in 1965 saw data obtained for 15 months of furnace operation but was not considered reliable due to long term drift in the instrumentation used. 'Although valuable experience in the use of electrical gauges under very adverse conditions was gained, no reliable results were obtained.' [6]

Measurements were made using mechanical strain measuring devices to remove the problem of electrical drift. Measurements were taken at intervals when the furnace was off blast: Figure 1. Corrosion problems were encountered with mechanical gauge measurement points, making accurate measurements over an extended period impractical.

Republic Steel Corp. reported the use of foil type strain gauges used to measure the stress in the shell of a blast furnace in 1971 [2]. Weld on gauges were used as they require less surface preparation, making installation easier in the dirty environment. A system of waterproofing the gauges using rubber compounds and protective caps was also developed. These experiments were aimed mainly at investigating the stress distribution in the furnace stack, particularly around plate coolers and reinforcing bands, but proved the importance and viability of the technology.

The strain gauging of blast furnace shells at British Steel[†] Scunthorpe Works has been undertaken on a regular basis during shut downs for maintenance or relining. In the period from 1984 to 1990 measurements were made on at least one furnace hearth jacket each year. During the 1990s this work focused on the first blow in after repair or rebuild or if there was some concern with shell condition.

[†] United Steel Companies, Scunthorpe became part of British Steel Corporation, later British Steel plc. British Steel plc became part of the Corus Group plc in 1999.

The first measurements made at Scunthorpe in the 1980s used tube type resistance strain gauges. The gauges were not encapsulated and so were extremely prone to problems associated with moisture entering electrical joints. These gauges exhibited large variations in sensitivity due to slight inconsistencies in manufacture, gauge drift and premature failure were common problems. Large numbers of gauges were used to ensure that consistent results were available during the first few months of furnace operation following blow in. Encapsulated foil type gauges were later used due to their improved moisture resistance. Improvements in manufacture of tube type gauges, now used almost exclusively, has removed previous problems of gauge drift and premature failure. Extensive waterproofing of the gauges is still necessary to prevent corrosion of the surface to which they are attached, although the gauges themselves are fully encapsulated to protect them from water ingress. Mechanical damage to gauges and leads is now the greatest cause of premature failure.

Early strain gauge instrumentation used transistor amplifiers that were prone to drift with time and changing atmospheric conditions. Data was recorded using paper chart recorders.

Electronic integrated circuit driven amplifiers were developed by Teesside Technology Centre in the early 1980s to provide long term measurement stability. This has provided the facility to record and display stresses on furnace process control computers.

More recent amplifier system developments now use programmable modular amplifier units to provide excellent long term stability and fast, accurate calibration. Computerized logging equipment is used almost exclusively, whether data is recorded on furnace control computers or stand alone data acquisition units.

The increased reliability of gauges and instrumentation coupled with confidence in the area in which gauges are placed has reduced the need for large numbers of gauges to be used. Typically pairs of gauges will be fitted around the furnace at two or three strategic locations. The gauges are mounted in the region of highest shell stress which practice and modelling has shown to be in the region of 300 mm above the top of the hearth pad. Calculated stresses are recorded on furnace process control computers so that furnace operators may accurately monitor the behaviour of the hearth jacket both when the furnace is blown in and during normal operation.

MODELLING OF THE HEARTH JACKET

An integral part of the design process when rebuilding a furnace in the late 1990s was the creation of a finite element model of the furnace hearth refractory and shell: Figure 2.

The model assumes the furnace to be axisymmetric. Material properties of the refractories and metals used were based on manufacturers data. They are both non-linear and temperature dependent.

The analysis assumes that heat is applied suddenly to the inside face of the refractory. The model is then iterated through time until steady state thermal conditions are reached. For each iteration the stresses in the model are calculated. This provides a complete stress history of the model, allowing for plastic deformation that occurs before steady state conditions are reached in the calculation of the final stresses in the furnace.

The analysis enables the shell of the furnace to be designed with the optimum compromise between shell strength and elasticity. Furnace designers can thus be confident that the shell will be strong enough given the most extreme conditions within the furnace whilst having sufficient elasticity to prevent crushing of the hearth refractory.

The model has been verified using measurements from thermocouples in the furnace hearth and sidewalls. The hot face temperature was calculated and the temperature in the model adapted to reflect these measurements. The resultant modelled stress in the furnace hearth jacket has been shown to be within the error bounds of the stress measured during blow in of this furnace.

The model has also been used to verify the point at which the highest stress is expected in the hearth jacket: Figure 3. This plot shows that the stress in the hearth jacket is highest at a point corresponding to 300 mm above the top of the hearth pad. This is the point that engineering judgement and empirical studies had suggested the highest stresses occur.

OBSERVATIONS FROM MEASUREMENTS

Figure 4 shows the stresses measured in the hearth jacket of a new furnace. The stresses are seen to rise to a peak after approximately fourteen days of operation and then relax slightly to a normal operating level. This supports the hypothesis describing relaxation of the refractory lining as the furnace heats up [2]. The relaxation in stress may also be attributable to the cooling of the refractory lining as a protective skull of frozen material is deposited on the walls of the furnace. N.B. Plots show data from more than one point around the circumference of the furnace.

Figure 5 shows the measured stress in a furnace hearth jacket after a stop of approximately three weeks. It can be seen that the maximum stress reached is higher than that seen when a new furnace was blown in. The amount of stress relaxation is also larger, whilst normal operating stresses are similar in both cases.

The larger stresses seen and subsequent relaxation is concurrent with the hypothesis of a solidifying and re-melting iron salamander [1]. This hypothesis is further supported by Figure 6. This figure shows that there is a trend of increasing stress in the furnace shell with increased length of stoppage. A longer stop will allow greater cooling of the iron salamander and hence larger voids will be formed as it cools. As previously described these voids will become filled before or during furnace re-start. The greater expansion of the cooler salamander on re-start will increase the stresses in the furnace hearth jacket. The peak stress is approximately independent of furnace size. Figure 6 shows data from furnaces from 8.3 to 9.45 m diameter. All have spray cooled hearths.

One technique used to reduce the peak stress experienced during blow in of a furnace with a spray cooled hearth is to heat the cooling water up to as 60 °C [1]. This expands the hearth jacket slightly, relieving the pressure on the refractory pushing against the jacket. This reduces the peak stress in the shell by 30-50 Nmm^{-2} (Figure 7). It is now common practice on Corus' iron works to heat hearth cooling water as a furnace is blown in if the stresses in the hearth jacket become large.

DISCUSSION

Finite element modelling of the furnace hearth has been proved as a tool to ensure that designs comply with pressure vessel design codes whilst maintaining the optimum balance of strength and elasticity in the hearth jacket. Current models assume a furnace to be uniform around it's circumference and do not allow for shell plate or refractory features such as iron notches and taphole buttresses.

Future models may incorporate these features to allow greater understanding of areas of potential weakness. They may also be used to explain uneven stress distribution around the shell, which has the potential to induce local yielding and failure. Furnace designers may then use this information to modify hearth designs to minimise the likelihood of failure.

Over the past twenty years there has been a trend of decreasing stresses in furnace hearth jackets as new or repaired furnaces are blown in. This reflects changes in the design of refractory walls with more conductive materials now being used to line the furnace hearth. The increased conductivity allows greater conduction of heat from the furnace, promoting the rapid formation of a protective 'skull' of frozen material on the hot face of the refractory. The skull formed insulates the hot face of the refractory so that the temperature remains between 200-600 °C [5]. The lower temperature has the benefit of reducing the thermal stresses induced in the refractory and the furnace hearth jacket, as well as protecting the refractory material from heat and abrasion.

The value of more conductive refractories was demonstrated by the very low stresses seen during the blow in of a recently rebuilt furnace. Hot face temperatures estimated from thermocouple measurements were less than 200 °C. This will greatly increase the life of both the refractory and the hearth jacket.

By monitoring the stresses in the furnace hearth jacket the furnace operator will gain a greater understanding of conditions and processes taking place within the furnace. This will allow greater control of the process, improving product quality and reducing cost by improving the understanding of the cause of operational problems.

In extreme cases monitoring of the stresses in the furnace hearth may warn an operator if failure of the hearth jacket is likely, allowing removal of personnel from the area and remedial action.

CONCLUSIONS

Measurements of the stresses in the hearth jacket of a blast furnace provide vital information on its condition. This is particularly important when a furnace is blown in from new or after a stop when stresses in the hearth jacket are highest.

The stresses measured in a furnace hearth jacket provide furnace designers and engineers with information from which they may predict the life of the furnace. The data informs them when high stresses occur preventing safety being compromised and allowing calculation of resultant damage.

Improved process knowledge from monitoring of the furnace hearth jacket may enable furnace operators to improve product quality and reduce costs caused by production problems.

Finite element models can be used to provide a good prediction of the stresses that a furnace hearth jacket may experience during operation. Future models might predict areas of the hearth jacket vulnerable to localised yielding allowing such areas to be 'designed out' of the furnace.

REFERENCE LIST

(1) James, T. E., *Cooling hazards in high tonnage carbon hearths*, Bethlehem Steel Corp., ISS-AIME Ironmaking Proceedings, Vol. 35, 1976.

(2) Markarian, K. M., Maloney, T. W., *Understanding blast furnace shell behaviour with modern engineering techniques*, Republic Steel Corp., AIME Ironmaking Proceedings, Vol. 30, April 1971.

(3) Yabe, Y. et al, *A policy for the prevention of cracking in the steel shells of blast furnaces*, Iron and Steel Institute of Japan, March 1975.

(4) Makhov, A. P. et al, *Low-cycle fatigue calculation of blast furnace shell,* Siberian Steel Institute, Izvestiya VUZ Chernaya Metallurgiya, 1980, (6), 133-136.

(5) Dzermejko, A. J., *Blast furnace hearth design theory, materials and practice*, Iron and Steel Engineer, December 1991.

(6) Babb, A., Baguley, M., Haynes, J., *Stresses in blast furnace steelwork*, United Steel Companies Ltd., January 1967, Internal Report.

(7) Babb, A., Hurd, T., Haynes, J., *Stresses in blast furnace steelwork*, British Steel Corporation, February 1971, Internal Report.

FIGURE 1   Stresses after reline, 1966

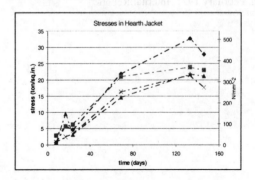

FIGURE 2   Contour plot of modelled stresses in furnace hearth

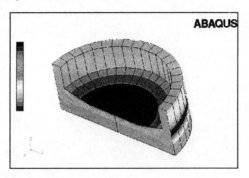

FIGURE 3   Plot showing point of highest stress

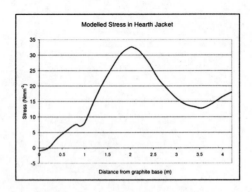

FIGURE 4 Stresses in hearth jacket of new furnace

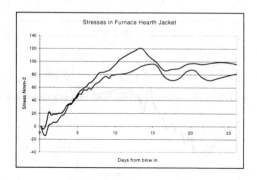

FIGURE 5 Stresses in hearth jacket following three week stop

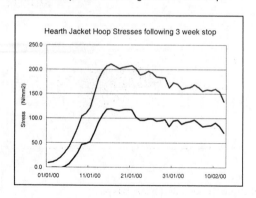

FIGURE 6 Plot of maximum stress vs stop length

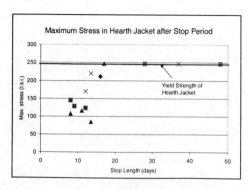

FIGURE 7   Stress peak reduced by heated coolant

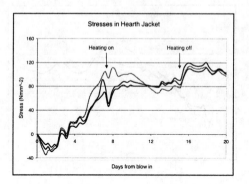

4. CONTACT ANALYSIS

A PARAMETRIC SURVEY OF A CURVIC COUPLING USING THE TWO-DIMENSIONAL FINITE ELEMENT CONTACT METHOD

I.J. Richardson*, T.H. Hyde*, A.A. Becker* and J.W. Taylor†.

Curvic couplings transmit torque between parallel in-line shafts or turbine/compressor discs. They are used extensively within the aero-engine industry but can also be found in industrial gas turbines. The manufacture of Curvic couplings involves the precision cutting and grinding of mating teeth on the adjacent ends of the components; the assembly is then clamped together with bolts. The use of Curvic couplings in engineering transmissions components is relatively widespread, although the publication of work in the open literature is currently limited.

The two-dimensional finite element contact method with Curvic couplings is a limited but useful technique to gauge the effect of geometrical changes on the displacements and stresses within Curvic teeth. The effect of changing the pressure angle and the fillet radius was analysed along with the effect of friction. This paper gives an overview of the type of results that can be obtained using the current techniques for modelling Curvic couplings with the loadcases of bolt loading and torque.

1. INTRODUCTION

Curvic couplings (see Figure 1) were first introduced in 1942; Curvic™ is a trademark of the Gleason Works [1], USA. Previous work has been carried out on Curvic couplings by Pisani and Rencis [2] in two and three dimensions. They compared the results from the finite and boundary element methods of a single tooth non-contact model, and then used the corresponding stress concentration factor in an axisymmetric non-contact finite element analysis in order to evaluate the nominal hoop stress in the Curvic coupling.

The use of the three-dimensional finite element contact method with Curvic couplings was validated by Richardson et al [3]. A simple demonstration model Curvic coupling was used as a die to produce photoelastic specimens of a known geometry. These photoelastic specimens were then tested and the results analysed by manual and automatic methods. The results from the photoelastic experiment were then compared to the results from a three-dimensional finite element contact model of

* School of Mechanical, Manufacturing, Materials and Management, The University of Nottingham, Nottingham, United Kingdom.

† Rolls-Royce plc, Aerospace Group, Derby, United Kingdom.

the same geometry. Considering the small scale of the photoelastic models, the comparison between the two sets of data was very good. This was considered to validate the use of the three-dimensional finite element contact method for use with Curvic couplings.

The two-dimensional finite element contact method has been used for the purpose of stress analysis on Curvic couplings by Richardson et al [4]. A comparison was carried out with a three-dimensional finite element model to determine the validity of the use of the two-dimensional finite element contact method with Curvic couplings. It was found that detailed analysis of Curvic couplings would require three-dimensional analysis; the two-dimensional finite element contact method, however, was shown to be useful in determining the relative effect of changing parameters such as the fillet radius and pressure angle.

This paper uses the ABAQUS [5] commercial finite element package to determine the effect of geometrical and material parameters on the geometry of a large aero-space Curvic coupling. The work presented in this paper is intended to provide data to help in the initial understanding of the effect of geometric parameters such as the fillet radius and pressure angle, as well as the effect of friction.

2. CURVIC COUPLING GEOMETRY AND MANUFACTURE

To obtain contact over the entire length of the coupling halves, one of the halves is machined by the external tool surface and the other by the internal tool surface. This produces a different geometry on either side of the coupling. If the coupling half is machined by the external tool surface then the teeth will have a concave geometry. If the coupling half is machined by the internal tool surface then the teeth will have a convex geometry; this is illustrated in Figure 2.

3. NOTATION AND DIMENSIONS

A large number of dimensions are required in order to define the geometry of a Curvic coupling. Referring to Figure 1, the dimensions used at the inside radius for the present investigation were as follows: -

w, tooth width=(varies according to radius); h_c , chamfer height=0.3mm; r_f , fillet radius=1mm; b_h , bedding height=2.2mm; λ_g , angle of inclination of the gable(i.e. the gable angle)=1.5°; λ_c , angle of inclination of the chamfer=40°; θ, the tooth pressure angle=30°; a, addendum=2.2mm; d, dedendum=3mm; t_t , tooth thickness=(varies according to radius); f_h , flange height=0.9mm; h_t , whole depth(total depth)=5.2mm and h_g , gable height=0.05mm.

The overall dimensions of the coupling are defined in Figure 3 by r_i, inside radius=141.5mm; r_{ig}, radius of outside surface of inner ring of teeth=153.9mm; r_{og},

radius of inside surface of outer ring of teeth=176.1mm and r_o, outside radius=188.5mm.

Other parameters or symbols used in the present work include, μ, coefficient of friction; r_{gw}, grinding wheel radius; R_T, tangency radius; B_f, flange backing thickness=22mm on shaft Curvic half and 23mm on fan disc Curvic half (for B_f see Figure 4).

4. FINITE ELEMENT ANALYSIS

Finite element contact analysis is a method where a contact definition is applied at the contact surface between two contacting bodies. If this contact definition is applied at the interface between the coupling halves, then nodal sliding at the contact surfaces is possible. By using this technique, it is possible for the two coupling halves to behave realistically when a load is applied, thus producing an accurate representation of the displacements and the stresses of a Curvic coupling under load.

ABAQUS input files were generated by the use of FEMGV 5.1-01 [6] Femsys Pre- and Post-processor. The contact surfaces were constructed as perfectly conforming straight lines with the same thickness specification as the model. The ABAQUS 5.8 commercial finite element package used for the present analyses is installed on a Silicon Graphics Origin2000™ server. The Material properties used to obtain the results presented in the figures, for the finite element models, are those of a high strength steel which has a Young's Modulus of 208000N/mm^2 and a Poisson's ratio of 0.28 and Titanium which has a Young's Modulus of 115000N/mm^2 and a Poisson's ratio of 0.32.

When defining the contact pair in ABAQUS the user must decide whether relative sliding is small or finite. All contact analyses in this paper have used the small sliding option. This implies that the relative motion of the two surfaces is a small proportion of the characteristic length of an element face.

The analyses in this paper have all used a non-linear geometry parameter. This is used in the small sliding algorithm to account for any rotation and deformation of the master surface and updates the load path through which the contact forces are transmitted. An isotropic Coulomb friction model was used with the Lagrange multiplier contact method. The finite element models used linear 4-noded reduced integration plane stress elements. These elements are recommended for contact problems with slipping, since they reduce the number of iterations needed to reach convergence of the finite element program.

A two-dimensional finite element model that is typical of the models used in the present investigation can be seen in Figure 4 and in more detail in Figure 5. The Curvic used in the current work used both Titanium and a high strength steel; in the models presented the Titanium Curvic half is at the bottom. Zero displacement boundary conditions were applied in all current models to the bottom surface in the

X-direction (horizontal) and the Y-direction (vertical). The geometry and loads of the models presented in the current work are taken from a global radius of 141.5mm i.e. the inside surface, r_i.

Two load cases were investigated, the first was the bolt load produced from the clamping load that holds the two halves of the coupling together. This is applied by nodal forces of 129.0N to the top surface in the negative Y-direction. The second load case was a combination of the bolt load and a torque load which was applied as a pure shear load with 63.4N/node applied to the top surface and 69.5N/node applied to the sides. The directions and relative magnitudes of these nodal forces can be seen in Figure 4.

5. THE EFFECT OF FRICTION

A comparison of the results is presented for the two-dimensional finite element contact models described above with different values of the coefficient of friction. Two data sets are presented, the first is the contact pressure which is shown in Figure 6, and the second is the relative contact slip which is shown in Figure 7. The data is presented for a node in the centre of the contact surface on the bottom Titanium Curvic half, which was shown in more detail in Figure 4 and Figure 5.

It can be seen from the results presented in Figure 6 that the contact pressure at the centre node is higher for bolt loading and torque than for bolt loading only, as would be expected. For both loadcases the effect of increasing the coefficient of friction is to reduce the contact pressure, which is obviously in agreement with Amontons Law of friction relating the normal and tangential forces.

The effect of the two loadcases in the figures presented is considerable, particularly for the relative contact slip with almost all of the slip occurring in the bolt load step. For the contact pressure the application of the torque load significantly increases the contact pressure, not only at the node shown in the data presented, but over the whole contact surface between the two Curvic halves. The two anomalies in Figure 7 at μ=0.0 and μ=0.5 are probably caused by the pure shear loading method of the two-dimensional model; it would be expected that the application of the torque load in a full 3D model would probably decrease rather than increase the relative contact slip.

6. THE EFFECT OF VARYING THE SIZE OF THE FILLET RADIUS

The effect of changing the fillet radius at the midpoint node of the contact surface is presented in Figure 8 for three values of the coefficient of friction, μ=0.0, 0.1 and 0.3. This data set shows the peak stress at the fillet radius in question; the location of these peaks can be seen in Figure 9. The Gable bottom is the raised area between the two fillet radii that separates the teeth. Only the fillet stress and location are presented here, as the contact pressure and the relative contact slip varied by insignificant amounts between the models for fillet radii between 0.3mm and 2.0mm.

It can be seen from the results that the effect of the coefficient of friction is very significant on the magnitude of the results at the fillet radius. The actual value of the coefficient of friction that is obtained between the Titanium and the steel is unknown in the plane of the two-dimensional model. The irregular shape of the curves in Figure 9 is due to the discrete nature of the results obtainable from the linear element density in this region of the model.

7. THE EFFECT OF CHANGING THE PRESSURE ANGLE

Analyses are presented for models that were constructed with pressure angles from 20° to 40° in 5° increments. This was achieved by rotating the geometry for each contact surface about the Curvic pitch plane, thus keeping the geometry of the rest of the Curvic constant. The fillet radius, r_f and the tooth thickness, t_t, remain constant, but the tooth width, w, will change with pressure angle. It is considered however, that the tooth width will have an insignificant effect on the results presented here.

The standard pressure angle for Curvic couplings is generally 30°. The effect of changing this parameter is presented, for the contact pressure in Figure 10, relative contact slip in Figure 11 and the peak von Mises equivalent stress at the fillet radius in Figure 12 for μ=0.0, 0.1 and 0.3.

The effect of the pressure angle appears to affect all the data sets plotted here in the same way. The shapes of the curves are similar for contact pressure, relative contact slip and the peak von Mises equivalent stress. For all three of these factors it would seem to be preferential to increase the pressure angle, however, the disadvantage of increasing the pressure angle is the increased likelihood of the separation of the coupling halves due to the torque load.

8. DISCUSSION AND CONCLUSIONS

There are many geometrical parameters that are included in the design specification of a Curvic coupling. For the majority of geometrical parameters, a three-dimensional model would be needed to analyse the effect of altering the size or location of the particular parameter. Two of the parameters that can be easily assessed using two-dimensional models are the fillet radius and the pressure angle.

Knowledge of the magnitude of a change in the peak stress at the fillet radius could be useful in conjunction with other stress analysis methods, such as simple design calculations and three-dimensional finite element analyses. By using a combination of these methods, it is possible to estimate the likely increase or decrease in the fillet stresses due to a change of radius at the fillet. As the majority of the results can be obtained from two-dimensional analyses, results can be obtained relatively quickly and cheaply in terms of both user time and processing time.

A change in the pressure angle of the teeth was found to be beneficial to the data sets measured, but any change made to this very important parameter would have a significant effect on the characteristics and behaviour of a whole Curvic coupling. It is likely that a change of 2 to 3 degrees in the pressure angle could result in beneficial changes in the stress state or magnitude of the displacements of the coupling, but this will be dependent heavily on the coupling's specific service requirements.

The work presented on the effect of the coefficient of friction illustrates the importance of obtaining an accurate value of the coefficient of friction between the two Curvic halves. If an accurate comparison or assessment of the displacements or stresses obtained in a real Curvic application is to be achieved, some assessment of the value of the coefficient of friction will probably be necessary. Due to the manufacturing process used in the construction of the teeth, it is likely that the coefficient of friction used for a two dimensional model will be different from that related to the direction across the facewidth of the teeth.

REFERENCE LIST

(1) Gleason Works, 1000 University Ave, Rochester, NY, 14603, USA. 1942.

(2) Pisani S.R. and Rencis J.J., 'Investigating Curvic Coupling behaviour by utilizing the two- and three-dimensional boundary and finite element methods', *International Conference on Boundary Element Methods, XV : Fluid Flow and Computational Aspects*, August 10-13, Computational Mechanics pp 597-608, 1993.

(3) Richardson I.J., Hyde T.H., Becker A., and Taylor J.W. 'A validation of the three-dimensional finite element contact method for use with Curvic couplings by comparing predictions with photoelastic test data', *Coupling and Shaft Technology for Aerospace Transmissions Seminar*, Lucas EES, Solihull, UK, 9 June 1999.

(4) Richardson I.J., Hyde T.H., Becker A., and Taylor J.W. 'A comparison of two and three-dimensional finite element contact analyses of Curvic coupling', *Computational Methods in Contact Mechanics IV*, Stuttgart, Germany, 3-5 August 1999, pp 389-400.

(5) ABAQUS, 'Users Manual', Hibbitt, Karlsson and Sorenson INC. 1998.

(6) FEMGV, Version 5.1 'Users Manual', FEMSYS Limited, Leicester, 1998.

ACKNOWLEDGEMENTS

The authors wish to acknowledge the financial and technical support of Rolls-Royce plc Aerospace Group, for this research which was carried out in the Rolls-Royce University Technology Centre (UTC) in Gas Turbine Transmission Systems at the University of Nottingham.

Figure 1. Tooth profile in the radial direction.

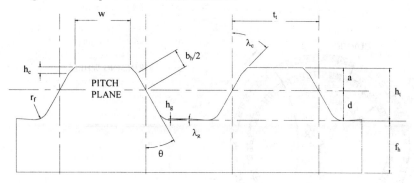

Figure 2. Convex and Concave Tooth Manufacture.

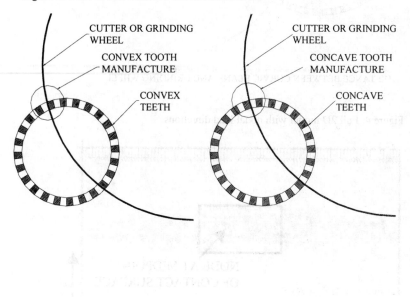

Figure 3. Sectioned view from above of a convex Curvic coupling.

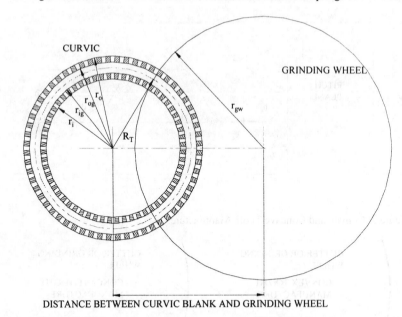

DISTANCE BETWEEN CURVIC BLANK AND GRINDING WHEEL

Figure 4. Full 2D model with nodal load directions.

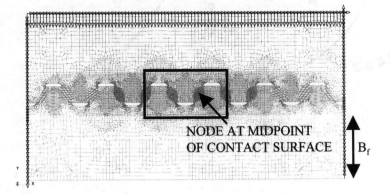

Figure 5. Close up view of highlighted box in Figure 4.

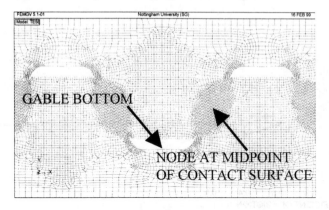

Figure 6. Variation of contact pressure with coefficient of friction.

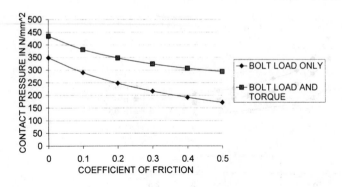

Figure 7. Variation of the relative contact slip with coefficient of friction.

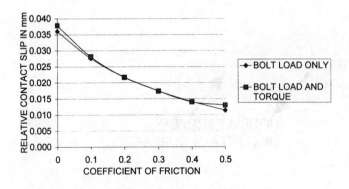

Figure 8. Variation of the peak von Mises equivalent stress with fillet radius for bolt load and torque.

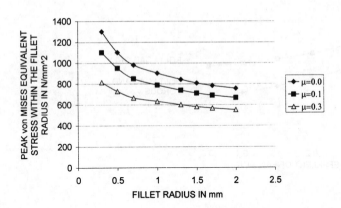

Figure 9. Variation of the location of the peak von Mises equivalent stress with fillet radius for bolt load and torque.

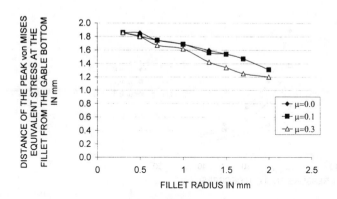

Figure 10. Variation of the contact pressure with pressure angle for bolt loading and torque.

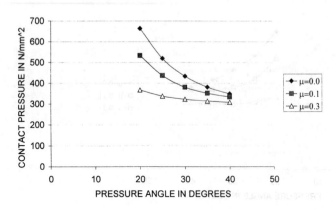

Figure 11. Variation of the relative contact slip with pressure angle for bolt loading and torque.

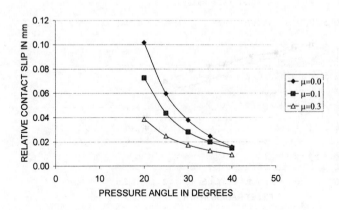

Figure 12. Variation of the peak von Mises equivalent stress with pressure angle for bolt loading and torque.

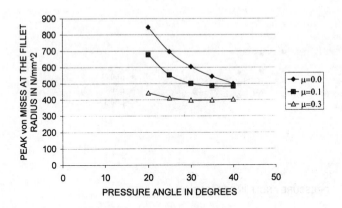

FULL NON-LINEAR FINITE ELEMENT ANALYSIS OF A SMALL PUNCH TEST

W. Li [1], D.J. Brookfield[2], J.E. Mottershead[2], T.K. Hellen[2], A. Zidan[2] and M. Whelan[3]

The small punch test has been applied to determine material properties from small specimens in the power generation industry for many years. Since there is no available analytical approach to analyse stress and strain states of such a test, the behaviour of the specimen has not been fully understood. In this paper, an FE model of a small punch test system has been created and a convergence analysis performed. The FE model has been validated by comparing its displacement-load curve of the punch with that from experiment. The convergence analysis and the validation make the FE model reliable. Based on the FE model, an FE simulation with all non-linearities, i.e. large strain, elasto-plastic behaviour and contact with friction, has been carried out. The stress and strain states and deflections of the specimen have been fully analysed, and the displacement vs force curve of the punch has been obtained, which could provide more information in determining other material properties.

1. INTRODUCTION

The small punch test has now prevailed as an important method to determine material properties, i.e., in the power generation industry where a large volume of specimens for standard tests cannot be obtained from working components without degradation of component integrity and strength. Since there is no available closed form analytical formulae for analysing stress and strain states within the disc and the tools, the stress and strain distributions in the disc and the tools have not been fully investigated so far. In the foreseeable future, such an analytical approach is unlikely to become available. Therefore the finite element method tends to be a very important method in analysing and understanding the physical behaviour of the test and in determining material properties more efficiently. However, there has been very limited work done in applying FEM to analysing the test.

Manahan [1] undertook some pioneering work in finite element analysis of a miniaturised disk bend test (MDBT), in which the experimentally measured load-deflection data was converted into useful engineering information by using ABAQUS.

[1] Advanced Safety Technologies Ltd., Sir William Lyons Road, Coventry, CV4 7EZ, UK

[2] Department of Engineering, The University of Liverpool, Liverpool, L69 3GH, UK (djb@liv.ac.uk)

[3] European Commission JRC, ISIS-TP210, 21020 Ispra (Va), Italy

However, due to the fact that ABAQUS was far from mature at that time, the FE model employed was very coarse and was limited to elastic response only.

Foulds [2] utilised the large strain FEM to calculate local strain energy density as an aid to determine material properties, i.e., fracture toughness. It was noted in their FE analysis that friction effects due to the contact between punch head and test specimen were negligible for friction coefficients between 0 and 0.8.

Cheon [3] studied initial deformation during small punch testing, which provided a more detailed analysis of stress and strain within the disc studied, using ABAQUS. A relationship between the load at the breakaway from initial linearity and the yield stress was predicted by the FE analysis and compared with the experimental results.

Yang [4] analysed the deformation behaviour of a thin disk clamped at the circumference and loaded at the centre by a rigid flat-end cylindrical punch, also using ABAQUS. The contact between the punch and the disk was assumed frictionless. Only the elastic deflection of the thin disk was studied. It was also concluded that the linear plate theory can be applied only when the internal stress is zero and the maximum deflection of the disk is less than one third of the disk thickness.

As can be seen from the previous work being done so far, pertinent to the finite element analysis of the small punch testing, there has been a need to perform a complete FE analysis of the stress and strain states of the test with all non-linearities, i.e. material non-linearity, geometrical non-linearity and boundary non-linearity, so that a more realistic FE simulation can be achieved, which is definitely important to a more confident and effective application of the small punch test.

2. SETTING-UP OF AN FE MODEL

The configuration of a small punch test system is shown in Fig. 1. It is obviously unnecessary to model every detail of the test system in the FE model to be created. With some simplifications, an FE model of the simplified system has been created as shown in Fig. 2. Due to the axisymmetry, only half of the radial segment of the system has been taken into account.

2.1 Model configuration

In the model, the punch diameter is 2.5 mm, the diameter of die guide hole is 4 mm, the outer diameter of die is 8.4 mm and the die corner radius is 0.2 mm. The holder has the same dimensional parameters as the die. From previous simulation results[5], it has been found that simplification of the holder as rigid body would not affect the responses of the disc, which is of main interest in the test. Therefore, the holder was modelled using analytical rigid surface provided in ABAQUS [6]. For the same reason, the thickness of the lower die was determined as 0.75 mm. The elements CAX4R were used for modelling the disc, which are 4-noded bilinear axisymmetrical elements with reduced integration. There are 2339 nodes and 1981 elements in total in the model. It is recommended that it is better, in general, to use first-order elements for those parts of a model which will form a slave surface, i.e. the disc, due to the confusion the contact algorithms in ABAQUS have in calculating consistent nodal loads for a contact pressure [6].

2.2. Material properties

The material properties for the specimen, which was punch cut from mild steel, were determined by standard tensile tests. It was found that the disc material has an approximately elastic/perfectly plastic characteristic with a yield stress $\sigma_y = 652 MPa$, a Young's Modulus $E = 206 GPa$. A Poisson's ratio $v = 0.3$ was assumed. The properties for the die and the punch are the same as those of the disc but without plastic behaviour.

2.3. Boundary conditions

The die was fixed in both directions at the bottom. The holder was just in contact with the disc resting on the die. This was in consistent with the situation in the experiment. Also the friction between the contact interfaces i.e. the interfaces between the punch and the disc, the holder and the disc, and the die and the disc, was taken into account. An assumed friction coefficient of 0.3 was used.

3. FE SIMULATION

The FE simulation of the testing was performed in a multi-step and multi-increment process by ABAQUS/STANDARD [6] V5.7-7 to ensure a smooth and stable convergence. The punch load was applied via a prescribed displacement of the punch. Fig. 3 is FE mesh deformation of the punch test.

3.1 Punch process simulation

In finite element contact simulation, contact conditions are a special class of discontinuous constraint, which allows contact forces to be transmitted from one part of the model to another. This constraint is applied only when the two contacting surfaces come into contact and no constraint is applied when two surfaces separate. The analysis must be able to apply or to remove the contact constraints according to whether two surfaces are in contact or not. Therefore the contact simulation is said to be the most difficult and complicated one in FE analyses [6].

Since it was expected for the relative motion between the contacting surfaces to be very significant, far larger than a typical element dimension, finite-sliding contact formulations were used. The Coulomb friction model was used in the simulation, which characterises the frictional behaviour between the surfaces using a coefficient of friction and describes the interaction of contacting surfaces. Since a large deflection was expected in the test, large strain capacity in ABAQUS was employed.

There are two major sources of difficulty in the contact simulations. The first is rigid body motion of the contact components before contact conditions occur. The second one is sudden changes in contact conditions, leading to severe discontinuity iteration during the simulation. These often result in a failure in contact simulations. Therefore special attention must be paid to ensure a successful contact analysis. To avoid the rigid body motion, it is important to constrain properly all unwanted degrees of freedom during the punch process simulation accordingly without over constraints. This can only be achieved in a multi-step simulation. Multi-iteration steps are absolutely needed to obtain a smooth convergence.

3.2 Convergence analysis

A convergence analysis was performed to ensure that the FE results have converged. This was done by carrying out two FE simulations each with different mesh densities and comparing their results. If the results are identical or the difference between them is very small, it can be said that the results have converged. This is especially important in a sensitivity analysis since the discretisation error could affect the conclusions drawn from such an analysis. The disc mesh in the coarse model consists of 500 elements while the fine model has 720 elements. This provides a clear difference between the mesh densities. Fig. 5 shows a very good agreement in the comparison of the deflection profiles on the upper and lower surfaces of the disc from different mesh densities. Comparisons of Von Mises stresses and equivalent plastic strains on the both sides of the disc have been made and excellent agreements have also been achieved, which have been shown in Fig. 6. and Fig. 7 respectively. The finer mesh was used in this work. For the convergence analysis, the punch was pressed down by 1 mm during the simulations and the yield stress used was 300 MPa.

4. VALIDATION OF THE FE MODEL

Before any further use of the created FE model, an experimental validation of the FE model is also necessary whenever it is possible. Based on feasibility, the criteria for this validation was determined to be the punch displacement-force curve. A physical experiment was conducted and the curve was obtained by the University of Limerick. This curve was then compared with the corresponding curve from the FE simulation, which was shown in Fig. 8. The comparison shows good agreement, especially when the punch displacement is less than 1.4 mm. Beyond this point, fracture of the real disc appeared due to the micro defects and the punch force dropped rapidly while the force in the FE simulation kept increasing further until a punch displacement of 1.5 mm. After that, the force in the simulation began to decrease due to the obvious reduction of thickness of the disc. This results in the obvious deviation of the FE curve from the experimental one. The comparison validates the FE model. During this comparison, the punch was pressed down to 2.0 mm in the FE simulation.

5. STRESS AND STRAIN ANALYSIS

As mentioned previously, stress and strain analysis of the small punch testing cannot be undertaken analytically. A thorough investigation of stress and strain states within the disc has been presented in the following. Fig. 4 shows the contour plot of Von Mises stress for the FE model. This plot shows that the stresses in the disc are much higher than those in the punch and the die. Actually the maximum stress within the punch is only about 40% of the yield stress and the maximum stress in the die is just over 50% of the yield stress so that there is no possibility for permanent deformation to occur within the tools [5]. Therefore the detailed stress and strain analysis have focused on the disc only. It is very difficult to have a detailed view over the stress distributions inside the disc. To view the stress distributions clearly, it is necessary to show a zoomed contour for each stress component respectively.

5.1 Propagation of stresses and strains

To understand how the stresses and strains propagate within the disc during the punch process, a series of Mises contour plots for different punch deflections are shown in Fig. 9a-c, corresponding to the punch displacements of 0.7, 1.4 and 2.0 mm respectively. As can be seen in the figures, with the punch progress downwards, the highest stress area tends to retreat away from the centre, which means the stresses around the centre were released due to the fracture appearance in the transit area from contact to non-contact. Fig. 10a-c provide the images of equivalent plastic strain variations with the punch progress of 0.7, 1.4 and 2.0 mm. It has been shown in these figures that the area where the maximum plastic strains occur also retreat away from the centre with the progress of the punch displacement, which is consistent with what is observed in the above stress analysis.

5.2. Final states of stress and strain in the disc

Figures 11a-d are stress component contours within the disc. It has been shown that the dominant stress component is that in third axis, or hoop direction which results from the forced movement of the disc towards the disc centre. The maximum value exists in the area contacting with die corner and is compressive stress, and the second highest stress appears in an area just opposite to the contact transit area and is tensile stress. The equivalent plastic strain components are also shown in Fig. 12 a-d. Fig. 13 and 14 show the Von Mises and equivalent plastic strain on the lower and upper surfaces of the disc.

5.3. Deflection profiles of the disc

Fig. 15 shows the deflection profiles of the lower and upper surfaces of the disc. It can be seen that due to plastic deformation, the vertical displacement of lower mid point is less than that of the upper mid point.

5.4. Radial displacement

It would be very interesting to know what is the magnitude of radial displacements of the disc part under the clamping between the holder and the die. From the FE simulation, it has been noted that these displacements on the lower, middle and upper surfaces of the disc are very small, as shown in Fig. 16. It has been noted that the radial displacements of the upper surface of the die are at the level of 10^{-6} m. However the displacements of other parts of the disc appear quite large up to 0.4 mm. The maximum displacements on all three surfaces occur at about 0.7-1.5 mm away from the centre. All displacements of the nodes on the unclamped lower surface are positive, that is, away from the centre. The displacements of the nodes on the unclamped middle surfaces (about a length of 5/12 of the radius) are positive and less than one third of nodes on the upper surface has a positive displacement.

6. FURTHER ANALYSIS

6.1 Contact pressure on the disc surface

Fig. 17 plots the contact pressure on the upper surface of the disc, which shows that the pressure between the punch and the disc increases from zero at the disc centre to a peak value at around the middle between the centre and the fracture zone and then goes down to zero at the fracture area. After that it rises again up to the second peak value at the middle between the fracture zone and the transit boundary of the contact and non-contact, and finally drops to zero at the boundary. The contact pressures within the clamping area are relatively small.

6.2 Shear stress

From Fig. 18, it can be seen that though there is no pressure within some area of the disc, referring to Fig. 17, the shear stresses exist almost everywhere. It is interesting to observe that within the contacting area with the punch, the variation trend of the shear stresses is opposite to that of the contact pressure, i.e. when the pressure vary from zero to a peak value, the stresses change from a peak value to a minimum. Compared with other stress components (see Fig. 11a-d), the shear stresses are quite small.

6.3 The holder force

Fig. 19 shows the force curves, in vertical direction, of the punch and the holder with the punch displacement. It is noted that the holder force is larger than that of the punch from the beginning until the punch displacement is over 1.03 mm. Only at two points during the punch progress, i.e. 1.03 and 2.0 mm, the forces at the punch and the holder are equal.

7. DISCUSSION AND CONCLUSIONS

A full non-linear finite element model of the small punch test has been set up and the corresponding simulation has been performed with success. The comparison of the results between the FE simulations and the experiment work shows an excellent agreement. Based on the FE simulation results, a detailed stress and strain analysis has been undertaken, which provides an insight of the stress and strain states within the disc. From the work reported above, some important and useful conclusions may be extracted as follows:

a. HKS/ABAQUS has an ability to model small punch and bulge test with all non-linearities.

b. FE stress and strain analyses have revealed that the stresses within the tools are quite low compared with those within the disc itself and this excludes the possibility of yielding occurring within the tools.

c. Similarly the strains within the tools could be ignored when compared with those of the disc. This may justify simplification of tools as rigid surfaces.

d. With existing friction force between the disc and the die and the holder, induced by just in-touch contact, the radial displacements of the part of the disc under the clamping are very small and can be ignored.

e. Compared with other stress components within the disc, the shear stresses are quite small.

ACKNOWLEDGEMENT

Part of the work reported here was undertaken with the support of the European Union under project 13663-1998-02 F1PCA ISP GB "Characterisation of Punch and Bulge Testing of Small Specimens employing Theoretical, Finite Element and Experimental Methods and a Technical Market Survey". In addition, one of the authors (AZ) is supported by a grant from the Ministry of Education of the Islamic Republic of Libya. This support is gratefully acknowledged.

REFERENCES

(1). Manahan, M.P., Argon, A.S. and Harling, O.K., 1981, the development of a minaturaized disk bend test for the determination of postirradiation mechanical properties, Journal of Nuclear Materials, Vol 103 &104, pp1545-1550.

(2). Foulds, J.R., Woytowitz, P.J., Parnell, T.K. and Jewett, W.J., 1995, Fracture toughness by small punch testing, Journal of Testing and Evaluation, Vol. 23, No. 1, pp3-10.

(3). Cheon, J.S. and Kim, I.S., 1996, Initial deformation during small punch testing, Journal of Testing and Evaluation, Vol. 24, No. 4, pp255-262.

(4). Yang, F., Hackett, E. and Li, J.C.M., 1997, Large deformation of a thin disk by a cylindrical punch, Mechanics of Materials, Vol. 26, pp15-22.

(5). Li, W., Finite element analysis of small punch and bulge testing, The University of Liverpool contribution to the final report of the EU Joint Research Council project: punch and bulge testing, May, 1999.

(6). HKS, 1997, ABAQUS User's Manuals I, II, III and ABAQUS Theory Manual.

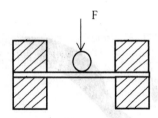

Fig. 1 Schematic of the punch test

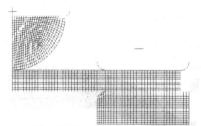

Fig. 2 FE mesh of the punch test

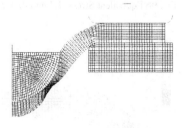

Fig. 3 FE mesh deformation of the punch test

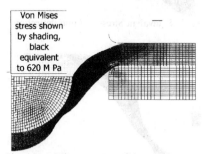

Fig. 4 Von Mises contour of the punch test

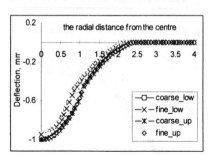

Fig. 5 Comparison of Deflection

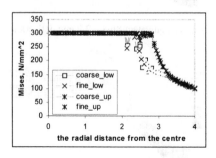

Fig. 6 Comparison of Equivalent Stress

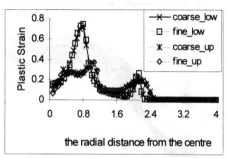

Fig. 7 Comparison of Equivalent Plastic Strain

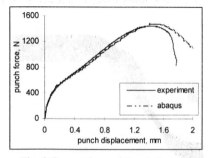

Fig. 8 Comparison of Force Curves

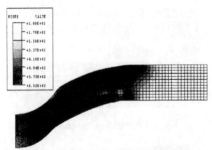

Fig. 9a Equivalent Stress, 0.7 mm deflection

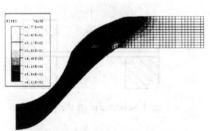

Fig. 9b Equivalent Stress, 1.4 mm deflection

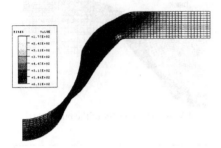

Fig. 9c Equivalent Stress, 2.0 mm deflection

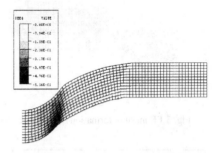

Fig. 10a Equivalent Strain, 0.7 mm deflection

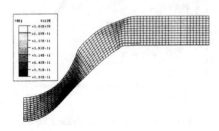

Fig. 10b Equivalent Strain 1.4 mm deflection

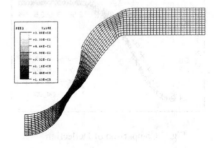

Fig. 10c Equivalent Strain, 2.0 mm deflection

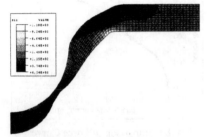

Fig. 11a 'x' Direction Stress

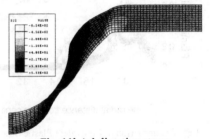

Fig. 11b 'y' direction stress

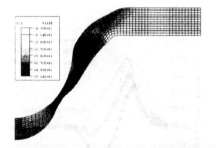

Fig. 11c 'z' Direction stress

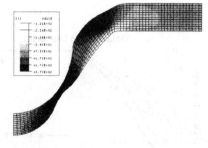

Fig. 11d 'xy' Shear Stress

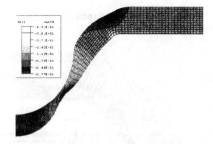

Fig. 12a 'x' Direction Strain

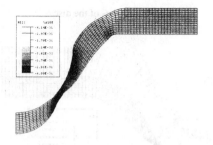

Fig. 12b 'y' Direction Strain

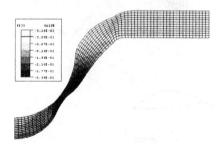

Fig. 12c 'z' Direction Strain

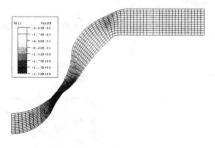

Fig. 12d 'xy' Shear Strain

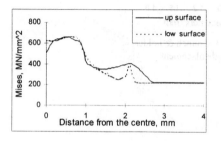

Fig. 13 Effective Equivalent Stresses

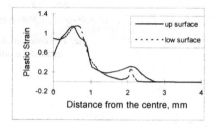

Fig. 14 Equivalent Plastic Strains

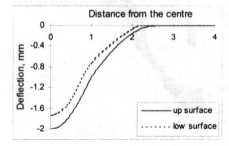

Fig. 15 Deflections of the disc

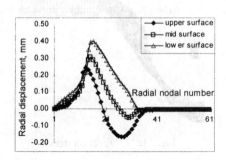

Fig. 16 Radial displacements of the disc

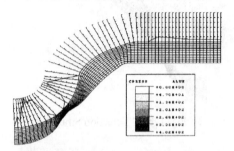

Fig. 17 Contact pressure on the upper surface

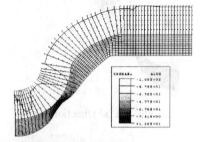

Fig. 18 Shear stress in 'x' direction

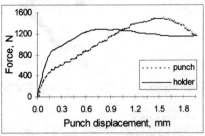

Fig. 19 Force curves of the punch & holder
against the punch displacement

FINITE ELEMENT MODELLING OF STAB IMPACT ON BODY ARMOUR

L Shedden*, D H Nash* and C A Walker*

The progressive development of a numerical model to simulate stab impact and penetration on body armour is outlined. The completion of this model allows a set of parametric studies to be undertaken which ultimately assesses the optimal material property solution required to best resist penetration by a knife. Initial studies undertaken are described. A hemi-spherical shaped projectile utilised in initial studies was progressively sharpened into a square pyramid, which was then elongated to form a blade shape. Comparisons were made for three different pointed projectiles, and graphs of projectile penetration displacement and velocity were obtained. Several numerical problems were identified and are reported. These were ultimately overcome and point towards a more stable solution. Other practical problems that require to be overcome before a realistic knife model can be produced were identified and are described. This paper demonstrates that finite element analysis can be successfully applied to the stabbing process.

INTRODUCTION

One of the most serious threats to the safety of police and prison officers is that of 'knife attacks'. Evidence shows that more than 50% of homicides in Strathclyde Region of Scotland each year are carried out by stabbing [1]. As a preventative measure, police officers in the UK are issued with 'stab-resistant' jackets. However these jackets are often not worn because they are impractical, cumbersome, heavy and inflexible and the wearing of them can be as much of a safety risk as not wearing them. Ideally police officers want to be able to wear such a jacket for a whole shift, without it hindering their ability to undertake their duties. For a jacket to allow a person to move freely, an anti-stab jacket must be light, flexible and not bulky, together with offering maximum protection against knife attacks. Central to this

* Department of Mechanical Engineering, University of Strathclyde, Glasgow.

problem is identifying a material that will be able to stop penetration by the knifepoint, but will also be lightweight.

The purpose of the present study is to create a computer simulation of a knife penetrating through a material or combination of materials. The aim is to improve the design process in the anti-stab jacket industry, streamlining the task of discovering a material, or system of materials that will provide maximum penetration prevention for

a minimum mass and thickness. The cycle of 'design, build and test' is time-consuming and expensive. The purpose of a completed model is to reduce this to selective testing so that the bulk of the analysis would be done using a computer simulation. A completed model reduces the need for time-consuming testing. It may ultimately model a more realistic situation, including stabbing motions such as twisting and follow-through. Computer simulations make it easier to change dimensions of weapons, shapes of scales, individual materials and combinations of materials. The effects of these changes can be seen quickly and the effect on the performance of the jacket assessed. Another benefit of simulation is the ability to examine the stab event as a function of time. It is also possible to see the interaction between individual materials, and materials and weapon. As the knife progressively penetrates, material failure can be pinpointed, analysed and replayed. A computer simulation can potentially produce very accurate results, from measuring the degree of penetration to plotting graphs of changes in stress and strain within the materials. This paper documents the development of a pointed projectile from a round indenter, and then onto a blade-shaped projectile, which is somewhat more like an axe than a knife.

The computer model was created using ANSYS, combined with LS-DYNA 3D, an explicit dynamic solver. LS-DYNA is a powerful tool in ballistics problems. In this case an important feature was its 'eroding contact' capability which is utilised in situations involving impact and penetration. Elements fail when their stress or strain exceeds pre-defined values. Failed elements are then deleted, allowing penetration of the projectile.

The use of the finite element method in this field is a relatively recent development. However there is some limited material available on related topics. The research undertaken by Chen [2] documents the comparison between numerical analysis and experimental results for 152mm diameter 6061-T651 aluminium alloy bars impacted by steel spherical-nose projectiles at impact velocities between 300 and 1000 m/s. This paper was useful for a number of reasons:

- It utilised LS-DYNA's eroding contact capability, which is an important aspect of all penetration problems.

- It indicated that mesh refinement around the axes of symmetry was required to capture the large deformations.

- It demonstrated the importance of friction in the problem, and the effect of neglecting it on the comparison between computer model and experimental results.

All of these points must be considered in the construction of a model to simulate stab impact on body armour.

PRELIMINARY STUDIES

Finite element analysis can be used to accurately model contact between flat plates, because the contact elements are parallel to each other, and the contact normals line up. However the problem becomes more complicated if one of the plates is curved, and an angle exists between the contact elements. This situation is further complicated if the projectile is a pointed objected, with its contact elements at almost 90 degrees to the contact elements on the plate.

With these problems in mind, a relatively simple ballistics model was created to gain confidence in modelling contact. The starting point for this work was the analysis of a round indenter impacting a thin plate. This problem utilised LS-DYNA's eroding contact capability. Comparisons were made between the results obtained from the ANSYS/LS-DYNA model, a 3D ABAQUS model, and drop-tower experiments. Plots of plate and indenter displacement for each computer model were compared. Correlation was good, see Figure 2, and demonstrated the use of eroding contact, as well as validating the modelling technique. The sides of this round indenter were then sharpened to create a square pyramid, and the development of a pointed weapon shape had begun.

SHARP INDENTOR ANALYTICAL MODEL

The square pyramid is shown in Figure 3. The square top has a length of 50mm, and the pyramid has a height of 78mm. The target plate is square, 0.6m long, and has a thickness of 1mm. Since the geometry and loading possess symmetry only a quarter model was created, and appropriate symmetry conditions imposed.

The target plate is assumed to be aluminium, with density of 2700 kg/m^3, Young's modulus of 70GN/m^2, and Poisson's ratio of 0.32. The pyramid indentor is steel, with density of 7800kg/m^3, Young's modulus of 207GN/m^2, and Poisson's ratio of 0.28. However, these properties are used only for mass calculations but the indentor is specified to be rigid, i.e. will remain undeformed upon impact with the plate, due to its high stiffness. This represents the worst case scenario, where all the energy in the indenter is transferred to the plate.

Failure criteria used within the LS/DYNA programme are in the form of 'Power Law 1'. This law requires only yield stress and failure strain be specified, unless there is hardening in the material or strain rate dependency. Elements fail when their stress or strain exceeds these pre-defined values. Failed elements are then deleted, allowing progressive penetration through the plate. This, put simply, is how the eroding contact capability operates.

Both the plate and the pyramid are meshed using solid eight-node brick elements, used for explicit dynamic analyses. The plate is meshed using the fully integrated form of this element, for the purpose of eliminating hourglassing (see Numerical Problems). After meshing, eroding contact is set, and it is specified that the surface of the projectile can erode the surface of the plate. Friction is neglected to simplify the analysis. Lastly, the boundary conditions of the plate are such that it is assumed to be fully fixed around the outer edges.

For the purposes of comparison the projectile has an initial velocity of 5m/s. This value was chosen, as it resulted in a realistic and reasonable degree of penetration, which made it easier to compare models. In addition, gravity is neglected, as it has little effect for this type of problem. It is noted that the solution time for such a problem on a 450MHz PC was obtained in around 8 hours.

ALTERNATIVE INDENTOR FORMS

The square pyramid modelled in the analysis described above, is the first step towards modelling an actual blade shape. To get a step closer to achieving a model of an actual knife this pyramid shape was elongated to create a thinner, longer projectile, more like a knife. The basic dimension of 50mm remained the same, but the ratio of length to width was increased from 1:1 (in the case of the square pyramid) to 2:1, 4:1, and finally to 8:1. Sectioned views of these projectiles at the end of the analysis can be seen in Figure 4 (2:1), Figure 5 (4:1) and Figure 6 (8:1)

NUMERICAL PROBLEMS

There were a number of numerical problems associated with a pointed object penetrating a plate. The first of these is hourglassing. This is an effect that occurs in solid and shell elements in their reduced, one point integration form. Hourglassing means that these reduced integration elements are prone to zero-energy modes, known as hourglassing modes. These modes are oscillatory in nature and tend to have periods that are much shorter than the modes of the overall structure. They result in mathematical states that are physically impossible. They have no stiffness and give the mesh a zig-zag appearance, known as hourglass deformations, see Figure 7. The presence of these hourglass deformations can invalidate the results of an analysis, and should be minimised. Meshing the plate with fully integrated elements solved this problem. However this increase in accuracy was accompanied by the penalty of longer solution run times (up to 4 times as long).

During the analyses, several anomalies resulted. Specifically this meant that although the projectile appeared to have passed through the plate, indicating none of the elements that made up the plate had failed, and therefore had not been deleted. A possible cause of this physical impossibility was that the contact stiffness between the projectile and the plate was too low, due to the angle between the contact surface on the side of the projectile and the contact surface on the flat face of the plate being too large. A stiffness relationship between two bodies must be established for contact to occur. Without sufficient contact stiffness bodies will pass through each other. Changing the penalty factor value may alter contact stiffness. Increasing the penalty factor had no effect, and further more incurred the risk of numerical instabilities. Changing the way in which the failure criteria was specified overcame this problem. Up to this point, 'power law 8' had been used, requiring that a stress-strain curve be input. By using 'power law 1' [5], and entering only a yield stress and failure strain, these anomalies were eliminated.

RESULTS

Comparison between 2:1, 4:1 and 8:1 projectiles were made. The effect of each of the three new projectile shapes on three factors was plotted, over the 0.02 seconds of the analysis. These factors were :

- Projectile displacement

- Projectile velocity

These plots were produced in the ANSYS time history post-processor. During the solution LS-DYNA recorded such items as displacement, velocity and force for every node, at each time step. Only one node requires to be selected on the projectile, since the projectile is defined to be a rigid body and thus all nodes have the same displacement and velocity, therefore it is not important which node is chosen. An item is then selected in this case displacement or velocity, and then a component of that item. The component of interest is the Y-component, of both displacement and velocity as this is the component that which induces the most damaging effect on the body underneath the armour in a real life situation. Although X and Z displacements could conceivably produce slashing effects, the main concern is the depth of the wound inflicted. It is assumed in this case that the knife would have only one component of velocity, normal to the armour surface. Constraining the rigid projectile in the X and Z directions, and allowing movement only in the Y direction reflects this in this case. The plots produced for each of the projectiles were then transferred into a spreadsheet, for the purposes of direct comparison. These graphs are shown in Figure 8 and Figure 9. For the purposes of the graph labelling, **'knife 1'** is the 2:1 projectile, **'knife 2'** is the 4:1 projectile, and **'knife 3'** is the 8:1 projectile.

DISCUSSION

As can be seen from the graph shown in Figure 8, projectile displacement increases as the knife profile lengthens. This can be attributed to a number of factors.

- A slight increase in the mass of the projectile due to its increased length, and hence volume. A heavier object will travel a further distance before coming to rest, due to its increased momentum.

- Increases the length of sharp edge coming into contact with the plate. The longer profile ensures a shallower angle between the cutting edge and the plate. Hence for the same vertical displacement more of the cutting edge comes into contact with the plate.

- An increase in the area of the cutting surface.

These results are as expected, with a projectile with a comparatively longer, thinner profile penetrating further through the plate. In terms of body armour this shape of weapon would inflict a deeper wound on the body underneath. It was also noticed that at some point in all three analyses the projectile stopped travelling downwards, and began to move upwards again.

All projectiles had an initial velocity of 5m/s. In all three analyses this speed decreases, as the projectile contacts the plate, until it is instaneously stationary, before the speed becomes positive, and the projectile begins to move upwards. As the knife profile became longer and thinner the time taken to slow the projectile to rest increased. This is again due to the factors mentioned above.

These graphs are useful in identifying a material, which will provide maximum protection against knife attacks since they form a pattern. Such characteristics could be used to investigate the effectiveness of a range of materials at preventing penetration. In these investigations the future aim, for the projectile displacement graph, would be to move all the three curves upwards, i.e. produce smaller degrees of penetration by the projectile. In the same way, the aim, with respect to the projectile velocity graph, would be to move the curves to the left, i.e. to slow the projectiles to rest in a faster time. Varying the material properties to represent different materials can be done in ANSYS/LS-DYNA, and finding a material to move these curves as described above, to decrease penetration, would result in body armour that could provide maximum resistance against penetration.

These models provide a qualitative approach to the problem of analysing potential materials for body armour. However there are several issues that have to be tackled to produce a more realistic model, one that would compare accurately with experimental stabbing results.

One problem that was apparent from these investigations was that of the projectile penetrating the plate and then travelling upwards again. In reality a knife would remain lodged in the armour, due to the effect of friction, unless it was pulled out.

The reason that the projectile began to travel upwards again was that, in this case, friction had been neglected. To create a more realistic model in the future the effects of friction must be taken into account.

Another factor that must be considered is the material's properties. For simplicity in this case it was assumed that the material deformed elastically, and then in a perfectly plastic manner until the failure strain was reached. This is not realistic, as most materials deform elastically and plastically, often involving a very complex stress-strain curve, including hardening. A quantitative model would require to model this complicated material behaviour, in order to accurately predict deformation and strain. However another problem that exists in this area is that of 'strain rate dependency'. High strain rates can have a significant impact on the failure behaviour of a material [4]. The deformation occurs over such a short period of time that the material has no chance to reach the plastic zone, but fails elastically, at low strain, and high stress. High strain rates are experienced in the problem of a knife impacting body armour, due to the high velocities and large deformations involved, and the issue of strain rate dependency in this situation is one which requires further research.

CONCLUSIONS

This study presents an important step towards accurately modelling stab impact on body armour using finite element methods. It identifies the effect of projectile shape on degree of penetration and velocity of projectile. It provides a qualitative approach to investigating suitable materials for body armour, allowing materials to be compared and their effectiveness at resisting penetration by a knife assessed. This paper has also identified some problems that require investigation before a realistic model of stab impact on body armour could be produced. The main research issue identified is that of the failure behaviour of materials, including the importance of strain rate dependency. Once these areas have been tackled and have been overcome it would be possible to produce a model which could be favourably compared to experimental stabbing results. Such a model could then be used to identify the most effective materials for preventing penetration, for use in 'stab resistant' body armour.

REFERENCES

1   Ankersen, J, Birkbeck, A, Thomson, R and Vanezis, P, 'Computational modelling of penetration of biomaterials by a sharp knife', *Journal of Modern Practice in Stress and Vibrational Analysis* (1997).

2   Chen, E P, 'Numerical simulation of penetration of aluminium targets by spherical-nose steel rods', *Journal of Theoretical and Applied Fracture Mechanics 22* (1995) 159-164.

3   Ankersen, J, Birkbeck, A, Thomson, R and Vanezis, P, 'The effect of knife blade profile on penetration force in flesh simulants', *Journal of Technology, Law and Insurance* 1998 3, 125-128.

4   Pronin, A, 'Dynamic Deformation at High Strain Rates', *'Applications of Laser Generated Stress Pulses for Materials Characterization'*, December 1997

5   ANSYS/LS-DYNA User's Guide for Release 5.5. September 1998.

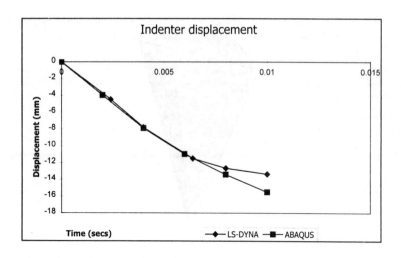

Figure 1 Indenter displacement comparison between ANSYS/LS-DYNA and ABAQUS models

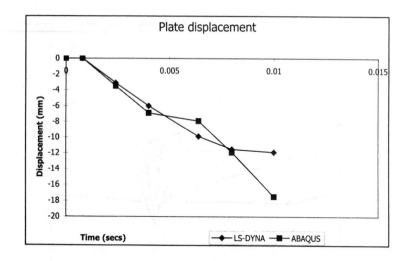

Figure 2 Plate displacement comparison between ANSYS/LS-DYNA and ABAQUS models

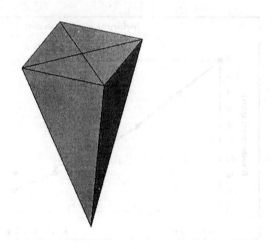

Figure 3 Square pyramid shaped indenter

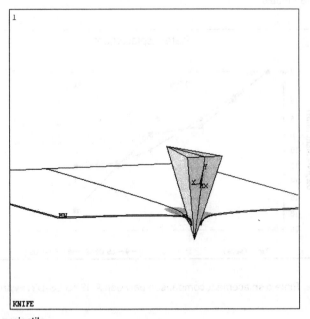

Figure 4 2:1 projectile

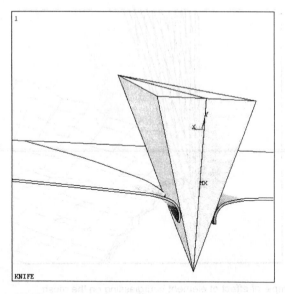

Figure 5 4:1 projectile

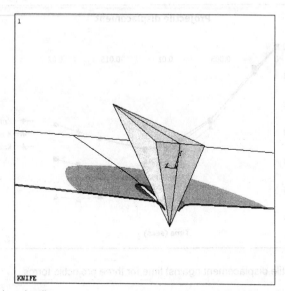

Figure 6 8:1 projectile

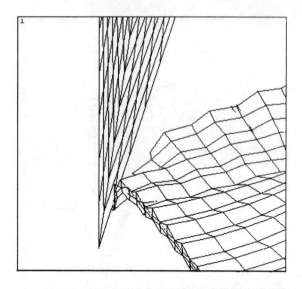

Figure 7 Example of effect of element hourglassing on the mesh

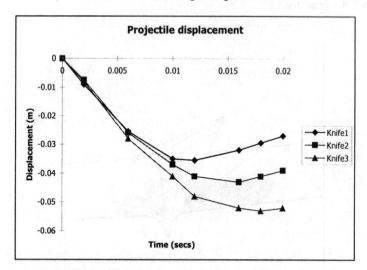

Figure 8 Projectile displacement against time for three projectile forms

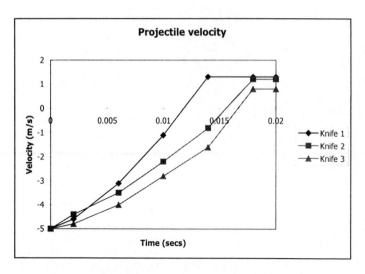

Figure 9 Projectile velocity against time for three projectile forms

PREDICTION OF FRETTING FATIGUE LIFE USING AVERAGED MULTIAXIAL INITIATION PARAMETERS

J.A. Araújo[*] and D. Nowell[*]

This paper examines the use of critical plane fatigue initiation parameters in fretting fatigue. An experiment is presented, where fatigue lives are found to vary with contact size under identical stress conditions. The existence of a critical stressed volume is used to explain these results qualitatively and averaging methodologies are then developed to allow the extension of the critical plane approach to cases of rapidly varying stress fields. It is shown that a critical averaging dimension of the order of the grain size of the material appears to give realistic estimates of fatigue life and predicts the observed size effect.

INTRODUCTION

Fretting fatigue can occur when contacting surfaces in engineering assemblies are subjected to cyclic force or displacement, e.g. as a result of vibration loading. High local stresses at the contact interface may give rise to microcracks. If one or both of the contacting components carry a bulk oscillatory load, the microcracks can propagate, leading to a fretting fatigue failure. Experimental evidence shows that fretting can lead to a dramatic reduction in the fatigue strength of a structural component [1].

As in plain fatigue, the fretting fatigue life of structural components is usually divided into two phases: i) crack initiation and ii) crack propagation. A number of approaches have been employed to analyse each of these phases. Fracture mechanics has been used to analyse fretting cracks in the LEFM regime with some degree of success [2], although the situation is complicated by the presence of multiaxial non-proportional loading, and significant crack closure. These approaches have also been extended into the short crack regime and used to predict a threshold for non-propagating cracks [3]. Fretting cracks nucleate in a region where the stress field is multiaxial and the principal stress magnitudes and directions vary with time. It therefore seems appropriate to seek to apply multiaxial fatigue damage models [4, 5] in order to predict the initiation life. Such models are generally based on

[*] Department of Engineering Science, University of Oxford, Parks Road, Oxford, OX1 3PJ, UK.

combinations of stress and/or strains in the absence of cracks. Szolwinski and Farris [6] have recently shown that, for components with a relatively slowly varying contact stress field, reasonably accurate predictions of fretting initiation life may be obtained using the Smith/Watson/Topper parameter. For more rapidly varying stress fields, however, the use of these parameters appears to give over-conservative predictions of crack life [7]; very high localised peaks of damage parameter are observed. Averaging the stresses or the initiation parameter over a suitable volume or critical depth might give more accurate estimates of initiation life, but there are difficulties involved in choosing an appropriate averaging methodology. The current paper will discuss these issues, using a series of experiments based on the Hertzian geometry which demonstrate a size effect [8].

MULTIAXIAL FATIGUE INITIATION CRITERIA

Multiaxial initiation criteria have generally been divided into a) equivalent stress/strain methods, e.g. [9]; b) critical plane methods, e.g. [10, 11, 12, 13] and c) energy and plastic work methods, e.g. [14, 15]. Although there is no universally accepted method to tackle this problem, it has been reported that better predictions are often achieved using critical plane methodologies [16], and here we will concentrate on applying this approach to the fretting situation, including modifications to account for steep stress gradients.

Critical plane parameters

Critical plane models are based upon a physical interpretation of the fatigue process whereby cracks were observed to initiate and grow on certain preferential material planes. In such an approach, stresses and strains during the loading cycle are determined for various planes at the same spatial position in the component. An empirical combination of these is used to predict the most severely loaded plane or "critical plane", where cracks are expected to nucleate. Besides the location of crack initiation, these empirical parameters also provide the direction of early growth of the crack and a measure of the multiaxial fatigue damage that can be correlated with simple uniaxial fatigue data to estimate initiation life. Moreover, it has been shown that there are at least two distinct modes of crack initiation and early growth. Depending upon strain amplitude, material type, and state of stress, materials generally form either shear cracks or tensile cracks. For cracks that grow in planes of high tensile strain Socie proposed a model, which is basically an extension of the celebrated Smith, Watson and Topper (SWT) parameter [17] to a multiaxial fatigue case. It can be expressed as

$$SWT = \sigma_{max}\left(\frac{\Delta\varepsilon}{2}\right) \tag{1}$$

where $\Delta\varepsilon$ is the difference between the maximum and minimum strain perpendicular to the plane experienced during the cycle and σ_{max} is the maximum value of the stress component perpendicular to the plane at any point in the cycle. Thus, the critical plane is one that experiences the largest value of combination of $\Delta\varepsilon\sigma_{max}$. To find the global maximum SWT parameter (SWT_{MAX}) and corresponding critical location and plane one must calculate the stress and strain fields for the complete loading cycle at each different location (x,y) in the component. At each location, all possible planes must be examined in order to find the critical one. It is now possible to estimate the component life by reference to a fully reversing uniaxial test (e.g. bending). For such a test, the stress-life and strain-life curves can often be modelled satisfactorily using the Coffin-Manson and Basquin 'Laws' as

$$\frac{\Delta\sigma}{2} = \sigma_{max} = \sigma_f \left(2N_f\right)^b \tag{2}$$

and

$$\frac{\Delta\varepsilon}{2} = \frac{\sigma_f}{E}\left(2N_f\right)^b + \varepsilon_f\left(2N_f\right)^c \tag{3}$$

where σ_f' and b are the fatigue strength coefficient and exponent, ε_f' and c are the fatigue ductility coefficient and exponent, E is the Young's Modulus and N_f is the number of cycles to initiate a crack of a given length (e.g. 1mm). These equations may now be used in conjunction with (1) to correlate the SWT fatigue parameter with life giving:

$$\sigma_{max}\frac{\Delta\varepsilon}{2} = \frac{\left(\sigma_f\right)^2}{E}\left(2N_f\right)^{2b} + \sigma_f\varepsilon_f\left(2N_f\right)^{b+c} \tag{4}$$

For situations where the crack grow on planes of high shear strain Fatemi and Socie [18] suggested the following fatigue parameter:

$$FS = \frac{\Delta\gamma}{2}\left(1 + \alpha\frac{\sigma_{max}}{\sigma_y}\right) \tag{5}$$

Where $\Delta\gamma$ is the difference between maximum and minimum values of shear strain experienced during the cycle σ_{max} is the maximum value of the stress normal to the chosen plane, σ_y is the yield strength, and α is a constant which approaches unity at long lives and is reduced at shorter lives. The ratio σ_y/α is often very close to the value of σ_f' [19]. Once again the critical plane is that having the largest value of the parameter and to find the global maximum FS parameter (FS_{MAX}) a procedure similar to that used to find SWT_{MAX} must be used. Again an empirical equation fitted to the results of simple fully reversing tests (this time under pure shear) can be used to correlate the FS fatigue parameter with life, giving

$$\frac{\Delta\gamma}{2}\left(1+\alpha\frac{\sigma_{max}}{\sigma_y}\right) = \frac{(\tau_f')^2}{G}(2N_f)^b + \gamma_f'(2N_f)^c \quad (6)$$

where G is the shear modulus and τ_f', γ_f', b, and c are constants. As the early growth mode depends on a number of variables such as load amplitude and material type, in most practical cases it is not possible to know a priori which fatigue initiation parameter should be used to evaluate life. A possible conservative approach to solve this problem is to calculate both multiaxial fatigue parameters and estimate the life according to each one. The expected life will then be the most conservative of the two estimates.

Cyclic Elastic Stress/Strain Field

As has been discussed above, we expect crack initiation to be controlled by the stress and strain components in the uncracked body. It is therefore necessary to to evaluate the cyclic stress and strain fields developed under the contact in the experimental configuration. To validate the analysis experiments carried out by Hills et al.[8] were used. A Hertzian configuration was employed, as depicted in Fig. 1. Two cylindrical pads were clamped against the specimen by a static normal load, P. An oscillatory fretting load $Q\sin(\omega t)$ was subsequently applied to the pads together with a bulk fatigue load $\sigma_B\sin(\omega t)$ to the specimen. The first step towards a solution is to determine the history of tractions. Due to the static normal force a constant contact area and Hertzian pressure will be developed. The cyclic shear load on the other hand will give rise to history dependent tractions as described firstly by Cattaneo [20] and Mindlin [21]. Once the tractions have been found the cyclic stress field can be obtained at each load step by using Muskhelishvili's potential theory [22]. Since the macroscopic stresses remain elastic, Hooke's law may be used to evaluate the strains.

AVERAGING METHODOLOGIES

In a similar way to cracks at notches, fretting cracks nucleate at points of high local stress where the material is under a complex multiaxial stress state. Moreover the stress concentration is extremely localised, fading away very rapidly as the crack grows. However, as discussed above, multiaxial initiation parameters based on critical plane approaches do not account for the effects of stress gradients. Rather, they suggest that surface stress-strain behaviour at some particular high stressed point is sufficient to quantify fatigue damage. This may well be the case for fretted components with a relatively slowly varying contact stress field [7]. However, for more rapidly varying stress fields, it appears sensible to argue that a high localised maximum is insufficient and that high values of the initiation parameter must be sustained over a characteristic length or volume in order for initiation to take place. The concept of a "critical layer" for the analysis of the elastic shakedown limit at notch roots were introduced by Stieler as early as 1954 [23]. More recently Flavenot and Skalli [24] have defined a critical layer for characterising the microstructural state of materials. They suggested that this critical layer is a constant for a specific material and could be related to microstructural dimensions such as grain boundaries. Miller's short crack work [25], showing that the material fatigue limit is related to the strongest microstructural barrier, seems to corroborate this idea

Here, we propose to develop an averaging methodology which, combined with a multiaxial fatigue initiation criterion, will give a less conservative prediction of fretting fatigue initiation life. In contrast to Flavenot and Skalli [24] we will not initially assume a dimension which is a material constant. Rather, we will search for a dimension or volume, which will best fit the experimental data. In order to do this we propose two averaging methodologies as follows.

Methodology 1: Averaging SWT and FS fatigue parameters over a characteristic depth (d_c) on the critical plane

Averaging the multiaxial SWT and FS fatigue parameters for a given depth along the critical plane direction is perhaps the simplest and most intuitive averaging methodology that may be proposed. We proceed as follows:

i) Find the maximum non-averaged fatigue parameter on the surface, the corresponding crack initiation site and critical plane orientation, θ_C.

ii) Assume a critical depth, d_c, evaluate the fatigue parameters at a number of different positions on the critical plane (up to a depth d_c) and average them.

iii) From the averaged multiaxial fatigue parameters and equations (4), (6) evaluate life. Adjust d_c and repeat (ii) and (iii) to find a good fit to the experimental data

Methodology 2: Averaging stresses over a characteristic element of volume, V_c

An alternative averaging technique can be developed by arguing that high stresses must be sustained over a critical volume, V_c in order for a crack to breach the strongest microstructural barrier. This characteristic volume might be thought of as corresponding to the grain size or other microstructural dimension, but we will proceed by assuming that the volume may not be a material constant. The averaging methodology is similar to that described above, but this time a square area element surrounding the initiation site is used to delineate the volume (the current analysis is 2D plane strain, so although a volume is the appropriate physical parameter to discuss, actual averaging is carried out over an area).

EXPERIMENTAL DATA

To validate the averaging methodologies, experimental data published in [8] will be used, where a contact size effect was reported. Five series of fretting fatigue tests were carried out at different stress levels. Exploiting the Hertzian nature of the experimental configuration, the contact size, a, was varied while keeping the peak contact pressure, p_0, constant for the experiments in each series. This is possible since a is proportional to $\sqrt{(PR)}$, where R is the radius of curvature of the pads, while p_0 is proportional to $\sqrt{(P/R)}$. Thus the magnitude of the stress field was constant for different contact sizes but it varied in extent. Table 1 summarises the characteristic contact parameters for the data series analysed here.

TABLE 1 Contact parameters for the experimental series analysed.

Series No.	p_0 (MPa)	σ_0 (MPa)	Q/P	Friction coefficient
1	157	93	0.45	0.75
3	143	93	0.45	0.75
4	143	77	0.45	0.75
5	120	62	0.45	0.75

The material chosen for both specimens and pads was an Al/4%Cu alloy, HE15-TF. Table 2 contains relevant static and fatigue material properties: ν and E are provided in [8], σ_f', b, ε_f' and c were obtained from [26], and the Paris-Gomez constants from [6]. Note that to use the FS parameter we require fatigue data under pure shear loading. Such data is limited, but it is possible to estimate these constants from tests under pure bending [27]. The microstructure of this alloy revealed highly elongated grains along the specimen; typical grains were 50 to 100 μm in cross-sectional diameter.

TABLE 2 Static and Fatigue properties of Al4%Cu alloy used in [8].

ν	E (GPa)	σ_f' (MPa)	b	ε_f'	c	Paris Constant, C (MPa^{-4}m^{-1})	Paris Exponent, m
0.33	68.9	1015	-0.11	0.21	-0.52	1.74×10^{-10}	4

Cracks in fretting experiments initiate and propagate under the contact and it is difficult to measure initiation life and subsequent crack growth rate. Normally, total life to failure is reported. In order to estimate initiation life (to a given defect size), it is necessary to subtract the number of cycles consumed in crack propagation. This may be estimated using Paris Law data and linear elastic fracture mechanics. Crack loading is often mixed mode, for part of the cycle, but it is usually assumed that the growth rate in the propagation phase is characterised by ΔK_I. This assumption was made in the current analysis and the distributed dislocation technique [27, 28] was used to calculate propagation life from a 1mm defect to failure.

RESULTS

In this section we will compare the results of our analysis with the experimental results. Methodology 1 was applied as follows: the global maximum of each parameter, SWT_{MAX} and FS_{MAX} was found by examining the stress field at spatial intervals $\Delta x/a = \Delta y/a = 0.01$. At each point eight different load steps in the cycle and thirty six candidate critical plane orientations (separated by five degrees) were examined. Once the crack initiation location and critical plane had been found, the fatigue parameters were averaged on the critical plane for to $y \leq d_c$. Note that a fairly large number of points along the critical plane must be examined in order to get an accurate value for the averaged parameter. For most of the cases studied here, a normalised point spacing (Δ/a) of 0.002 was used.

Fig. 2 shows total experimental fretting fatigue life versus contact size for Series 1 data. As can be seen from the results, there is a contact size range below which fretting lives are very long. On the other hand, for larger contacts fatigue life was dramatically reduced. Plotted on the same graph is estimated total life using non-averaged multiaxial fatigue parameters. Eqs. (4) and (6) were used to obtain initiation life, and the Paris Law to obtain propagation life. Notice that while estimated lives agree reasonably well with the experimental data for large contacts, for small contacts predicted lives were over conservative by a factor of 75 or more[1]. In this case, total life is dominated by the initiation stage and the results demonstrate the underestimation of initiation life if the parameters are not averaged. Also worthy of note is that lives predicted by either the SWT or the FS parameter are very similar, although the FS parameter nearly always predicts a slightly shorter initiation life.

If we now apply methodology 1 to average the parameters, the results shown in Fig. 3 emerge. The FS and SWT parameters were averaged according to methodology 1 over three different critical depths (d_c=20, 50 or 80 µm). It is clear that the averaged results give a much better fit to the experimental results than the non-averaged results. For both FS and SWT parameters the value of d_c which best fits the experimental data appears to be between 20 and 80 µm. However, an over-estimation of the critical depth, e.g. d_c=80 µm, generates very non-conservative predictions. Therefore, a critical depth of 20 µm seems to be a sensible lower bound for d_c for all experiments in Series 1, reducing the level of conservatism to a factor of 8 in the worst case.

---

[1] Fretting fatigue tests were stopped when the life reached 10^7 cycles. Thus, predicted lives for these tests are conservative by a factor larger than 75.

Similar results emerged when we applied this technique to the results of the other three series of experiments.

Methodology 2 may now be applied to assess the same experimental data in a similar manner. Application of Methodology 2 to Series 3 data generated the set of results shown in Fig 4. In this case the FS and SWT parameters were averaged over three different critical volumes (l_c x l_c x unit thickness in the z-direction). Once again, for both parameters values of l_c between 20 and 80 μm provide a good fit to the experimental data. Applying Methodology 2 to the other series of experiments produced similar results. Using lc = 20 μm, estimates of life were always conservative by a factor of 8.4 or less.

DISCUSSION AND CONCLUSIONS

The results presented above demonstrate that the use of two different critical plane approaches to estimate fretting fatigue initiation life may not be adequate if calculations are based solely on surface stress/strain behaviour at highly stressed points. It seems clear that the reason for the poor performance of the predictive methodology is the presence of a high stress gradient. The averaging methodologies presented here provide means of extending the critical plane approaches to cope with the existence of stress gradients. Comparison of both methodologies with experimental data suggests that:

1) The averaging procedure provides a qualitative explanation of the contact size effect observed in [8]. Two averaging methodologies were used; in each case there was no single averaging dimension or volume which could capture the sharp transition in life observed in the experiments at the critical contact size. These results suggest that either the averaging parameter is not a true material constant, or that the multiaxial parameters do not accurately characterise the initiation process in cases where high stress gradients are present.

2) Although the averaging dimension may not be a material constant, the adoption of a constant critical depth or critical volume (d_c = 20 μm or l_c = 20 μm) appeared to give satisfactory conservative life estimates for the Hertzian contact geometry across a range of loading conditions. Adoption of a larger averaging dimension (d_c, l_c = 50 μm) provided generally better estimates of life, but some non-conservative predictions resulted

3) Both averaging methodologies appeared to give similar results and led to similar characteristic dimensions. This suggests that the life estimates are more sensitive to the characteristic dimension than to the averaging methodology itself.

4) The averaging dimension appears to be of a similar order of magnitude as the grain size. This might be expected physically as initiation is likely to take place on a slip plane within a single grain.

Due to the limited amount of data used to validate this work it is difficult to draw further firm conclusions. More work is required to validate the approach with different materials and under different contact configurations. It is hoped that such work would provide the basis for choosing an averaging parameter in practical fretting contacts, allowing better predictions of fretting fatigue initiation life to be obtained.

REFERENCES

(1) Lindley, T.C., *Int. J. Fatigue*, Vol. **19**, No. 1, 1997, pp. S39-S49.

(2) Hills, D. A. and Nowell D., *Mechanics of fretting fatigue*, Dordrecht, 1994.

(3) Araújo, J.A., and Nowell,D., Analysis of pad size effects in fretting fatigue using short crack arrest methodologies, *Int. J. Fatigue*, Vol. **21**, No. 9, 1999, pp. 947-956.

(4) Balthazar, J. C., and Araújo, J. A.. Biaxial Fatigue: An Analysis of the Combined Bending/Torsion Loading Case, Proc. 5th Int. Conf. on Biaxial/Multiaxial Fatigue and Fracture, Cracow 97, Poland, 1997, pp 9-23.

(5) You, B. R., and Soon-Bok Lee, S. B., *Int. J. Fatigue*, Vol. **18**, No. 4, 1996, pp. 235-244.

(6) Szolwinski, M.P., and Farris, T.N., *Wear*, Vol. **221**, No. 1, 1998, pp. 24-36.

(7) Fouvry, S., Kapsa, P., and Vincent, L., A multiaxial fatigue analysis of fretting contact taking into account the size effect, in *Fretting fatigue: current technology and practices, ASTM STP 1367*, Ed. D.W. Hoeppner, V. Chanrasekaran, and C.B. Elliot, ASTM, West Conshohocken, PA, 1999.

(8) Hills,D.A., Nowell, D., and O'Connor, J.J., *Wear*, Vol. **125**, 1988, pp.129-156.

(9) Sines, G., and Ohgi, G., ASME, J. Eng. Mats. and Tech., Vol. **103**, 1981, pp. 82-90.

(10) Brown, M.W., and Miller, K.J., *Proc. I.Mech.E*, Vol. **187**, 1973, pp. 745-755.

(11) Socie, D., *J. Eng. Mats. and Tech.*, Vol. **109**, 1987, pp.293-298.

(12) Fatemi, A., and Socie, D. F., *Fatigue Fract. Eng. Mats Struct.*, Vol. **11**, 1988, pp. 149-165.

(13) Socie, D. F., Critical Plane Approaches for Multiaxial Fatigue Damage Assessment, in *Advances in Multiaxial Fatigue ASTM STP 1191*, Ed. D. L. McDowell and R. Ellis, ASTM, Philadelphia, 1993.

(14) Garud, Y. S., A New Approach to the Evaluation of Fatigue under Multiaxial Loading, *Proc. Symposium on Methods for Predicting Material Life in Fatigue*, ASME, New York, 1979.

(15) Ellyin, F., and Kujawski, D., A Multiaxial Fatigue Criterion Including Mean Stress Effect, *Advances in Multiaxial Fatigue ASTM STP 1191*, Ed. D. L. McDowell and R. Ellis, ASTM, Philadelphia, 1993.

(16) Szolwinski, M. P., and Farris, T. N., *Wear*, Vol.**198**, 1996, pp.93-107.

(17) Smith, K.N., Watson, P., and Topper, T.H., *J. Mater.*, Vol. **5**, No. 4, 1970, pp. 767-778.

(18) Fatemi, A., and Socie, D.F., *Fatigue Fract. Eng. Mats Structs*, Vol. 11, 1988, pp. 149-165.

(19) Neu, R. W., Pape, J. A., and Swalla-Michaud, D. R., Methodologies for Linking Nucleation and Propagation Approaches for Predicting Life under Fretting Fatigue, in *Fretting Fatigue: Current Technology and Practices, ASTM STP 1367*, Ed. D.W. Hoeppner, V. Chandrasekaran, and C.B. Elliots, ASTM, West Conshohocken, PA, 1999.

(20) Cattaneo, C., *Rendiconti dell'Academia nazionale dei Lincei*, Vol. 27, Ser. 6, 1938, pp 342, 434, 474.

(21) Mindlin, R. D., *J. App. Mech.*, Vol. 16, pp.259-268.

(22) Muskhelishvili, N.I., Some Basic Problems of Mathematical Theory of Elasticity, Noordhoff, Gröningen, 1953.

(23) Stieler, M., Untersuchungen über die Daverchwing festigkeit metallisher Bauteile ein Raumtemperatur, Thèse de Dr Ingr., Technische Hochschule Stuttgart, 1954.

(24) Flavenot, J. F., and Skalli, N., A Critical Depth Criterion for the Evaluation of Long-Life Fatigue Strength under Multiaxial Loading and a Stress Gradient, *Biaxial and Multiaxial Fatigue, EGF 3*, Ed. M.W. Brown and K.J. Miller, Mechanical Engineering Publications, London, 1989.

(25) Miller, K. J., *Fatigue Fract. Eng. Mats Structs*, Vol. 16, No 9, 1993, pp. 931-939.

(26) Hertzberg, R. W., Deformation and Fracture Mechanics of Engineering Materials, John Wiley & Sons, 1983.

(27) Dowling, N. E., Mechanical Behavior of Materials – Engineering Methods for Deformation, Fracture and Fatigue, Prentice-Hall, 1993.

(28) Nowell, D., and Hills, D.A., *J. Strain Analysis*, Vol. 22, 1987, pp. 177-185.

(29) Hills, D.A., Kelly, P.A., Dai, D.N., and Korsunsky, A.M., *Solution of crack problems: The distributed dislocation technique*, Kluwer, Dordrecht, 1996.

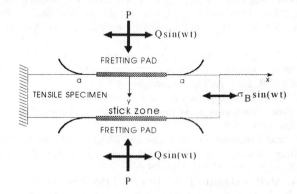

FIGURE 1 Schematic diagram of the experimental configuration used in [8].

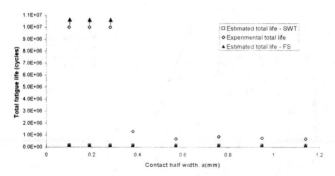

FIGURE 2 Total fretting fatigue life versus contact size for Series 1 data

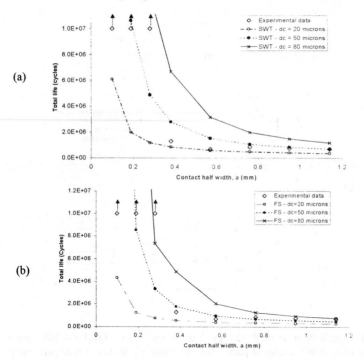

FIGURE 3 Application of methodology 1 to Series 1 data. (a) Total life versus contact size using SWT averaged parameter. (b) Total life versus contact size using FS averaged parameter.

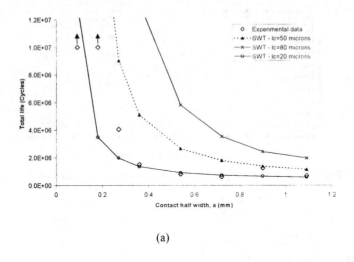

(a)

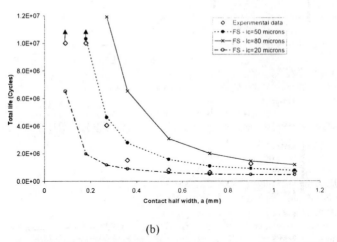

(b)

FIGURE 4 Application of methodology 2 to Series 3 data. (a) Total life versus contact size using SWT averaged parameter. (b) Total life versus contact size using FS averaged parameter.

ELASTOPLASTIC ANALYSIS OF PUNCH CONTACT USING BIE

H. Gun[*]

In this paper the elastoplastic BIE formulation in the framework of small displacements and small strains is briefly reviewed and the elastoplastic stress analysis of a frictional punch problem is presented with emphasis on a robust implementation of the BIE method in elastoplastic frictional contact applications.

INTRODUCTION

The boundary integral equation (BIE) method is well established as an accurate numerical tool particularly well suited for linear elastic problems. Due to its high resolution of stresses on the surface, the BIE approach has been shown to be well suited to problems involving stress concentration, fracture mechanics and contact analysis. However, its extension to non-linear problems including material and geometric non-linearity is not widespread and is under –developed when compared to the Finite Element (FE) method. In many non-linear BIE formulations the interior of the solution domain has to be discretized, thus losing the main BIE advantage of boundary –only modelling. Another difficulty encountered in the non-linear BIE formulations is the accurate evaluation of strongly singular integral functions.

Although the elastoplastic boundary element formulation has been covered in a number of publications, the details of the analytical and numerical details were not available. Furthermore, a degree of ambiguity was present in some implementations, which may explain the reason why the BIE method is lagging behind the FE method in nonlinear applications. Because of the nature of boundary integral identities, the elastoplastic BIE needs special attention in incremental-iterative processes. In the literature it can be observed that the most of the presented algorithms tend to cause a stiff response.

In this paper the elastoplastic BIE formulation is briefly reviewed and the elastoplastic stress analysis of the indentation problem is presented with particular emphasis on how the BIE method handles the elastoplastic frictional contact problems.

GOVERNING EQUATIONS

[*]The University of Afyon Kocatepe, Usak Engineering Faculty, Usak , Turkey

By considering a two-dimensional isotropic homogeneous body, which has a boundary S and a domain A during time-independent plastic deformation, the Navier rate equation for plane strain and plane stress can be written as follows:

$$\frac{\partial^2 \dot{u}_i}{\partial x_j \partial x_j} + \frac{1}{(1-2\nu)} \frac{\partial^2 \dot{u}_j}{\partial x_i \partial x_j} - \left(k_1 \frac{\partial \dot{\varepsilon}_{ij}^p}{\partial x_i} + 2 \frac{\partial \dot{\varepsilon}_{ij}^p}{\partial x_j} \right) = \frac{-\dot{f}_i}{\mu} \tag{1}$$

in which $\dot{u}_i$ is the displacement rate, $\dot{f}_i$ is the body-force rate, $\dot{\varepsilon}_{ij}^p$ is the plastic strain rate and the parameter k_1 is either 0 (for plane strain) or $2\nu/(1-2\nu)$ (for plane stress).

For a material obeying the von Mises yield criterion the plastic stain rates are given by the following incremental elastoplastic flow rules:

$$\dot{\varepsilon}_{ij}^p = \frac{9}{4} \left(\frac{\dot{S}_{kl} \dot{\sigma}_{kl}}{H} \right) \frac{\dot{S}_{ij}}{(\dot{\sigma}_{eq})^2} \tag{2}$$

$$\dot{\varepsilon}_{ij}^p = \frac{3}{2} \left(\frac{\dot{S}_{kl} \dot{\varepsilon}_{kl}}{1 + H/3\mu} \right) \frac{\dot{S}_{ij}}{(\dot{\sigma}_{eq})^2} \tag{3}$$

in which $\dot{S}_{ij}$ and $\dot{\sigma}_{eq}$ denote the current deviatoric stress tensor and the equivalent stress respectively, $\dot{\varepsilon}_{ij}$ is the total strain rate and H represents the plastic modulus.

Axelsson and Samuelson [1] proposed that the plastic strain rate is decomposed into its isotropic and kinematic parts as follows:

$$d\varepsilon_{ij}^{p(i)} = M d\varepsilon_{ij}^p \tag{4}$$

$$d\varepsilon_{ij}^{p(k)} = (1-M) d\varepsilon_{ij}^p \tag{5}$$

in which M is defined as the mixed hardening parameter which is equal to -1 for isotropic softening, 0 for kinematic hardening and 1 for isotropic hardening .

The slope of the stress-plastic strain curve in a uniaxial tensile test, H, is given as follows:

$$H = \frac{d\sigma_{eq}}{d\varepsilon_{eq}^{p(i)}} \tag{6}$$

The equivalent plastic strain rate, $\dot{\varepsilon}_{eq}^p$ is given as follows:

$$\dot{\varepsilon}_{eq}^p = \left(\frac{2}{3} \dot{\varepsilon}_{ij}^p \dot{\varepsilon}_{ij}^p \right)^{1/2} \tag{7}$$

and the equivalent plastic strain, ε_{eq}^p, is given by

$$\varepsilon_{eq}^p = \int \dot{\varepsilon}_{eq}^p dt \tag{8}$$

ANALYTICAL FORMULATION

By considering the plastic strain rates as initial strain rates then modifying Betti's reciprocal theorem to include plasticty, the pseudo-boundary integral equation for initial strain approach can be written as follows (see, for example, Lee and Fenner [2]):

$$C_{ij}(P)\dot{u}_i(P) + \int T_{ij}(P,Q)\dot{u}_j(Q)dS(Q) = \int U_{ij}(P,Q)\dot{t}_j(Q)dS(Q)$$

$$+ \int U_{ij}(P,Q)\dot{f}_j(q)dA(q) + \int W_{kij}(P,q)\dot{\varepsilon}_{ij}^p(q)dA(q) \qquad (9)$$

In this expression U_{ij} and T_{ij} are fundamental displacements and tractions at x in the jth direction at the field point Q or q due to a unit load at load point P acting in i^{th} direction. W_{kij} represents the third-order tensor for the stress at the field point due to a unit load at load point P. The tensors, U_{ij}, T_{ij}, W_{kij}, are derived from the fundamental solution to Kelvin's problems (see, for example, Lee and Fenner [2]). The free-term tensor, C_{ij}, is defined as follows:

$$C_{ij}(P) = \delta_{ij} + \lim_{\varepsilon \to 0} \int_{\varepsilon(P)} T_{ij}(P,Q) \; dS(Q) \qquad (10)$$

In order to obtain the correct expression of the plastic deformation rate in the solution domain, differentiation of the boundary integral identities can be employed. At internal points the total plastic rate can then be given as follows:

$$\dot{\varepsilon}_{ij}(P) + \int_S S_{kij}^\varepsilon(P,Q)\dot{u}_k(Q)dS(Q) = \int_S D_{kij}^\varepsilon(P,Q)\dot{t}_k dS(Q)$$

$$+ \int_A D_{kij}^\varepsilon(P,q)\dot{f}_k(q)dA(q)$$

$$+ \int_A W_{ijkh}^\varepsilon(P,q)\dot{\varepsilon}_{kh}^p dA(q) + \int_A \overline{W}_{ijkh}^\varepsilon(P,q)\dot{\varepsilon}_{kh}^p dA(q) + F_{ij}^\varepsilon(\dot{\varepsilon}_{kh}^p(P)) \qquad (11)$$

in which D_{kij}^ε, S_{kij}^ε, W_{ijkh}^ε, and $\overline{W}_{ijkh}^\varepsilon$ are the derivatives of the aforementioned fundamental solutions. $F_{ij}^\varepsilon(\dot{\varepsilon}_{kh}^p(P))$ is an integral-free term that depends on the plastic deformation at the load point.

By using both equation (11) and the stress-strain relationship, a similar expression for the stress rate at domain points can be obtained (see, for example, Lee and Fenner [2]).

NUMERICAL IMPLEMENTATION

It is obvious from the elasto-plastic BIE formulation discussed previously that both boundary elements and domain cells (internal cells) are necessary in order to perform the integrals arising in the BIE formulation. In a manner similar to the elastostatic BIE analysis, the boundary is represented as a collection of boundary elements. The zones, where the plastic deformation is expected in the solution domain are discretised into domain cells in order to perform domain integrals.

The elastoplastic BIE in the initial strain approach (without considering body forces), in discretised form, can be written as follows:

$$C_{ij} \dot{u}_i(P) + \sum_{m=1c=1}^{M} \sum_{c=1}^{3} \dot{u}_j(Q) \int_{-1}^{+1} T_{ij}(P,Q)N_c(\xi)J(\xi)d\xi$$

$$= \sum_{m=1c=1}^{M} \sum_{c=1}^{3} \dot{t}_j(Q) \int_{-1}^{+1} U_{ij}(P,Q)N_c(\xi)J(\xi)d\xi$$

$$\sum_{m=1c=1}^{D} \sum_{c=1}^{8} \dot{\varepsilon}_{ij}^P(q) \int_{-1}^{+1}\int_{-1}^{+1} W_{ijk}(P,q)N_c(\xi_1,\xi_2)J(\xi_1,\xi_2)d\xi_1 d\xi_2 \qquad (12)$$

where P denotes the node where the integration is performed, Q indicates the cth node of the mth boundary element and q indicates the cth node of the mth domain cell. $N_c(\xi)$ is the quadratic shape function and $J(\xi)$ is the Jacobian of transformation. The details of an efficient integration process for the discretized BIE are presented by Gun and Becker [3]. It should be noted that the integration process is performed separately for each domain in contact. For each contacting domain, the linear algebraic equations obtained from the discretized BIE can be formed as follows:

$$[A][\dot{u}] = [B][\dot{t}] + [W][\dot{\varepsilon}^p] \qquad (13)$$

in which the matrices $[A]$, $[B]$ and $[W]$ contain the integrals of the displacement, traction and domain kernel integrals, respectively. For two-dimensional problems, if the total number of boundary nodes is N and the total number of the domain cell points is H, then the solution matrices $[A]$ and $[B]$ will be square matrices of size $2N \times 2N$, whereas the matrix $[W]$ will be a rectangular matrix of size $2N \times 2H$. All matrices are fully populated.

CONTACT ITERATIONS

It is obvious from the nature of the contact problems that the proper numerical algorithms for contact problems require an iterative and / or incremental procedure.

One of the iterative procedures used in the presented algorithm is an efficient automatic iterative scheme in order to perform the contact iterations without load increments. This iterative processes checks the possibilities which are overlap, tensile stress and frictional slip that may arise in determining the proper contact conditions. Since a contact area is based on compressive forces, contacting nodes with normal tensile stresses, which suggest that the contact area is too large for the given load, must be released from the contact in the next iteration. Overlapping nodes indicate that the contact area is too small for the given load. Therefore the associated elements must be included in the contact area for the next iteration in order to prevent any inter-penetration of the bodies in contact. Finally, in the presence of Coulomb friction slip, which occurs when the absolute value of the ratio of the tangential to the normal traction exceeds the coefficient of friction, μ, the related nodes have to be allowed to slip in the next iteration. It should be worth mentioning that all node pairs are assumed to be sticking for the first iteration. The details of such iterative scheme can be found in the textbook by Becker [4].

COUPLING THE SYSTEM OF EQUATIONS

In order to form the overall system of equations for two bodies in contact, the linear algebraic equations obtained from the discretized BIE for each contacting domain can be formed as follows:

$$
\begin{bmatrix} [A]^{(a)} & 0 \\ 0 & [A]^{(b)} \end{bmatrix} \begin{bmatrix} [\dot{u}]^{(a)} \\ [\dot{u}]^{(b)} \end{bmatrix} = \begin{bmatrix} [B]^{(a)} & 0 \\ 0 & [B]^{(b)} \end{bmatrix} \begin{bmatrix} [\dot{t}]^{(a)} \\ [\dot{t}]^{(b)} \end{bmatrix} + \begin{bmatrix} [W]^{(a)} & 0 \\ 0 & [W]^{(b)} \end{bmatrix} \begin{bmatrix} [\dot{\varepsilon}^p]^{(a)} \\ [\dot{\varepsilon}^p]^{(b)} \end{bmatrix} \quad (14)
$$

In order to arrive at the solution matrix, both prescribed displacement and prescribed traction are imposed on the system of equations obtained from the discretized BIE for each solution domain and the resulting matrices are coupled together according to the contact conditions, thus the following final form of the system of equation can be obtained.

$$
[A^*] [\dot{x}] = [C^*] \quad (15)
$$

in which the matrix $[A^*]$ is the final coefficient matrix of the overall system of equations, the vector $[\dot{x}]$ includes the unknown traction and displacement rates and $[C^*]$ is the known vector. The details can be found in the work of Gun[5].

Because of the nature of boundary integral identities and the nature of the contact problems, the equations have to be solved in an iterative manner. Therefore, two different iterative procedures are incorporated in order to find the proper contact area and the plastic deformations. Gaussian elimination processes can be employed in order to solve the resulting set of simultaneous equations. It is worth mentioning that the solution matrices should have roughly the same order of the magnitude. To do this, a reasonable scaling factor can be used. The stresses at the boundaries are obtained from the local displacement gradients and traction rates.

It should be mentioned that the elastoplastic formulation adopted in the present BIE formulation is similar to that presented by Karami [6], but an efficient automatic iterative scheme without load incrementation is employed in the present algorithm in order to handle the contact iterations.

PUNCH PROBLEM

This BIE application represents the plane strain analysis of the frictional contact of a punch of height H_p and half-width W_p indenting the foundation of height H_f and half-width W_f. The subscripts p and f refer to the punch and foundation respectively. Boundary and loading conditions are given in Figure 1. The relevant data for dimensions employed in this analysis are $H_p/W_p=2$, $W_f/W_p =4$, $H_f / W_p =4$. This problem was investigated by Zhong and Wu [7] and Bujang [8], who used a commercial finite element package, ABAQUS, in his work. In order to be able to compare the BIE results with Zhang and Wu's analysis and the FE results presented by Bujang [8], the same material properties and loading conditions were employed in the BIE analysis. It should be noted that the overall dimensions are different, but still in portion with the model analysed by Zhong and Wu [7]. In their analysis, the yield stress of the foundation is 100 times greater then that of the punch (σ_p =1.96 10^6). However, for the FE analysis Bujang [8] swapped the values of σ_y in order to make σ_{yp} greater than σ_{yf} which is more in line with engineering applications. Poisson's ratio, v, and Young's modulus E are assumed to be both at 0.3 and 206 10^9 Pa respectively. The applied uniform loads are within the range of 2.5 and 3 MPa with two different values of coefficient of friction, $\mu = 0$ and $\mu = 0.2$.

The mesh design for the present BIE analysis has 83 line elements and 144 domain cells, as shown in Figure 2. It is clear that two major differences between element modeling strategies of the BIE and finite element method appear. The first difference is that the BIE mesh for interior elements is designed to cover only the regions where yielding is expected to occur. This makes the BIE method more attractive for problems displaying limited plastic deformation. Secondly the domain and boundary meshes in BIE method are independent each other. This allows more flexibility in BIE mesh design.

The foundation starts to plasticise at the load of 2.4 MPa. Therefore the results are plotted in terms of load ratios, r, which is the ratio of the applied load to 2.4 MPa. Figures 3 and 4 show the normal contact pressure versus the normalized contact interface for r=1.33 and r=1.04 respectively for frictionless contact (μ=0). The elastic-plastic curves by Zhong and Wu [7] for r=1.04 and r=1.33 indicate a smooth increase of pressure towards the end of the contact interface. While the FE results did not give completely this trend, the present BIE results are in good agreement with Zhong and Wu's analysis.

The main feature of the present algorithm is that it allows the user to attempt to reduce load increments to a minimum and to find average values for strain and stress rates that are reasonably representative of the particular load-step. This is the fundamental key for a robust BIE algorithm. In the frictionless case, 7 and 3 load increments were employed for the load ratios, r=1.33 and r=1.04 respectively, whereas in the frictional case ($\mu = 0.2$) 5 and 3 load increments were employed for r=1.125 and r=1.046 respectively.

Figures 5 and 6 show the rate of the increase in tangential friction stresses at the load rations, r=1.125 and r=1.046 respectively when μ=0.2. The BIE results give a similar relationship to that suggested by Zhong and Wu [7], but it is clear from the work of Bejung [8] that the FE solutions were not able to give results including part of the contact region sliding, while the rest is sticking. The dashed lines in Figure 5 and Figure 6 represent the BIE elastic solutions.

CONCLUSION

In this paper the elasto-plastic BIE formulation is briefly reviewed and the elastoplastic stress analysis of a frictional punch contact problem is presented in order to reveal how well the BIE method handles the elasto-plastic frictional contact problems.

REFERENCES

(1)   Axelsson, K., and Samuelsson, A., *Int. J. Numer. Math. Engng.*, Vol. 14, 1979, pp. 211-225.

(2)   Lee, K.H., and Fenner, R.T., *J. Strain Analysis*, Vol. 21, 1986, pp. 159-175.

(3)   Gun, H. and Becker, A.A., A Reviev of Boundary Element Quadratic Formulation in Elastopaltic Stress Analysis Problems, *Proceedings of 4th International Conference on Computational Structures Technology*, Edited by B.H.V. Topping, Civil-Comp Press, Edinburg, 1998.

(4)   Becker, A.A., *The Boundary Element Method in Engineering - a Complete Course*, McGraw-Hill, London, England, 1992.

(5)   Gun, H., An Efficient Implementation of the Boundary Integral Equation Method in Elastoplastic Stress Analysis of Frictional Contact Problems, *Proceedings of 21st Conference on Boundary Element Methods,* Edited by C.A. Brebbia and H.Power, WIT Press, Southampton, England, 1999.

(6)   Karami, G., *Int. Numer. Methods in Engng.*, Vol. 36, 1993, pp. 221-235.

(7)   Zhong, W.X. and Wu, C.W., *Elastic-plastic Contacts using Parametric Quadratic Programing Computational Methods in Contact Mechanics*, Computational Mechanics Publications, Southampton, England, 1993.

(8)   Bujang, H.,*Contact Analysis with Plasticity using Finite Elements*, Bsc., The university of Nottingham, Nottingham,1995.

(9)   ABAQUS version 5.2, HKS inc., Rhode Island, 1994.

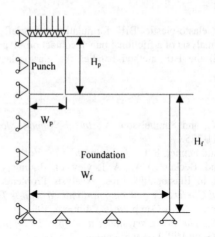

FIGURE 1 The punch problem.

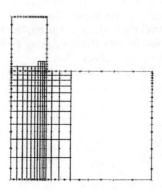

FIGURE 2   BIE mesh design for the punch problem.

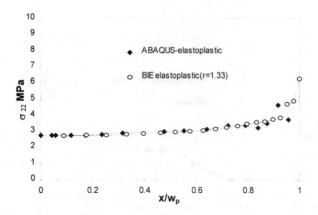

FIGURE 3   Normal contact pressure distribution when $\mu = 0.0$ (r=1.33)

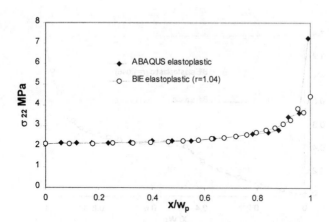

FIGURE 4   Normal contact pressure distribution when $\mu = 0.0$ (r=1.04)

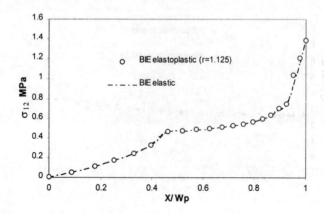

FIGURE 5   Shear stress distribution when $\mu = 0.2$ (r=1.125)

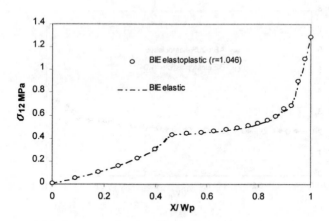

FIGURE 6   Shear stress distribution when $\mu = 0.2$ (r=1.046)

5. DAMAGE AND FRACTURE ANALYSIS

8. DAMAGE AND FRACTURE ANALYSIS

AN FRF-BASED DAMAGE IDENTIFICATION TECHNIQUE AND ITS APPLICATION TO A SPACE ANTENNA

C. Zang * and M. Imregun *

This paper discusses a structural damage detection methodology based on feature extraction from measured vibration data using artificial neural networks. The size of measured FRF data was reduced by applying a principal component analysis (PCA) compression technique. The compressed FRFs, represented by their projection onto the most significant principal components, were used as neural network input variables, an approach that has very significant computational advantages over using raw FRF data. The output is a prediction for the actual state of the specimen, i.e. healthy or damaged. A further advantage of this particular approach was found to be its ability to deal with relatively high measurement noise. The methodology was applied to detect three different states of a space antenna: healthy, slight mass damage and slight stiffness damage. The results showed that it was possible to distinguish between these states with good accuracy and repeatability.

1. INTRODUCTION

Recent advances in data acquisition and numerical modelling techniques have resulted in the development of a large number of damage detection and health monitoring techniques. Such work is particularly important for high-safety and high-cost structures in order to prevent the catastrophic failures and to prolong their in-service lifetime. Doebling et al. (1996, 1998) and Friswell and Penny (1997) gave detailed surveys of structural damage detection methods. Generally speaking, current vibration-based approaches use time domain data, frequency domain data or extracted modal parameters. In practical cases, the successful

* Mechanical Engineering Department, Imperial College of Science, Technology & Medicine, Exhibition Road, London SW7 2BX

implementation of any of them is fraught with major difficulties. Time signals are often polluted with noise. FRF methods dealing with FRF data require an accurate baseline FE model. In spite of their popularity, modal parameters are difficult to apply to large industrial structures. The modal analysis is not always straightforward, especially for damped structures with high modal density. Furthermore, the modal parameters are not necessarily sensitive to the effects of the damage and analysis errors can easily be larger than differences in structural behaviour with and without the damage.

Recent years, artificial neural network techniques have been applied to structural damage detection (Doebling et al 1996, Zeng 1998). Rather than using a validated reference model, the FRFs from healthy and damaged specimens can be used directly via an artificial neural network (ANN) approach (Wu et al 1992, Chaudhry et al 1994). However, such an undertaking presents a major practical difficulty. In order to be able to use all available FRF data, one must build very large ANNs, the training and convergence of which is not possible with routinely-available computational power (Bishop 1995). Researchers who have utilised ANNs either used modal data (Levin and Lieven 1998), or they selected key spectral points from available FRF data (Attala and Inman 1998). Marwala & Hunt (1999) used a combination of modal data and spectral reduction. In all cases, some of the frequency response information is lost, either by modal analysis, or the omission of FRF data points.

The approach here is to reduce the FRF data using a novel data reduction technique. The basic idea is to compute the so-called principal components (PCs) of a measured FRF matrix. The PC-compressed FRFs are represented by their projections onto the most significant principal components and have the additional benefit of containing less measurement noise. Such a route provides a very significant data reduction, thus allowing the use of FRF data with ANNs. The methodology will be demonstrated in the case of a space antenna undergoing a small amount of damage caused by missing screws and/or mass.

2. METHODOLOGY

2.1 Feature Extraction by Principal Component Analysis

Principal component analysis (PCA) is a well-known multivariate analysis method for achieving a dimensionality reduction (Jolliffe 1986 and Bishop 1995). Using an orthogonal projection, the original set of variables in an N-dimensional space is transformed into a new set of uncorrelated variables, the so-called principal components, in a P-dimensional space such that P<N.

Let $[H] = [\{h\}_1, \{h\}_2, \cdots, \{h\}_m]$ denote a measured FRF matrix, where m is the number of measured FRFs. If each FRF $\{h\}_i$ contains n spectral lines, the mean value of the i-th FRF measurement can be expressed as:

$$\bar{h}_i = \frac{1}{n} \sum_{j=1}^{n} \{h_j\}_i \tag{1}$$

One can now define a response perturbation matrix by subtracting the mean value from each actual FRF value:

$$[\tilde{H}] = [\{h\}_1 - \{\bar{h}\}_1, \{h\}_2 - \{\bar{h}\}_2, \cdots, \{h\}_m - \{\bar{h}\}_m] \tag{2}$$

Using (2), a covariance matrix can be defined as:

$$[C] = [\tilde{H}][\tilde{H}]^T \tag{3}$$

By definition, the principal components are the eigenvalues and associated eigenvectors of the correlation matrix:

$$[C]\{\Psi_i\} = \lambda_i \{\Psi_i\} \tag{4}$$

where i is the principal component index.

The first principal component, i. e. the highest eigenvalue and its associated eigenvector, represents the direction and amount of maximum variability in the original data. The next principal component, which is orthogonal to the first component, represents the next most significant contribution from the original data, and so on. The projection of the response perturbation matrix onto the principal components is given by:

$$[A] = [\tilde{H}]^T [\Psi] \tag{5}$$

The projection matrix [A] and the eigenvector matrix [Ψ] can be partitioned into two sub-matrices with P principal components and $(N-P)$ principal components. Setting those sub-matrices representing principal components (N-P), one obtains a reduced response variation matrix:

$$[\tilde{H}_R] = [A][\Psi]^T = [[A]_{MXP} \vdots [0]_{MX(N-P)}][[\Psi]_{NXP} \vdots [0]_{NX(N-P)}]^T \approx [A]_{MXP}[\Psi]_{PXN}^T \tag{6}$$

The reduced FRF matrix can now be obtained by simply adding the mean value of each measurement column, given by (1), to (6).

2.2 Artificial Neural Networks

ANNs provide a general, non-linear parametric mapping between a set of inputs and a set of outputs. Once trained on available sample data, they can recognise patterns and hence they are ideally suited to signature analysis. Although many types of ANNs are used in practice, a back-propagation (BP) type network, shown in FIGURE 1, will be used here (Bishop 1995). The number of nodes for the input and output layers is determined by the nature of the problem to be solved. The number of nodes in the hidden layers is selected according to various stability and convergence criteria.

An ANN analysis consists of two stages, namely training and testing. During the training stage, an input-to-output mapping is determined iteratively using the available sample data. The actual output error, propagated from the current input set, is compared with the target output and the required compensation is transmitted backwards to adjust the node weights so that the error can be reduced at the next iteration. The learning stage is terminated once a pre-set error threshold is reached and the node weights are frozen at this point. During the testing stage, data from specimens with unknown properties are provided as input and the corresponding output is calculated using the fixed node weights.

3. CASE STUDY: SPACE ANTENNA

3.1 Preliminaries

The total mass of the antenna, a wire-frame mesh of which is shown in FIGURE 2, is 10.4 kg. The FRFs in the x, y and z directions were obtained at various measurement nodes for an excitation in the x direction. Interest was confined to the 0-256 Hz frequency range which was covered with 1,024 spectral lines. Three different states were considered:

- Healthy antenna - HS
- Slight damage caused by removing two of the four screws from the plate at the intersection of tangential and radial stiffener bars – the so-called DS1 state.
- Slight damage caused by removing a mass 0.110 kg from the same plate – the so-called DS2 state

The damage location is shown in FIGURE 2. It should be noted that DS1 will cause a local loss of stiffness while DS2 will cause a local loss mass. The response functions corresponding to these three states are shown in FIGURES 3 to 5.

Although a visual inspection reveals that there are differences between the FRFs of the healthy and damaged cases, an objective assessment of the actual damage state is not possible. Furthermore, the FRFs appear to be polluted by measurement noise, especially at the lower end of the frequency spectrum. It is further observed that the frequency shifts between the healthy and damaged states are not systematic and that the modal analysis of such FRF data is not straightforward. Such considerations make the space antenna a suitable test case for damage detection using the methodology offered by feeding PC-compressed FRFs to ANNs.

3.2 Feature Extraction

A total of 600 FRFs, 300 corresponding to state HS, 150 to DS1 and 150 to DS2, were used to form a 1,024x600 FRF matrix, where 1,024 is the number of spectral lines in each measured FRF. Clearly, the amount of data is prohibitive for using ANNs and a data compression technique must be used. The principal components of the FRF matrix were determined and the results are listed in TABLE 1, together with their relative and cumulative percentages. It is observed that the first 16 eigenvalues account for 98.03% of the variance of the response about the mean FRF values. Therefore, the reconstruction of the response using 16 principal components would represent a reduction of 1,024:16=64 and the error would be 2.0%. Using the first 30 principal components will yield a reconstruction quality of 99.5% and a compression ratio of 1,024/30=34.

The original and the reconstructed FRFs are compared in FIGURE 6 for an increasing number of principal components. The results are given for a response in the x direction, though very similar trends are observed for the y and z directions. As expected, better agreement is observed as more principal components are included. The final set of FRFs, was reconstructed using 60 principal components and a typical overlay is plotted in FIGURE 7 for a response in the z direction. It can easily be seen that the agreement is almost perfect and that the noise in the low-frequency region has been filtered.

TABLE1 Principal components and the cumulative percentage of variance

No	PC Eigenvalue	Cumul. Percentage(%)	No	PC Eigenvalue	Cumul. Percentage(%)
1	578.0	55.0	13	54.0	96.9
2	297.0	69.5	14	51.8	97.3
3	228.0	78.1	15	45.0	97.7
4	206.0	85.1	16	40.7	98.0
5	130.0	87.9	30	14.9	99.5
10	70.5	95.1	40	7.55	99.7
11	63.4	95.8	60	4.84	99.8
12	62.7	96.4	600	0.04	100.0

3.3 Neural network model for damage identification

It is known that a three-layer network with a single hidden layer can approximate any input/output mapping to a required accuracy. If the number of hidden layers is increased, better mapping may be obtained with fewer nodes. In this particular case, it was decided to use a BP network with two hidden layers. The PCA-compressed FRFs are fed into the input layer, processed in the hidden layers and the damage information is produced by the output layer.

It was decided to use 4 neural networks, NN1 to NN4, each corresponding to a different PCA compression level. Although it would have been desirable to keep the network architecture identical for all four cases for a direct comparison of results, practical considerations, such as network stability and convergence, led to the individual optimisation of each network. Using the PCA compression, the original FRF matrix of size 600X1,024 was reduced to a reconstructed FRF matrix of size 600x16 for NN1, 600x28 for NN2, 600x43 for NN3 and 600x60 for NN4. At each spectral point, a given FRF is represented by a mean value onto which projections of the principal components are added. The aim is to monitor the training and testing of each network in order to provide guidelines as to which reduction ratios should be used. The properties of each network are listed in TABLE 2. As shown in TABLE 3, each network has the same output that consists of three nodes, representing the three possible states: HS, DS1 & DS2.

TABLE 2 Properties of the networks used

(I: input, H1: 1st hidden layer, H2: 2nd hidden layer, O:output)

Network	No of principal components	Nodes in each layer (I-H1-H2-O)
NN1	16	16-9-9-3
NN2	28	28-15-15-3
NN3	43	43-23-12-3
NN4	60	60-31-15-3

TABLE 3 Output layer definition

State	Node1	Node2	Node3
HS	1	0	0
DS1	0	0	1
DS2	0	1	0

The available 600 reconstructed FRFs were first divided into a training group with 480 FRFs and a testing group with 120 FRFs. The training group consisted of 240 FRFs for state HS, 120 FRFs for DS1 and 120 FRFs for DS2. The testing group consisted of 60, 30 and 30 FRFs for HS, DS1 and DS2 respectively. During training, 0.01% random noise was added to each reconstructed FRF in order to avoid local minima and overfitting. The network error and training effort are listed in TABLE 4. The computational effort for each network depends on the number of iterations, the time required for each iteration and the actual network architecture. Broadly speaking, small training errors and fewer iterations indicate a better mapping ability.

TABLE 4 Network error and training effort

Network	Training error (% RMS)	Number of iterations
NN1	18.2	5,000
NN2	9.1	2,400
NN3	5.6	1,500
NN4	5.4	1,600

As can be seen from TABLES 2, 4, the convergence of the ANNs is a function of the number of principal components and the number of nodes. The largest training error is for NN1, which corresponds to the lowest number of principal components. This network also requires the largest training effort with 5,000 iterations. On the other hand, NN3 and NN4 with 43 and 60 principal components (i. e. input layer nodes) converged to an RMS error of about 5.5 % in about 1,600 iterations.

3.4 Damage detection

The network performance during the training with 480 FRFs and the damage detection results, obtained for the 120 FRFs of the testing group, are listed in TABLE 5. The following features were noted:

(i) The NN1 network has the highest error rates of both training and testing. Its shortcomings can easily be explained by the fact that 16 principal components were not adequate to describe the response of the specimens.

(ii) The NN2 network, the FRFs of which are reconstructed using 28 principal components, shows a marked improvement over the NN1 network. The training error was reduced from 20% to 5%, and the worst testing error from 40% to 3.3%.

(iii) The success rate is much better with the NN3 networks, the FRFs of which have 43 principal components. Only 4 of 480 training samples and 4 of 120 testing samples have failed for NN3. For DS1 detection, the training and detection errors are 0% and 3.3% respectively.

(iv) One would intuitively expect that any increase in the number of principal components will yield better training and detection results. The findings from the NN4 network, the FRFs of which use 60 principal

253

components, seem to contradict such a supposition. Although the training errors are lower than those for NN3, the detection errors are somewhat higher at 6.7% compared to 3.3% for NN3. It is believed that one is observing the adverse effects of noise in the data, which is re-introduced as more principal components are introduced. In any case, the main conclusion is that there must be an optimum number of principal components for each case.

TABLE 5 Training and damage detection results

Network (No of PCs)	Structural State	Training results			Testing (damage detection) results		
		Samples	Failed	Error rate	Samples	Failed	Error rate
NN1 (16)	HS	240	6	2.5%	60	1	1.6%
	DS1	120	24	20.0%	30	12	40.0%
	DS2	120	8	6.7%	30	3	10.0%
	Overall	480	38	7.9%	120	16	13.3%
NN2 (28)	HS	240	2	0.8%	60	3	5.0%
	DS1	120	6	5.0%	30	1	3.3%
	DS2	120	0	0.0%	30	0	0.0%
	Overall	480	8	1.7%	120	4	3.3%
NN3 (43)	HS	240	0	0.0%	60	2	3.3%
	DS1	120	0	0.0%	30	1	3.3%
	DS2	120	4	3.3%	30	1	3.3%
	Overall	480	4	0.8%	120	4	3.3%
NN4 (60)	HS	240	1	0.4%	60	3	5.0%
	DS1	120	1	0.8%	30	3	10.0%
	DS2	120	0	0.0%	30	2	6.6%
	Overall	480	2	0.4%	120	8	6.7%

TABLE 6 shows the successful detection output of NN3 when 30 testing FRFs, 10 FRFs for HS, 10 FRFs for DS1, and 10 FRFs for DS2 respectively, were fed into the network.

4. CONCLUDING REMARKS

The results indicate that the combination of FRF data reduction via the principal component analysis with the use of artificial neural networks provides a suitable methodology for damage detection. Once the size problem is circumvented through the reduction of the FRF data and a suitable network configuration is devised, the training of the network for several damage configurations is relatively straightforward. The proposed technique is particularly suited to detecting slight damage, a situation that is difficult to characterize via modal parameter changes.

The technique has the capability to cope with incomplete FRF data obtained from a few sensors. In any case, the routine availability of measured FRF data and relatively modest computational requirements make the method well suited to on-line industrial applications.

The PCA-compression acts as a noise filter since random noise is not expected to be a global feature in all measured FRFs. Such a feature will have further data processing applications, an obvious one being the modal analysis of noise-removed FRF data.

In the case of measured data that are contaminated by measurement errors, there appears to be an optimum number of principal components for FRF reconstruction. Too few components are not adequate to describe the response and the use of too many components impairs noise-filtering properties of the reduction process.

TABLE 6 Output from 30 testing FRFs

	Test1	Test2	Test3	Test4	Test5	Test6	Test7	Test8	Test9	Test10
HS	1.0000	1.0000	1.0000	0.9996	0.9999	0.9973	1.0000	0.9729	0.9979	1.0000
DS1	0.0004	0.0002	0.0002	0.0002	0.0001	0.0024	0.0002	0.0001	0.0003	0.0001
DS2	0.0000	0.0000	0.0000	0.0003	0.0001	0.0002	0.0000	0.0157	0.0007	0.0000
	Test11	Test12	Test13	Test14	Test15	Test16	Test17	Test18	Test19	Test20
HS	0.0000	0.0000	0.0012	0.0068	0.0741	0.0000	0.0138	0.0000	0.0001	0.0000
DS1	0.9569	0.9994	0.9335	0.9997	0.9747	0.9999	0.8393	1.0000	0.8568	1.0000
DS2	0.0064	0.0015	0.1552	0.0000	0.0000	0.0001	0.0003	0.0004	0.2925	0.0002
	Test21	Test22	Test23	Test24	Test25	Test26	Test27	Test28	Test29	Test30
HS	0.0023	0.0000	0.0001	0.0013	0.0014	0.0001	0.0049	0.0124	0.0000	0.0001
DS1	0.0001	0.0057	0.0010	0.0002	0.0000	0.0008	0.0001	0.0010	0.0006	0.0006
DS2	0.9939	0.9999	0.9999	0.9984	0.9791	0.9998	0.9925	0.8516	1.0000	0.9999

5. ACKNOWLEDGMENTS

The financial support of the European Commission under the Brite/Euram Programme (Contract No: BRPR-CT98-0688 AMADEUS) is gratefully acknowledged. The authors also wish to thank CASA for supplying the measured FRF data. Thanks are also due to Dr. K. Alexiou for many useful discussions.

REFERENCES

(1) Alleyne, D. N., Lowe, M. J. S. & Cawley, P., *J. of Applied Mechanics*, Vol. 65, 1998, 635-641

(2) Atalla, M. J. & Inman, D. J., *Mechanical Systems and Signal Processing*, Vol.12, No. 2, 1998, 135-161

(3) Bishop, C. M., *Neural networks for pattern recognition*. Oxford University Press,1995

(4) Doebling, S. W., et al., *Damage identification and health monitoring of structural and mechanical systems from changes in their vibration characteristics: a literature review*. Los Alamos National Laboratory, Report No. LA-13070-MS, 1996

(5) Doebling, S. W., Farrar, C. R., and Prime, M. B. *Shock and Vibration Digest*, Vol. 30, No. 2, 1998, 91-105

(6) Friswell, M. I. and Penny, J. E. T. 1997 Is damage location using vibration measurements *EUROMETH365*. Sheffield, UK, 1997

(7) Jolliffe, I. T. *Principal component analysis*. Springer-Verlag, New York,1986

(8) Levin, R. I. & Lieven, N. A. J., *J. of Sound and Vibration,* Vol. 210, No. 5, 1998, 593-607

(9) Marwala, T. & Hunt, H. E. M., *Mechanical Systems and Signal Processing* Vol. 13, NO. 3, 1999, 475-490

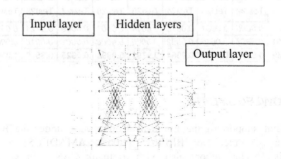

FIGURE 1 Back-propagation network

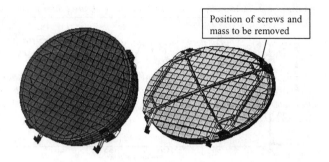

FIGURE 2 Wire-frame mesh of the space antenna

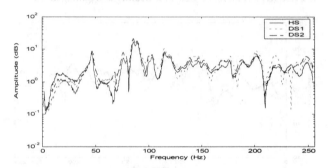

FIGURE 3 X direction FRFs for healthy and damaged states

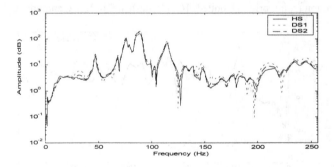

FIGURE 4 Y direction FRFs for healthy and damaged states

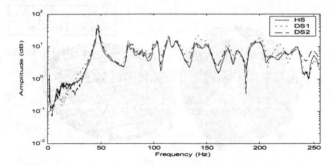

FIGURE 5 Z direction FRFs for healthy and damaged states

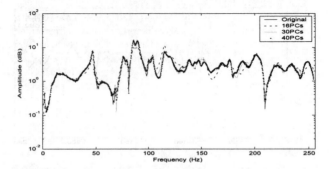

FIGURE 6 Original and FRFs reconstructed with PCs – response in the x
direction (solid: original, dotted: 16 PCs, dashed: 30 PCs, diamond: 40 PCs)

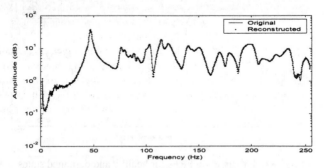

FIGURE 7 Original and final reconstructed FRF set using 60 PCs – response in
the z direction (solid blue: original, red diamond: 60 PCs)

Ultrasonic Detection of Defects in Thin Plates Using Rayleigh-Lamb Waves

M. Conry,* L.J. Crane,† M.D. Gilchrist*

The current work examines the interaction of symmetric Rayleigh-Lamb waves with defects normal to the surface of a plate. Symmetric waves are chosen due to their non-dispersive nature at low frequencies (the frequencies studied here) [1]. These defects are of various sizes and orientations, and have been modelled in an isotropic material (aluminium). This has been done by means of finite element modelling techniques. The results obtained to date indicate that Rayleigh-Lamb waves can successfully detect and characterise defects significantly faster than conventional ultrasonic waves. The results indicate that embedded defects as small as 20% of plate thickness can be detected. For surface defects, sizes that are at least 25% of plate thickness can be detected. These and anticipated future results should be of value in the design of novel ultrasonic NDT&E techniques. Specifically, this information should provide guidance on what sizes and geometries of defect can detected, and also the frequencies and modes of vibration which should be used in their experimental detection.

1 Introduction

Non-destructive Testing and Evaluation (NDT&E) is critical in the safety assurance of modern engineering structures. This is particularly the case when using high performance materials, such as fibre-reinforced polymer matrix composites. Frequently, such materials are subject to mechanisms of damage uncommon in metallic structures. Additionally, many high performance alloys such as advanced aerospace aluminiums are more susceptible to fatigue failure than more traditional metals. In all such cases, it is essential to have good knowledge of the defects present in a component in order to assess its soundness. One of the most common and versatile techniques used in NDT&E is ultrasonic testing, where a component is tested using acoustic waves.

Conventional ultrasonic NDT&E relies principally on through thickness wave propagation. In order to fully examine a component, its entire area must be scanned. For plate-like sections, this is a very slow process.

*Dept. of Mechanical Engineering, University College Dublin, Dublin 4, Ireland. (All correspondence to be addressed to Dr. Gilchrist)
†Dept. of Applied Mathematics, Trinity College Dublin.

The research presented here is focused on exploring an alternative form of propagating waves: Rayleigh-Lamb waves [2, 3]. Rayleigh-Lamb waves are waves that propagate longitudinally along a plate (as opposed to transversely through the plate thickness). Although the governing equations for such plate vibrations can be easily written down, plate, α and β are simple functions of frequency and material properties.) they are deceptively difficult to explore. In general there are many different symmetric and antisymmetric modes possible for any given frequency and plate thickness.

The paper begins with an exposition of the mathematics of Rayleigh-Lamb waves. Following from this, a finite element model is constructed to model the propagation of the waves in a plate of isotropic material (aluminium). The results of this model are validated against those arising from analytical work. Models are then constructed to investigate the reflection of waves from embedded and surface-breaking vertical cracks. The results obtained are commented upon with reference to practical engineering applications.

2 Mathematical Analysis

2.1 Introduction

In order to investigate the use of Rayleigh-Lamb waves, it is necessary to first understand the fundamental wave equations. The analysis begins with the elastic equations of an isotropic medium, in this case aluminium, which has Lamé physical constants satisfying $\lambda = 2\mu$. The geometry studied is that of an infinite plate. Plane strain is assumed, and displacements within the medium are expressed in terms of partial waves. Using elasticity theory, expressions are found for these partial waves in terms of constants. A dimensionless notation is introduced to simplify matters, and geometric boundary conditions are used to evaluate the constants. Subsequently the expressions for displacement and stress are fully derived, together with the characteristic equation of Rayleigh-Lamb waves.

2.2 Partial Wave Analysis

This analysis is carried out on an infinite plate, using an x, y, z coordinate system (Fig.7). The displacements in these directions are denoted by u, v and w respectively. The $x-y$ plane coincides with the median plane of the plate. The z axis is normal to the plate. The coordinate system is arranged so that the x axis coincides with the direction of wave propagation. It is assumed that the plate, being infinite in its y direction, and with a wave propagating in the x direction, is in a state of plane strain (all strains being in the $x-z$ plane).

The dynamic equation for a uniform elastic solid can be found in many standard texts (e.g. Jaeger [4]). It will be assumed that the displacements all vary in the time domain as $e^{-i\omega t}$, and along the x axis as e^{ifx}. Using this, the dynamic equation components can be written as follows:

$$\left(\nabla^2 + \frac{\rho\omega^2}{\mu}\right) u = \left(1 - \frac{\lambda + 2\mu}{\mu}\right) \frac{\partial\theta}{\partial x} \qquad \&c. \tag{2.1}$$

where θ represents the dilation, and in a 2-D system is expressed as:

$$\theta = \frac{\partial u}{\partial x} + \frac{\partial w}{\partial z} \tag{2.2}$$

In equation (2.1), each component is differentiated along the corresponding axis. The three components are then summed to give:

$$\left(\nabla^2 + \frac{\rho\omega^2}{\lambda + 2\mu}\right) \theta = 0 \tag{2.3}$$

where ρ is density, ω is frequency in rad/s, and where λ and μ are the Lamé constants. A solution of equation (2.1) is given by:

$$u = -\frac{(\lambda + 2\mu)}{\rho\omega^2} \frac{\partial\theta}{\partial x} + \alpha \quad \text{and} \quad w = -\frac{(\lambda + 2\mu)}{\rho\omega^2} \frac{\partial\theta}{\partial z} + \gamma \tag{2.4}$$

The complementary solution terms α and γ satisfy the following relations:

$$\left(\nabla^2 + \frac{\rho\omega^2}{\mu}\right) [\alpha, \gamma] = 0 \quad \text{and} \quad \frac{\partial\alpha}{\partial x} + \frac{\partial\gamma}{\partial z} = 0 \tag{2.5}$$

From equations (2.5), and introducing a new term χ, we see that it is possible to write:

$$\alpha = \frac{\partial\chi}{\partial z} \quad \text{and} \quad \gamma = \frac{-\partial\chi}{\partial x} \tag{2.6}$$

where χ is a function of x and z which satisfies

$$\left(\nabla^2 + \frac{\rho\omega^2}{\mu}\right) \chi = 0 \tag{2.7}$$

Now, combining (2.4) and (2.6), the two parts of the solution for u and w leads to the expressions:

$$u = \frac{-\partial\phi}{\partial x} + \frac{\partial\chi}{\partial z} \quad \text{and} \quad w = \frac{-\partial\phi}{\partial z} + \frac{-\partial\chi}{\partial x} \tag{2.8}$$

the omitted constants being absorbed into the function θ to form a new function ϕ.

By introducing a dimensionless notation, characterised by unit length (d, the half thickness of the plate) and unit time ($1/\eta$), then equations (2.3) and (2.7) become much simpler. Dimensionless quantities will be denoted by uppercase letters (e.g. $X = x/d$,

$T = t\eta$). Our choice of dimensions d and η (2.9) and material (aluminium (2.10)) are as follows.

$$\rho d^2 \eta^2 = \mu \tag{2.9}$$

$$\lambda = 2\mu \tag{2.10}$$

Particular simplifications occur where a dimensionless frequency term, Ω, is introduced such that (with c_t as transverse wave speed)

$$\Omega = \frac{\omega d}{c_t} = \omega d \sqrt{\frac{\rho}{\mu}} = \frac{\omega}{\eta} \tag{2.11}$$

Substituting this into equations (2.7) (2.3), and setting $\lambda = 2\mu$, and $\rho d^2 \eta^2 = \mu$ gives

$$\left(\nabla^2 + \frac{\Omega^2}{4}\right) \phi = 0 \quad \text{and} \quad \left(\nabla^2 + \Omega^2\right) \chi = 0 \tag{2.12}$$

If we assert that the only dependence on x, or in the current notation X, is through an harmonic term, this gives:

$$\phi(X, Z) = \phi(Z) e^{iFX} \quad \text{and} \quad \chi(X, Z) = \chi(Z) e^{iFX} \tag{2.13}$$

This leads to solutions of the form (omitting $e^{i(FX - \Omega T)}$).

$$\phi = A \cosh(\bar{q} Z) \quad \text{where} \quad \bar{q} = \sqrt{F^2 - \Omega^2/4} \tag{2.14}$$

$$\chi = B \sinh(\bar{s} Z) \quad \text{where} \quad \bar{s} = \sqrt{F^2 - \Omega^2} \tag{2.15}$$

Also, putting equation (2.8) into dimensionless notation gives

$$U = -\frac{\partial \phi}{\partial X} + \frac{\partial \chi}{\partial Z} \qquad W = -\frac{\partial \phi}{\partial Z} - \frac{\partial \chi}{\partial X} \tag{2.16}$$

2.3 Stresses and Boundary Conditions

For plane strain conditions, the stress and strain expressions are as follows:

$$\sigma_{xx} = (\lambda + 2\mu)\epsilon_x + \lambda\epsilon_z \quad \sigma_{yy} = \lambda\epsilon_x + \lambda\epsilon_z \quad \sigma_{zz} = \lambda\epsilon_x + (\lambda + 2\mu)\epsilon_z$$
$$\tau_{xz} = \mu\varrho_{xz} \tag{2.17}$$

$$\epsilon_x = \partial u/\partial x \quad \epsilon_y = \partial v/\partial y = 0 \quad \epsilon_z = \partial w/\partial z$$
$$\varrho_{xz} = \varrho_{zx} = \partial u/\partial z + \partial w/\partial x \tag{2.18}$$

Boundary conditions prescribe that the plate surfaces ($Z = \pm 1$) be stress free surfaces ($\sigma_{zz} = \sigma_{xz} = 0$). Evaluating the terms in (2.17), using (2.14), (2.15) and (2.16) gives:

$$\sigma_{zz} = \left(A\left(F^2 + \bar{s}^2\right)\cosh\bar{q} + 2BiF\bar{s}\cosh\bar{s}\right)e^{iFX}e^{-i\Omega T} \tag{2.19}$$

$$\sigma_{xz} = \pm\left(2AiF\bar{q}\sinh\bar{q} - B\left(F^2 + \bar{s}^2\right)\sinh\bar{s}\right)e^{iFX}e^{-i\Omega T} \tag{2.20}$$

Setting these stresses to zero gives a system which produces non-trivial results only if its determinant is zero. The characteristic equation is thus:

$$\frac{\tanh\bar{s}}{\tanh\bar{q}} = \frac{4F^2\bar{q}\bar{s}}{\left(F^2 + \bar{s}^2\right)^2} \equiv \frac{4F^2\bar{q}\bar{s}}{\left(2F^2 - \Omega^2\right)^2} \tag{2.21}$$

This equation is an example of the fundamental characteristic equation for the vibration of a thin isotropic plate. By solving this equation numerically, it is possible to determine the frequency–velocity curves of the waves.

It is possible to express B in terms of A using equation (2.19). With this information, along with equations (2.14–2.18) the expressions for all the stresses can be fully expressed as follows (M is a simple constant):

$$\tau_{xz} = 2\mu MF\bar{q}\left(\frac{\sinh\bar{q}Z}{\sinh\bar{q}} - \frac{\sinh\bar{s}Z}{\sinh\bar{s}}\right)e^{i(FX - \Omega T)} \tag{2.22}$$

$$\sigma_{zz} = i\mu M\left(\frac{-\cosh\bar{q}Z}{\sinh\bar{q}}(F^2 + \bar{s}^2) + \frac{\cosh\bar{s}Z}{\sinh\bar{s}}\frac{4\bar{q}\bar{s}F^2}{F^2 + \bar{s}^2}\right)e^{i(FX - \Omega T)} \tag{2.23}$$

$$\sigma_{xx} = i\mu M\left(\frac{\cosh\bar{q}Z}{\sinh\bar{q}}\left(2F^2 + \frac{\Omega^2}{2}\right) - \frac{\cosh\bar{s}Z}{\sinh\bar{s}}\frac{4\bar{q}\bar{s}F^2}{F^2 + \bar{s}^2}\right)e^{i(FX - \Omega T)} \tag{2.24}$$

While the displacements are given as:

$$U = MF\left(\frac{\cosh(\bar{q}Z)}{\sinh\bar{q}} - \frac{2\bar{q}\bar{s}}{F^2 + \bar{s}^2}\frac{\cosh(\bar{s}Z)}{\sinh\bar{s}}\right)e^{i(FX - \Omega T)} \tag{2.25}$$

$$W = -iM\bar{q}\left(\frac{\sinh(\bar{q}Z)}{\sinh\bar{q}} - \frac{2F^2}{F^2 + \bar{s}^2}\frac{\sinh(\bar{s}Z)}{\sinh\bar{s}}\right)e^{i(FX - \Omega T)} \tag{2.26}$$

3 Basic Modelling

3.1 Introduction

This section of the paper focuses on the finite element model used to evaluate the reflection coefficients of the studied defects. Before any model is constructed, it is necessary to evaluate the time scaling factor. The basic model of an undamaged plate is then discussed, and validated against theoretical results. Subsequently two distinct classes of defects are modelled and the results of these analyses are presented.

TABLE 1: Frequencies of Analysis

Ω	0.12	0.34	0.74	1.02	1.23	1.39	1.53	1.64	1.74	1.91	1.98
p (Hz)	58.4	170.1	367.8	510.0	612.7	694.2	761.7	819.3	869.2	952.4	987.7

3.2 Calculation of Time Scaling Factor

First recall the results given in equations (2.9) and (2.10). To find the value of η in (2.9), we must determine μ (ρ and d having been already set). Young's Modulus (E) and Poisson's Ratio (ν) can be defined in terms of the Lamé constants μ and λ. Equally, the reverse applies, in particular:

$$\lambda = (E\nu)/\left[3\nu\left(1 - 2\nu\right) + \left(1 - 2\nu\right)^2\right] \qquad \lambda = 0 \qquad (3.1)$$

$\lambda = 0$ is not a useful solution. The other solution value of λ can be calculated by substituting values for E (7.07×10^{10} Pa) and ν ($1/3$) into (3.1). Then, from equations (2.9) and (2.10) it immediately follows

$$\mu = \lambda/2 = 2.651250 \times 10^{10} \text{Pa} \qquad (3.2)$$
$$\eta = 3.1336 \times 10^3 \text{ s}^{-1} \qquad (3.3)$$

3.3 Constructing the Model

The model constructed is purely two dimensional. It is necessary to fix three sets of parameters: the elastic properties of the material (aluminium), the dimensions of the model and the frequencies of the ultrasonic wave.

The elastic properties (for aluminium) have already been established, given by Young's Modulus ($E = 7.07 \times 10^{+10}$ Pa), Poisson's Ratio ($\nu = 1/3$) and density ($\rho = 2700$ kg/m^3).

The analysis will be maintained in dimensionless form. The plate half-thickness is set as unity ($d = 1.0$ m). The very lowest frequency which will be examined here is $\Omega \approx 0.12$. From the analysis of Section 2.3, the equation on wavelengths (2.21) establishes that a plate length of $80.0\,d$ is appropriate.

The dimensionless frequencies (Ω) for analysis were converted into equivalent values in Hz for use in the model according to equation (2.11), and using η as calculated in Section 3.2. The frequencies used are shown in Table (3.3), both in dimensionless form (Ω), and in absolute form ($p = \omega/2\pi$) (as they are specified in the model). The range of frequencies is selected such that only the zeroth order symmetric mode can exist. This avoids mode conversion issues [1].

We are interested only in the symmetric modes of vibration of the model. It is therefore only necessary to model half the thickness of the plate. The bottom surface

264

TABLE 2: Dimensionless Wavelengths From FEA Model and Calculations

Ω	0.12	0.34	0.74	1.02	1.23	1.39	1.53	1.64	1.74	1.91	1.98
FEA	79.4	28.93	14.2	10.04	8.5	7.57	6.65	6.11	5.8	5.1	4.81
Eqn(2.21)	92.9	31.86	14.64	10.46	8.63	7.54	6.79	6.24	5.81	5.15	4.88

of the model (the central surface of the plate) is constrained by a symmetry boundary condition (no motion perpendicular to the surface).

A steady state dynamics analysis was performed on the model. The loads specified were applied sinusoidally at each frequency, and the response of the model was evaluated. A uniform pressure load of unit amplitude was applied to the right hand side of the model. During the analysis, this load varied in a sinusoidal fashion.

20 elements were used to mesh the half thickness of the plate. 320 uniform elements were used along its length. The element chosen for modelling the plate was a 2-D plane strain element. The material was modelled as entirely isotropic and linearly elastic (as is approximately true for aluminium). On the left hand end of the model (the end furthest from the point of application of the loads), 20 4-node, linear, one-way infinite elements were used. These elements provide "quiet boundaries" to the finite element model in steady state dynamics analyses [5], and allow our finite model to approximate the behaviour of an infinite plate. It is possible to check agreement between the calculated frequency dispersion curve and that of the model (Fig.7) by comparing the variation of wavelength with frequency for the two cases.

As can be seen from Fig.7, there is close agreement between the finite element model wavelengths, and those calculated analytically from equation (2.21).

4 Modelling of Embedded and Surface Defects

4.1 Basic Principles

The two defects studied in this paper are very similar. Both are perpendicular to the plate surface, and both are cracks (having zero dimension in the direction of the plate surface). In both cases, it is assumed that the faces of the crack do not touch. Therefore, the surface of the crack represents a stress free surface.

$$\tau_{xz} = 0 \qquad\qquad \sigma_{xx} = 0 \qquad\qquad (4.1)$$

Examination of the stresses as described by equations (2.22) and (2.24) reveals that the latter of these two stresses is the more significant. These equations provide expressions for the stresses arising from the incident wave. In order for the crack surface to be stress free, equal and opposite stresses must occur there [6]. The stress required (as given by the analytic expressions (2.22–2.23)) is coded into the finite element model, and applied to the crack surface. The amplitude of the resulting reflected wave is compared to that of the equivalent incident wave and the ratio is referred to as the reflection coefficient.

4.2 Centrally Embedded Vertical Crack

The model used was very much the same as that described in Section 3.3. Again, 20 elements were used to mesh the half thickness of the plate. On one edge of the model (where the defect is placed), 10 elements were used to mesh the crack face, and 10 to mesh the intact part of the plate above the crack. The ratio of crack length to plate thickness was varied by changing the vertical position of the nodes. As before, 20 infinite elements were used along the non-cracked end of the plate, to provide a quiet boundary to the finite element model. An illustration of the cracked region, and the x-displacements of the reflected wave is shown in Fig.7. In this diagram, the defect is at the bottom right corner. The centreline (of the plate) is the bottom surface of the model. The absolute values of displacements are unimportant here, but the regions near the centre line experience the largest displacement, while the material near the free surface displaces the least.

In this model, the stress equation for the S_o wave was programmed into a user subroutine which then applied the required stress to the free surface of the crack. The intact portion of the plate, above the crack, was fixed in the x-direction by means of a plane of symmetry.

The displacement-amplitude of the reflected wave was divided by that of the corresponding incident wave to give a reflection coefficient. A representative selection of results from this model are shown in Fig.7.

4.3 Vertical Symmetrical Surface Crack

The model used is identical to that described in Sections 3.3 and 4.2. The only difference between this model and that of Section 4.2 is in the boundary conditions (the plane of symmetry for the median plane of the plate is now on the edge of the model opposite that of the crack). Loading is applied in the same way as before. An illustration of the cracked region, and the x-displacements of the reflected wave is shown in Fig.7. In this diagram, the defect is located in the top right corner of the model. The centreline (of the plate) is the bottom surface of the model. Again, the absolute values of displacements do not matter (it should be noted though that away from the defect, the displacements are very similar to those in Fig.7). The results from this model for a selection of the frequencies tested are shown in Fig.7.

5 Discussion

On the evidence of Section 3, it is possible to conclude that the finite element model constructed is indeed a good model of the phenomenon studied. That is to say, the waves occurring in the model behave in the manner of waves excited in an infinite plate of isotropic matter.

Several conclusions can be drawn from the results of the defect analyses presented in Sections 4.2 and 4.3. If it is assumed that the resolution of a signal processing system can distinguish reflection coefficients greater than 10% from background noise, it is clear that that embedded defects as small as 20% of plate thickness can be detected. For surface defects, sizes that are at least 25% of plate thickness can be detected. The difference between the reflection coefficients associated with these different classes of defects is understandable when one considers the mode shapes, which can be seen in equation (2.25), and graphically in Fig.7 and Fig.7. The x-displacement is greatest near the centre line ($z = 0$), and consequently defects located there (embedded defects) will reflect more of the incident wave than will defects that are located at the plate surface.

Both classes of defect exhibit a high degree of sensitivity to the defect size. This is apparent from the quite steep slopes of the curves for all frequencies in Fig.7 and Fig.7.

6 Conclusions

The results established within this work are of direct practical relevance to NDT&E applications. Clearly, if a structure is scanned along its edge, rather than over its area, there is an order of magnitude reduction in the time required to detect any damage. This increase in efficiency can translate either into a reduction of costs, or an opportunity to perform more extensive and thorough defect assessment. Furthermore, since it is only necessary to have access to one edge of the structure, it should prove possible to scan regions of a structure which might not otherwise be accessible. This is particularly important for the in-service inspection of components and structures. Greater use of in-service testing helps to reduce the cost of operating and servicing components.

The present work has shown that it is theoretically possible to use propagating symmetric Rayleigh-Lamb waves to detect vertical defects that are embedded within a thin plate-like structure. The reflection coefficient shows quite a high degree of sensitivity to the size of the component, which means that it should be possible to quite accurately size a defect if it is detected. The main weakness of the technique presented here is that it gives little information on the *location* of the defect, fixing it only along one axis. However, such information could be obtained either by time-of-flight measurements, or by scanning along two edges of the surface.

In summary, Rayleigh-Lamb waves have dramatic potential in the field of ultrasonic NDT&E to significantly reduce costs and improve efficiency for certain component geometries. It has been shown here that such waves offer promise in the detection of vertical cracks, whether located at the surface of a plate or fully embedded within its material.

Future work that will be undertaken within this programme of research will attempt to establish the extent to which other classes of defects can be detected using Rayleigh-Lamb waves. These other defects include skew cracks, lozenge shaped defects, and defects in non-planar thin structures (such as pipes).

7 Acknowledgements

The authors would like to acknowledge the support provided by Enterprise Ireland (Basic Research Grant SC/1997/710) and University College Dublin (Research Doctoral Scholarship and Centre for High Performance Computing Applications).

References

[1] I. A. Viktorov, *Rayleigh and Lamb Waves*, Plenum Press, New York, 1967.

[2] H. Lamb, *Proc. Roy. Soc., London*, **Vol. 93**, 1917, pp. 114–128.

[3] Lord Rayleigh, *Proc. London Math. Soc.*, **Vol. xx**, 1889, pp. 225–234.

[4] J. C. Jaeger, *Elasticity, Fracture and Flow with Engineering and Geological Applications*, Chapman & Hall, London, 1969.

[5] Hibbitt, Karlsson & Sorensen, Inc., *ABAQUS/Standard User's Manual Volume 1*, edition 5.4, 1994.

[6] R. D. Mindlin, Waves and vibrations in isotropic, elastic plates, *Structural Mechanics, Proceedings of the first symposium on naval structural mechanics*, Edited by J. N. Goodier and N. J. Hoff, pp. 199–232, Pergamon Press, Oxford, 1960.

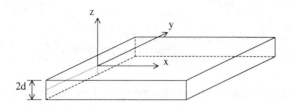

FIGURE 1: Orientation of Axes

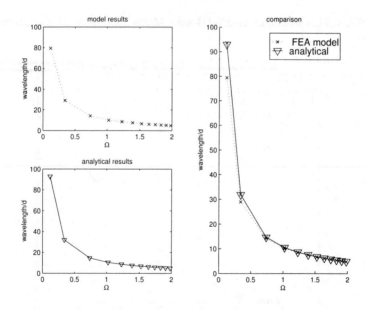

FIGURE 2: Comparison of FEA Model and Analytical Results

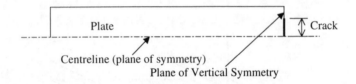

FIGURE 3: Schematic of Model Geometry for Embedded Crack in Quarter Plate

FIGURE 4: FEA Model, Embedded Crack. (Mode Shapes for U1 displacement)

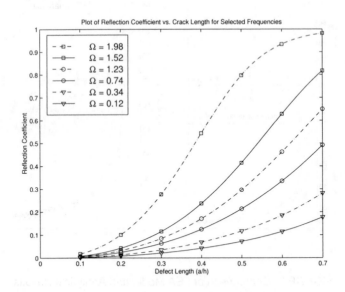

FIGURE 5: Reflection Coefficients for Embedded Vertical Crack

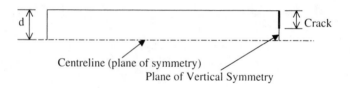

FIGURE 6: Schematic of Model Geometry for Surface Crack in Quarter Plate

FIGURE 7: FEA Model, Surface Crack. (Mode Shapes for U1 displacement)

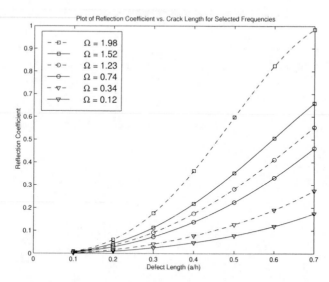

FIGURE 8: Reflection Coefficients for Surface Vertical Crack

THE NON-LINEAR VIBRATIONS OF RC BEAMS WITH DISTRIBUTED CRACKS

C. M. Tan*, J. S. Owen* and B S Choo*

When using vibration measurements in the structural health monitoring of structures it may be necessary to take account of any non-linearity in the structural system. This has led to various models for the vibration behaviour of a cracked beam being proposed. However, the nature of reinforced concrete structures is such that traditional models for the vibration of structures with an isolated crack are inappropriate. This paper considers 5 non-linear models for the vibration of a cracked RC beam and compares the results with experimental observations. It is shown that a simple bi-linear model of crack behaviour is not able to reproduce the softening spring non-linearity observed in practice and a more complex model is required that includes a gradual transition from crack open to crack closed.

INTRODUCTION

Although vibration measurements have been used for structural health monitoring (SHM) for many years, a systematic approach has only become possible with the development of computer based signal processing. Much progress has been made with these techniques since the initial work of Cawley & Adams [1], though there are still many issues to be addressed. This is especially so for Civil Engineering applications, like bridges, where the sensitivity of modal parameters to damage has not been fully established. Moreover, the need to know details of the undamaged structure and for detailed computer modelling raises problems for older bridges where data are not available.

One important issue when considering using vibration measurements for SHM is that of non-linearity as a cracked structure or component will vibrate in a non-linear fashion as the stiffness changes across each vibration cycle. This has led to research into the vibration characteristics of cracked beams to develop an understanding of this non-linear behaviour. Although much of this work has concentrated on the vibration of uniform beams with a single crack (Friswell [2], Shen and Pierre [3], Abraham and Brandon [4]) this approach is not appropriate for reinforced concrete structures. Here the material is non-homogeneous, the structure may have many distributed cracks and

*University of Nottingham, School of Civil Engineering, University Park, Nottingham, NG7 2RD

there is extensive micro-cracking. A previous investigation by the authors (Eccles et al [5]) confirmed that the vibration characteristics of cracked RC beams were non-linear and that this non-linearity was significant if the modal properties were to be used for SHM. In this paper the authors present a further investigation into the non-linear vibration of cracked RC beams. Numerical studies were performed using five different non-linear models for the beam stiffness and the results were compared with data from tests on RC beams.

NUMERICAL STUDIES

Assumptions

The single crack models noted above are not applicable to the case of a RC beam with multiple distributed cracks. This is not only because there are more than one crack, but also because the exact location and severity of the cracks is impossible to determine due to micro cracking, which occurs between the coarse aggregate and cement paste. In addition, the crack behaviour is complicated by the presence of the reinforcement and aggregate interlock. The reinforcement bridges the crack and carries tensile and, by dowel action, shear loads. Aggregate interlock generates friction as the crack surfaces separate in bending and, although tensile forces cannot be resisted, this provides a mechanism to transfer shear across the crack. The accurate modelling of cracks in concrete structures is therefore not a straightforward process and a simplified modal approach has been used. The equivalent modal stiffness used in the numerical modelling can then be found, assuming Euler Bernoulli beam theory, from:

$$k = \int_0^\ell EI\phi''(x)dx \qquad (1)$$

There are two more assumptions implicit in using this expression – firstly that there is a uniform reduction in second moment of area along the length of the beam and secondly that the mode shape does not change with damage. Previous experiments (Das et al [6]) have shown that, for the RC beams discussed here, there is very little change in mode shape with damage and so the second assumption is valid. This also suggests that, although the first assumption clearly does not hold, the loss of accuracy is acceptable. Hence, the dynamic response of a cracked RC beam can be modelled using a modal approach, with each mode described as a single degree of freedom (SDOF) system with non-linear stiffness:

$$m\ddot{u} + c\dot{u} + k(u)u = p(t) \qquad (2)$$

where m and c are the mass and damping for the system, $p(t)$ is the excitation force and $k(u)$ is a stiffness model which varies across the vibration cycle.

Non-linear Stiffness Models

Five non-linear stiffness models were considered. The first was a simple bilinear stiffness model where a different stiffness was defined for the two crack states, open and closed. This model assumes that the crack instantaneously opens when the displacement of the beam creates tensile forces in the crack region, leading to a reduced value of stiffness for negative displacements:

$$k = k_i \left(1 + \frac{(1-\mu)}{2} \left(\frac{u}{|u|} - 1 \right) \right) \tag{3}$$

where k_i is the stiffness of the uncracked beam and μk_i is the stiffness of the system with an open crack.

The simple bi-linear crack model is often criticised as it neglects the self weight of the beam. Hence, the second model included the effect of the beam self weight, ρAL, which moves the static equilibrium position of the beam into the cracked stiffness region:

$$k = k_i \left(1 + \frac{(1-\mu)}{2} \left(\frac{(u+u_0)}{|u+u_0|} - 1 \right) \right) \tag{4}$$

where:

$$u_0 = -\frac{1}{2} \frac{\rho AL}{\mu k_i} g \tag{5}$$

However, this model still assumes an abrupt transition from the cracked to the uncracked state, whereas the authors (Eccles et al [7]) and others (Brandon and Mathias [8]) have previously suggested that there is a more complicated transition between the cracked and uncracked states. The third model assumes a hyperbolic tangent relationship between the stiffness and displacement:

$$k = k_i \left(1 + \frac{(1-\mu)}{2} (\tanh(a.u - b) - 1) \right) \tag{6}$$

where parameters a and b define how sharply the transition occurs and the static equilibrium position respectively.

Alternative models for this transition have been suggested by Eccles [9] and Cheng et al [10], and both these were also considered in this study. Eccles proposed an exponential model, which gives a sudden closure of the crack:

$$k = \begin{cases} k_i\left(\mu + (1-\mu)e^{a(u-b(1-\mu))}\right) & u \leq 0 \\ k_i & u > 0 \end{cases} \qquad (7)$$

whereas, Cheng et al relate the stiffness directly to the amplitude of response

$$k = k_i\left(\mu + \frac{(1-\mu)}{2}(1 + \cos(\omega_l t))\right) \qquad (8)$$

where ω_l is the excitation frequency. The above stiffness model assumes that the crack is completely closed when $\omega_l = 2l\pi$ ($l = 1,2,3...$), and completely open when $\omega_l t = (2l - 1)\pi$ ($l = 1,2,3...$). Otherwise the crack is in a state of partial closure. In order to be comparable with the other models discussed in this paper, Cheng's model has been recast in terms of u, the displacement of the beam:

$$k = Max\left(\mu k_i, k_i\left(\mu + \frac{1}{2}(1 - \mu^2)\right)\right) \qquad (9)$$

The variation of stiffness with displacement for all the models considered is shown in Figure 1, and the corresponding force/displacement curves in Figure 2.

Methodology

The SDOF equations of motion were simplified by assuming a unit mass (equivalent to mass normalised mode shapes) and expressing the modal damping in terms of the damping ratio ξ:

$$\ddot{u} + 2\omega_n\xi\dot{u} + k(u)u = p\cos(t) \qquad (10)$$

The influence of changes in natural frequency on damping was ignored. The equations of motion were then solved numerically using MATLAB (ode45 for non-stiff differential equation, medium-order method). Initial conditions of zero displacement and unit velocity were assumed and the simulations were run until a steady state response was reached. From these, time histories and phase portraits for different values of μ were obtained.

The variation of response with frequency of excitation for each model was obtained by increasing the excitation frequency in steps of $0.005\omega_n$ and calculating the response at each increment. This process was then repeated with the excitation frequency decreasing in steps of $0.005\omega_n$. Finally, the excitation force was varied to determine the influence of response magnitude on the natural frequency.

Results

Typical time histories and phase portraits for the five models are shown in Figures 3 – 7. Each of the phase portraits shows a significant asymmetry, which is as expected for a system with a difference in stiffness between each half of the vibration cycle. Figure 7 suggests that the asymmetry is less marked for the trigonometric stiffness model, reflecting the more gradual change in stiffness evident in Figures 1 and 2.

Typical variations of response with frequency are shown in Figures 8 – 13. None of the models showed any notable difference between results obtained with an increasing frequency and those obtained with a decreasing frequency. This suggests that the systems are only very weakly non-linear. However, the effect of changing the amplitude of the FRF does indicate non-linearity for some of the models. As expected, the natural frequency of the bi-linear model is independent of response level (Figure 8). When the self-weight is included (Figure 9) there is an initial hardening behaviour - typified by an increase in natural frequency with amplitude - but for larger amplitude response the natural frequency remains almost constant. With parameter $b<0$, the hyperbolic tangent model, shows a marked softening behaviour (Figure 10) which is in keeping with the results of experimental work [5,7,9]. For the exponential model the non-linearity is dependent on the value of b chosen as is shown by Figures 11 and 12. For $b=0$ (Figure 11) the system shows a softening behaviour, but for $b>0$ (Figure 12) – which moves the static equilibrium point as if some self weight was included - there is significant hardening behaviour. The trigonometric model (Figure 13) is slightly softening.

EXPERIMENTAL WORK

Test Setup

A set of laboratory tests were carried out on three reinforced concrete beams (Figure 14). Each beam was tested in its undamaged state to determine the mode shapes and natural frequencies of its first four vibration modes. The beams were then incrementally loaded in four point bending until yielding of the reinforcement occurred. At each load increment, the static load was removed and the dynamic behaviour of the beam investigated using a stepped sine sweep excitation around each natural frequency. This sine sweep was repeated using both increasing and decreasing frequencies, and three different amplitudes of excitation. The location of the excitation and the instrumentation are shown in Figure 14.

Data Processing

The variation of response with frequency was obtained for both forward and backward sweeps by plotting the amplitude of the response against the frequency of excitation. The restoring force surface method - first introduced by Masri and Caughey [11] and improved by Worden [12] - was also used to investigate the non-linear behaviour. This method is based on Newton's second law for a SDOF system:

$$m\ddot{u}(t) + f(u,\dot{u}) = p(t) \tag{11}$$

where $f(u,\dot{u})$ is the internal restoring force of the system and can be regarded as a surface over the phase plane. If the force $p(t)$ and acceleration $\ddot{u}(t)$ are sampled simultaneously at regular intervals, then at each sampling instant the value of the restoring force can be calculated from

$$f_i = p_i - m\ddot{u}_i \tag{12}$$

where p_i is the ith sampled value of the input etc. By integrating the acceleration data to acquire the estimated displacements and velocities, a sequence of triplets $(u_i, \dot{u}_i, f_i)$ for each sampling instant is obtained. Each triplet specifies a point in the phase plane and the height of the restoring force surface above that point. A continuous representation of the force surface can then be constructed and the section of the plane at $\dot{u} = 0$ will give the force displacement curve of the system.

To plot the restoring force surface for this case, typical experimental acceleration data were integrated twice numerically, using the trapezoidal method. To eliminate the integration errors, the mean value and best fit linear trend were removed from the velocity and displacement data.

Experimental Results

Figure 15 shows typical results from a sweep test for one of the modes of the test beams. If a system is linear the shape of the frequency response function (FRF) would be independent of both the force amplitude and tuning direction, i.e. all FRFs would coincide, Weiland and Link [13]. Figure 15 shows that the results of the forward and backward sweeps do not match. This shows that the FRF of the test beam is not independent of tuning direction. Although this did not always occur, it suggests that a RC beam with distributed cracks is a weakly non-linear system.

Figure 16 is a typical set of data of the first mode of the beam at different static load increments. When the beam is undamaged, it is clear that the beam behaves in a linear manner and the natural frequency does not change with excitation amplitude. Increasing the static load level causes damage to the beam and a clear drop in natural frequency can be seen at load levels 10kN, 20kN and 30kN. The results also show a clear softening spring behaviour, as the natural frequency decreases with increasing amplitude. At a static load level of 40kN, the beam behaves linearly again. This is because the damage to the beam is so great that the main reinforcement has yielded and prevents the cracks from closing.

A typical restoring force surface from the experimental data is plotted in Figure 17 and the corresponding force displacement curve in Figure 18. As the experimental data were not initially intended for this purpose tests were only conducted at three different amplitudes, which is not sufficient to plot an accurate force/displacement graph. Nevertheless, from the restoring force surface and restoring force/displacement graph, non-linear behaviour can clearly be seen.

CONCLUDING REMARKS

Experimental results have shown that RC beams with distributed cracks exhibit a drop in natural frequency with increasing crack height. They also show that cracked RC beams exhibit a marked non-linear behaviour with the characteristics of a softening spring. However, neither the simple bi-linear nor the bi-linear with self-weight models of crack vibration reproduce this non-linear behaviour correctly. To model the observed behaviour it is necessary to consider the transition of the crack from open to closed in more detail. The models considered here do reproduce this behaviour if appropriate parameters are used, although it has not been possible to determine these parameters empirically. Further experimental studies are now being performed to obtain more data, which will be used to obtain empirical models for the cracked beam.

ACKNOWLEDGEMENTS

This work was sponsored by the UK Highways Agency. The testing was performed by Marina Lute of TU of Timisoara, Romania, as part of an EU Tempus project.

REFERENCES

(1) Cawley P. and Adams R.D., *J. of Strain Analysis*, **14**, 1979, pp. 49-57.

(2) Friswell M.I., A simple non-linear model of a cracked beam, *Proc. of the 10th IMAC*, San Diego, California, USA, 1992.

(3) Shen M.H.H. and Pierre C., *J. of Sound and Vib.*, **170**, Pt. 2, 1994, pp. 237-259.

(4) Abraham O.N.L. and Brandon J.A., *Trans. ASME: J. of Vib. & Acous.*, **117**, 1995, pp. 370-377.

(5) Eccles B.J., Owen J.S., Woodings M.A., & Choo B.S., A proposed new approach to full life quantitative bridge assessment, *Proc. of the 7th Int. Conf. on Structural Faults & Repair*, Edited by M.C. Forde, Edinburgh, 1997

(6) Das P.C., Owen J.S., Eccles B.J., Woodings M.A. & Choo B.S., *Transport Research Record Pt 2: Structures*, **1594**, 1997, pp. 115-124.

(7) Eccles B.J., Owen J.S., Choo B.S. & Woodings M.A., Non-linear vibrations of cracked reinforced concrete beams. *Proc. of the 4th European Conf. on Structural Dynamics*, Edited by L. Frýba & J. Náprstek, Prague, Czech Republic, 1999.

(8) Brandon J.A. and Mathias M.H., *J. of Sound and Vib.*, **186**, Pt. 2, 1995, pp. 350-354.

(9) Eccles B.J., *The use of non-linear dynamics in the health monitoring of reinforced concrete structures*, PhD thesis, University of Nottingham, 1999

(10) Cheng S.M., Wu X.J. and Wallace W., *J. of Sound and Vib.*, **225**, Pt. 1, 1999, pp. 201-208.

(11) Masri S.F. and Caughey T.K., *J. of App. Mech.*, **46**, 1979, pp 433-447.

(12) Worden K., *Parametric and non-parametric identification of non-linearity in structural dynamics*, PhD thesis, Heriot-Watt University, Edinburgh, 1989

(13) Weiland M. and Link M., Influence of measurement noise and incomplete model assumptions on the quality of identification results of weak nonlinear systems, *Proc. of 2nd Int. Conf. Structural Dynamics Modelling*, Windermere, UK, 1996

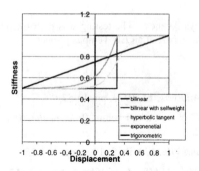

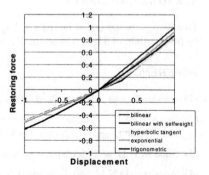

Figure 1 – Stiffness/displacement relationship for different models ($\mu = 0.5$)

Figure 2 – Displacement/force relationship for different models

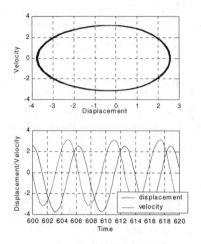

Figure 3 – Phase plot and time history of a bilinear model

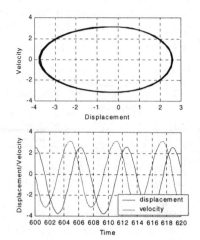

Figure 5 – Phase plot and time history of a hyperbolic tangent model, a = 5, b = - 1.5

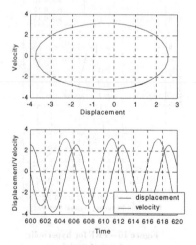

Figure 4 – Phase plot and time history of a bilinear with selfweight model

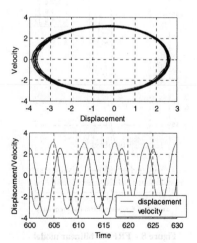

Figure 6 – Phase plot and time history of a exponential model, a = 10, b = -3

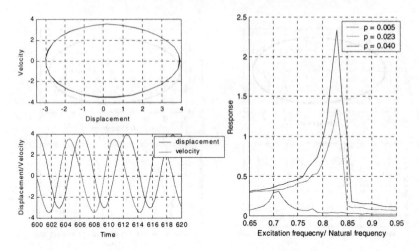

Figure 7 – Phase plot and time history of a trigonometric model

Figure 9 – FRF for bilinear with selfweight model

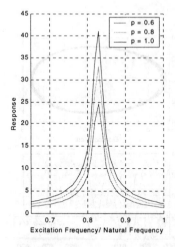

Figure 8 – FRF for bilinear model

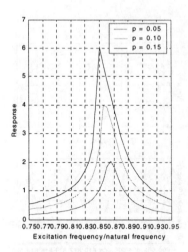

Figure 10 – FRF for hyperbolic tangent model

282

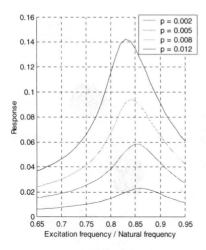

Figure 11 – FRF for exponential model,
a = 10, b = 0

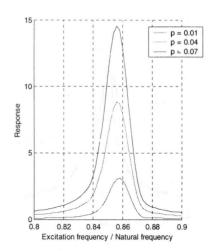

Figure 13 – FRF for trigonometric model

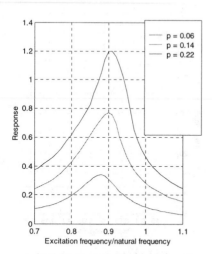

Figure 12 – FRF for exponential mode
a = 1, b = 5

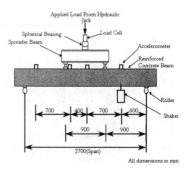

Figure 14 – Static load test setup

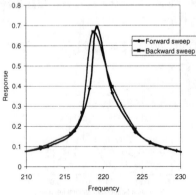

Figure 15 - Frequency Response Function for Beam 2 Mode 2 Load level

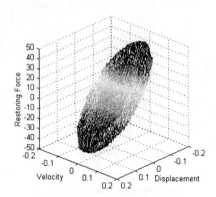

Figure 17 – Restoring force surface for beam 3 mode 2

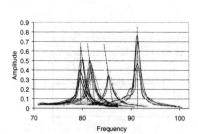

Figure 16 - Beam 2 Mode 1 for load level 0, 10, 20, 30, 40

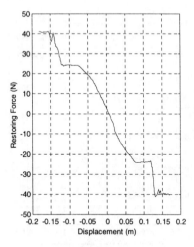

Figure 18 – Displacement / restoring force relationship

THERMOELASTIC INVESTIGATION OF IMPACT DAMAGED WOVEN GRP COMPOSITES

C. Santulli[†], J.M. Dulieu-Barton[‡] and W. Cantwell[*]

The feasibility of using the thermoelastic stress analysis technique to measure damage severity in woven composite materials is investigated. Controlled levels of impact damage are introduced into strip specimens manufactured from laminated woven E-glass polyester material. Thermoelastic data is obtained for the material in the damaged and undamaged state using the Deltatherm system. The readings are compared and it is demonstrated that, with knowledge of the impact location, the thermoelastic signal level increases with damage severity.

INTRODUCTION

Thermoelastic stress analysis [1] is a well-established experimental technique that has been used in a wide range of engineering applications. The technique is based on the measurement of the small temperature change that occurs in materials subjected to elastic cyclic stresses. For linear elastic, homogeneous materials it is readily shown that the stress changes in the material are directly related to the small temperature change. Until recently the standard equipment for thermoelastic stress analysis was the SPATE (Stress Pattern Analysis by the measurement of Thermal Emissions) system [1]. This system uses a single cell scanning infra-red detector to 'measure' the small temperature change. As a result of the SPATE system's scanning mode and its analogue signal processing and in order to obtain noise-free data typical scanning times can be up to three hours. Now [2], a new equipment, known as Deltatherm, is available that uses a detector focal plane array and digital processing techniques so that 'scan' times have reduced to as little as 1.2 seconds. Both systems provide a high resolution full-field digital image of the stress distribution on the surface of a test component.

Damage assessment and monitoring are topics that are receiving much current research interest; in particular the evolution and mechanisms of damage in laminated fibre reinforced plastic composites. The thermoelastic technique offers an advantage in studying these materials, in that it is non-contact and therefore does not use any specimen attachments (such as gauges) that may reinforce the material. However, as thermoelastic stress analysis requires cyclic loading, scan times of the length associated with SPATE often means that the component may damage or existing damage might grow during testing. The reduced data collection time associated with the Deltatherm system means

[†] University of Nottingham, School of Mechanical, Materials, Manufacturing Engineering and Management, University Park, Nottingham, NG7 2RD
[‡] University of Southampton, School of Engineering Sciences (Ship Science), Highfield, Southampton, SO17 1BJ
[*] University of Liverpool, Department of Engineering, Brownlow Hill, Liverpool, L69 3GH

that the application of thermoelastic stress analysis to damage studies in composite materials has become a more realistic proposition and has introduced the possibility of 'real time' monitoring of damage growth. The underlying theory that relates the thermoelastic response or signal, S, given by the infra-red detection system to the surface stresses in an orthotropic material is identical for both systems [1] and is as follows

$$S = \frac{1}{A^*}(\alpha_{11}^P \sigma_{11} + \alpha_{22}^P \sigma_{22}) \tag{1}$$

where A^* is a calibration constant based on the detector and material properties, α_{11}^P and α_{22}^P are the coefficients of thermal expansion in the principal material directions, and σ_{11} and σ_{22} are the changes in the co-ordinate direct stresses in the principal material directions.

It is clear from equation (1) that for a general orthotropic material quantitative stress values cannot be obtained from thermoelastic data alone. The use of thermoelastic techniques for the analysis of orthotropic components should not be dismissed as the quantity $(\alpha_{11}^P \sigma_{11} + \alpha_{22}^P \sigma_{22})$ is an important stress metric and with calibration (e.g. [3]) can be used for validation purposes. Moreover, as $(\alpha_{11}^P \sigma_{11} + \alpha_{22}^P \sigma_{22})$ is directly related to the stress level in a component it can be used as the basis for a damage parameter.

In the past successful damage studies have been carried out using the SPATE system; these are described in the review given in Ref. [4]. Impact damage in sandwich construction material has been studied using the SPATE system [5] and damage evolution under fatigue load in a woven glass fibre polyester composite has been monitored using the Deltatherm system [6].

In the present paper the feasibility of using thermoelastic stress analysis to quantify the level of impact damage in woven composites is assessed. The output from the infra-red detector is related to the surface stresses and hence the orientation of the surface weave. Therefore the surface weave must be accurately related to the 'stress pattern' obtained from the Deltatherm system and the position of the impact must be located. A detailed description of the test specimens and the means of introducing the impact damage is provided, along with the application of the theory to the specimens. An analysis routine that relates the Deltatherm output from an undamaged region to that from an equivalent damaged region is developed, the results of which form the basis of the feasibility study.

TEST SPECIMENS AND EXPERIMENTAL ARRANGEMENTS

The test specimen material was an E-glass reinforced polyester; the E-glass was in the form of a woven mat and the resin was an unsaturated polyester (1629 NT) with styrene as a coupling agent. The fibre mats and the resin were laminated into sheets using a resin transfer moulding process to give a fibre fraction for the laminate of 63% by volume. Ten plies of the woven mat were used which gave the sheets a nominal thickness of 3 mm. Four strips of material 200 mm long by 20 mm were cut from the sheet in a '0°/90°' orientation. To prevent any damage being introduced by the action of the gripping pressure of the loading machine glass fibre/epoxy end tabs (40 mm long by 20 mm wide by 3 mm thick) were bonded at each end and on both sides of the strips.

The impact damage was produced using a hemispherical drop-weight steel impactor mounted in a Ceast Fractovis impact tower. Each of the four specimens was pneumatically clamped on an annular support and different mass impactors (2.53 kg, 3.89 kg, 4.99 kg and 7.54 kg) were used to provide increasing levels of impact energy (5 J, 7.5 J, 10 J and 15J) and hence increasing damage in each specimen. (The impact tower was fitted with an anti-rebound device so that each specimen only received a single impact.) After impact there was no visible damage on any of the specimens, so micrographs and c-scans [7] were used to locate the damage. The micrographs provided a more detailed view of the surface damage and the c-scans revealed the location of internal damage. It was clear from both the micrograph and c-scan data that the position of impact was not in the centre of the specimen but offset towards one edge or the other.

After the impact had been introduced the thermoelastic tests were carried out. The specimens were mounted in an Instron 8501 servo hydraulic test machine and loaded to a stress level of 105 ± 35 MPa. This meant that the maximum load was approximately 50% of the tensile strength of the material. A major assumption in developing the theory that leads to equation (1) is that the temperature changes occur adiabatically [1]. It has been shown that in laminated reinforced plastic composites that this assumption may not be valid [8]. In metals a cyclic loading frequency of around 10 to 20 Hz is usually sufficient to achieve adiabatic conditions; in composites this may not be the case. Therefore the specimens were tested at six loading frequencies of 5, 10, 15, 20 25 and 30 Hz. In TSA it is standard practice to coat the test specimens with a matt black paint in order to standardise and enhance the surface emissivity [1]. It has been shown [5] that for glass reinforced polyester that this is unnecessary. As the paint coating can also influence the surface thermal conditions and cause non-adiabatic behaviour [9], the specimens used in this work were not coated. The thermoelastic data was obtained using a Deltatherm 1000 system fitted with a 25 mm lens; for each test the accumulation time was set to 1.2 seconds and to reduce noise the data was integrated over 2.5 minutes.

ANALYSIS PROCEDURE

A Deltatherm image of the specimen impacted with an energy of 10 J is shown in Figure 1. The impacted region is clearly visible to the right of the centre of the image. The regular pattern of the woven surface structure is also evident away from the damaged region. To analyse this data the surface was divided into 'structural units' that represented one complete 'cycle' of the surface weave pattern. The surface weave configuration of a structural unit is shown in Figure 2, along with the direction of the applied load. In the analysis the data from the edges of the specimen was disregarded so that the width of the structural unit was less than the width of the specimen as indicated in Figure 2.

It is clear from Figure 2 that the specimen is made-up two weave orientations, one parallel to the applied stress, σ_{app}, and the other transverse to the applied stress. This means that for the parallel weave orientation equation (1) reduces to

$$\sigma_{11} = \sigma_{app} = A^* \alpha_{11}^P S \tag{2}$$

and for the transverse ply orientation

$$\sigma_{22} = \sigma_{app} = A^* \alpha_{22}^P S \tag{3}$$

These equations show that the signal from each weave orientation will be different and mean that there will be two distinct signals from the specimen, i.e. one from the parallel weave and the other from the transverse weave. An inspection of Figure 1 shows that approximately this is so, however there is a variation in the signal from the parallel weave. As the variations occur in a regular manner it is likely that they are caused by the manufacturing technique and by the woven nature of the surface structure resulting in an uneven distribution of fibre to resin on the surface.

To aid analysis and to quantify the variation in the readings from the parallel weave the structural unit was divided into twelve sections as shown in Figure 2. The B sections indicate the transverse weave, the C sections indicate the parallel weave either side of the transverse weave and the A and D sections indicate the parallel weave above and below the B/C sections. Readings were taken from each of the sections in the damaged and undamaged regions of each of the four specimens and processed as described in the following two sections.

RESULTS FROM UNDAMAGED REGION

For each specimen and loading frequency readings were taken from a structural unit approximately 30mm away from the impacted region. The average of the readings for each section group (e.g. A1, A2 and A3) was obtained and in each case gave a variation of around 5%. For the A and the D sections the values were virtually identical and the combined coefficient of variation of the average of the A and D sections was less than 5%.

Figure 3 shows uncalibrated signal readings plotted against frequency for the specimen impacted with an energy of 5 J; the A and D weaves are shown as combined values. From 10 to 25 Hz there is a clear decrease in the signal for the A, C and D weaves from around 7100 U to 6500 U indicating there may be some non-adiabatic behaviour at these frequencies; between 25 and 30 Hz there is practically no change in the signal. For weave B there is a slight reduction in the signal although not as marked as in the parallel weaves. It is noteworthy that the readings from weave C is almost the same as those for weaves A and D, which confirms that only small variations arise in the signal as a result of manufacturing.

A similar procedure was carried out on the other three specimens. The specimens with the 7.5 J and 10 J impacts yielded much the same results. However the specimen with the 15 J impact gave slightly increased results of the order of 10 %; this may be due to matrix cracking remote from the impact region caused by a greater specimen deflection at the higher impact energy.

RESULTS FROM DAMAGED REGION

The purpose of this section of work is to quantify the effects of damage on the thermoelastic signal from the material at the point of impact and on the signal from the area surrounding the impact. To avoid any possible discrepancies due to non-adiabatic behaviour it was decided that only the readings taken at 30 Hz should be used (see above). The signal from each section of the structural unit in the damaged region was normalised by dividing it by the appropriate average reading taken from the undamaged region, e.g.

$$S_{NAI} = \frac{S_{DAi}}{S_{UAI}} = \frac{(\sum_1^{n_{AI}} S_{DAI})/n_{AI}}{(\sum_1^{n_{AI}} S_{UAI} + \sum_1^{n_{A2}} S_{UA2} + \sum_1^{n_{A3}} S_{UA3} + \sum_1^{n_{D1}} S_{UDI} + \sum_1^{n_{D2}} S_{UD2} + \sum_1^{n_{D3}} S_{UD3})/N} \quad (4)$$

where the subscripts U and D denote undamaged and damaged readings and n is the number of signal readings from each section and N is the total number of readings from the six sections (or three for B and C) used in the averaging process.

The normalised results for each impact energy are plotted as histograms in Figure 4, 5, 6, and 7 for 5, 7.5, 10 and 15 J respectively. For this type of presentation an S_D/S_U value of unity means that the damage has had no effect and that the material is in its 'normal' condition. Because of signal noise the normal condition should be regarded as somewhere between 1.10 and 0.90. Values of outside this range indicate that a change in the stress state and/or material properties has occurred and that the damage is influencing the signal. In assessing the results in Figures 4 to 7 it is important to locate the position of the impact; the Deltatherm images were used to identify an approximate position, along with the c-scan and micrograph data. The approximate positions of the impacts within the structural unit is given in Table 1.

TABLE 1 Approximate position of impact

Impact energy (J)	Section
5	A1
7.5	C2
10	B2
15	A3/B3

Figure 4 shows the results for the 5 J impact energy. From examination of the Deltatherm image and the micrographs it appeared that for this specimen the impact occurred in section A1, this is confirmed by the fact that the largest normalised reading is given by section A1. This means that sections B1, B3, C1, C3 and D3 were adjacent to the impact; these regions have S_D/S_U readings of greater than one indicating that these regions were also affected by the impact.

Figure 5 shows the results for the 7.5 J impact. Here the impact took place in section C2, which gives a normalised reading of 1.2. Sections A2, A3, B3, D2 and D3 were adjacent to the impact region and the impact appears to have little effect on the A and D sections. (This indicates that it is likely that the 5 J impact (see Figure 4) occurred at the interface between A1 and D3 as the D3 reading is comparatively large.) Although only section B3 is adjacent to the impact all of the B readings are in excess of 1.2. This points to the possibility that the transverse weave signal response is more sensitive to damage than the parallel weave.

In Figure 6 the impact took place in section B2, which gave a S_U/S_D value of 1.6, i.e. 30% greater than all the other values obtained from this specimen. The adjacent sections are A2, A3, C3 D2 and D1, with the exception of A2 these appear not to have been affected by the impact. As with the 7.5 J test the readings from the non-adjacent B sections are large, once again indicating that the transverse fibre signal response is more susceptible to damage.

Figure 7 shows the results for the 15 J impact that took place at the interface of section A3 and B3. Although, A3 and B3 give large S_D/S_U readings the most noticeable trend is that all of the readings are greater than unity indicating that the impact damage is provided by the higher energy level is spreading to influence the thermoelastic readings from the entire structural unit.

DISCUSSION

This work is not intended to provide an in-depth study of the effect of impact damage on woven composites, but to show that thermoelastic data obtained from impact damaged specimen can be interpreted in a meaningful way in respect to the level of impact damage. The results given in the previous section have demonstrated that despite the complex surface structure of the material this can be done. It is clear that without prior knowledge of the point of impact the interpretation of the results would not be straight-forward. However, the Deltatherm images provided an indication of the impact position, which was confirmed by other non-destructive techniques.

A notable feature of this work was that the damage was mainly sub-surface and it was detected and quantified using the thermoelastic technique. The impact damage clearly disrupted the regular pattern of the data obtained from the undamaged regions and gave a good indication of the damage location. The technique of taking the signal readings from small sections of the specimens and normalising them with respect to equivalent undamaged signal proved successful as the point of impact was identified as that with the greatest S_U/S_D value for each specimen. Most notable is the general increase in the thermoelastic response of the transverse sections as the impact energy increases (see Figure 8) regardless of the location of the impact. This indicates that the thermoelastic response of the transverse orientation is more sensitive to low levels of damage in comparison to the parallel orientation. This result may only be valid for the tensile loading mode, as the transverse weave will be weak in comparison to the parallel weave and any minor damage will be exaggerated. Another possibility is that the resin material properties dominate the response from this mode (see equation (3)) and comparatively small matrix cracks may serve to change the thermoelastic properties of the material. The change in the signal from the transverse weave as damage increases is certainly an important finding of the work and clearly warrants further investigation.

A cautionary note is the change in the thermoelastic response in the undamaged material over the frequency range. A similar variation was noted in the damaged region and hence the decision to use the highest frequency achievable with the loading machine. Non-adiabatic behaviour is clearly a topic that requires further detailed examination, in particular the changes in the thermal conditions that occur as the damage progresses.

CLOSURE

The thermoelastic stress analysis technique has been used to study damage in woven glass polyester composites. The work has clearly shown that the thermoelastic technique has great potential in this area and that it is feasible to use the thermoelastic signal as a damage indicator.

REFERENCES

(1)   Dulieu-Barton J.M. and Stanley, P., *J. Strain Analysis*, Vol. 33, 1998, pp 93-104.

(2)   Lesniak, J. R. and Boyce, B.R., A high speed differential thermography camera, *Proceedings of the SEM Spring Conference on Experimental Mechanics*, Baltimore, 1994, pp 491-497

(3)   Dulieu-Smith, J.M., Shenoi, R.A., Read, P.J.C.L., Quinn, S. and Moy, S.S.J., *J. Applied Composite Materials*, Vol. 4, 1997, pp 283-303.

(4)   Dulieu-Barton, J.M. and Stanley, P., *Strain*, Vol. 35, 1999, pp 41-48

(5)   Dulieu-Barton, J.M. and Chapman, L.E., On the thermoelastic analysis of impact damage on foam-cored sandwich construction composites, *Proceedings of the 3rd International Conference on Damage Assessment of Structures (DAMAS 99), (Key Engineering Materials Vols. 167-168)*, 1999, Dublin, pp 35-42.

(6)   Dulieu-Smith, J.M., Quinn, S. and Minervini, D., Thermoelastic analysis of damage on woven glass/polyester panels, *Proceedings of the SEM Spring Conference on Experimental Mechanics*, Seattle, 1997, pp 359-360.

(7)   Santulli, C., *Impact damage evaluation in woven composites using acoustic and thermoelastic techniques*, PhD Thesis (submitted) University of Liverpool, 2000.

(8)   Wong, A.K., *J Phys. Chem. Solids*, Vol. 51, 1991, 483-494

(9)   McKelvie, J. and Mackenzie, A.K., Signal attenuation due to internal and external factors, in *Thermoelastic Stress Analysis*, IOP Publishing Ltd., Bristol, 1991, pp 85-104.

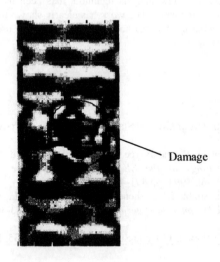

Damage

FIGURE 1 Deltatherm image of specimen impacted with an energy of 10 J

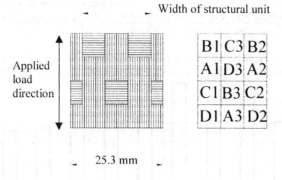

FIGURE 2 A structural unit of surface ply

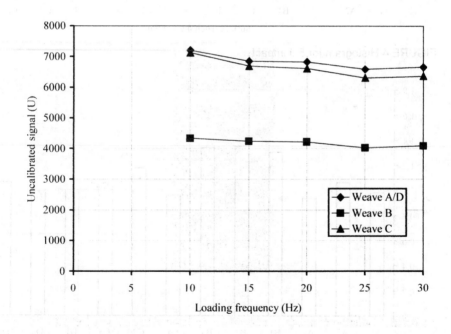

FIGURE 3 Thermoelastic signal against loading frequency for undamaged
material

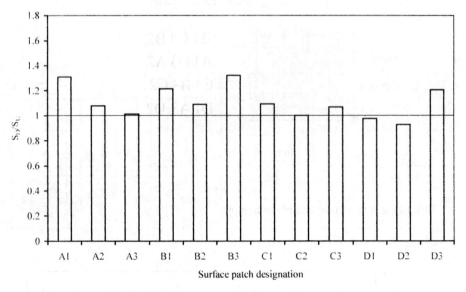

FIGURE 4 Histogram for 5 J impact

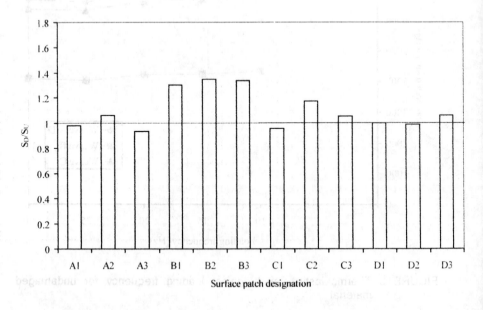

FIGURE 5 Histogram for 7.5 J impact

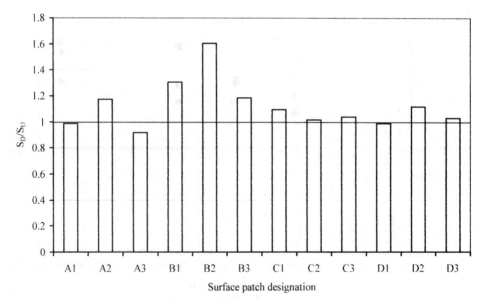

FIGURE 6 Histogram for 10 J impact

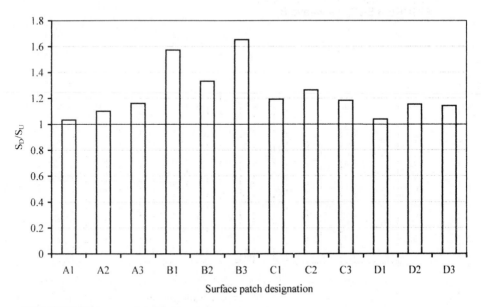

FIGURE 7 Histogram for 15 J impact

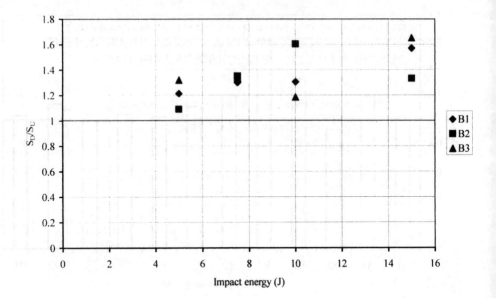

FIGURE 8 S_D/S_U for weave B

PREDICTION OF FATIGUE STRENGTH OF ADHESIVELY BONDED COMPOSITE JOINTS IN A HOSTILE ENVIRONMENT USING A FRACTURE MECHANICS APPROACH

M.M. Abdel Wahab[*], I. A. Ashcroft[♣], A.D. Crocombe[*],

D. J. Hughes[♣] and S. J. Shaw[♠]

The prediction of fatigue strength of adhesively bonded joints is investigated using a fracture mechanics approach. Composite substrates made of Unidirectional (UD) and Multidirectional (MD) laminates are bonded together using epoxy film adhesive. The joints are exposed to different environmental conditions. From linear and non-linear finite element analyses, elastic and elasto-plastic fracture parameters are calculated for two different inherent cracks. The first crack is initiated at the adhesive/adherend interface, while the second is in the centre of the adhesive layer. The fracture parameters extracted from the results of the UD joints are used to predict fatigue thresholds of the MD ones. Both, the elastic strain energy release rate and the J-integral that accounts for plasticity, have been shown to correlate with the threshold load for the different joints.

INTRODUCTION

The effects of environmental conditions on the fatigue life are one of the most important topics in the design of adhesively bonded structures. In most cases, bonded joints are prone to fail under static or cyclic loads in hostile environmental conditions, which cause deterioration to the adhesive and interface. This indicates the importance of studying the effect of environmental condition on the mechanical behaviour of bonded joints in order to enhance their design and extent their service life.

[*] School of Mechanical & Materials Engineering, University of Surrey, Guildford, GU2 7XH, UK

[♣] Department of Mechanical Engineering, Loughborough University, Leicestershire, LE11 3TU, UK

[♠] Structural Materials Centre, DERA, Farnborough, Hants, GU14 0LX, UK

Many papers that discuss the effect of environments on the performance of bonded joints, have been reported in the literature. Brewis et al [1,2] have studied the effect of temperature on the strength of aluminium lap joints bonded with epoxide adhesive. They found that the joint strength significantly decreases as the test temperature increases. Girifalco and Good [3] have shown that the strength of the joint interface decreases with increasing temperature. Although they studied the case of polymer-to-polymer interface, it is likely that adhesive/substrate interface would have the same trend of results. Crocombe [4,5] has presented a numerical technique coupling diffusion and mechanical analysis in order to predict the residual strength of adhesive joints exposed to moisture degradation. He concluded that the wet and dry joint strength can be predicted using the adhesive failure strains.

In this paper, numerical simulations and fracture mechanics analysis are carried out for Lap Strap (LS) joints in order to predict the fatigue threshold. The fatigue thresholds of Multidirectional (MD) carbon fibre composite bonded joints are predicted using the results of the Unidirectional (UD) joints. The experimental results of the LS joints tested under fatigue loading, at different test temperatures and aged in dry or wet environments are reported in [6]. It has been found that the fatigue threshold of the joint is not affected by temperature until the glass transition temperature is reached. The combination of moisture and temperature has the most severe effect on the fatigue resistance.

The strain energy release rate is calculated using two different methods. The first method is the crack closure integral (G) [7] that is based on linear elastic fracture mechanics and can be valid when the plastic zone is limited to a very small distance at the crack tip. This method assumes also that as the crack extends by a small amount the energy dissipation in the body is only due to this crack extension and therefore does not account for any plastic deformation. The second method is the J-integral [8] that is applicable to any stress-strain relationship and therefore takes into account the size of the plastic zone at the crack tip. The J-integral is more appropriate than G when the plastic zone size becomes larger.

JOINT CONFIGURATIONS, AGEING AND TEST CONDITIONS

Carbon Fibre Reinforced Polymers (CFRP) substrates are made of a modified bismaleimide/epoxy reinforced with 60% carbon fibres. Two types of laminates are manufactured; UD of 16 plies at $0°$ and MD of $[(0/-45/+45/0)_2]_s$. Table 1 summarises the material properties of the composite laminates. It is worth mentioning that the manufacturers have reported that the temperature does not have a large effect on these material properties in the temperature range of -50 to 90°C.

TABLE 1 Material properties of UD and MD laminates

Property	E_1 (GPa)	E_2 (GPa)	G_{12} (GPa)	v_{12}	v_{21}
UD	174	9.64	7	0.36	0.02
MD	99.8	28.1	25.7	0.69	0.2

The mechanical properties of the adhesive are determined in [6] for different temperatures and moisture contents. The tests were carried out on dumbell shaped specimens under a constant cross head speed of 1mm/min. The E-modulus, yield stress, ultimate stress and strain at failure are summarised in table 2 for different ageing/test conditions. In the first column of table 2, the first number refers to the test temperature (-50°C, 22°C or 90°C), while the expression after the comma refers to the ageing conditions, i.e., dry (room temperature) or wet (45°C, 85% relative humidity). LS joints are manufactured using epoxy film adhesive as shown in figure 1. The LS joint is similar to the Cracked Lap Shear (CLS) joint except that no crack is initiated in the adhesive layer. The fillet at the overlap edge can be either square or tapered.

TABLE 2 Mechanical properties of adhesive

	E-modulus (MPa)	Yield stress (MPa)	Ultimate stress (MPa)	Strain to failure (%)
-50°C	2850	53.0	94.4	7.0
22°C, dry	2241	27	57.7	8.3
22°C, wet	1990	30	51.3	10.7
90°C, dry	800	13	21.8	61.6

Sinusoidal waveform fatigue loading at frequency of 5Hz and stress amplitude ratio of 0.1 is applied to the different joints. The fatigue thresholds are determined as the highest load at which no damage is observed for 10^6 cycles. Table 3 summarises the measured fatigue thresholds for the UD and the MD joints for the different ageing and testing conditions. From table 3, it can be seen that testing in cold environment (-50°C) has little effect on the joint strength. The wet ageing has little effect if the joint is tested at 22°C. Also, testing at 90°C after dry ageing does not affect the fatigue threshold significantly. Cracking was always initiated in the adhesive layer near the corner point or at the interface and then propagated in the fillet, along the fillet/substrate or the adhesive/substrate interfaces.

TABLE 3 Fatigue threshold (kN) - Lap strap joints

Test temperature	Ageing conditions	UD	MD
-50°C	-	14±1	11±1
22°C	dry	15±1	11±1
22°C	45°C, 85RH	15±1	9±1
90°C	dry	14±1	9±1

ELASTIC AND ELASTO-PLASTIC FRACTURE ANALYSIS

Fracture mechanics is a convenient technique that can be used to predict the crack initiation load. In order to be able to calculate a fracture parameter at the corner point, an inherent crack should be considered. This crack might be at the interface between the adhesive and the substrate or in the adhesive layer. As a first step an interface crack is introduced. In the finite element model, the mid-side nodes at the crack tip are shifted to the quarter position to produce square root stress singularity. Although in this case (interface crack, elasto-plastic analysis), the stress singularity will be complex and different from 0.5, this approximation can provide acceptable results for G [9]. It should also be noted that because J-integral is a path independent integral and can be taken away from the crack tip, it is not affected by the approximation in modelling the stress and strain fields at the crack tip. This is of course one of the main advantages of the J-integral beside its applicability to elasto-plastic analysis. For the quarter-point element shown in figure 2, the strain energy release rate (G) is calculated from the opening displacement ahead of the crack tip and the nodal forces behind the crack tip using the crack closure technique [10]:

$$G_I = \frac{u_{yl}}{\Delta}(F_{yj} + (1.5\pi - 4)F_{yi})$$

$$G_{II} = \frac{u_{xl}}{\Delta}(F_{xj} + (1.5\pi - 4)F_{xi}) \tag{1}$$

Where G_I and G_{II} are the mode I and II strain energy release rate. u_y and u_x are the opening and sliding displacement and F_y and F_x the nodal forces in the y and x directions, respectively. The total strain energy release rate is simply the sum of G_I and G_{II}.

The J-integral method is an energy approach based on calculating a certain path-independent integral inside the solution domain. Rice [8] has shown that the following integral quantity is path independent when taken along any line path, which encloses the crack tip and has initial and end points lying on the two crack faces:

$$J = \int_{\Gamma}[W \, dy - (t_x \frac{\partial u_x}{\partial x} + t_y \frac{\partial u_y}{\partial x})ds] \tag{2}$$

Where Γ is the path, *ds* is the differential distance on this path, W is the strain energy density, (t_x, t_y) and (u_x, u_y) are the tractions and the displacements, respectively, in the x and y directions. The J-integral method has been widely used in fracture problems since it involves only the evaluation of a contour integral from the far field solution without any special treatment in the region surrounding the crack tip. Furthermore, it has been demonstrated that the J-integral for a delaminated crack in composite laminates is conservative [11] and has been applied to an interface crack [12]. In the finite element calculation, the differentiation of the second term in equation (2) is calculated numerically by shifting the path a small amount in the x-direction. It is therefore important to ensure that the finite element mesh is fine enough where the path should be defined to minimise the numerical error.

Figure 3 shows the finite element idealisation at the crack tip of a typical LS joint. As a first step, the crack length that should be assumed at the interface is investigated. This crack length should be as small as possible in order to represent the non-cracked joint. The elastic strain energy release rate is calculated for different small crack lengths for the case of 22°C/dry UD at threshold load and plotted in figure 4. For a crack length '*a*' below 0.5mm, the variation of G as a function of *a* is very high (G goes to zero as the crack length approaches zero). However, for crack lengths greater than 0.5mm, the strain energy release rate is almost linear as a function of *a* (constant slope dG/d*a*). Therefore, the most convenient crack length that should be used must be larger than 0.5mm. In the rest of this paper, a crack length of 0.5mm is used for all analyses. It should be noted that the concept of inherent flaw size introduced by Anderson and DeVries [13] can be applied. However, the fatigue threshold toughness of the interface should be measured for different crack sizes. Because in the present analysis a comparison will be made between the UD and MD joints, the exact value of the inherent flaw size is of minor importance. A typical deformation at the crack tip is shown in figure 5.

Next, the plastic zone that is formed at the crack tip due to the non-linear behaviour of the adhesive layer is considered. The load is applied in different steps. At each load step, the plastic zone size, G and J are calculated. Figure 6 shows a contour plot of the von-Mises plastic strain at the crack tip at the threshold load. The plastic zone is formulated only around the lower crack face (adhesive side). This is because only adhesive was modelled with elastic-plastic mechanical properties. The variation of G and J as a function of loading for different test/ageing conditions is shown in figure 7 for the UD joints. For small load values, when the plastic zone is small, G agrees very well with J. However, for higher loading and larger plastic zones, the difference between G and J is very high. In fact, at this stage the crack closure technique is no longer applicable as it does not account for the effect of plasticity. The highest discrepancy between G and J is for the 90°C dry case in which the plastic zone is the largest. The results for the different cases at threshold loads are summarised in table 4. The elastic strain energy release rate (denoted as G_e in table 4) is also given for convenience.

Assuming that the interface fracture toughness of the adhesive/UD is equal to that of the adhesive/MD (the fibre orientation of the first ply in the UD and MD laminates adjacent to the adhesive is the same), the fatigue thresholds for the MD can be predicted from the results of the UD joints as given in table 5. The prediction were carried out by plotting the load against G for the MD joints. The threshold load was calculated from the intercept of the fracture energy (G_{th} calculated from UD joints) with the curve. The predictions using J and G_e are presented in the third and the fourth columns, respectively. In general, J gives better prediction than G_e. It should be noted that large deformations have not been considered in the FE analysis for the linear elastic case (G_e).

TABLE 4 Comparison between G and J (N/m^2) - Interface crack

	UD				MD			
Test/ageing conditions	P (kN)	J	G	G_e	P (kN)	J	G	G_e
-50°C	14	205.6	219.7	316.8	11	202.9	229.7	424.3
22°C/dry	15	184.3	229.7	343.0	11	168.2	211.3	429.2
22°C/wet	15	184.0	227.5	348.8	9	125.1	143.3	354.7
90°C/ dry	14	75.7	244.7	329.4	9	71.12	184.6	403.1

TABLE 5 Prediction of MD threshold load - Interface crack

Test/ageing conditions	Measured P (kN)	Predicted P (kN) (J)	Predicted P (kN) (G$_e$)
-50°C	11	11.09	8.21
22°C/dry	11	11.65	8.79
22°C/wet	9	11.76	8.8
90°C/ dry	9	10.86	8.17

Initiating the crack in the adhesive layer rather than at the adherend/adhesive interface is further investigated. A crack of 0.5mm is initiated in the centre of the adhesive layer and similar procedures as described above are followed. The plastic von-Mises strain contour for the 22°C/dry joint at threshold load is shown in figure 8. The results are summarised in table 6. Comparing table 4 to table 6, it can be seen that the elastic strain energy release rate (G$_e$) is about the same for the interface crack and the adhesive crack for all joints. Except for the 90°C/dry joints, the J for the interface crack agrees well with that for the adhesive crack. The prediction of the fatigue thresholds for the MD joints using the J and G$_e$ of the UD joints at thresholds load is presented in table 7. In the last column of table 7, the predicted P using the strain energy release rate calculated from non-linear geometric analysis (G$_{ng}$) but linear material model is presented. The threshold loads predicted using G$_e$ and J (-50°C, 22°C/dry and 22°C/wet) are similar to those predicted by the interface crack (table 5). For large plastic deformation, as in the case of 90°C/dry, J is more sensitive to the position of crack initiation. The results obtained using G$_{ng}$ are comparable to those obtained using J except for the 90°C/dry case.

TABLE 6 Comparison between G and J (N/m^2) - Lap strap joint - Adhesive crack

	UD				MD			
Test/ageing conditions	P (kN)	J	G	G$_e$	P (kN)	J	G	G$_e$
-50°C	14	197.8	203.3	318.5	11	201.3	212.8	432.2
22°C/dry	15	181.0	202.3	344.0	11	166.8	186.0	435.0
22°C/wet	15	178.9	193.5	346.0	9	124.0	130.7	356.7
90°C/ dry	14	54.56	175.7	327.6	9	56.5	113.4	400.6

TABLE 7 Prediction of MD threshold load - Adhesive crack

Test/ageing conditions	Measured P (kN)	Predicted P (kN) (J)	Predicted P (kN) (G_e)	Predicted P (kN) (G_{ng})
-50°C	11	11.11	8.1	11.5
22°C/dry	11	11.60	8.69	11.0
22°C/wet	9	11.59	8.73	11.0
90°C/ dry	9	7.94	8.17	11.0

CONCLUSIONS

A fracture mechanics approach has been used to analyse the fatigue thresholds of composite Lap Strap adhesively bonded joints. The fracture parameters have been extracted from linear and non-linear FE results using the crack closure technique and the J-integral method. Two inherent cracks are considered; an interface crack and an adhesive crack at the corner point where stress singularity is expected. It is found that both G_e and J of the UD and MD joints correlate reasonably at threshold. In case of large plastic deformation, J is sensitive to the position of the initiated crack.

REFERENCES

(1) Brewis, D., Comyn, J. and Shalash, R., The effect of moisture and temperature on the properties of an epoxide-polyamide adhesive in relation to its performance in single lap joints, Int. J. Adhes. Adhes., 1982, Vol.2, pp.215-222.

(2) Brewis, D., Comyn, J. and Shalash, R., The effect of water and heat on the properties of an epoxide adhesive in relation to its performance in single lap joints, 1983, Polymer, Vol.24, pp.67-70.

(3) Girifalco, L. and Good, R., A theory for the estimation of surface and interfacial energies: part I, Derivation and application to interface tension, 1957, J. Phys. Chem, Vol.61, pp.904-909.

(4) Crocombe A.D., "Durability modelling concepts and tools for the cohesive environmental degradation of bonded structures", Int J Adhesion and Adhesives, 1997, 17-3, 229-238.

(5) Crocombe, A.D., Hambly, H. and Pan, J., 1st World Congr on Adhes. And Rel. Phen., Dechema, 1998, e.V., 1.2.

(6) Ashcroft, I.A., Abdel Wahab, M.M., Crocombe, A.D., Hughes, D.J. and Shaw, S.J., The effect of environment on the fatigue of composite joints: Part 1 testing and fractography, September 1999, Composites part A, Submitted.

(7) Irwin, G. R., Fracture, Handbuch de physik, vol. VI, Springer, Berlin, 1958.

(8) Rice, J. R., A path-independent integral and the approximate analysis of strain concentration by notches and cracks, Trans. ASME, J. Appl. Mech., 1968, vol.35, pp.379-386.

(9) Abdel Wahab, M. M., Finite elements for general power type singularity problems in fracture mechanics, Ph.D. thesis, Department of Civil Engineering, Katholieke Universiteit Leuven, Belgium, 1995.

(10) Sethuraman, R. and Maiti, S.K., Finite element based computation of strain energy release rate by a modified crack closure integral, Eng. Fracture Mechanics, 1988, Vol.30, pp.227-231.

(11) Yan, X.Q., Du, S. and Wang D., Engng Frac, Mech., 1991, No 1, pp.67-74.

(12) Lee, L.J. and Tu, D.W., Composite Science and Technology, 1993, 47, pp.67-74.

(13) Anderson, G.P. and DeVries, K.L., "Predicting strength of adhesive joints from test results", Int. J. of Fracture, 1989, Vol. 39, 191-200.

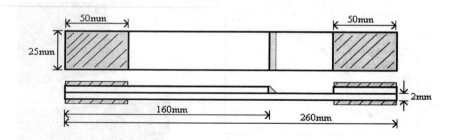

FIGURE 1 Lap strap joint

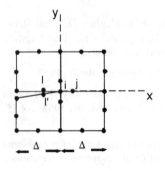

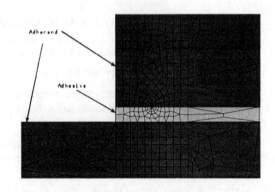

FIGURE 2 Crack closure method

FIGURE 3 FE idealisation at the
crack tip - Interface crack

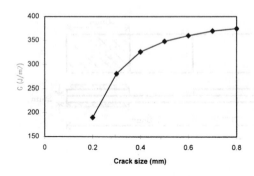

FIGURE 4: Elastic SERR versus a

FIGURE 5: Deformation at crack tip -
Interface crack

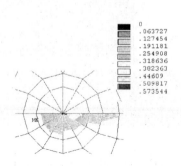

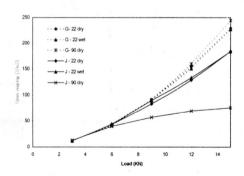

FIGURE 6: von-Mises plastic strain
- Interface crack

FIGURE 7: Comparison between G and J
- Interface crack

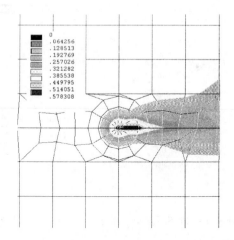

FIGURE 8: von-Mises plastic strain - Adhesive crack

FINITE ELEMENT SIMULATION OF THE MECHANICALLY COUPLED COOK OFF EXPERIMENT FOR HIGH EXPLOSIVES

J.M. Gerken[*], J.G. Bennett[*], and F.W. Smith[†]

This paper develops and applies a method to model dynamic crack propagation in structures. The technique is developed via the three field Hu-Washizu Energy Principle for the implicit finite element method. This method is then incorporated into simulation of an experiment called the Mechanically Coupled Cook Off (MCCO) experiment in which a confined sample of polymer bonded explosive is heated and then ignited. High-speed photographs of the experiment show a pattern of cracks propagating through the explosive. The results of the numerical simulation show that the general features of the experiment are reproduced.

INTRODUCTION

There has been considerable interest in developing numerical models having the capability to predict the structural static and dynamic response of structures in the presence of failure by fracture. There are several challenges that must be addressed in modeling of dynamic crack propagation. Primary among these challenges are producing the correct material behavior in the presence of fracture and modeling geometry changes that are a result of crack propagation. Previous and ongoing efforts to model fracture in structures include most, if not all, of the well developed computational methods (Liebowitz et al. [1] and Aliabadi [2]). In reviews given by Nishioka [3] and De Borst [4], among others, it can be seen that much of this effort has been dedicated to fracture modeling using the finite element method. Some of the techniques employed include special element formulation to model crack tip singularities and discontinuities (e.g. Banks-Sills and Sherman [5], and Lotfi and Shing, [6]), adaptive meshing (e.g. Nishioka et al. [7]), fracture parameter calculation (e.g. Li et al. [8], and Parks [9]), damage evolution (e.g. Lemaitre [10]) and discrete fracture models (e.g. Hoff et al. [11], Liaw et al. [12], and Xu and Needleman, [13]). While these methods provide valuable computational abilities with specific applications, the main goal of this work is to provide an accurate fracture model that is comparable in complexity and application to current structural finite element simulations.

[*]Los Alamos National Laboratory, ESA-EA MS P946, Los Alamos, New Mexico 87545, USA

[†]Colorado State University, Department of Mechanical Engineering

This paper presents an implicit finite element method, developed by Gerken [14], that models discrete fracture in two-dimensional structures and addresses the primary challenges of discrete fracture modeling. The method incorporates discrete fracture by allowing the propagation of cracks along pre-existing element interfaces. The approach to developing such a method is to first develop a 2 dimensional finite element from the Hu-Washizu Energy Principle, which has a small, "virtual", crack on its edge. The finite element mesh then contains a virtual crack at each element interface along which discrete cracks can propagate. The analysis is formulated on the element level and the implicit finite element code ABAQUS/Standard [15] is used to enforce the boundary conditions, assemble the global equations and solve for the nodal variables.

This method is then used in a finite element model of the Mechanically Coupled Cook Off (MCCO) of High Explosives Experiment. The MCCO experiment is one in which the "cook-off" of a plastic bonded explosive material is produced by confining a thick circular ring of the explosive material in a thin circular metal ring and then subjecting the assembly to a uniform temperature increase. After the explosive becomes highly reactive, several optical photographs of the explosive are recorded. One of the phenomenon observed in the photographs is 3 to 5 distinct narrow zones of luminous activity propagate from the inner surface of the explosive ring outward towards the confinement ring. These luminous zones are postulated to be the ignition of newly exposed surface as discrete cracks propagate through the explosive.

The remainder of this paper will present a detailed development of the discrete fracture model and its application in the finite element simulation of the MCCO experiment. In the results section it is shown that by introduction of a size distribution of initial "virtual" cracks, both the mechanical and temporal features of the experiment are reproduced.

FINITE ELEMENT EQUATIONS

The Hu-Washizu Energy Principle is a three-field principle in which the displacement, strain and stress fields are independent. Following that of Weissman and Taylor [16], the Hu-Washizu Principle is stated as

$$\Pi_{HW}(\mathbf{u},\sigma,\varepsilon) = \int_{\Omega}\left[\frac{1}{2}\varepsilon^{T}\mathbf{D}\varepsilon - \varepsilon^{T}\mathbf{D}\varepsilon_{0} + \varepsilon^{T}\sigma_{0} + \sigma^{T}(\mathbf{Lu}-\varepsilon)\right]d\Omega - \Pi_{EXT} \quad (1)$$

where Ω is the volume, $\mathbf{u}$, σ, and ε are the displacement stress and strain fields respectively, $\mathbf{D}$ is the elastic moduli coefficients matrix, ε_{0} and σ_{0} are the initial strain and stress tensors respectively, Π_{EXT} is the external work, and $\mathbf{L}$ is the strain displacement operator.

Then, taking the first variation of eqn. (1) and equating it to zero,

$$\int_{\Omega}\left[\delta\sigma^{T}\left(\mathbf{Lu}-\varepsilon-\varepsilon^{a}\right)+\delta\varepsilon^{T}\left(\mathbf{D}\varepsilon-\mathbf{D}\varepsilon_{0}+\sigma_{0}-\sigma\right)+\delta\mathbf{u}^{T}\left(\mathbf{L}^{T}\sigma-\mathbf{b}\right)\right]d\Omega-\int_{\Gamma_{\sigma}}\delta\mathbf{u}^{T}\mathbf{t}^{a}d\Gamma=0$$

$$(2)$$

where $\mathbf{b}$ is the body force, $\mathbf{t}^{a}$ is the applied traction, ε^{a} are the external strains.

The region Ω is subdivided into a finite number of subdomains (elements), Ω_{i}, and each region is defined by a finite number of points (nodes). Over these elements, the approximations for σ, $\mathbf{u}$, and ε along with their respective variations are

$$\sigma = \mathbf{Ss}; \ \delta\sigma = \mathbf{S}\delta\mathbf{s} \qquad (3\ a, b)$$

$$\varepsilon = \mathbf{Ee}; \ \delta\varepsilon = \mathbf{E}\delta\mathbf{e} \qquad (4\ a, b)$$

$$\mathbf{u} = \mathbf{Nd}; \ \delta\mathbf{u} = \mathbf{N}\delta\mathbf{d} \qquad (5\ a, b)$$

where $\mathbf{S}$ and $\mathbf{E}$ are the stress and strain interpolation functions, $\mathbf{s}$ and $\mathbf{e}$ are nodal point parameters, $\mathbf{N}$ are the shape functions, and $\mathbf{d}$ is the vector of nodal point displacements. Substituting eqns. (3) – (5) into eqn. (2) and noting that the variations $\delta\mathbf{s}$, $\delta\mathbf{e}$, and $\delta\mathbf{d}$ are arbitrary, the following three equations result,

$$\int_{\Omega_{i}}\left(\mathbf{E}^{T}\mathbf{DEe}-\mathbf{E}^{T}\mathbf{D}\varepsilon_{0}+\mathbf{E}^{T}\sigma_{0}-\mathbf{E}^{T}\mathbf{Ss}\right)d\Omega=0 \qquad (6)$$

$$\int_{\Omega_{i}}\left(\mathbf{S}^{T}\mathbf{LNd}-\mathbf{S}^{T}\mathbf{Ee}-\mathbf{S}^{T}\varepsilon^{a}\right)d\Omega=0 \qquad (7)$$

$$\int_{\Omega_{i}}\left(\mathbf{LN}^{T}\mathbf{Ss}-\mathbf{N}^{T}\mathbf{b}\right)d\Omega-\int_{\Gamma_{i}}\left(\mathbf{N}^{T}\sigma^{a}\right)d\Gamma=0 \qquad (8)$$

The following are defined,

$$\mathbf{H}\equiv\int_{\Omega_{i}}\mathbf{E}^{T}\mathbf{DE}d\Omega; \ \mathbf{A}\equiv\int_{\Omega_{i}}\mathbf{S}^{T}\mathbf{E}d\Omega; \ \mathbf{G}\equiv\int_{\Omega_{i}}\mathbf{S}^{T}\mathbf{LN}d\Omega \qquad (9a, b, c)$$

$$\mathbf{Q}\equiv\int_{\Omega_{i}}\mathbf{S}^{T}\varepsilon^{a}d\Omega; \ \mathbf{f}\equiv\int_{\Omega_{i}}\mathbf{N}^{T}\mathbf{b}d\Omega+\int_{\Gamma_{i}}\mathbf{N}^{T}\sigma^{a}d\Gamma; \ \mathbf{f}_{0}\equiv\int_{\Omega_{i}}\left(\mathbf{E}^{T}\mathbf{D}\varepsilon_{0}-\mathbf{E}^{T}\sigma_{0}\right)d\Omega$$

$$(10a, b, c)$$

By substitution of the above definitions, eqns. (6) – (8) become

$$\begin{bmatrix} \mathbf{H} & -\mathbf{A}^{T} & 0 \\ -\mathbf{A} & 0 & \mathbf{G} \\ 0 & \mathbf{G}^{T} & 0 \end{bmatrix} \cdot \begin{bmatrix} \mathbf{e} \\ \mathbf{s} \\ \mathbf{d} \end{bmatrix} = \begin{bmatrix} \mathbf{f}_{0} \\ \mathbf{Q} \\ \mathbf{f} \end{bmatrix} \qquad (11)$$

If A is invertible[1], elimination of **e** and **s** yields

$$\mathbf{G}^T\mathbf{A}^{-T}\mathbf{H}\mathbf{A}^{-1}\mathbf{G}\mathbf{d} = \mathbf{f} + \mathbf{G}^T\mathbf{A}^{-T}\mathbf{f}_0 + \mathbf{G}^T\mathbf{A}^{-T}\mathbf{H}\mathbf{A}^{-1}\mathbf{Q} \tag{12}$$

Stiffness matrix

The stiffness matrix is the coefficient on **d** in eqn. (12). The element is transformed from its global curvilinear coordinates, $[x, y]$, into local linear coordinates, $[\xi \ \eta]$, where $-1 \le \xi \le 1$, and $-1 \le \eta \le 1$. The interpolation functions for a 4 node plane element are chosen to be the following [17]

$$\mathbf{N} = \begin{bmatrix} N_1 & 0 & N_2 & 0 & N_3 & 0 & N_4 & 0 \\ 0 & N_1 & 0 & N_2 & 0 & N_3 & 0 & N_4 \end{bmatrix} \tag{13}$$

$$\mathbf{S} = \mathbf{E} = \begin{bmatrix} 1 & \xi & \eta & 0 & 0 & 0 & 0 & 0 & 0 \\ 0 & 0 & 0 & 1 & \xi & \eta & 0 & 0 & 0 \\ 0 & 0 & 0 & 0 & 0 & 0 & 1 & \xi & \eta \end{bmatrix} \tag{14}$$

where the nodal shape functions are

$$N_I = \frac{1}{4}\left(1 + \xi_I\xi\right)\left(1 + \eta_I\eta\right) \tag{15}$$

The elastic moduli matrices for plane stress and plane strain respectively are

$$\mathbf{D} = \frac{E}{1-v^2}\begin{bmatrix} 1 & v & 0 \\ v & 1 & 0 \\ 0 & 0 & \dfrac{1-v}{2} \end{bmatrix} ; \mathbf{D} = \frac{E(1-v)}{(1+v)(1-2v)}\begin{bmatrix} 1 & \dfrac{v}{1-v} & 0 \\ \dfrac{v}{1-v} & 1 & 0 \\ 0 & 0 & \dfrac{1-2v}{2(1-v)} \end{bmatrix} \tag{16a,b}$$

where E is the equivalent Young's modulus and v is Poisson's ratio. By substitution of eqns. (13) – (16) into eqn. (9) the stiffness matrix is formed and integrated symbolically in the computational software package Maple V Release 4 [18].

Load Vector

The load vector is the left-hand side of eqn. (12). It includes terms for body forces, initial stress and strain, and externally applied stress and strain. The externally applied strain field, ε^a, is assumed to be due to a small crack on the element edge. The other

---

[1] See [16] for conditions on the invertability of **A**. In this work, the conditions are satisfied and **A** is invertable.

terms in the load vector are given standard treatment and are integrated symbolically in Maple V as with the stiffness matrix.

Shown in Fig. 1, the externally applied strain field is due to a small crack embedded in an infinite elastic plate subjected to the far field stresses σ_0, σ_1, and τ_0. The applied strain field is the strain in the adjacent element due only to the presence of the crack on its edge.

The strain field in the plate subject to the far field stresses shown is determined by introducing a complex stress function $Z(z)$, where $z = \xi + i\eta$ and $i = \sqrt{-1}$ [19],

$$Z(z) = \frac{z}{\sqrt{z^2 - a^2}} \; ; \; Z'(z) = \frac{-a^2}{\left(z^2 - a^2\right)^{\frac{3}{2}}} \tag{17}$$

where a is the half crack width.

By superposition of the Mode I and Mode II stresses, the stresses in the plate are

$$\sigma_{\xi\xi} = \sigma_0\left(\text{Re}(Z) - \eta\,\text{Im}(Z')\right) + \sigma_1 + \tau_0\left(2\,\text{Im}(Z) + \eta\,\text{Re}(Z')\right) \tag{18}$$

$$\sigma_{\eta\eta} = \sigma_0\left(\text{Re}(Z) + \text{Im}(Z')\right) + \tau_0\left(-\eta\,\text{Re}(Z')\right) \tag{19}$$

$$\tau_{\xi\eta} = -\sigma_0\eta\,\text{Re}(Z') + \tau_0\left(\text{Re}(Z) - \eta\,\text{Im}(Z')\right) \tag{20}$$

where Re and Im denote the real and imaginary parts.

Using the elasticity relations for plane stress and plane strain, the strain field in the plate is calculated. Far field strains analogous to the far field stress are defined as ε_0, ε_1, and γ_0. The strain in the vicinity of the crack, due only to the presence of the crack, is the total strain field around the crack minus the far field strain given by

$$\varepsilon^a = \begin{Bmatrix} \varepsilon_{\xi\xi} - (\varepsilon_0 + \varepsilon_1) \\ \varepsilon_{\eta\eta} - \varepsilon_0 \\ \varepsilon_{\xi\eta} - \gamma_0 \end{Bmatrix} \tag{21}$$

This strain field is inserted into eqn. (10a) and integrated numerically with Gauss Quadrature and the complete load vector is assembled. By assuming superposition of the strains given by eqn. (21), additional cracks can be placed on each of the element edges by summing the load vector over the number of edge cracks[2]. This allows for the insertion of a crack at each element interface in the mesh so that each element would have at least one edge crack and at most four.

---

[2] This assumes that additional cracks in the plate in Fig. 1 can be treated independent of each other.

Interface Failure

To allow for discrete fracture, each element is defined by unique node numbers and displacement continuity is enforced across each element interface until the interface crack fails. While many criteria may be chosen for the failure of the interface crack, it is a simple matter to apply elastic plastic fracture mechanics as shown below.

First it is assumed that the strain energy release rate, G, is a function of the interface crack size. A common form of the curve is an exponential of the form

$$G = \lambda(a - a_0)^n + R_1 \tag{22}$$

where λ, R_1, and n are material parameters and a_0 is the initial crack half width. The local strain energy release rate at the interface crack is calculated as follows

$$G = \frac{K_I^2 + K_{II}^2}{E} = \frac{\left(\sigma_0 \sqrt{\pi a}\right)^2 + \left(\tau_0 \sqrt{\pi a}\right)^2}{E} \tag{23}$$

where the far field Mode I and Mode II stresses, σ_0 and τ_0, are the average of the stresses from the two elements that are adjacent to the interface crack. Equation (22) can be inverted to give the change in crack length as follows

$$\Delta a = (a - a_0) = \left(\frac{G - R_1}{\lambda}\right)^{\frac{1}{n}} \tag{24}$$

The change in crack length is calculated based on the calculated strain energy release rate at each interface. If the new crack length is greater than the previous crack length, the interface crack grows. If this growth causes the crack width to exceed the interface width, the interface fails and displacement continuity across the interface is no longer enforced.

MECHANICALLY COUPLED COOK OFF EXPERIMENT

A cartoon of the MCCO experiment performed by Dickson et al. [20] is shown in Fig. 2. A small flat cylinder of the high explosive (HE) PBX 9501 is confined in a metal ring of copper. The HE and ring assembly is confined between a window at the top and a solid metal surface at the bottom. The HE specimen has an outer diameter of 25 mm and an inner diameter of 3.175 mm. To simulate the cook-off event, the cylinder of HE is heated uniformly from both the top and bottom to a temperature below the auto-ignition temperature, at which point ignition is initiated at the inner surface of the cylinder by means of an electrically heated NiCr wire.

Experimental observations are made in several ways including the use of a camera that photographs the HE at intervals of 3 to 5 μsec through the top window. The sequence of photographs presented in Fig. 3 shows the typical behavior of HE in a

MCCO experiment after ignition. The photographs show narrow regions of lumination propagating from the inner surface outward toward the confinement ring. This lumination is caused by the ignition of fresh HE surface behind cracks as they propagate. The photographs show that early in the process there are three narrow cracks starting to propagate outward. As time progresses, much of the HE has started to chemically react and the lumination overwhelms the details of the discrete cracks and branching phenomena observed earlier. It is typically observed that 3 to 4 radial cracks propagate after ignition and that such cracks may subsequently bifurcate.

MECHANICALLY COUPLED COOK OFF SIMULATION

Shown in Fig. 4 is a plane strain model of the copper confinement ring and the PBX 9501. The PBX 9501 consists of 1200 discrete fracture elements described above. The element dimensions vary from 0.24 mm x 0.17mm on the inner surface to 0.87 mm x 1.33 mm at the copper ring. The confinement ring consists of 180 standard plane strain elements. The interface between the copper and the HE is modeled as a perfect bond so that the interface is allowed to deform, but no relative motion between the HE and the copper is allowed.

The copper used in the experiment is oxygen free copper. An isotropic elastic plastic material model was used to model the response of the copper. The material has an elastic modulus of 117×10^9 Pa and a Poisson's ratio of 0.33. The stress vs. plastic strain was obtained using a power law model with a yield stress of 65 MPa, a strain hardening exponent of 0.2 and a yield stress coefficient of 292 MPa. The coefficient of thermal expansion (CTE) of copper is a constant $16.56 \times 10^{-6}/°C$ and the density is 8.9×10^3 kg/m^3.

A material model developed by Hackett and Bennett [21] called ViscoSCRAM is used to model the mechanical and thermal behavior of the explosive. The mechanical behavior is characterized by a viscous model coupled with a damage model so that it is rate dependent but loses strength with the buildup of stress. The thermal behavior includes both mechanical work and chemical decomposition of the explosive. The material properties of importance for the explosive are the constant CTE of $55 \times 10^{-6}/°C$ and the density of 1.849×10^3 kg/m^3. For the conditions of the experiment it is likely that the material properties are not constant. However, for the present analysis, they are taken to be constant throughout the entire temperature range.

For the discrete fracture model, each element interface in the explosive has been seeded with a small crack. The size of these interface cracks is randomly distributed throughout the mesh according to an approximately flat distribution such that the largest crack is approximately 90% of the smallest element width and the smallest crack is approximately 10% of the smallest element width. This type of definition allows for the failure conditions for fracture to be different for each interface. Also, by choosing several different sets of samples to represent the same flat distribution and mean crack size, the relationship between the general features of the results and any particular set of interface cracks can be ascertained.

The fracture properties of PBX 9501 have been estimated based on the limited information that is available for HE. The parameters from eqn. (22) are $\beta = 2.0$, $\gamma = 0.1$, and $\lambda = 0.0$.

The interface failure criteria have been modified for this simulation to exclude shear contributions. This is partially due to the difficulties in modeling shear deformation with bilinear finite elements. This difficulty, coupled with the extremely low fracture toughness of PBX 9501, tends to cause prediction of disperse shear cracking that is inconsistent with experimental results. Because the deformation in the experiment is dominated by primarily Mode I type loading, it is felt that this exclusion will not cause significant error in modeling.

To reproduce the conditions of the experiment, the analysis simulated heating from room temperature at a rate of 0.6 °C/sec for 200 seconds. After this initial phase, a pressure of 5 MPa/μsec is applied to the inner surface of the explosive to simulate the rapid pressurization caused by the ignition in the cavity. This internal pressure causes a tangential stress to develop in the explosive and, as a result, cracks begin to open. As these cracks open, the pressure applied to the inner surface is also instantly applied to the crack faces.

RESULTS

During the heat-up phase of the experiment, both the confinement ring and the explosive thermally expand. Because the CTE of PBX 9501 is greater than that of copper, the copper ring serves as a restraint to the expansion of the explosive. At the end of the heating phase, the tensile tangential stress in the copper ring has exceeded the material's yield strength. The compressive tangential stresses in the explosive have caused enough damage that the inner row of elements no longer supports as much stress as the next row of elements.

After the heat-up, a pressure of 5MPa/μsec is applied to the inside of the explosive. As this pressure is applied, it is likely that the inner row of elements is further damaged to the point that they can no longer support tensile stresses, therefore never satisfy the interface failure criterion. However, the stresses in the second (from the inner surface) row of elements transitions to tension. This tension creates strain energy that causes the interface cracks to eventually fail. Shown in Fig. 5 is a graphic of a typical simulation in which many small discrete fractures appear early in the simulation. While the random nature of the interface crack sizes produces some variability in the results, different sets of samples with the same distribution and mean crack size produces generally the same results.

As cracks fail and open up, tensile stresses in the vicinity of the crack are relieved, thereby reducing the strain energy in nearby elements. In addition to relieving nearby tensile stresses, these discrete cracks also create large stress concentrations in front of the crack, encouraging further growth in the radial direction. Crack growth is further encouraged by the application of the internal pressure to the crack faces, which increases the tensile stress acting on the crack. As simulation time progresses, some of these small cracks will continue to propagate radially outward and some will arrest. In all of the simulations run to date, 3 to 5 large cracks appear and propagate from near the inner surface to near the copper confinement ring with several smaller arrested cracks. Shown in Fig. 6 are the final deformed shapes of four simulations. Each model is the same except that different sets of random crack sizes, with the same distribution and mean size, has been used to seed the element interfaces. The models show that 3 to 5 large cracks appear and propagate out toward the copper ring. In addition to reproducing the fracture patterns, the total simulation time is similar in all cases with the times relative to the end of the heat-up phase being: a) 27.4 μsec, b) 26.9 μsec, c) 29.0 μsec, and d) 28.8 μsec.

SUMMARY AND CONCLUSIONS

A finite element model of the Mechanically Coupled Cook Off experiment conducted on PBX 9501 has been developed. Photographs from the experiment show the formation of 3 to 5 large discrete cracks that propagate from the inner surface radially outward toward the confinement ring. The finite element model developed to simulate the experiments includes the behaviors thought to be essential to modeling the observed behavior. One key component of the numerical model is a discrete fracture model which models macroscopic fracture based upon standard fracture criteria. Although much is still not known about the behavior of PBX 9501, the incorporation of this model with other finite element modeling techniques has produced a model of the MCCO that reproduces the photographic observations of the experiment.

REFERENCE LIST

(1) Liebowitz, H., Sandhu, J. S., Lee, J. D., Menandro, F. C. M., *Eng. Fract. Mech.,* Vol. 50, 1995, pp. 653-670.

(2) Aliabadi, M. H., ed., *Dynamic Fracture Mechanics,* Computational Mechanics Publications, Boston, 1995.

(3) Nishioka, T. *Int. J. Fract.,* Vol. 86, 1997, pp. 127-159.

(4) De Borst, R., *Int. J. Fract.,* Vol. 86, 1997, pp. 5-36.

(5) Banks-Sills, L., Sherman, D., *Int. J. Fract.,* Vol. 41, 1989, pp. 177-196.

(6) Lotfi, H. R., Shing, P. B., *Int. J. Numer. Meth. Eng.,* Vol. 38, 1995, pp. 1307-1325.

(7) Nishioka, T. Stonesifer, R. B., Atluri, S. N., *Eng. Fract. Mech.,* Vol. 15, 1981, pp. 205-218

(8) Li, F. Z., Shih, C. F., Needleman, A., *Eng. Fract. Mech.,* Vol. 21, 1985, pp. 405-421.

(9) Parks, D. M., *Int. J. Fract.,* Vol. 10, 1974, pp. 487-502.

(10) Lemaitre, J., *Eng. Fract. Mech.,* Vol. 25, 1986, pp. 523-537.

(11) Hoff, R., Rubin, C.A., Hahn, G.T., *Eng. Fract. Mech.,* Vol. 23, 1986, pp. 105-118.

(12) Liaw, B. M., Kobayashi, A. S., Emery, A. F., *Int. J. Numer. Meth. Eng.,* Vol. 20, 1984, pp. 967-977.

(13) Xu, X. P., Needleman, A., 1994, *J. Mech. Phys. Solids,* Vol. 42, pp. 1397-1434.

(14) Gerken, J.M., *An Implicit Finite Element Method for Discrete Dynamic Fracture,* MS Thesis, Colorado State University, 1998.

(15) ABAQUS/Standard, Version 5.8, Hibbit, Karlsson and Sorenson Inc.

(16) Weissman, S. L., Taylor, R. L., *Int. J. Numer. Meth. Eng.,* Vol. 33, 1992, pp. 131-141.

(17) Bennett, J. G., Personal Communication, 1997.

(18) Maple V Release 4, Version 4.00f, Waterloo Maple Inc.

(19) Anderson, T. L., *Fracture Mechanics: Fundamentals and Applications,* 2nd *Edition,* CRC Press, New York, 1995.

(20) Dickson, P.M., Asay, B.W., Henson, B.F., and Fugard, C.S., Observation of the Behavior of Confined PBX 9501 following a Simulated Cookoff Ignition, *Proceedings of the 11th International Symposium on Detonation,* Office of Naval Research, Washington, D.C., 1998.

(21) Hackett, R.M., and Bennett, J.G, *An Implicit Finite Element Material Model for Energetic Particulate Composite Materials,* Los Alamos National Laboratory, Technical Report, LA-UR-99-3139, Los Alamos, New Mexico, 1999.

Figure 1. Crack in an infinite plate on the edge of a 2-D solid element

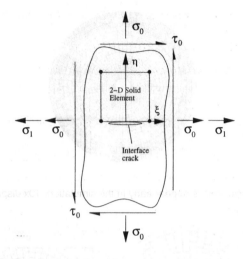

Figure 2. Setup of MCCO experiment.

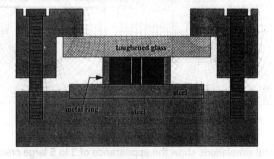

Figure 3. Optical photographs of MCCO experiment.

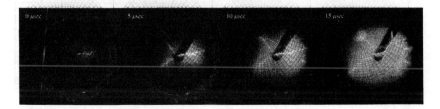

Figure 4. Mesh of the MCCO experiment.

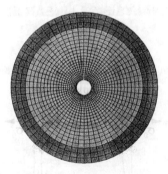

Figure 5. Many small cracks appear early in the simulation. 10x displacement.

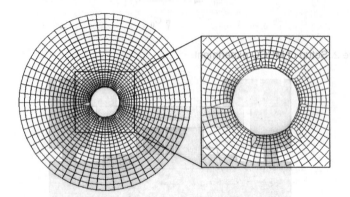

Figure 6. Several simulations show the appearance of 3 to 5 large cracks.

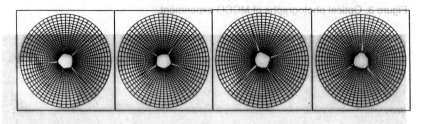

FAST ESTIMATION OF STRESS INTENSITY FACTORS IN FINITE ELEMENT ANALYSIS OF LINEAR ELASTIC FRACTURE MECHANICS

Z.J. Yang, J.F. Chen, G.D. Holt and K. Kibble[*]

ABSTRACT The energy-based virtual crack extension (VCE) technique is widely used in calculating stress intensity factors in finite element analysis of linear elastic fracture problems. It has been reported that the accuracy of the predicted stress intensity factor can be significantly improved by adding a small rosette around the crack tip in the finite element mesh, but the choice of rosette size has to date been somewhat arbitrary. This paper presents a numerical study on calculating the stress intensity factors for Mode I, Mode II and mixed-mode planar fracture problems using the VCE technique. Results show that whilst the improvement of accuracy can be very significant, it is strongly dependent on the size of the rosette. A new procedure is developed in this study to estimate the stress intensity factor by using only two calculations using two different rosette sizes. Numerical examples show that this new procedure gives good estimation for even very coarse meshes.

INTRODUCTION

Various methods are available for calculating stress intensity factors in finite element (FE) analysis of linear elastic fracture mechanics (LEFM). The most widely used have been the displacement correlation first proposed by Chan et al. [1], the path-independent J-integral (Rice [2]), Griffith's energy method [3], and virtual crack extension technique (VCE) (Hellen [4]) or stiffness derivative approach (Parks [5]). In the displacement correlation technique, reasonable accuracy can only be achieved by using well-shaped crack-tip singular elements and fine meshes near the crack tip (Saouma and Schwemmer [6]). The J-integral algorithm needs to conduct complex curvilinear integration of stresses and there is some indecision regarding the choice of

---

[*] School of Engineering and the Built Environment, The University of Wolverhampton, Wolverhampton WV1 1SB, UK.

integration path (Banks-Sills and Sherman [7]). Griffith's energy method requires two FE analyses to calculate each stress intensity factor [7].

Over the last two decades, great attention has been attracted to energy-based methods, especially the VCE technique, because energy converges much faster than other physical quantities (e.g. Xie [8], Xie et al. [9], Xie and Gerstle [10], Hellen [11], Ishikawa et al. [12], Ishikawa [13], Sha [14], Dlorenzi [15], Suo and Combescure [16]). A comparison study [7] showed that the VCE technique results in more accurate predictions for stress intensity factors than J-integral, displacement correlation and Griffith's energy methods.

During meshing (and re-meshing during crack propagation analysis), a small rosette is usually added around the crack tip (e.g. [8], [9], Bocca et al. [17], Wawrzynek and Ingraffea [18]) in FE analysis. This leads to improved symmetry condition with respect to the crack, and significant improvement of accuracy, compared with a VCE analysis without a rosette. However, numerical studies show that this improvement is very much dependent on the size of the rosette. It was reported ([8], [9]) that the size ratio of this rosette to the elements from which it is formed should be between 0.2-0.4, but the results can still be very different even within this range. Because a user cannot determine which rosette size gives more accurate results in practice, this severely constrains the applicability of the method.

This paper presents an extensive FE analysis on calculating the stress intensity factors in Mode I, Mode II and mixed-mode 2D LEFM problems using the VCE method. Through analysing the characteristics of the numerical results, a simple procedure is devised to determine the stress intensity factors with good engineering accuracy. This makes the method applicable in practice with significant reduction of computational effort.

VIRTUAL CRACK EXTENSION TECHNIQUE

The VCE technique (or stiffness derivative approach) was first proposed in [4] and [5] to calculate stress intensity factors. It was subsequently generalised for application in mixed-mode crack propagation analysis ([13], [14]) after Ishikawa [12] proved that the total energy release rate can be decomposed into the Mode-I and Mode-II energy release rates. The Mode-I and Mode-II strain energy release rates, G_I and G_{II}, are calculated by using:

$$G_I = -\frac{1}{2}\mathbf{u}_I{}^T\frac{\partial \mathbf{K}}{\partial a}\mathbf{u}_I + \mathbf{u}_I{}^T\frac{\partial \mathbf{P}}{\partial a} \tag{1a}$$

$$G_I = -\frac{1}{2}\mathbf{u}_{II}{}^T\frac{\partial \mathbf{K}}{\partial a}\mathbf{u}_{II} + \mathbf{u}_{II}{}^T\frac{\partial \mathbf{P}}{\partial a} \tag{1b}$$

where $\mathbf{u}_I$ and $\mathbf{u}_{II}$ are the symmetric and anti-symmetric displacement vectors respectively; $\mathbf{K}$ is the stiffness matrix; $\mathbf{P}$ is the external load vector; a is the crack length and ^{T} denotes transpose.

If the external load remains unchanged, Eq. 1 shows that the energy release rate is solely determined by the derivative of the stiffness matrix with respect to the crack length. Figure 1 shows a simple method for conducting a virtual crack extension as proposed in [8] and [9], in which only the crack tip elements contribute to the energy release rates. By using finite difference approximation, Eq. 1 may be expressed as:

$$G_I = -\frac{1}{2\Delta A} \sum_{i=1}^{N_{ce}} \mathbf{u}_{Ii}^{e\,T} \Delta \mathbf{K}_i^e \mathbf{u}_{Ii}^e + \frac{1}{\Delta A} \sum_{j=1}^{N_{cef}} \mathbf{u}_{Ij}^{e\,T} \Delta \mathbf{P}_j^e \tag{2a}$$

$$G_I = -\frac{1}{2\Delta A} \sum_{i=1}^{N_{ce}} \mathbf{u}_{IIi}^{e\,T} \Delta \mathbf{K}_i^e \mathbf{u}_{IIi}^e + \frac{1}{\Delta A} \sum_{j=1}^{N_{cef}} \mathbf{u}_{IIj}^{e\,T} \Delta \mathbf{P}_j^e \tag{2b}$$

in which N_{ce} and N_{cef} are the total number of elements and the number of elements with applied force around the crack tip respectively; $\mathbf{u}_{Ii}^e$ and $\mathbf{u}_{IIi}^e$ are the Mode-I and Mode-II displacement vectors of the ith crack tip element respectively; $\Delta \mathbf{K}_i^e$ is the change of ith crack tip element stiffness matrix due to virtual crack extension; $\Delta \mathbf{p}_j^e$ is the change of the nodal force vector of the jth crack tip element due to virtual crack extension; and ΔA is the increase of crack surface area after a virtual crack extension Δa and $\Delta A = t\Delta a$ for a 2D structure with a thickness t.

The Mode-I and Mode-II stress intensity factors, K_I and K_{II}, can then be calculated from the strain energy rates:

$$K_I = \sqrt{E'G_I} \tag{3a}$$

$$K_{II} = \sqrt{E'G_{II}} \tag{3b}$$

in which $E' = E$ for plane stress and $E' = E/(1-v^2)$ for plane strain; E is the Young's modulus; and v is the Poisson's ratio.

DISPLACEMENT DECOMPOSITION

In the above method, the displacement field around the crack-tip needs to be decomposed into symmetric and anti-symmetric fields with respect to the crack. Similar decomposition procedures in three dimensions have been used by several researchers ([8], [9] and Cervenka [19]). In 2D, the displacement $\mathbf{u}_A$ at Node A

(Fig. 1) is decomposed into Mode-I and Mode-II displacements, $\mathbf{u}_{AI}$ and $\mathbf{u}_{AII}$, in the global X-Y coordinate system as follows:

$$\mathbf{u}_A = \begin{Bmatrix} u_A \\ v_B \end{Bmatrix} = \mathbf{u}_{IA} + \mathbf{u}_{IIA} = \begin{Bmatrix} u_{IA} \\ v_{IA} \end{Bmatrix} + \begin{Bmatrix} u_{IIA} \\ v_{IIA} \end{Bmatrix} \tag{4a}$$

where

$$u_{IA} = \tfrac{1}{2}[u_A + (\cos^2\theta - \sin^2\theta)\, u_B + 2\cos\theta\sin\theta\, v_B] \tag{4b}$$

$$v_{IA} = \tfrac{1}{2}[v_A + (\sin^2\theta - \cos^2\theta)\, v_B + 2\cos\theta\sin\theta\, u_B] \tag{4c}$$

$$u_{IIA} = \tfrac{1}{2}[u_A + (\sin^2\theta - \cos^2\theta)\, u_B - 2\cos\theta\sin\theta\, v_B] \tag{4d}$$

$$v_{IIA} = \tfrac{1}{2}[v_A + (\cos^2\theta - \sin^2\theta)\, v_B - 2\cos\theta\sin\theta\, u_B] \tag{4e}$$

in which u and v are global displacements at a point in X and Y directions respectively; subscribes I and II denote global displacement components for Mode-I and Mode-II respectively; subscribes A and B denote Node A and its mirror image B respectively; and θ is the crack propagation angle (Fig. 1). The displacements at Point B may be calculated from the deformations of the element where it lies by using the same interpolation functions as used for the element.

ROSETTE AROUND CRACK TIP AND VIRTUAL CRACK EXTENSION

The use of an efficient adaptive meshing technique is vital for the success of a crack propagation analysis. Several adaptive meshing techniques are available for this purpose (e.g. [8], [9], [17] and [18]). The procedure proposed by Xie [8] was used in this research, in which a small rosette can be automatically added around the crack tip node to improve the symmetry condition with respect to the crack line and the accuracy of the prediction as described earlier. For convenience, the relative size of the rosette R_r is defined here as:

$$R_r = \frac{L_r}{L_m} \tag{5}$$

where L_r is the radius of the rosette; and L_m is the minimum radial dimension of all the 'mother elements' around the crack tip from which the rosette is formed (Fig. 2).

For convenience of discussion, a virtual crack extension ratio is defined here as:

$$R_i = \frac{\Delta a}{L_r} \tag{6}$$

NUMERICAL EXAMPLES

Examples

Three numerical examples, corresponding to Mode-I, Mode-II and mixed-mode LEFM respectively, were carried out to investigate the effects of mesh density, element type and the use of the rosette. Each example was modelled using 12 different meshes, 6 with a rosette around the crack tip node and 6 without. Either quadratic six-node triangular elements (T6) or linear three-node triangular elements (T3) were used to represent the rosette elements. All other areas were modelled by using either quadrilateral eight-node elements (Q8) or quadratic four-node elements (Q4). Each mesh was assigned a name, with the first character identifying the problem (O for open mode (i.e. Mode I), S for slide mode (i.e. Mode II) and M for mixed mode), the last character defining the density of the mesh (a for coarse, b for medium and c for fine meshes), and the middle number(s) indicating the type of element(s) used (8, 6, 4 and 3 for Q8, T6, Q4 and T3 respectively).

The fracture analysis program FRAP, originally developed by Xie [8] for workstations, was transplanted to PCs and extensively modified by the authors to improve its maintainability, portability and readability. This modified program was used in this research.

The first example is a square plate with a horizontal central crack subjected to remotely applied uniform vertical stress $\sigma = 1$MPa (Mode I). Only half the plate was modelled by taking advantage of the symmetry (Fig. 3). The analytical solution is $K_I = 4.72$MPa$\sqrt{m}$ (Teda [20]).

The second example is a square plate with a horizontal central crack subjected to a uniform shear stress $\tau = 1$MPa on all the four edges (Mode II) (Fig. 4). The analytical solution can be calculated by using $K_{II} = \tau\sqrt{\pi a}$ in LEFM (Aliabadi and Rooke [21]): $K_{II} = 1.772$MPa$\sqrt{m}$ for the parameters given in Fig. 4a.

The third example is a square plate with a diagonal central crack (mixed-mode) (Fig. 5a). The results are compared with the solution of $K_I = 1.15$ and $K_{II} = 1.12$ obtained by Xie and Gerstle [9] using the VCE technique and crack tip singular elements with very fine meshes.

Results and discussion

Effect of virtual extension ratio R_i: Figure 6 shows the effects of the virtual crack extension ratio R_i on the calculated K_I for six meshes without a rosette for the open mode fracture example. It is seen that the predictions converge quickly to their stable values as R_i decreases and no variation of K_I is seen for all meshes when R_i is smaller than 10^{-3}. Similar calculations were conducted for all other meshes used in this study,

325

including those for the Mode-II fracture example and the mixed-mode fracture example. No difference is seen in the predicted K_I and K_{II} values in all cases if $K_i<10^{-3}$. This confirms that the range of R_i values from 10^{-3} to 10^{-6} used by many researchers (e.g. [7]) is sufficiently small to give converged predictions. $R_i = 10^{-6}$ was used in all other calculations in this paper.

Figure 6 also shows that, not surprisingly, the use of higher order elements (Q8 and T6) resulted in consistently more accurate predictions than that of lower order elements (Q4 and T3). This is further confirmed in Figs 7-10, where the relative errors of predicted stress intensity factors for the three examples are shown.

Effect of rosette size ratio R_r: Figure 7 shows that the addition of a rosette around the crack tip can significantly improve the accuracy of the predicted stress intensity factor K_I if $R_r>0.2$, with one exception that the predicted K_I for $R_r=0.99$ is less accurate than without rosette for Mesh O43a. Except for Mesh O43a for which $R_r=0.14$ results in the exact K_I values, the optimal R_r value is about 0.2 for all other meshes. The value of R_r, which results in the exact stress intensity factor for a given mesh, may be termed critical rosette size. All three examples (Figs 7-10) show that the accuracy of the predicted stress intensity factor increases as R_r decreases if the rosette is larger than the critical size. For rosettes smaller than the critical size, the error of prediction increases fast as R_r decreases. Obviously, the prediction can be far less accurate than that without a rosette, if the rosette is too small compared with the critical size.

For the Slide Mode example, the critical rosette size varies from 0.17 for the coarsest Mesh S43a to about 0.7 for the finest Mesh S86c (Fig. 8). It varies from 0.25 to 0.5 for K_I (Fig. 9), and 0.22 to 0.8 for K_{II} (Fig. 10) for the Mixed Mode example. In general, the critical rosette size is smaller for coarser meshes and larger for finer meshes. It may therefore be concluded that the critical rosette size varies with the mesh density, the element type(s) being used and the problem being investigated (including geometry, crack type, loading etc.).

The strong sensitivity of the predicted stress intensity factors with the rosette size, and the fact that numerous factors affect the critical rosette size, severely limit the applicability of using a rosette in practice. This is because no 'exact solution' is known before a convergence test is carried out for a practical problem, so it is not possible to know whether a prediction has acceptable accuracy. The use of very fine meshes to carry out a convergence test would lose computational efficiency which is the prime purpose of using a rosette. Furthermore, for a given value of R_r, the refinement of mesh may not converge to the exact solution even if it does converge. For example, an analysis may converge to a solution with a large error at $R_r=0.2$ for the second example (Fig. 8).

A NEW METHOD FOR DETERMINING STRESS INTENSITY FACTORS

Characteristics of K versus R_r curves

Figures 11-14 show the predicted stress intensity factors at various R_r values for all the three examples. All these curves show that a FE prediction of stress intensity factor K is smaller than the exact solution at R_r close to 1. K increases almost linearly as R_r decreases in the range of R_r=0.5-1. For small R_r values, K increases fast and approaches to infinity as $R_r \to 0$.

The tangent near R_r=0.5-1 is also shown for each curve in these figures. It is seen that all these tangents intersect the vertical axis (K at R_r=0) close to the exact solution. This important feature, together with the characteristic that K is almost linear to R_r in the range of R_r=0.5-1 may be used to devise the following simple procedure to estimate the stress intensity factors very efficiently.

Fast evaluation of K values

Based on the above discussion, stress intensity factors may be evaluated using the following procedure:

a) For a given mesh, carry out two FE analyses with two different R_r values between 0.5 and 1, giving two sets of K values for Mixed Mode fracture problems (one set for single mode);

b) Each set of these values represents two points in the R_r-K coordinate system. Drawing a straight line through these two points intersecting the vertical (K) axis gives a good estimation of the exact stress intensity factor.

Figures 15-18 show the errors of the predicted stress intensity factors using this procedure for all the meshes studied for the three examples using R_r=0.6 and 0.99. Errors of those predicted using R_r=0.2 and 0.4 and those without a rosette are also shown for comparison. For the Open Mode example (Fig. 15), this new procedure predicts K_I with errors ranging from –8% for the coarsest Mesh O43a to –2% for the finest Mesh O86c, compared with errors ranging from –32% to –3% for those predicted without rosette. The error is typically within ±5% for the Slide Mode except that for the coarsest Mesh S43a which is –10% (Fig. 16). Figures 17 and 18 show similar results for the Mixed Mode example. Figure 18 also shows that the predictions using R_r=0.2 are less accurate than that without a rosette for Meshes M86a and M86b, highlighting that using a rosette may result in less accurate predictions.

Note that at least two (more often a number of) analyses with different meshes, of which one must be very fine, are needed to carry out a convergence test in calculating stress intensity factors in normal FE analysis. The use of a rosette around the crack tip may improve the accuracy for a given mesh (thus coarser meshes may be used), but a

327

convergence test using different meshes is unavoidable. This new procedure, however, only needs to generate one mesh and it may be very coarse. This can lead to potentially significant savings in both manpower and computing resources. However, the new procedure has been devised based on limited numerical analyses in this study. Further theoretical/numerical analyses are needed to elaborate it and confirm its robustness.

CONCLUSIONS

This paper has presented an extensive FE analysis of stress intensity factors in planar Mode-I, Mode-II and Mixed Mode LEFM using the VCE technique. Numerical results have shown that the virtual crack extension ratio should be smaller than 10^{-3} to give converged results. Adding a small rosette around the crack tip may significantly improve the accuracy of prediction if the size of the rosette is properly chosen, but may lead to less accurate results than that without a rosette otherwise.

Numerical results have shown that there exists a critical rosette size for each mesh, with which the stress intensity factors may be very accurately predicted. However, this critical size varies with mesh density, element type and is problem specific. The size of a rosette has a very strong effect on the results of prediction, and it is not possible to judge what rosette size results in more accurate predictions for a practical problem.

A new simple procedure has been devised to estimate the stress intensity factors by using only two FE calculations for one mesh with two different rosette sizes. While the results are also dependent on mesh density, limited numerical results show that errors of predictions are generally within 5%, and within 10% for even very coarse meshes. This new method may thus be used in practice to estimate stress intensity factors very efficiently.

ACKNOWLEDGEMENT

The numerical calculations were carried out using a modified version of program FRAP. Dr Ming Xie and Prof. Walter H. Gerstle in the Department of Civil Engineering in the University of New Mexico in the United States provided the source code of FRAP. Their generous contribution is most gratefully acknowledged.

REFERENCES

(1)   Chan, S. K., Tuba, L. S. & Wilson, W.K., *Eng. Fracture Mech.*, Vol. 2, 1970, pp1-17.

(2)   Rice, J. R., *J. of App. Mech.*, Vol. 35, 1968, pp379-386.

(3)   Griffith, A. A., *Philosophical Transactions of Royal Society*, A221, 1920, pp163-198.

(4)   Hellen, T. K., *Int. J of Num. Method in Eng.*, Vol. 9, 1975, pp187-207.

(5)   Parks, D. M., *Int. J of Fracture*, Vol. 10, No. 4, 1974, pp487-502.

(6)   Saouma, V.E. and Schwemmer, D., *Int. J of Num. Method in Eng.*, Vol. 20, No. 9, 1984, pp1629-1641.

(7)   Banks-Sills, L. & Sherman, D., *Int. J of Fracture*, Vol. 32, 1986, pp127-140.

(8)   Xie, M., *Finite Element Modelling of Discrete Crack Propagation*, Doctoral Dissertation, University of New Mexico, USA, 1995.

(9)   Xie, M., Gerstle, W. H., & Rahulkumar, P., *J. of Eng. Mech, ASCE*, Vol. 121, No. 8, 1995, pp914-923.

(10)   Xie, M., & Gerstle, W.H., *J of Eng. Mech., ASCE*, Vol. 121, No. 12, 1995, pp1349-1458.

(11)   Hellen, T. K., *Int. J of Num. Method in Eng.*, Vol. 28, 1989, pp929-942.

(12)   Ishikawa, H., Kitagawa, H. & Okamura, H., *Proc., 3rd Int. Conf. on Mech. Behaviour of Materials*, Vol. 3, 1979, pp447-455.

(13)   Ishikawa, H., *Int. J of Fracture*, Vol. 16, No. 5, 1980, pp243-246.

(14)   Sha, G. T., *Int. J of Fracture*, Vol. 25, No. 2, 1984, pp33-42.

(15)   Dlorenzi, H. G., *Eng. Fracture Mech.*, Vol. 21, No. 1, 1985, pp129-143.

(16)   Suo, X.Z. & Combescure, A., *Nuclear Eng. & Design*, Vol. 135, 1992, pp207-224.

(17)   Bocca, P., Carpinteri, A. & Valente, S., *Int. J of Solid Struct.*, Vol. 27, No. 9, 1991, pp1139-1153.

(18)   Wawrzynek, P. A. & Ingraffea, A. R., *Finite Element in Analysis and Design*, Vol. 5, 1989, pp87-96.

(19)   Cervenka, J., *Discrete crack modelling in concrete structures*, Ph.D Thesis, University of Colorado, Boulder, USA, 1994.

(20)   Tada, H., Paris, P. & Irwin, G., *The stress analysis of cracks handbook*, Del Research Corporation, Hellertown, Penn., 1993.

(21)   Aliabadi, M. H. & Rooke, D. P., *Num. Fracture Mech.*, Kluwer Academic Publishes, London, 1991.

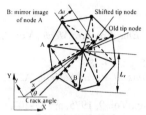

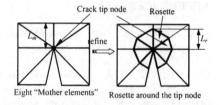

Fig. 1 Virtual crack extension   Fig. 2 A rosette and its "mother elements"

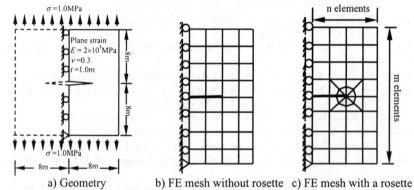

a) Geometry   b) FE mesh without rosette   c) FE mesh with a rosette
Fig. 3 A square plate with a horizontal central crack: Mode-I fracture

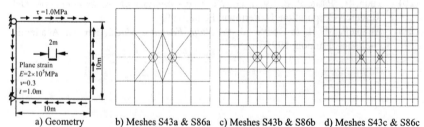

a) Geometry   b) Meshes S43a & S86a   c) Meshes S43b & S86b   d) Meshes S43c & S86c
Fig. 4 A square plate with a horizontal central crack: Mode-II fracture

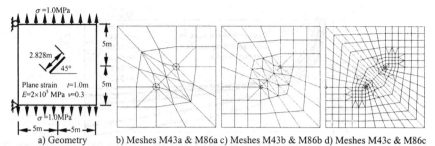

a) Geometry   b) Meshes M43a & M86a   c) Meshes M43b & M86b   d) Meshes M43c & M86c

Fig. 5 A square plate with a 45 degree inclined central crack: Mixed-mode fracture

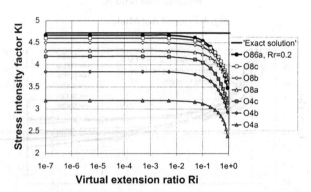

Fig. 6 Effect of virtual extension ratio R_i on calculated stress intensity factor

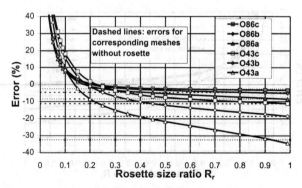

Fig. 7 Error of K_I: Mode-I

331

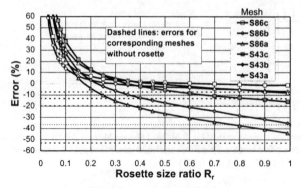

Fig. 8 Error of K_{II}: Mode-II

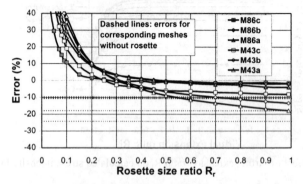

Fig. 9 Error of K_I: Mixed Mode

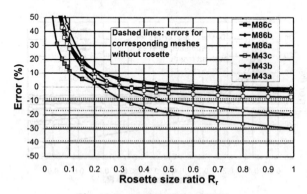

Fig. 10 Error of K_{II}: Mixed Mode

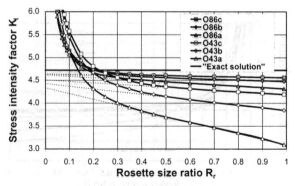

Fig. 11 Predicted K_I: Mode-I

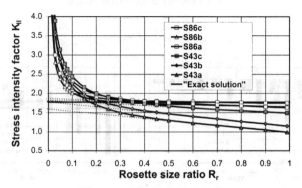

Fig. 12 Predicted K_{II}: Mode-II

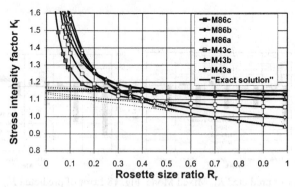

Fig. 13 Predicted K_I: Mixed Mode

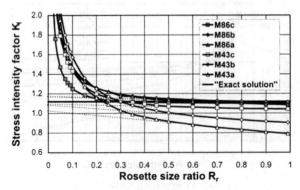

Fig. 14 Predicted K_{II}: Mixed Mode

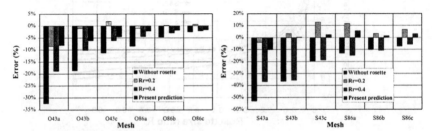

Fig. 15 Error of predicted K_I: Mode-I   Fig. 16 Error of predicted K_{II}: Mode-II

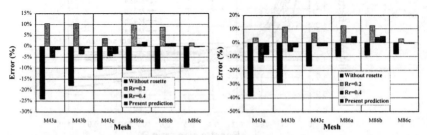

Fig. 17 Error of predicted K_I: Mixed Mode Fig. 18 Error of predicted K_{II}: Mixed Mode

6. VIBRATIONS AND DYNAMIC ANALYSIS

BLOCKED DYNAMIC STIFFNESS MATRIX OF A RUBBER BUSH MOUNTING

L.Kari †

A waveguide model of the complete blocked dynamic stiffness matrix of a long rubber bush mounting in the audible frequency range is presented, where influences of geometrical and material dispersion are investigated. The model relies on a dispersion relation extending the Pochhammer-Chree theory, which is resolved into various modes; yielding the sought stiffness matrix including axial, torsional, radial and tilting stiffness. The paper applies a nearly incompressible material model with shear modulus based on a fractional standard linear solid, the main advantage being the minimum parameter number required to successfully model the material properties over a broad structure borne sound frequency domain. The low-frequency stiffness asymptotes of the presented model are shown to agree with those of static theories.

1. INTRODUCTION

Rubber bush mountings are widely used in engineering for their great axial and torsional flexibility, the large radial and tilt rigidy and their compact size. Their static stiffness formulas in many directions are provided in standard textbooks; such as, Gent [1], Lindley [2], Göbel [3], Payne and Scott [4] and Freakley and Payne [5], while their dynamic properties – particularly within the audible frequency range - are missing. However, increasing interest in noise abatement has heightened the need for effective isolation within the audible frequency domain, requiring structure-borne sound property data from the source, the vibration isolator – such as the rubber bushing - and the receiving structure. In this paper, the audible dynamic stiffness of a rubber bush mounting is focussed upon; covering all the six directions of freedom.

The rubber material is assumed to be nearly incompressible with the deviatoric response based on a fractional standard linear (or three element) solid, Koeller [6], the main advantage being the minimum parameter number required to successfully model the material properties over a broad structure borne sound frequency domain.

† MWL/Department of Vehicle Engineering, Kungliga Tekniska Högskolan, 100 44 Stockholm, Sweden.

2. METHOD

2.1 Rubber bush mounting

The rubber bush mounting in Figure 1 consists of an l long rubber tube with inner radius r_1 and outer radius r_2, firmly bonded to an inner and outer steel shaft.

A practical field representation at the junctions between the rubber tube and the outer and inner shafts is by variables acting at the geometrical centers of the junctions; that is, at the center of the rubber bush mounting. In Figure 2, the displacement fields at the inner and outer shaft junctions are represented by generalized displacement vectors $\mathbf{U}_{In} = [U_1, U_1, \ldots, U_6]^T$ and $\mathbf{U}_{Out} = [U_7, U_8, \ldots, U_{12}]^T$, respectively, both including three translational and three rotational displacements, where T denotes a transpose, with the stress fields (acting at the bonded rubber surfaces) represented by corresponding generalized force vectors $\mathbf{F}_{In}$ and $\mathbf{F}_{Out}$. As this paper aims chiefly at the dynamic stiffness description of the rubber bush mounting, only rigid body motions of the junctions at inner and outer shafts are allowed. A suitable description of the structure-borne sound properties of the mounting provides the blocked dynamic driving point and transfer stiffnesses; $\widetilde{\mathbf{K}}_{InIn}$ or $\widetilde{\mathbf{K}}_{OutOut}$ and $\widetilde{\mathbf{K}}_{InOut}$ or $\widetilde{\mathbf{K}}_{OutIn}$, respectively, being (6×6) matrices and defined through

$$\widetilde{\mathbf{F}}_{In} = \widetilde{\mathbf{K}}_{InIn}\widetilde{\mathbf{U}}_{In} + \widetilde{\mathbf{K}}_{InOut}\widetilde{\mathbf{U}}_{Out} \tag{1}$$

and
$$\widetilde{\mathbf{F}}_{Out} = \widetilde{\mathbf{K}}_{OutIn}\widetilde{\mathbf{U}}_{In} + \widetilde{\mathbf{K}}_{OutOut}\widetilde{\mathbf{U}}_{Out}, \tag{2}$$

where $(\tilde{\,}) = \int_{-\infty}^{\infty}(\cdot)e^{-i\omega t}dt$ is the temporal Fourier transformation, i is the imaginary unit, ω is angular frequency and t is natural time. More compactly

$$\widetilde{\mathbf{F}} = \widetilde{\mathbf{K}}\widetilde{\mathbf{U}}, \tag{3}$$

where $\mathbf{F} = [\mathbf{F}^T_{In}, \mathbf{F}^T_{Out}]^T$, $\mathbf{U} = [\mathbf{U}^T_{In}, \mathbf{U}^T_{Out}]^T$ and the (complete) blocked dynamic stiffness (12×12) matrix

$$\widetilde{\mathbf{K}} = \begin{bmatrix} \widetilde{\mathbf{K}}_{InIn} & \widetilde{\mathbf{K}}_{InOut} \\ \widetilde{\mathbf{K}}_{OutIn} & \widetilde{\mathbf{K}}_{OutOut} \end{bmatrix}. \tag{4}$$

Reciprocity implies $\widetilde{\mathbf{K}}_{InOut} = \widetilde{\mathbf{K}}^T_{OutIn}$, $\widetilde{\mathbf{K}}_{InIn} = \widetilde{\mathbf{K}}^T_{InIn}$ and $\widetilde{\mathbf{K}}_{OutOut} = \widetilde{\mathbf{K}}^T_{OutOut}$. The particular isolator geometry - coinciding mass centers, inertia centers, excitation and response points - results in diagonal stiffness submatrices

$$\tilde{\mathbf{K}}_{\text{InIn}} = Diag\big[\tilde{K}_{11}, \tilde{K}_{22}, \dots, \tilde{K}_{66}\big], \ \tilde{\mathbf{K}}_{\text{InOut}} = Diag\big[\tilde{K}_{17}, \tilde{K}_{28}, \dots, \tilde{K}_{612}\big] \qquad (5,6)$$

$$\tilde{\mathbf{K}}_{\text{OutOut}} = Diag\big[\tilde{K}_{71}, \tilde{K}_{82}, \dots, \tilde{K}_{126}\big] \text{ and } \tilde{\mathbf{K}}_{\text{OutIn}} = Diag\big[\tilde{K}_{77}, \tilde{K}_{88}, \dots, \tilde{K}_{1212}\big], \quad (7,8)$$

where $\tilde{K}_{17} = \tilde{K}_{71}$, $\tilde{K}_{28} = \tilde{K}_{82}$, $\dots$, $\tilde{K}_{612} = \tilde{K}_{126}$ due to reciprocity and $\tilde{K}_{22} = \tilde{K}_{33}$, $\tilde{K}_{28} = \tilde{K}_{39}$, $\tilde{K}_{55} = \tilde{K}_{66}$, $\tilde{K}_{511} = \tilde{K}_{612}$, $\tilde{K}_{88} = \tilde{K}_{99}$, $\tilde{K}_{1111} = \tilde{K}_{1212}$ due to the specific isolator symmetry. Thus, the total number of non-zero elements of the stiffness matrix $\tilde{\mathbf{K}}$ is 24 of which 12 are 'independent'. These matrix elements are determined in Sections 2.2.1 to 2.2.4 while the general solution, which extends Pochhammer [7] and Cree [8] theories of wave propagation in solid cylinders to thick-walled cylinders with arbitrary boundary conditions, is derived in next Section.

2.2 General solution

Consider the infinite, thick walled rubber cylinder in Figure 3 where a convenient representation of the geometry is in a cylindrical co-ordinate system with z-axis directed along main axis. Subsequently, the field variables are assumed to be z independent.

Helmholtz theorem, Fung [9], gives $\boldsymbol{u} = \text{grad}\phi + \text{curl}\boldsymbol{\psi}$, where $\boldsymbol{\psi} = [\psi_r, \ \psi_\varphi, \ \psi_z]^T$ and ϕ are the vector and scalar potentials, respectively. Through the gauge transformation $\boldsymbol{\psi}' = \boldsymbol{\psi} - \text{grad}\phi'$, where $\text{div}\boldsymbol{\psi}' = 0$, the Helmholtz equations become

$$\nabla^2\tilde{\phi} + k_L^2\tilde{\phi} = 0 \text{ and } \nabla^2\tilde{\boldsymbol{\psi}}' + k_T^2\tilde{\boldsymbol{\psi}}' = \mathbf{0}, \qquad (9,10)$$

where ∇^2 is the Laplacean, reading

$$\nabla^2\tilde{\phi} = \frac{\partial^2\tilde{\phi}}{\partial r^2} + \frac{1}{r}\frac{\partial\tilde{\phi}}{\partial r} + \frac{1}{r^2}\frac{\partial^2\tilde{\phi}}{\partial\varphi^2} \qquad (11)$$

and

$$\nabla^2\tilde{\boldsymbol{\psi}}' = \left[\nabla^2\tilde{\psi}_r' - \frac{\tilde{\psi}_r'}{r^2} - \frac{2}{r^2}\frac{\partial\tilde{\psi}_\varphi'}{\partial\varphi}\right]\mathbf{e}_r + \left[\nabla^2\tilde{\psi}_\varphi' - \frac{\tilde{\psi}_\varphi'}{r^2} + \frac{2}{r^2}\frac{\partial\tilde{\psi}_r'}{\partial\varphi}\right]\mathbf{e}_\varphi + \nabla^2\tilde{\psi}_z'\mathbf{e}_z, \quad (12)$$

the longitudinal wavenumber $k_L = \omega / c_L$, the transversal wavenumber $k_T = \omega / c_T$, the longitudinal phase velocity $c_L = \sqrt{[\hat{\kappa} + \frac{4}{3}\hat{\mu}]/\rho}$, the transversal phase velocity $c_T = \sqrt{\hat{\mu}/\rho}$; ρ is the density while $\hat{\kappa}$ and $\hat{\mu}$ are the bulk and shear modulus, respectively. In order to minimize the material parameter number the shear modulus is based on a fractional standard linear (or three element) solid [6], reading

$$\hat{\mu}(\omega) = \mu_\infty \frac{1 + \frac{1+\Delta}{\Delta}(\frac{\mu_v}{\mu_\infty}i\omega)^\alpha}{1 + \frac{1}{\Delta}(\frac{\mu_v}{\mu_\infty}i\omega)^\alpha}, \tag{13}$$

where μ_∞ is equilibrium shear modulus; $\Delta \gg 1$, $0 < \alpha \le 1$ and μ_v are material constants. This material model results in an admissible behavior with a finite instantaneous shear modulus $\lim_{\omega\to\infty} \hat{\mu}(\omega) = \mu_\infty [1 + \Delta]$. The model embodies a rubber, a transition and a glassy region. Furthermore, a nearly incompressible material model, suitable for rubber, assumes that the bulk and equilibrium shear moduli are dependent as

$$\hat{\kappa}(\omega) = \kappa = b\mu_\infty, \tag{14}$$

where the positive real valued constant $b \gg 1$, typically $\sim 10^2$ to 10^5. Thus, the longitudinal and transversal wavenumbers become

$$k_L = \omega\sqrt{\frac{\rho}{b\mu_\infty}\frac{1}{1+\frac{4\hat{\mu}}{3b\mu_\infty}}} \quad \text{and} \quad k_T = \omega\sqrt{\frac{\rho}{\hat{\mu}}}, \tag{15,16}$$

respectively, where shear modulus is given by (13).

The boundary conditions at $r = r_1$ and r_2 depend on the stiffness matrix element and will be detailed in Sections 2.2.1 to 2.2.4. In order to solve the partial differential equations (9) and (10), the variables are separated as follows

$$\tilde{\phi} = \tilde{R}_\phi(r)\vartheta_\phi(\varphi), \ \tilde{\psi}'_r = \tilde{R}_r(r)\vartheta_r(\varphi), \tag{17,18}$$

$$\tilde{\psi}'_\varphi = \tilde{R}_\varphi(r)\vartheta_\varphi(\varphi) \text{ and } \tilde{\psi}'_z = \tilde{R}_z(r)\vartheta_z(\varphi), \tag{19,20}$$

giving

$$\frac{d^2\tilde{R}_\phi}{dr^2}\vartheta_\phi + \frac{1}{r}\frac{d\tilde{R}_\phi}{dr}\vartheta_\phi + \frac{\tilde{R}_\phi}{r^2}\frac{d^2\vartheta_\phi}{d\varphi^2} + k_L^2\tilde{R}_\phi\vartheta_\phi = 0, \tag{21}$$

$$\frac{d^2\tilde{R}_r}{dr^2}\vartheta_r + \frac{1}{r}\frac{d\tilde{R}_r}{dr}\vartheta_r + \frac{\tilde{R}_r}{r^2}\frac{d^2\vartheta_r}{d\varphi^2} + \left[k_T^2 - \frac{1}{r^2}\right]\tilde{R}_r\vartheta_r - \frac{2\tilde{R}_\varphi}{r^2}\frac{d\vartheta_\varphi}{d\varphi} = 0, \tag{22}$$

$$\frac{d^2\tilde{R}_\varphi}{dr^2}\vartheta_\varphi + \frac{1}{r}\frac{d\tilde{R}_\varphi}{dr}\vartheta_\varphi + \frac{\tilde{R}_\varphi}{r^2}\frac{d^2\vartheta_\varphi}{d\varphi^2} + \left[k_T^2 - \frac{1}{r^2}\right]\tilde{R}_\varphi\vartheta_\varphi + \frac{2\tilde{R}_r}{r^2}\frac{d\vartheta_r}{d\varphi} = 0 \tag{23}$$

and
$$\frac{d^2\tilde{R}_z}{dr^2}\vartheta_z + \frac{1}{r}\frac{d\tilde{R}_z}{dr}\vartheta_z + \frac{\tilde{R}_z}{r^2}\frac{d^2\vartheta_z}{d\varphi^2} + k_T^2\tilde{R}_z\vartheta_z = 0. \tag{24}$$

Requirements of single valuedness and later demands in Sections 2.2.1 to 2.2.4 narrow the ϑ – solutions down to

$$\vartheta_\phi \propto \begin{cases}\cos(n\varphi)\\ \sin(n\varphi)\end{cases}, \ \vartheta_r \propto \begin{cases}\sin(n\varphi)\\ \cos(n\varphi)\end{cases}, \ \vartheta_\varphi \propto \begin{cases}\cos(n\varphi)\\ \sin(n\varphi)\end{cases} \text{ and } \vartheta_z \propto \begin{cases}\sin(n\varphi)\\ \cos(n\varphi)\end{cases}, \quad (25\text{-}28)\begin{cases}a\\b\end{cases}$$

where $n \in \mathbb{N}$. The remaining R-functions are determined by ordinary Bessel equations, where (22) and (23) are coupled, with solutions

$$\tilde{R}_\phi = A_\phi J_n(k_L r) + B_\phi Y_n(k_L r), \tag{29}$$

$$\tilde{R}_r = A_{r\varphi}J_{n+1}(k_T r) + B_{r\varphi}Y_{n+1}(k_T r) + C_{r\varphi}J_{n-1}(k_T r) + D_{r\varphi}Y_{n-1}(k_T r), \tag{30}$$

$$\tilde{R}_\varphi = -A_{r\varphi}J_{n+1}(k_T r) - B_{r\varphi}Y_{n+1}(k_T r) + C_{r\varphi}J_{n-1}(k_T r) + D_{r\varphi}Y_{n-1}(k_T r) \tag{31}$$

and
$$\tilde{R}_z = A_z J_n(k_T r) + B_z Y_n(k_T r), \tag{32}$$

where A and B are constants; J_k and Y_k are Bessel functions of first and second kind, respectively, and of order k. It is possible to set $C_{r\varphi} = D_{r\varphi} = 0$, without any loss of generality, inasmuch as the number of boundary conditions is 6; 3 on the outer and 3 on the inner surface, while the number of constants is 8. Helmholtz theorem with (17) to (20) and (25) to (28) result in the displacements

$$\tilde{u}_r = \left[\frac{d\tilde{R}_\phi}{dr} \begin{Bmatrix}+\\-\end{Bmatrix}\frac{n}{r}\tilde{R}_z\right]\begin{Bmatrix}\cos(n\varphi)\\ \sin(n\varphi)\end{Bmatrix}, \quad (33)\begin{cases}a\\b\end{cases}$$

$$\tilde{u}_\varphi = \left[\left\{\begin{matrix}-\\+\end{matrix}\right\}\frac{n}{r}\tilde{R}_\phi - \frac{d\tilde{R}_z}{dr}\right]\begin{Bmatrix}\sin(n\varphi)\\ \cos(n\varphi)\end{Bmatrix} \quad (34)\begin{cases}a\\b\end{cases}$$

and
$$\tilde{u}_z = \left[\frac{\tilde{R}_\varphi}{r} + \frac{d\tilde{R}_\varphi}{dr}\begin{Bmatrix}-\\+\end{Bmatrix}\frac{n}{r}\tilde{R}_r\right]\begin{Bmatrix}\cos(n\varphi)\\ \sin(n\varphi)\end{Bmatrix}, \quad (35)\begin{cases}a\\b\end{cases}$$

where R-functions are explicitly given by (29) to (32). The stress components become

$$\tilde{\sigma}_{rr} = \left[-[b\mu_\infty - \tfrac{2}{3}\hat{\mu}]k_L^2\tilde{R}_\phi + 2\hat{\mu}\left(\frac{d^2\tilde{R}_\phi}{dr^2}\begin{Bmatrix}+\\-\end{Bmatrix}\frac{n}{r}[\frac{d\tilde{R}_z}{dr} - \frac{\tilde{R}_z}{r}]\right)\right]\begin{Bmatrix}\cos(n\varphi)\\ \sin(n\varphi)\end{Bmatrix},$$

$$\tilde{\sigma}_{r\varphi} = \hat{\mu}\left[\left\{\begin{matrix}+\\-\end{matrix}\right\}\frac{2n}{r}[\frac{\tilde{R}_\phi}{r} - \frac{d\tilde{R}_\phi}{dr}] - k_T^2\tilde{R}_z - 2\frac{d^2\tilde{R}_z}{dr^2}\right]\left\{\begin{matrix}\sin(n\varphi)\\\cos(n\varphi)\end{matrix}\right\},$$

$$\tilde{\sigma}_{rz} = \hat{\mu}\left[\left\{\begin{matrix}-\\+\end{matrix}\right\}\frac{n}{r}[\frac{d\tilde{R}_r}{dr} + \frac{\tilde{R}_r}{r}] + [\frac{n^2}{r^2} - k_T^2]\tilde{R}_\varphi\right]\left\{\begin{matrix}\cos(n\varphi)\\\sin(n\varphi)\end{matrix}\right\},$$

$$\tilde{\sigma}_{\varphi\varphi} = \left[-[b\mu_\infty - \tfrac{2}{3}\hat{\mu}]k_L^2\tilde{R}_\phi + \frac{\hat{\mu}}{r}\left(\frac{d\tilde{R}_\phi}{dr} - \frac{n^2\tilde{R}_\phi}{r}\left\{\begin{matrix}-\\+\end{matrix}\right\}n[\frac{d\tilde{R}_z}{dr} - \frac{\tilde{R}_z}{r}]\right)\right]\left\{\begin{matrix}\cos(n\varphi)\\\sin(n\varphi)\end{matrix}\right\},$$

$$\tilde{\sigma}_{\varphi z} = \hat{\mu}\frac{n}{r}\left[\frac{n\tilde{R}_r}{r}\left\{\begin{matrix}-\\+\end{matrix}\right\}[\frac{\tilde{R}_\varphi}{r} + \frac{d\tilde{R}_\varphi}{dr}]\right]\left\{\begin{matrix}\sin(n\varphi)\\\cos(n\varphi)\end{matrix}\right\}$$

and

$$\tilde{\sigma}_{zz} = -[b\mu_\infty - \tfrac{2}{3}\hat{\mu}]k_L^2\tilde{R}_\phi\left\{\begin{matrix}\cos(n\varphi)\\\sin(n\varphi)\end{matrix}\right\}. \qquad (36\text{-}41)\left\{\begin{matrix}a\\b\end{matrix}\right.$$

The displacements (33) to (35) and stresses (36) to (41), together with (13) to (16) and (29) to (32), are subsequently used to determine the blocked dynamic stiffness matrix elements (5) to (8).

2.2.1 Axial stiffness

The axial stiffness is determined by setting all U_k in Figure 2, except U_1 or U_7, to zero. The motion in the rubber is primarily in the z-direction and is essentially z-independent; particularly for long bush mountings. The desired displacement field is attained by setting $n = A_\phi = B_\phi = C_{r\varphi} = D_{r\varphi} = 0$ in (33a) to (35a) with (29) to (32), giving $\tilde{u}_r = \tilde{u}_\varphi = 0$

and

$$\tilde{u}_z = -k_T[A_{r\varphi}J_0(k_Tr) + B_{r\varphi}Y_0(k_Tr)], \qquad (42)$$

by using the identities $J_1(x)/x + dJ_1(x)/dx = J_0(x)$ and $Y_1(x)/x + dY_1(x)/dx = Y_0(x)$, Abramowitz and Stegun [10]. The shear stress becomes

$$\tilde{\sigma}_{rz} = k_T^2\hat{\mu}[A_{r\varphi}J_1(k_Tr) + B_{r\varphi}Y_1(k_Tr)], \qquad (43)$$

by using (38a). The axial forces

$$\tilde{F}_{1,7} = -2\pi r_{1,2}l\tilde{\sigma}_{rz}(r_{1,2}), \qquad (44)$$

with the boundary conditions $U_1 = U_0$ or $U_7 = U_0$, $U_0 \neq 0$, the remaining displacements set to zero, result in the axial stiffnesses

$$\widetilde{K}_{11} = 2\pi r_1 l k_T \hat{\mu} \frac{J_1(k_T r_1) Y_0(k_T r_2) - J_0(k_T r_2) Y_1(k_T r_1)}{J_0(k_T r_1) Y_0(k_T r_2) - J_0(k_T r_2) Y_0(k_T r_1)}, \tag{45}$$

$$\widetilde{K}_{77} = 2\pi r_2 l k_T \hat{\mu} \frac{J_1(k_T r_2) Y_0(k_T r_1) - J_0(k_T r_1) Y_1(k_T r_2)}{J_0(k_T r_1) Y_0(k_T r_2) - J_0(k_T r_2) Y_0(k_T r_1)} \tag{46}$$

and
$$\widetilde{K}_{17} = \widetilde{K}_{71} = \frac{4l\hat{\mu}}{J_0(k_T r_1) Y_0(k_T r_2) - J_0(k_T r_2) Y_0(k_T r_1)}, \tag{47}$$

by using the Wronskian [10] $J_1(x) Y_0(x) - J_0(x) Y_1(x) = 2/(\pi x)$. Their low-frequency asymptotes are achieved by the ascending series $J_0(x) = 1 + O(x^2)$, $J_1(x) = x/2 + O(x^3)$, $Y_0(x) = (2/\pi)\log_e(x/2) + O(1)$ and $Y_1(x) = -2/(\pi x) + O(x \log_e(x))$, resulting in

$$\lim_{\omega \to 0}[\widetilde{K}_{11} = \widetilde{K}_{17} = \widetilde{K}_{71} = \widetilde{K}_{77}] = \frac{2\pi l \mu_\infty}{\log_e(r_2/r_1)} = \frac{2\pi}{\log_e(10)} \frac{l \mu_\infty}{\log_{10}(r_2/r_1)}. \tag{48}$$

This is identical to the standard static formula; such as in [2] with $2\pi/\log_e(10) = 2.7287\ldots$, valid for mountings that are at least as long as their outer diameter; $l \geq 2r_2$.

2.2.2 Torsional stiffness

The torsional stiffness is determined by setting all U_k, except U_4 or U_{10}, to zero. For all bush mounting lengths, the motion in the rubber is z-independent and directed along the φ-direction only. Therefore, the torsional stiffness solution is 'exact' within an infinitesimal displacement domain where linear theory applies. The desired displacement field is attained by setting $n = 0$ in (33b) to (35b) with (29) to (32), giving $\tilde{u}_r = \tilde{u}_z = 0$ and

$$\tilde{u}_\varphi = k_T[A_z J_1(k_T r) + B_z Y_1(k_T r)], \tag{49}$$

by using the formula $dJ_0(x)/dx = -J_1(x)$. The shear stress becomes

$$\tilde{\sigma}_{r\varphi} = -k_T^2 \hat{\mu}[A_z J_2(k_T r) + B_z Y_2(k_T r)], \tag{50}$$

by means of (37b) and $d^2 J_0(x)/dx^2 = [J_2(x) - J_0(x)]/2$. The rotational forces

$$\widetilde{F}_{4,10} = -2\pi r_{1,2}^2 l \tilde{\sigma}_{r\varphi}(r_{1,2}), \tag{51}$$

with the boundary conditions $U_4 = U_0$ or $U_{10} = U_0$, $U_0 \neq 0$, the remaining displacements set to zero, result in the torsional stiffnesses

$$\widetilde{K}_{44} = 2\pi r_1^3 l k_T \hat{\mu} \frac{J_2(k_T r_1)Y_1(k_T r_2) - J_1(k_T r_2)Y_2(k_T r_1)}{J_1(k_T r_1)Y_1(k_T r_2) - J_1(k_T r_2)Y_1(k_T r_1)}, \tag{52}$$

$$\widetilde{K}_{1010} = 2\pi r_2^3 l k_T \hat{\mu} \frac{J_2(k_T r_2)Y_1(k_T r_1) - J_1(k_T r_1)Y_2(k_T r_2)}{J_1(k_T r_1)Y_1(k_T r_2) - J_1(k_T r_2)Y_1(k_T r_1)} \tag{53}$$

and
$$\widetilde{K}_{410} = \widetilde{K}_{104} = \frac{4l\hat{\mu} r_1 r_2}{J_1(k_T r_1)Y_1(k_T r_2) - J_1(k_T r_2)Y_1(k_T r_1)}, \tag{54}$$

by using the Wronskian $J_2(x) Y_1(x) - J_1(x) Y_2(x) = 2/(\pi x)$. Their low-frequency asymptotes are achieved by the ascending series $J_1(x) = x/2 + O(x^3)$, $J_2(x) = x^2/8 + O(x^4)$, $Y_1(x) = -2/(\pi x) + O(x \log_e(x))$ and $Y_2(x) = -4/(\pi x^2) + O(1)$, resulting in

$$\lim_{\omega \to 0}[\widetilde{K}_{44} = \widetilde{K}_{410} = \widetilde{K}_{104} = \widetilde{K}_{1010}] = \frac{4\pi l \mu_\infty r_1^2 r_2^2}{r_2^2 - r_1^2}, \tag{55}$$

which is identical to the standard static formula; such as in [2], valid for all mounting lengths.

2.2.3 Radial stiffness

The radial stiffness is determined by setting all U_k, except U_2, U_3, U_8 or U_9, to zero. The motion in the rubber is primarily in the r- and φ- directions and is essentially z-independent; particularly for long bush mountings. The desired displacement field is attained by setting $n = 1$ and $A_{r\varphi} = B_{r\varphi} = C_{r\varphi} = D_{r\varphi} = 0$ in (33a) to (35a) for U_2 or $U_8 \neq 0$ or in (33b) to (35b) for U_3 or $U_9 \neq 0$. The equations (33a) to (35a) with (29) to (32) give $\widetilde{u}_z = 0$,

$$\widetilde{u}_r = \{k_T A_z J_0(k_T r) + k_L A_\phi J_0(k_L r) + k_T A_z J_2(k_T r) - k_L A_\phi J_2(k_L r)$$

$$+ k_T B_z Y_0(k_T r) + k_L B_\phi Y_0(k_L r) + k_T B_z Y_2(k_T r) - k_L B_\phi Y_2(k_L r)\} \cos(\varphi)/2 \tag{56}$$

and
$$\widetilde{u}_\varphi = -\{k_T A_z J_0(k_T r) + k_L A_\phi J_0(k_L r) - k_T A_z J_2(k_T r) + k_L A_\phi J_2(k_L r)$$

$$+ k_T B_z Y_0(k_T r) + k_L B_\phi Y_0(k_L r) - k_T B_z Y_2(k_T r) + k_L B_\phi Y_2(k_L r)\} \sin(\varphi)/2, \tag{57}$$

by using the formulas $dJ_1(x)/dx = [J_0(x) - J_2(x)]/2$ and $J_1(x)/x = [J_0(x) + J_2(x)]/2$. The displacement boundary conditions read

$$\frac{1}{2}\begin{bmatrix} J_{L0}^1 - J_{L2}^1 & Y_{L0}^1 - Y_{L2}^1 & J_{T0}^1 + J_{T2}^1 & Y_{T0}^1 + Y_{T2}^1 \\ J_{L0}^1 + J_{L2}^1 & Y_{L0}^1 + Y_{L2}^1 & J_{T0}^1 - J_{T2}^1 & Y_{T0}^1 - Y_{T2}^1 \\ J_{L0}^2 - J_{L2}^2 & Y_{L0}^2 - Y_{L2}^2 & J_{T0}^2 + J_{T2}^2 & Y_{T0}^2 + Y_{T2}^2 \\ J_{L0}^2 + J_{L2}^2 & Y_{L0}^2 + Y_{L2}^2 & J_{T0}^2 - J_{T2}^2 & Y_{T0}^2 - Y_{T2}^2 \end{bmatrix} \begin{pmatrix} A_\phi^{(2)} & A_\phi^{(8)} \\ B_\phi^{(2)} & B_\phi^{(8)} \\ A_z^{(2)} & A_z^{(8)} \\ B_z^{(2)} & B_z^{(8)} \end{pmatrix} = \begin{pmatrix} \tilde{U}_2 & 0 \\ \tilde{U}_2 & 0 \\ 0 & -\tilde{U}_8 \\ 0 & -\tilde{U}_8 \end{pmatrix} \tag{58}$$

where the first (unknown) coefficient column is for $U_2 \neq 0$, the second for $U_8 \neq 0$; $J_{xn}^P = k_x J_n(k_x r_p)$ and $Y_{xn}^P = k_x Y_n(k_x r_p)$; the first and third rows constrain u_r at $\varphi = 0$ while the second and fourth rows constrain u_φ at $\varphi = \pi/2$. The axial forces are

$$\tilde{F}_{2,8} = -2lr_{1,2} \int_0^\pi [\tilde{\sigma}_{rr}(r_{1,2})\cos(\varphi) - \tilde{\sigma}_{r\varphi}(r_{1,2})\sin(\varphi)]d\varphi, \tag{59}$$

giving

$$\begin{pmatrix} \tilde{K}_{22} & \tilde{K}_{28} \\ \tilde{K}_{82} & \tilde{K}_{88} \end{pmatrix} = \pi l \begin{bmatrix} M_{11} & M_{12} & M_{13} & M_{14} \\ M_{21} & M_{22} & M_{23} & M_{24} \end{bmatrix} \begin{pmatrix} A_\phi^{(2)} & A_\phi^{(8)} \\ B_\phi^{(2)} & B_\phi^{(8)} \\ A_z^{(2)} & A_z^{(8)} \\ B_z^{(2)} & B_z^{(8)} \end{pmatrix} \begin{bmatrix} \dfrac{1}{\tilde{U}_2} & 0 \\ 0 & \dfrac{1}{\tilde{U}_8} \end{bmatrix}, \tag{60}$$

where

$$M_{11} = r_1 k_L^2 J_1(k_L r_1)[\tfrac{4}{3}\hat{\mu} + b\mu_\infty], \quad M_{12} = r_1 k_L^2 Y_1(k_L r_1)[\tfrac{4}{3}\hat{\mu} + b\mu_\infty], \tag{61,62}$$

$$M_{13} = r_1 k_T^2 J_1(k_T r_1)\hat{\mu}, \quad M_{14} = r_1 k_T^2 Y_1(k_T r_1)\hat{\mu}, \tag{63,64}$$

$$M_{21} = r_2 k_L^2 J_1(k_L r_2)[\tfrac{4}{3}\hat{\mu} + b\mu_\infty], \quad M_{22} = r_2 k_L^2 Y_1(k_L r_2)[\tfrac{4}{3}\hat{\mu} + b\mu_\infty], \tag{65,66}$$

$$M_{23} = r_2 k_T^2 J_1(k_T r_2)\hat{\mu} \text{ and } M_{24} = r_2 k_T^2 Y_1(k_T r_2)\hat{\mu}, \tag{67,68}$$

by means of (36a), (37a), (29), (32), the formulas $[dJ_1(x)/dx - J_1(x)/x]/x = -[J_3(x) + J_1(x)]/4$ and $d^2 J_1(x)/dx^2 = [J_3(x) - 3J_1(x)]/4$, where the unknown coefficients are determined by (58). Reciprocity and isolator symmetry give $\tilde{K}_{28} = \tilde{K}_{82} = \tilde{K}_{39} = \tilde{K}_{93}$, $\tilde{K}_{22} = \tilde{K}_{33}$ and $\tilde{K}_{88} = \tilde{K}_{99}$.

2.2.4 Tilting stiffness

The tilting stiffness for a long rubber bush mounting is readily obtained by the radial and axial stiffness as

345

$$\widetilde{K}_{55} = \widetilde{K}_{66} = \frac{\widetilde{K}_{33}l^2}{12} + \frac{\widetilde{K}_{11}r_1^2}{2}, \quad \widetilde{K}_{1111} = \widetilde{K}_{1212} = \frac{\widetilde{K}_{99}l^2}{12} + \frac{\widetilde{K}_{77}r_2^2}{2} \qquad (69,70)$$

and
$$\widetilde{K}_{511} = \widetilde{K}_{115} = \widetilde{K}_{612} = \widetilde{K}_{126} = \frac{\widetilde{K}_{39}l^2}{12} + \frac{\widetilde{K}_{17}r_1 r_2}{2}. \qquad (71)$$

3. RESULTS

The formulas given above are implemented in MATLAB®; also graphically presenting the results. The test object is a $l = 100$ mm long rubber bush mounting of radii $r_1 = 25$ mm and $r_2 = 35$ mm, with material data from Kari [11]; $\rho = 984$ kg/m³, $\mu_\infty = 8.25 \ 10^5$ N/m², $\Delta = 276$, $b = 2222$, $\alpha = 0.657$ and $\mu_v = 12.6$ Ns/m². The calculated blocked dynamic stiffness matrix elements in the frequency range 20 to 2 000 Hz is in Figure 4, clearly showing a strong frequency dependence.

ACKNOWLEDGMENTS

The Swedish Board for Technical and Industrial Development (NUTEK) under their VAMP program is gratefully acknowledged for financial support.

REFERENCE LIST

(1) Gent, A., *Engineering with Rubber*, Carl Hansen Verlag, Munich, 1992.

(2) Lindley, P., *Engineering Design with Natural Rubber*, MRPRA, 1992.

(3) Göbel, E., *Rubber Springs Design*, Newnes-Butterworths, London, 1974.

(4) Payne, A. and Scott, J., *Engineering Design with Rubber*, Interscience Publishers, New York, 1960.

(5) Freakley, P. and Payne, A., *Theory and Practice of Engineering with Rubber*, Applied Science Publishers, London, 1978.

(6) Koeller, R., *Journal of Applied Mechanics*, **51**, 1984, 299-307.

(7) Pochhammer, L., *Journal für die Reine und Angewandte Mathematik*, **81**, 1876, 324-336.

(8) Chree, C., *Transactions of the Cambridge Philosophical Society*, **14**, 1889, 250-369.

(9) Fung, Y., *Foundations of Solid Mechanics*, Prentice Hall, New Jersey, 1965.

(10) Abramowitz M. and Stegun I., *Handbook of Mathematical Functions*, Ninth printing. Dover Publications, New York, 1972.

(11) Kari, L., *Kautschuk Gummi Kunststoffe*, Submitted.

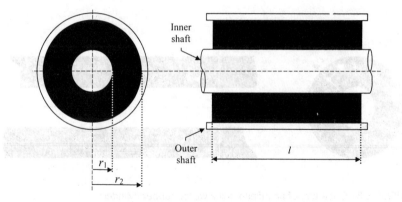

FIGURE 1   Rubber bush mounting.

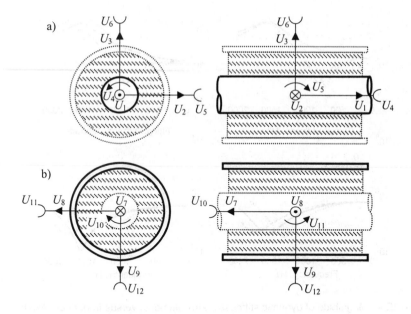

FIGURE 2   Generalized displacement at a) inner and b) outer shaft.

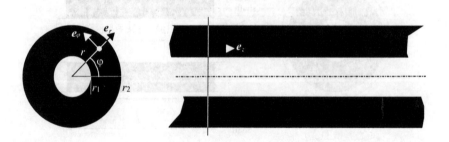

FIGURE 3   Geometry of an infinite, thick walled rubber cylinder.

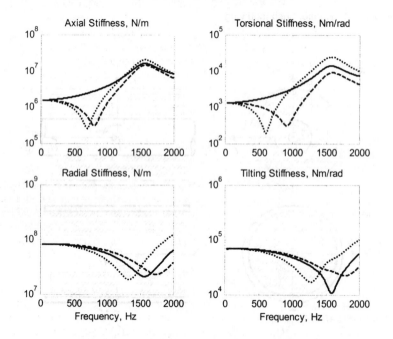

FIGURE 4   Magnitude of dynamic stiffness matrix elements versus frequency. Axial: $\widetilde{K}_{17}$ (solid), $\widetilde{K}_{11}$ (dashed) and $\widetilde{K}_{77}$ (dotted). Torsional: $\widetilde{K}_{410}$ (solid), $\widetilde{K}_{44}$ (dashed) and $\widetilde{K}_{1010}$ (dotted). Radial: $\widetilde{K}_{28}$ (solid), $\widetilde{K}_{22}$ (dashed) and $\widetilde{K}_{88}$ (dotted). Tilting: $\widetilde{K}_{511}$ (solid), $\widetilde{K}_{55}$ (dashed) and $\widetilde{K}_{1111}$ (dotted).

THE DYNAMIC STABILITY OF A LAMINATED NONHOMOGENEOUS ORTHOTROPIC ELASTIC CYLINDRICAL SHELL UNDER A TIME DEPENDENT EXTERNAL PRESSURE

O. Aksogan* and A. H. Sofiyev*

In this study, the dynamic stability of a nonhomogeneous orthotropic elastic cylindrical shell, with the elasticity modulus and density varying piecewise continuously in the thickness direction, subject to an external pressure which is a power function of time, has been considered. At first, the dynamic stability and compatibility equations of a nonhomogeneous elastic orthotropic cylindrical shell with n layers subject to an external pressure, have been obtained. Then, employing the method given in [1], the critical static and dynamic external pressures and the dynamic factor have been found analytically.

1. INTRODUCTION

Laminated bars, plates and shells, made up of materials with varying physical properties, are used to fabricate some members of modern structures and machines. The main reason for the wide use of laminated structural members is the development of new composite materials. Most materials are naturally laminated. Structural members made with these materials can be considered to comprise numerous thin layers. The theory of laminated structural members can be considered to be an extension of the classical theory of plates and shells [2-4].

Material can be saved by using thin shells made of composite materials with physical properties varying piecewise continuously in the thickness direction, rendering a decrease in the dimensions and weight possible. Hence, the research on the dynamic stability of thin shells made of laminated nonhomogeneous materials is extremely important [5-8].

* Cukurova University, Civil Engineering Department, 01330 Adana, Turkey

* Ondokuz Mayıs University, Civil Engineering Department, 55139 Samsun, Turkey

The aim of the present research is to study the dynamic stability of a laminated cylindrical shell made of orthotropic elastic materials with elasticity moduli and density varying piecewise continuously in the thickness direction subject to an external pressure varying with a power function of time, using the method presented in [1].

2. FUNDAMENTAL RELATIONS AND EQUATIONS

Consider a circular cylindrical shell of medium length, with thickness 2h, radius R and length L, having n layers of equal thickness made of nonhomogeneous orthotropic elastic materials. The contact condition between any two consecutive layers is one of perfectly rigid bonding, which ensures that the Kirschoff-Love hypothesis is satisfied for the whole shell, meaning that there is a single displacement and a single strain expressions for the whole shell and the pressures at the surfaces of contact do not need any particular attention. During the deformation there is no loss of contact or slip at the contact surfaces. The elasticity moduli and densities of all layers are defined as continuous functions of the coordinate in the thickness direction, in the following forms:

$$E_1^{(k+1)}(\overline{z}) = E_{01}^{(k+1)}\overline{\varphi}_1^{(k+1)}(\overline{z}), \quad E_2^{(k+1)}(\overline{z}) = E_{02}^{(k+1)}\overline{\varphi}_2^{(k+1)}(\overline{z}),$$

$$G^{(k+1)}(\overline{z}) = G_0^{(k+1)}\overline{\varphi}_3^{(k+1)}(\overline{z}), \quad \rho^{(k+1)}(\overline{z}) = \rho_0^{(k+1)}\overline{\varphi}_4^{(k+1)}(\overline{z}), \tag{1}$$

$$-h + k\delta \le z \le h + (k+1)\delta, \quad \overline{z} = z/h, \quad k = 0, 1, 2, ..., (n-1)$$

where $E_{01}^{(k+1)}$, $E_{02}^{(k+1)}$ and $G_0^{(k+1)}$ are the elasticity moduli and $\rho_0^{(k+1)}$ are the densities of the homogeneous materials, $\delta = 2hn^{-1}$ is the thickness of the layers and $\overline{\varphi}_i^{(k+1)}(\overline{z})$ (i=1, 2, 3, 4) are continuous functions expressing the nonhomogeneities of the corresponding quantities. In the above expression, μ expressing the coefficients of variation for the elasticity moduli and densities, $\overline{\varphi}_i^{(k+1)}(\overline{z}) = 1 + \mu\varphi_i^{(k+1)}(\overline{z})$ where $\left|\varphi_i^{(k+1)}(\overline{z})\right| \le 1$, and $0 \le \mu < 1$. It can be seen from equation (1) that the surface representing the middle surface is found for even values of n at z=0, whereas, for odd values of n, depending on the value of n, either on the left of z=0 or on the right of it. In Fig.1, the Ox and Oy axes are in the middle plane of the shell in the axial and tangential directions, respectively, and the Oz axis normal to them. The axes of orthotropy in all layers are parallel to the Ox and Oy axes [2].

350

According to Kirchhoff-Love hypothesis, in the case of small displacements, the strain at z distance from the middle surface is given as follows [2]:

$$\varepsilon_{11} = e_{11} - zW_{,xx} \; , \quad \varepsilon_{22} = e_{22} - zW_{,yy}, \quad \varepsilon_{12} = e_{12} - zW_{,xy} \qquad (2)$$

where e_{ij} ($i, j = 1, 2$) are the strains on the middle surface and W is the radial displacement, assumed to be much smaller than the thickness.

For the multi-layered physically linear shell described above, the stress-strain relations are as follows:

$$\sigma_{11}^{(k+1)} = \frac{E_{01}^{(k+1)}\overline{\varphi}_{1}^{(k+1)}(\overline{z})}{1 - v_{11}^{(k+1)}v_{22}^{(k+1)}}\left(\varepsilon_{11} + v_{22}^{(k+1)}\varepsilon_{22}\right),$$

$$\sigma_{22}^{(k+1)} = \frac{E_{02}^{(k+1)}\overline{\varphi}_{2}^{(k+1)}(\overline{z})}{1 - v_{11}^{(k+1)}v_{22}^{(k+1)}}\left(\varepsilon_{22} + v_{11}^{(k+1)}\varepsilon_{11}\right), \qquad (3)$$

$$\sigma_{12}^{(k+1)} = 2G_{0}^{(k+1)}\overline{\varphi}_{3}^{(k+1)}(\overline{z})\varepsilon_{12}, \qquad k = 0, 1, 2, ..., (n-1)$$

where $\sigma_{ij}^{(k+1)}$ ($i, j = 1, 2$) are the stresses in the layers and $v_{11}^{(k+1)}$, $v_{22}^{(k+1)}$ are the Poisson's ratios which are constant. The internal forces and moments are found using the following expressions [2]:

$$T_{ij} = \sum_{k=0}^{n-1} \int_{-h+k\delta}^{-h+(k+1)\delta} \sigma_{ij}^{(k+1)} \, dz, \quad M_{ij} = \sum_{k=0}^{n-1} \int_{-h+k\delta}^{-h+(k+1)\delta} \sigma_{ij}^{(k+1)} z \, dz, \quad (i, j = 1, 2) \qquad (4)$$

The relations between the forces T_{ij} ($i, j = 1, 2$) and the stress function $\overline{\Phi} = \Phi/(2h)$ are as follows:

$$T_{11} = \Phi_{,yy}, \qquad T_{22} = \Phi_{,xx}, \qquad T_{12} = -\Phi_{,xy} \qquad (5)$$

351

The cylindrical shell is under the effect of the following time dependent uniform external pressure [8]:

$$T_{11}^0 = 0, \qquad T_{12}^0 = 0, \qquad T_{22}^0 = -R\left(P_1 + P_0 t^\alpha\right) \qquad (6)$$

where T_{ij}^0 ($i, j = 1, 2$) are the shear forces for the case with zero initial moments, P_0 is the loading speed, P_1 is the static external pressure and α is the positive power which expresses the time dependence of the pressure. Considering relations (2-6) in the compatibility and dynamic stability equations of a cylindrical shell [9], after some mathematical operations, one gets

$$c_{12}\,\Phi_{,xxxx} + \left(c_{11} - 2c_{31} + c_{22}\right)\Phi_{,xxyy} + c_{21}\,\Phi_{,yyyy} - c_{13}\,W_{,xxxx} -$$
$$\left(c_{14} + 4c_{32} + c_{23}\right)W_{,xxyy} - c_{24}\,W_{,yyyy} + \Phi_{,xx}/R - R\left(P_1 + P_0 t^\alpha\right)W_{,yy} = \tilde{\rho}\,W_{,tt} \qquad (7)$$

$$b_{22}\,\Phi_{,xxxx} + \left(b_{12} + 2b_{31} + b_{21}\right)\Phi_{,xxyy} + b_{11}\Phi_{,yyyy} - b_{23}\,W_{,xxxx} -$$
$$\left(b_{13} - 4b_{32} + b_{24}\right)W_{,xxyy} - b_{14}W_{,yyyy} = -W_{,xx}/R \qquad (8)$$

where a subscript following a comma means a differentiation with respect to that variable and the following definitions apply:

$$c_{11} = A_{11}^1 b_{11} + A_{12}^1 b_{21}, \quad c_{12} = A_{11}^1 b_{12} + A_{12}^1 b_{22}, \quad c_{13} = A_{11}^1 b_{13} + A_{12}^1 b_{23} + A_{11}^2,$$

$$c_{14} = A_{11}^1 b_{14} + A_{12}^1 b_{24} + A_{12}^2, \quad c_{22} = A_{21}^1 b_{12} + A_{22}^1 b_{22}, \quad c_{23} = A_{21}^1 b_{13} + A_{22}^1 b_{23} + A_{21}^2,$$

$$c_{24} = A_{21}^1 b_{14} + A_{22}^1 b_{24} + A_{22}^2, \quad c_{31} = A_{33}^1 b_{31}, \quad c_{32} = A_{33}^1 b_{32} + A_{33}^2, \quad b_{11} = A_{22}^0 L_0^{-1},$$

$$b_{12} = -A_{12}^0 L_0^{-1}, \quad b_{13} = \left[A_{12}^0 A_{21}^1 - A_{11}^1 A_{22}^0\right]L_0^{-1}, \quad b_{14} = \left[A_{12}^0 A_{22}^1 - A_{12}^1 A_{22}^0\right]L_0^{-1}, \qquad (9a)$$

$$b_{21} = -A_{21}^0 L_0^{-1}, \quad b_{22} = A_{11}^0 L_0^{-1}, \quad b_{23} = \left[A_{21}^0 A_{11}^1 - A_{11}^0 A_{21}^1\right]L_0^{-1},$$

$$b_{24} = \left[A_{21}^0 A_{12}^1 - A_{11}^0 A_{22}^1\right]L_0^{-1},$$

$$b_{31} = 1/A_{33}^0, \quad b_{32} = -A_{33}^1/A_{33}^0, \quad L_0 = A_{11}^0 A_{22}^0 - A_{21}^0 A_{12}^0$$

$$A_{11}^{k_1} = h^{k_1+1} \sum_{k=0}^{n-1} \frac{E_{01}^{(k+1)}}{1 - v_{11}^{(k+1)} v_{22}^{(k+1)}} \int_{-1+\frac{2k}{n}}^{-1+\frac{2(k+1)}{n}} \bar{z}^{k_1} \overline{\varphi}_1^{(k+1)}(\bar{z}) d\bar{z},$$

$$A_{12}^{k_1} = h^{k_1+1} \sum_{k=0}^{n-1} \frac{v_{22}^{(k+1)} E_{01}^{(k+1)}}{1 - v_{11}^{(k+1)} v_{22}^{(k+1)}} \int_{-1+\frac{2k}{n}}^{-1+\frac{2(k+1)}{n}} \bar{z}^{k_1} \overline{\varphi}_1^{(k+1)}(\bar{z}) d\bar{z}$$

$$A_{22}^{k_1} = h^{k_1+1} \sum_{k=0}^{n-1} \frac{E_{02}^{(k+1)}}{1 - v_{11}^{(k+1)} v_{22}^{(k+1)}} \int_{-1+\frac{2k}{n}}^{-1+\frac{2(k+1)}{n}} \bar{z}^{k_1} \overline{\varphi}_2^{(k+1)}(\bar{z}) d\bar{z},$$

$$\tag{9b}$$

$$A_{21}^{k_1} = h^{k_1+1} \sum_{k=0}^{n-1} \frac{v_{11}^{(k+1)} E_{02}^{(k+1)}}{1 - v_{11}^{(k+1)} v_{22}^{(k+1)}} \int_{-1+\frac{2k}{n}}^{-1+\frac{2(k+1)}{n}} \bar{z}^{k_1} \overline{\varphi}_2^{(k+1)}(\bar{z}) d\bar{z},$$

$$A_{33}^{k_1} = 2h^{k_1+1} \sum_{k=0}^{n-1} G_0^{(k+1)} \int_{-1+\frac{2k}{n}}^{-1+\frac{2(k+1)}{n}} \bar{z}^{k_1} \varphi_3^{(k+1)}(\bar{z}) d\bar{z},$$

$$\tilde{\rho} = h \sum_{k=0}^{n-1} \rho_0^{(k+1)} \int_{-1+\frac{2k}{n}}^{-1+\frac{2(k+1)}{n}} \overline{\varphi}_4^{(k+1)}(\bar{z}) d\bar{z}, \quad k_1 = 0, 1, 2$$

3. THE SOLUTION OF THE DIFFERENTIAL EQUATIONS

Assuming the cylindrical shell to have hinged supports at the ends, the solution of the equation set (7-8) is sought in the following form [9]:

$$\Phi = \phi(t) \sin \frac{m_1 x}{R} \sin \frac{n_1 y}{R}, \qquad W = \xi(t) \sin \frac{m_1 x}{R} \sin \frac{n_1 y}{R} \tag{10}$$

where $m_1 = \dfrac{m\pi R}{L}$, m is the half wave number in the direction of the Ox axis, n_1 is the wave number in the direction of the Oy axis and $\phi(t)$ and $\xi(t)$ are the time dependent amplitudes. Substituting expressions (10) in the equation set (7-8) and eliminating $\phi(t)$, having in mind that when m=1 the wave parameters satisfy the inequality $n_1^4 \gg m_1^4$, the following differential equation is obtained:

$$\frac{d^2\xi(\tau)}{d\tau^2} + \frac{1}{\tilde{\rho}R^4}\left[\left(\frac{c_{24}b_{11}-c_{21}b_{14}}{b_{11}}\right)n_1^4 + \frac{m_1^4R^2}{b_{11}n^4} - R^3\left(P_1 + P_0 t_{kr}^\alpha \tau^\alpha\right)n_1^2\right]t_{kr}^2\xi(\tau) = 0 \ (11)$$

where $t = t_{kr}\,\tau$, t_{kr} is the critical time, and τ is the dimensionless time parameter such that $0 \le \tau \le 1$. Applying the method of reference [1] to equation (11), i.e. multiplying this equation by $d\xi/d\tau$ and integrating with respect to τ from 0 to 1 and from 0 to τ, in that order, one gets the following characteristic equation:

$$P_0 t_{kr}^\alpha = B_0(\alpha)\left[\left(\frac{c_{24}b_{11}-c_{21}b_{14}}{b_{11}R^3}\right)n_1^2 + \frac{1}{b_{11}R}\frac{m_1^4}{n_1^6} - P_1\right] + \frac{B_1(\alpha)\tilde{\rho}R}{t_{kr}^2 n_1^2} \qquad (12)$$

where $B_0(\alpha)$ and $B_1(\alpha)$ are defined as follows:

$$B_0(\alpha) = \frac{\int_0^1 [\xi(\tau)]^2\,d\tau}{2\int_0^1\int_0^\tau \eta^\alpha \xi'(\eta)\xi(\eta)\,d\eta d\tau}, \qquad B_1(\alpha) = \frac{\int_0^1 [\xi'(\tau)]^2\,d\tau}{2\int_0^1\int_0^\tau \eta^\alpha \xi'(\eta)\xi(\eta)\,d\eta d\tau} \qquad (13)$$

TABLE 1 The variation of $B_0(\alpha)$ and $B_1(\alpha)$ with α depending on the choice of approximating function $\xi(\tau)$

$\xi(\tau) = Ae^{50\tau}\tau\left(\frac{52}{51}-\tau\right)$, $\xi(0) = \frac{d\xi(1)}{d\tau} = 0$					
α	0.5	1.0	1.5	2.0	2.5	3.0
$B_0(\alpha)$	1.0182	1.0366	1.0552	1.0740	1.0931	1.1124
$B_1(\alpha)$	530.367	539.947	549.464	559.464	569.402	579.462

To minimize $P_0 t_{kr}^\alpha$, with respect to n_1^2 the following condition must be satisfied:

$$\frac{B_1(\alpha)\tilde{\rho}R}{t_{kr}^2 n_1^2} = B_0(\alpha)\left(\frac{c_{24}b_{11} - c_{21}b_{14}}{b_{11}R^3}\right)n_1^2 - \frac{3B_0(\alpha)}{b_{11}R}\frac{m_1^4}{n_1^6} \tag{14}$$

Substituting from (14) into (12), the following equation is found for finding the critical load:

$$P_0 t_{kr}^\alpha = 2B_0(\alpha)\left[\left(\frac{c_{24}b_{11} - c_{21}b_{14}}{b_{11}R^3}\right)n_1^2 - \frac{1}{Rb_{11}}\frac{m_1^4}{n_1^6} - \frac{P_1}{2}\right] \tag{15}$$

For $P_1=0$, eliminating t_{kr} from equations (12) and (15), one gets

$$(1 - 3\Omega)^{\frac{2\alpha}{1+\alpha}}(1-\Omega)^{\frac{4}{1+\alpha}} = \Lambda^{\frac{2\alpha}{1+\alpha}}\Omega \tag{16}$$

where the following definitions apply:

$$\Omega = \frac{R^2}{(c_{24}b_{11} - c_{21}b_{14})}\frac{m_1^4}{n_1^8}, \quad \Lambda = \frac{B_1(\alpha)P_0^\alpha R^{\frac{5+3\alpha}{\alpha}} b_{11}^{\frac{2+\alpha}{\alpha}} \tilde{\rho}}{2^{\frac{2}{\alpha}}(B_0(\alpha))^{\frac{2+\alpha}{\alpha}} m_1^{\frac{2(1+\alpha)}{\alpha}}(c_{24}b_{11} - c_{21}b_{14})^{\frac{3+\alpha}{2\alpha}}} \tag{17}$$

Since $\Omega < 1$ and the numbers on the two sides of the equation are positive, in the first approximation, due to the fact that $\Lambda \gg 1$, (16) yields

$$\Omega = \Lambda^{-\frac{2\alpha}{1+\alpha}} \tag{18}$$

Considering expression (18) in the first of expressions (17), the following expression is found for the wave number corresponding to the dynamic critical load:

$$n_{1d}^2 = \left(\frac{R^2 m_1^4}{c_{24}b_{11} - c_{21}b_{14}}\right)^{0.25} \Lambda^{\frac{\alpha}{2(1+\alpha)}} \tag{19}$$

Substituting n_{1d}^2 in (15), the dynamic critical load for $P_1 = 0$ is found as

$$P_{kr}^d = P_0 t_{kr}^\alpha = \frac{2B_0(\alpha)m_1}{b_{11}R^{2.5}}(c_{24}b_{11} - c_{21}b_{14})^{0.75}\Lambda^{\frac{\alpha}{2(1+\alpha)}} \tag{20}$$

In the static case $\left(t_{kr} \to \infty,\ P_0 \to 0\right)$, finding the wave number corresponding to the static critical load from equation (14) and substituting it in equation (15) the static critical load is found as

$$P_{kr}^{st} = \frac{4B_0(\alpha)m_1}{3^{0.75}b_{11}R^{2.5}}(c_{24}b_{11} - c_{21}b_{14})^{0.75} \tag{21}$$

Hence, the dynamic factor is found to be

$$K_d = \frac{P_{kr}^d}{P_{kr}^{st}} = \frac{3^{0.75}}{2}\Lambda^{\frac{\alpha}{2(1+\alpha)}} \tag{22}$$

When $\mu = 0$, $\alpha = 1$ and $n = 1$ the expressions for the critical load and dynamic factor for a cylindrical shell of single layer made of a homogeneous orthotropic elastic material are found as a special case.

4. NUMERICAL RESULTS

The numerical computations have been carried out for the composite material graphite/epoxy with the material constants $E_{01}^{(k+1)} = 1.724\text{x}10^5$ MPa, $E_{02}^{(k+1)} = 7.79\text{x}10^3$ MPa, $\nu_{11}^{(k+1)} = 0.35$, $\rho_0^{(k+1)} = 1.53\text{x}10^3$ kg/m^3 [10], shell parameters $R/h = 140$, $L/R = 2.86$, and speed of loading $P_0 = 200$ MPa/s making use of expressions (22) and (25).

356

For shells with odd number of symmetrical layers, as the number of layers increase, the values of the dynamic critical load (dynamic factor) approach a certain limit, whereas, for shells with even number of antisymmetrical layers, the values of the dynamic critical load and the dynamic factor do not change appreciably with the number of layers.

When the elasticity moduli and densities of the materials all change in the thickness direction $(i = 1, 2, 4)$, the effect of nonhomogeneity on the dynamic critical load is more pronounced, whereas, when the density of the material is kept constant $(i = 1, 2)$ the effect of nonhomogeneity on the dynamic factor is more pronounced (Table 2).

TABLE 2 The variation of the critical parameters for various laminated cylindrical shells

$\varphi_i^{(k+1)} = e^{-0.1|\overline{z}|} \cos(1.2\overline{z}), \quad (k = 0, 1, 2,..., 19), \quad P = P_0 t$						
	P_{kr}^d (MPa)			K_d		
Positioning of layers	$\mu = 0$	$\mu = 0.9$ $(i = 1,2,4)$	$\mu = 0.9$ $(i = 1,2)$	$\mu = 0$	$\mu = 0.9$ $(i = 1,2,4)$	$\mu = 0.9$ $(i = 1,2)$
(0°)	2.0670	2.6033	2.2901	16.0999	13.1158	11.5382
$(0^\circ - 90^\circ)$ ve $(90^\circ - 0^\circ)$	2.9811	3.7937	3.3373	9.0929	7.2554	6.3825
$(0^\circ - 90^\circ - 0^\circ)$	2.3884	3.0778	2.7075	13.2554	10.4581	9.1999
$(90^\circ - 0^\circ - 90^\circ)$	4.4430	5.5846	4.9127	4.4826	3.5795	3.1489
$(0^\circ - 90^\circ - 0^\circ - 90^\circ)$ and $(90^\circ - 0^\circ - 90^\circ - 0^\circ)$	3.6530	4.6613	4.1005	6.0554	4.8060	4.2278
$(0^\circ - 90^\circ - 0^\circ - 90^\circ - 0^\circ)$	3.1502	4.0802	3.5893	7.8082	6.0660	5.3362
$(90^\circ - 0^\circ - 90^\circ - 0^\circ - 90^\circ)$	4.2418	5.2936	4.6567	4.7234	3.8732	3.4072
$(0^\circ - 90^\circ - 0^\circ - 90^\circ - 0^\circ - 90^\circ)$ and $(90^\circ - 0^\circ - 90^\circ - 0^\circ - 90^\circ - 0^\circ)$	3.7437	4.7422	4.1717	5.7656	4.6434	4.0847
20 lays. $(0^\circ - 90^\circ - 0^\circ - ... - 90^\circ)$ 20 lays. $(90^\circ - 0^\circ - 90^\circ - ... - 0^\circ)$	3.8058	4.7958	4.2188	5.5790	4.5402	3.9940

As α increases the values of the dynamic critical load and dynamic factor decrease. Another point to be noted is that as α increases the effect of the variation of the elasticity moduli on the dynamic critical load increases, whereas, the effect on the dynamic factor decreases (Table 3).

TABLE 3 The variation of the dynamic critical load and dynamic factor with α

$$\varphi_i^{(k+1)} = e^{-0.1|\bar{z}|}\cos(0.8\bar{z}), \quad (i=1,2), \quad (k=0,1,2,3,4), \quad P=P_0 t^\alpha, \quad P_0 = 200\,\text{MPa/s}^\alpha$$

P_{kr}^d

α	$(0°)$		$(0° - 90°)$		$(0° - 90° - 0°)$		$(0° - 90° - 0° - 90°)$		$(0°-90°-0°-90°-0°)$	
	$\mu = 0$	$\mu=.9$	$\mu = 0$	$\mu=.9$	$\mu = 0$	$\mu=.9$	$\mu = 0$	$\mu=.9$	$\mu = 0$	$\mu=.9$
1.0	2.0670	2.3540	2.9811	3.4140	2.3884	2.7509	3.6530	4.1887	3.1502	3.6374
1.5	0.7288	0.8519	1.1310	1.3309	0.8669	1.0271	1.4435	1.7011	1.2085	1.4361
2.0	0.3659	0.4352	0.5963	0.7144	0.4437	0.5357	0.7819	0.9384	0.6418	0.7774
2.5	0.2248	0.2707	0.3793	0.4604	0.2764	0.3382	0.5071	0.6166	0.4104	0.5040
3.0	0.1567	0.1904	0.2714	0.3326	0.1946	0.2405	0.3681	0.4520	0.2948	0.3657

K_d

α	$(0°)$		$(0° - 90°)$		$(0° - 90° - 0°)$		$(0° - 90° - 0° - 90°)$		$(0°-90°-0°-90°-0°)$	
1.0	16.0999	10.7622	9.0929	6.0108	13.2554	8.7235	6.0554	3.9929	7.8082	5.0988
1.5	5.5768	3.8261	3.3890	2.3019	4.7262	3.1995	2.3506	1.5929	2.9425	1.9775
2.0	2.7507	1.9202	1.7552	1.2139	2.3765	1.6394	1.2508	0.8633	1.5352	1.0517
2.5	1.6604	1.1735	1.0971	0.7686	1.4544	1.0169	0.7971	0.5574	0.9647	0.6700
3.0	1.1371	0.8111	0.7712	0.5456	1.0063	0.7108	0.5686	0.4015	0.6808	0.4777

5. CONCLUSIONS

The dynamic stability of a cross-ply laminated cylindrical shell, made of orthotropic elastic materials with elasticity moduli and density varying piecewise continuously in the thickness direction, under the effect of an external pressure which varies with a power function of time, has been investigated and analytical expressions have been obtained for the dynamic and static critical external pressures and the dynamic factor.

The computations carried out using graphite/epoxy material properties reveal the following conclusions:

a) In the case of an odd number of symmetrical layers, when the positioning of the layers is changed, increasing the number of layers, the dynamic critical load (dynamic factor) values approach a certain limit.

b) In the case of an even number of antisymmetrically positioned layers, irrespective of the number of layers, the critical parameters do not change appreciably.

c) In the case of materials with elasticity moduli and densities both varying in the thickness direction, the effect on the dynamic critical load is more pronounced, whereas, when the density is kept constant, the effect on the dynamic factor is more pronounced.

d) When the power of time in the external pressure expression increases, the effect of the changes in the elasticity moduli on the dynamic critical load also increases, whereas, the effect on the dynamic factor decreases.

The foregoing observations, support the opinion that in the dynamic stability analysis of laminated cylindrical shells, the effect of nonhomogeneity and the variation of the power of time in the external pressure expression should be taken into consideration for obtaining a dependable solution.

6. REFERENCES

(1)   Sachenkov, A.V. and Baktieva, L. U., Approach to the Solution of Dynamic Stability Problems of Thin Shells, *Research on the Theory of Plates and Shells,* Kazan State University, Kazan, Vol.13, 1978, pp.137-152. (in Russian)

(2)   Ambartsumyan, S.A., *General Theory of Anisotropic Shells*, Nauka, Moscow, 1974. (in Russian)

(3)   Jones, R.M. and Morgan, H.S., Buckling and Vibration of Cross-Ply Laminated Circular Cylindrical Shells, *AIAA Journal*, Vol.13, No.5, 1975, pp.664-671.

(4)   Argento, A. and Scott, R.A., Dynamic Instability of Layered Anisotropic Circular Cylindrical Shells, Part I: Theoretical Development, *J. Sound and Vibr.*, Vol.162, No.2, 1993, pp.311-322.

(5)   Lomakin, V.A., *The Elasticity Theory of Nonhomogeneous Materials*, Nauka, Moscow, 1976. (in Russian)

(6)   Massalas, C., Dalamanagas, D. and Tzivanidis,G., Dynamic Instability of Truncated Conical Shells with Variable Modulus of Elasticity under Periodic Compressive Forces, *J. Sound and Vibr.*, Vol.79, No.4, 1981, pp.519-528.

(7)   Mecitoglu, Z., Governing Equations of a Stiffened Laminated Inhomogeneous Conical Shell, *AIAA Journal*, Vol.34, No.10, 1996, pp.2118-2125.

(8)   Sofiyev, A. and Aksogan, O., Dynamic Stability of a Nonhomogeneous Orthotropic Elastic Cylindrical Shell under a Time Dependent External

Pressure, *Technical J. Turkish Chamber of Civ. Eng.*, Vol.10, No.4, 1999, pp.2011-2028. (in Turkish)

(9) Volmir, A. S., *Nonlinear Dynamics of Plates and Shells.*, Nauka, Moscow, 1972. (in Russian)

(10) Tylikowski, A., Dynamic Stability of Nonlinear Antisymmetrically-Laminated Cross-Ply Rectangular Plates, *J. Appl. Mech.,* Vol.56, 1989, pp.375-381.

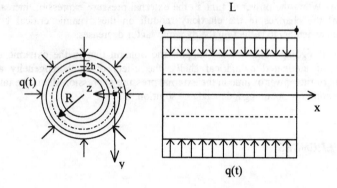

FIGURE 1 Cylindrical shell with n layers under a uniform external pressure

DUAL-MODE FREQUENCY TRIMMING OF IMPERFECT RINGS

A.K. Rourke[*], S. McWilliam[*] and C.H.J. Fox[*]

This paper investigates a method of trimming an imperfect ring in order to simultaneously eliminate the frequency splits that exist between two pairs of modes. Initially, the effect that the addition of two imperfection masses has on a perfect ring is investigated. The effect of performing this operation in reverse is then considered and it is shown that it is theoretically possible to trim two independent modes simultaneously and that a simple relationship exists between the angular positions of the two masses. For the purposes of validation and demonstration, the proposed method is applied to a specific example.

INTRODUCTION

This paper deals with the reduction and possible elimination of small frequency splits that occur in rings, or other nominally axi-symmetric structures, between pairs of modes of vibration with the same harmonic number. In a perfectly axi-symmetric ring, such modes occur in degenerate pairs with equal natural frequencies. In real rings, imperfections due to dimensional variations and material non-uniformity give rise to small frequency splits, and fix the positions of the modes relative to the ring. This problem is of particular importance in the manufacture of gyroscopic rate sensors that are based on the vibration of a ring-shaped resonator [1]. In such an application, it is often desirable to reduce frequency splits to the order of 0.01% to maintain strong resonant coupling between a given pair of modes.

It has previously been shown by Fox [2,3] that, for in-plane modes of flexural vibration, the addition of an appropriate single "trimming" mass at a particular position on the ring will eliminate the frequency split between one pair of $n\theta$ modes of the ring, and remove the fixed spatial orientation, where n is the number of nodal diameters of the mode. The effect of this trimming mass on modes with a different value of n can, similarly, be predicted but it is unlikely that the frequency splits associated with these modes will be eliminated simultaneously. This has previously been an acceptable result, but future developments in sensor technology may depend on the ability to trim more than one pair of modes at the same time.

The principal aim of the current paper is to report the results of an investigation that extends and generalises the procedure and results given in [2] to the simultaneous trimming of two pairs of modes using two trimming masses.

[*]School of Mechanical, Materials, Manufacturing Engineering and Management, University of Nottingham, University Park, Nottingham, NG7 2RD, U.K.

THE TRIMMING PROBLEM

Consider an imperfect ring for which the natural frequencies of the two similar orthogonal modes having n nodal diameters are ω_{n1} and ω_{n2} and of the two similar orthogonal modes having N nodal diameters are ω_{N1} and ω_{N2}, where $N \neq n$. Here it is assumed that the radial (w) and tangential displacements (u) of the ring in these four modes are given by:

$$
\begin{aligned}
w_1 &= W_1 \cos n(\phi - \psi_{n1}) \exp(i\omega_{n1}t) & u_1 &= U_1 \sin n(\phi - \psi_{n1}) \exp(i\omega_{n1}t) \\
w_2 &= W_2 \cos n(\phi - \psi_{n2}) \exp(i\omega_{n2}t) & u_2 &= U_2 \sin n(\phi - \psi_{n2}) \exp(i\omega_{n2}t) \\
w_3 &= W_3 \cos N(\phi - \psi_{N1}) \exp(i\omega_{N1}t) & u_3 &= U_3 \sin N(\phi - \psi_{N1}) \exp(i\omega_{N1}t) \\
w_4 &= W_4 \cos N(\phi - \psi_{N2}) \exp(i\omega_{N2}t) & u_4 &= U_4 \sin N(\phi - \psi_{N2}) \exp(i\omega_{N2}t)
\end{aligned}
\tag{1-8}
$$

where the orientations $\psi_{n2} = \psi_{n1} + \pi/2n$ and $\psi_{N2} = \psi_{N1} + \pi/2N$. The assumption of the above mode shapes is reasonable provided the degree of imperfection is sufficiently small. In practice the orientations of the modes and their natural frequencies would be determined from measurements performed on the ring.

The initial problem is to calculate the values of the two required masses, m_1 and m_2, and the angular positions, ϕ_1 and ϕ_2, of these masses which, when added to a perfect ring, would produce the described "imperfect" natural frequencies and mode positions (see figure 1). The effect of additional masses and springs on the natural frequencies and mode positions of a ring has been investigated previously by Fox [2], using a Rayleigh-Ritz approach. Using an identical procedure it may be shown that for the case of two imperfection masses m_1 and m_2 positioned at ϕ_1 and ϕ_2, the split natural frequencies for the mode with n nodal diameters are:

$$
\omega_{n1}^2 = \omega_{0n}^2 \left(\frac{1+\alpha_n^2}{(1+\alpha_n^2) + m_1[(1+\alpha_n^2)-(1-\alpha_n^2)\cos 2n(\phi_1-\psi_n)]/M_0 + m_2[(1+\alpha_n^2)-(1-\alpha_n^2)\cos 2n(\phi_2-\psi_n)]/M_0} \right)
\tag{9}
$$

$$
\omega_{n2}^2 = \omega_{0n}^2 \left(\frac{1+\alpha_n^2}{(1+\alpha_n^2) + m_1[(1+\alpha_n^2)+(1-\alpha_n^2)\cos 2n(\phi_1-\psi_n)]/M_0 + m_2[(1+\alpha_n^2)+(1-\alpha_n^2)\cos 2n(\phi_2-\psi_n)]/M_0} \right)
\tag{10}
$$

and the mode orientations $\psi_n = \psi_{n1} = \psi_{n2} - \pi/2n$ are such that:

$$\tan 2n\psi_n = \frac{m_1 \sin 2n\phi_1 + m_2 \sin 2n\phi_2}{m_1 \cos 2n\phi_1 + m_2 \cos 2n\phi_2}. \tag{11}$$

In these equations the ratio of the radial amplitude to the tangential amplitude of the $n\theta$ mode is α_n, the mass of the perfect ring is M_0, and the natural frequency of the perfect ring is ω_{0n}. A similar set of equations can be produced for the $N\theta$ mode.

For the purposes of calculating the magnitude and position of the masses needed to eliminate the frequency splits, it is necessary to manipulate equations (9) to (11) and the corresponding $N\theta$ equations so as to establish expressions for the natural frequencies of the perfect ring, and the magnitudes and positions of the trimming masses in terms of the known frequency splits, nodal positions and amplitude ratios. Using these equations it may be shown that:

$$\omega_{0n}^2 = \frac{2M\omega_{n1}^2\omega_{n2}^2}{(M - m_1 - m_2)(\omega_{n1}^2 + \omega_{n2}^2)} \tag{12}$$

$$\omega_{0N}^2 = \frac{2M\omega_{N1}^2\omega_{N2}^2}{(M - m_1 - m_2)(\omega_{N1}^2 + \omega_{N2}^2)} \tag{13}$$

$$m_1 = \frac{M\left(A_1 \cos 2N(\phi_2 - \psi_N) - A_2 \cos 2n(\phi_2 - \psi_n)\right)}{A_3\left(\cos 2n(\phi_1 - \psi_n)\cos 2N(\phi_2 - \psi_N) - \cos 2n(\phi_2 - \psi_n)\cos 2N(\phi_1 - \psi_N)\right)} \tag{14}$$

$$m_2 = \frac{M\left(A_2 \cos 2n(\phi_1 - \psi_n) - A_1 \cos 2N(\phi_1 - \psi_N)\right)}{A_3\left(\cos 2n(\phi_1 - \psi_n)\cos 2N(\phi_2 - \psi_N) - \cos 2n(\phi_2 - \psi_n)\cos 2N(\phi_1 - \psi_N)\right)} \tag{15}$$

$$\tan 2n\psi_n = \frac{\begin{pmatrix} A_2(\sin 2n\phi_2 \cos 2n(\phi_1 - \psi_n) - \sin 2n\phi_1 \cos 2n(\phi_2 - \psi_n)) \\ + A_1(\sin 2n\phi_1 \cos 2N(\phi_2 - \psi_N) - \sin 2n\phi_2 \cos 2N(\phi_1 - \psi_N)) \end{pmatrix}}{\begin{pmatrix} A_2(\cos 2n\phi_2 \cos 2n(\phi_1 - \psi_n) - \cos 2n\phi_1 \cos 2n(\phi_2 - \psi_n)) \\ + A_1(\cos 2n\phi_1 \cos 2N(\phi_2 - \psi_N) - \cos 2n\phi_2 \cos 2N(\phi_1 - \psi_N)) \end{pmatrix}} \tag{16}$$

$$\tan 2N\psi_N = \frac{\begin{pmatrix} A_2(\sin 2N\phi_2 \cos 2n(\phi_1 - \psi_n) - \sin 2N\phi_1 \cos 2n(\phi_2 - \psi_n)) \\ + A_1(\sin 2N\phi_1 \cos 2N(\phi_2 - \psi_N) - \sin 2N\phi_2 \cos 2N(\phi_1 - \psi_N)) \end{pmatrix}}{\begin{pmatrix} A_2(\cos 2N\phi_2 \cos 2n(\phi_1 - \psi_n) - \cos 2N\phi_1 \cos 2n(\phi_2 - \psi_n)) \\ + A_1(\cos 2N\phi_1 \cos 2N(\phi_2 - \psi_N) - \cos 2N\phi_2 \cos 2N(\phi_1 - \psi_N)) \end{pmatrix}} \tag{17}$$

where $M(=M_0 + m_1 + m_2)$ is the total mass of the ring and the constants A_1, A_2 and A_3 are:

$$A_1 = (\omega_{n2}^2 - \omega_{n1}^2)(\omega_{N2}^2 + \omega_{N1}^2)(\alpha_n^2 + 1)(\alpha_N^2 - 1)$$

$$A_2 = (\omega_{N2}^2 - \omega_{N1}^2)(\omega_{n2}^2 + \omega_{n1}^2)(\alpha_N^2 + 1)(\alpha_n^2 - 1)$$

$$A_3 = (\omega_{n2}^2 + \omega_{n1}^2)(\omega_{N2}^2 + \omega_{N1}^2)(\alpha_n^2 - 1)(\alpha_N^2 - 1)$$

Equations (12) to (15) may be used directly to calculate the natural frequencies of the perfect ring and the magnitude of the trimming masses once the positions of the masses have been determined. There appears to be no analytical solution for the angular positions, ϕ_1 and ϕ_2, of the masses and for this reason a numerical solution to simultaneous equations (16) and (17) is sought – details of the numerical method adopted are presented in the Numerical Analysis section. A number of solutions to equations (16) and (17) are possible, and for this reason it is worthwhile investigating whether any analytic relationships between these solutions exist. Manipulating equation (11) and the equivalent $N\theta$ equation it may be shown, after some algebra, that the following simple relationship between the angular positions holds:

$$\tan(n + N)(\phi_1 + \beta) = C \tan(N - n)(\phi_2 + \delta) \tag{18}$$

$$\tan(n + N)(\phi_2 + \beta) = C \tan(N - n)(\phi_1 + \delta) \tag{19}$$

where either:

(i) $\qquad \beta = -\left(\dfrac{n\psi_n + N\psi_N}{n + N}\right), \ \delta = \left(\dfrac{-n\psi_n + N\psi_N - \pi/2}{n - N}\right)$ and $C=D$ $\qquad$ (20)

or

(ii) $\qquad \beta = -\left(\dfrac{n\psi_n + N\psi_N - \pi/2}{n + N}\right), \ \delta = \left(\dfrac{-n\psi_n + N\psi_N}{n - N}\right)$ and $C=1/D$. $\qquad$ (21)

The constants β and δ are dependent on the number of nodal diameters and the original orientations of the modes, as indicated in equations (20) and (21). To date, the authors have not been able to find analytic solutions for the constant D. However, once a single numerical solution to equations (16) and (17) has been calculated, the constant D may be calculated from equations (18) and (19) and the remaining set of solutions obtained.

The above analysis indicates that it is theoretically possible to create an imperfect ring with specific frequency splits and mode orientations from an initially perfect ring by the addition of two trimming masses. It has also been shown that this process can be performed in reverse. Thus, by starting with an imperfect ring, it is possible to eliminate the natural frequency splits by removing two trimming mass at particular angular positions. The proposed procedure is demonstrated and validated below.

NUMERICAL ANALYSIS

The analysis presented in the previous section established that it is theoretically possible to trim an imperfect ring for two independent modes. To establish the validity of the analysis, it is necessary to investigate an example. The example chosen is from data provided in Table 4 of reference [2]. The method used to investigate this example is outlined first.

The Analysis Method

As was indicated earlier, the first step in calculating possible positions for the trimming masses is to calculate a single numerical solution to simultaneous equations (16) and (17). The numerical procedure adopted to achieve this is described below:

(i) Let $F(\phi_1,\phi_2)=tan(2n\psi_n)-f(\phi_1,\phi_2)$, where $f(\phi_1,\phi_2)$ is the term appearing on the right hand side of equation (16). Solutions to equation (16) occur when $F(\phi_1,\phi_2)=0$;

(ii) Similarly, let $G(\phi_1,\phi_2)=tan(2N\psi_N)-g(\phi_1,\phi_2)$, where $g(\phi_1,\phi_2)$ is the term appearing on the right hand side of equation (17). Solutions to equation (17) occur when $G(\phi_1,\phi_2)=0$;

(iii) Let $H(\phi_1,\phi_2)=F(\phi_1,\phi_2)^2+G(\phi_1,\phi_2)^2$. This equation ensures that solutions to equations (16) and (17) occur when $H(\phi_1,\phi_2)=0$.

(iv) Use standard numerical techniques to calculate a single numerical solution to $H(\phi_1,\phi_2)=0$.

Once a single numerical solution for the angular positions of the trimming masses has been calculated, the relevant value of C is calculated by substituting the results into equations (18) or (19) - values of β and δ having already been calculated from either equations (20) or (21). Other solutions for the mass positions may then be generated from the simultaneous solution of equations (18) and (19). The magnitudes of the required masses can then be calculated from equations (14) and (15) and the natural frequencies, that the modes will be trimmed to, calculated from equations (12) and (13).

The range of values of ϕ_1 and ϕ_2 that need to be considered can be determined by considering the influence of angular translations and reflections on equations (18) and (19). The basic symmetry of these two equations indicates that the choice of ϕ_1 and ϕ_2 is arbitrary and if ϕ_1 and ϕ_2 are interchanged, then the only difference will be that the angular positions of masses m_1 and m_2 will be exchanged. The other limitation on the necessary calculations of ϕ_1 and ϕ_2 is that an angular translation of either ϕ_1 or ϕ_2 by π/R will not affect equations (18) and (19), provided that R is a common factor of both $(n+N)$ and $(N-n)$. Thus the region that needs to be investigated so that the minimum number of valid angular solutions can be generated is $0<\phi_1<\pi/R$ and

$\phi_1 < \phi_2 < \pi/R$. The remaining natural frequency solutions can then be generated by appropriate angular translations of the solutions in this region, and by transposing ϕ_1 and ϕ_2.

As the example that is to be investigated here has been generated numerically from an initially perfect ring, the solutions to equations (9) to (19) can be checked by reconsidering the original problem [2]. Furthermore, the frequency splits produced by the original three imperfection masses and the two calculated trimming masses should be negligible when all are added to the originally perfect ring.

The example considered below checks that the theoretical solutions are observed numerically for several pairs of $n\theta$ and $N\theta$ modes.

A Numerical Example

Consider a perfect ring of mass 7.3984kg to which are attached three imperfection masses of 0.1kg, 0.2kg and 0.3kg at angular positions 0, 20 and 70 degrees respectively. The other dimensions of the ring are included in Appendix (I). Using the analysis reported by Fox [2], the effect that these masses have on the natural frequencies and the orientations of the mode shapes of the ring can be calculated and are recorded in Table 1 for the first four practical flexural modes. $n=1$ represents rigid body motion of an unsupported ring and so is not included in the data. The frequencies included in brackets in the table are the original frequencies of the perfect ring.

There are six possible pairs of modes that can be obtained from this data. Each of the six pairs are investigated and Figures 2 to 7 show the complete set of angular solutions to equations (18) and (19) for the specified modes. The solutions have been obtained over the full range $-180° < \phi_i < 180°$. Figures 8 and 9 have been included for comparison. Figure 8 is a plot of all the possible curves that can be obtained from equations (18), (19) and (21) for the $(n=2,N=3)$ mode test and the solutions can be observed from the points at which the curves intersect. The solutions along the line $\phi_1 = \phi_2$ are invalid as the trimming masses that need to be placed at these points are significantly larger than the mass of the ring. Figure 9 is a manipulated plot of equation (18), where the x-axis is given by $tan(N-n)(\phi_2+\delta)$ and the y-axis is given by $tan(N+n)(\phi_1+\beta)$, and the gradient of the graph is the constant C.

From the calculated angular positions, the respective magnitudes of the masses that are to be placed at these positions, and their effect on the frequencies, can be calculated. Tables 2 and 3 record all of the valid solutions for the $(n=2,N=3)$ modes and the effect that these trimming masses have on the ring. The masses recorded in both tables are the masses that need to be added to, or removed from, the imperfect ring of mass $M=7.9984$kg to achieve a perfect ring of mass M_0 that has frequencies of ω_n for mode $n=2$ and of ω_N for mode $N=3$. The masses have been calculated by reversing the sign of the solutions to equations (14) and (15). The values for ω_n and

ω_N, recorded in Table 2, have then been calculated from equations (12) and (13) using the original solutions to equations (14) and (15).

The four other values of ω_{n1}, ω_{n2}, ω_{N1} and ω_{N2}, which are recorded in Table 3, correspond to the total influence of the original three imperfection masses and the two calculated trimming masses onto the original perfect ring, which has a mass of M_0=7.3984kg. These values have been calculated in the same manner that the frequency splits of Table 1 were calculated. It can be observed that the frequency splits have been significantly reduced. For clarity, it should be noted that the difference between the ideal frequencies shown in Table 2 and the calculated frequencies are recorded instead of the absolute frequencies.

The calculated "trimmed" modes possess a degree of determinacy in their orientations. This determinacy has been included in the calculation of the frequencies, as required by the equations established in Fox [2], but it has not been recorded in the tabulated data. The remaining determinacy is due to the accuracy of the calculations of the masses and their angular positions. These variables will have to be calculated to a high degree of accuracy, or several iterations of the trimming procedure will have to be performed, to eliminate the determinacy of the modes.

Despite the remaining determinacy of the modes, the (two) trimming masses have significantly reduced the two required frequency splits to close to zero. It is often desirable in a practical gyroscopic sensor to reduce a frequency split to less than 0.01% to make any errors insignificant. These frequency splits have all been reduced to such a level. Thus, it is theoretically possible to modify an imperfect ring to simulate a perfect ring for two modes by the addition of two trimming masses. The effect that these masses have on the other modes is predictable but it is unlikely that the other frequency splits will be reduced to zero unless the imperfections happened to be identical to those created by the addition of two imperfection masses onto an imperfect ring.

TABLE 1 Imperfections created in the perfect ring by the three imperfection masses

	n=2	n=3	n=4	n=5
Frequencies of the imperfect ring, ω_{n1},ω_{n2} (Hz)	35.096	97.832	188.02	305.71
	36.656	102.423	195.89	314.97
	(36.779)	(104.026)	(199.46)	(322.57)
Orientations, ψ_{n1},ψ_{n2} (degrees)	-6.95	11.82	23.16	-4.14
	38.05	41.82	0.66	13.86

TABLE 2 Trimming masses and the natural frequencies for n=2, N=3

m_1 (kg)	ϕ_1 (deg.)	m_2 (kg)	ϕ_2 (deg.)	M_0 (kg)	ω_n (Hz)	ω_N (Hz)
-0.199	12.90	-0.262	71.00	7.538	36.437	103.059
-0.298	6.86	0.248	107.92	7.949	35.483	100.362
0.327	44.02	0.159	97.15	8.484	34.346	97.145
-0.523	3.95	-0.398	144.31	7.078	37.602	106.355
0.335	40.65	-0.133	134.82	8.200	34.934	98.809
0.406	37.63	0.195	172.18	8.599	34.115	96.493
-0.480	77.86	-0.293	119.16	7.226	37.216	105.263
-0.327	75.07	0.185	155.81	7.857	35.690	100.947
0.522	111.48	0.478	150.52	8.999	33.348	94.321

TABLE 3 Trimming masses and the frequency splits for n=2, N=3

m_1 (kg)	ϕ_1 (deg.)	m_2 (kg)	ϕ_2 (deg.)	$\omega_{n1}-\omega_n$ ($\times 10^{-4}$ Hz)	$\omega_{n2}-\omega_n$ ($\times 10^{-4}$ Hz)	$\omega_{N1}-\omega_N$ ($\times 10^{-4}$ Hz)	$\omega_{N2}-\omega_N$ ($\times 10^{-4}$ Hz)
-0.199	12.90	-0.262	71.00	-3.178	2.083	-16.39	8.293
-0.298	6.86	0.248	107.92	-2.970	1.903	-15.45	7.559
0.327	44.02	0.159	97.15	-2.721	1.688	-14.18	6.543
-0.523	3.95	-0.398	144.31	-3.462	2.331	-17.76	9.398
0.335	40.65	-0.133	134.82	-2.846	1.796	-14.71	6.944
0.406	37.63	0.195	172.18	-2.674	1.648	-13.89	6.309
-0.480	77.86	-0.293	119.16	-3.364	2.245	-17.30	9.024
-0.327	75.07	0.185	155.81	-3.012	1.939	-15.56	7.628
0.522	111.48	0.478	150.52	-2.513	1.511	-12.87	5.458

The results shown in Table 4 indicate the influence of the trimming masses on the frequency splits of some other modes. The order of the solutions corresponds with the order of the variables shown in Tables 2 and 3, such that the first solution of Table 4 is that of an imperfect ring with trimming masses of 0.199kg and 0.262kg removed from it. The frequency splits vary between a few Hertz and thirty Hertz for the $n=4$ modes and there is a similar variation of frequency splits for the $n=5$ modes.

TABLE 4 Effect of the trimming masses on the other modes

n=4			n=5		
ψ_1 (degrees)	ω_{n1} (Hz)	ω_{n2} (Hz)	ψ_1 (degrees)	ω_{n1} (Hz)	ω_{n2} (Hz)
6.037	199.246	196.004	-7.767	314.109	325.325
1.243	201.008	184.871	-5.359	301.529	321.880
6.745	185.616	186.921	0.011	298.012	304.555
4.607	220.359	190.692	4.086	348.526	313.784
5.532	192.782	186.296	2.547	298.519	314.921
10.340	190.561	179.926	-2.168	288.990	310.595
-9.837	210.913	193.828	-8.655	309.925	345.824
-4.632	199.084	188.463	4.495	317.660	308.579
-2.582	192.910	173.803	3.428	278.582	308.679

Comparison of the solutions for tests of different pairs of modes indicate that the smallest frequency splits shown in Table 4 correspond to angular positions of the trimming masses that are close to solutions for that mode. For example, a solution for the ($n=2,N=4$) mode test is at $\phi_1=43.24°$ and $\phi_2=96.95°$ which is close to the solution $\phi_1=44.02°$ and $\phi_2=97.15°$ for the ($n=2,N=3$) mode test and it is at this point that the frequency split is smallest for $n=4$ during the $n=2$, $N=3$ mode test. There is still a significant frequency split for the $n=4$ mode so it is unlikely that three modes may be deliberately trimmed using two trimming masses.

Conclusion

The theory outlined in [2] has been extended from a single trimming mass to a pair of trimming masses. It has been shown that a pair of trimming masses correctly placed around the circumference of an imperfect ring will simultaneously eliminate two frequency splits. It has also been shown that the angular positions of the two trimming masses are related by a simple pair of equations. A numerical example has been used to demonstrate and verify the proposed method.

Acknowledgement

The authors gratefully acknowledge the support for this work provided by BAE SYSTEMS and EPSRC under the Industrial CASE scheme.

Nomenclature

α_n – Constant of the nθ mode, the ratio of the radial amplitude to the tangential amplitude

β, δ, C – Constants of the solution model

ψ_n – Orientation of the nθ mode

ω_n – Natural frequency of the nθ mode

ω_{0n} – Natural frequency of the nθ mode of the perfect ring

ϕ – General angular position around the ring

ϕ_i – Angular position of the ith imperfection mass, m_i

m_i – Mass of the ith imperfection mass

M – Mass of the imperfect ring

M_0 – Mass of the simulated perfect ring

N, n – Number of nodal diameters of a specific node

t – Time

T_{0n} – Kinetic energy of the ring

u_j – Tangential displacement of the ring

w_j – Radial displacement of the ring

REFERENCE LIST

(1) Hopkin, I., Performance and design of a silicon micro-machined gyro, *Proceedings of DGON Symposium on Gyro Technology,* Stuttgart, 1997, Chap. 1

(2) Fox, C.H.J., *Journal of Sound and Vibration*, Vol. 142(3), 1990, pp. 227–243.

(3) Fox, C.H.J., Mode trimming in nominally axi-symmetric structures, *Proceedings of XV International Modal Analysis Conference,* Tokyo, 1997, pp566-572

Appendix (I) – The Dimensions and Properties of the Perfect Ring

Mean radius = 0.3 m   Radial thickness = 0.005 m

Axial length = 0.1 m   Mass of the ring, M_P = 7.3984 kg

Density = 7850 kg/m^3 Young's modulus = 206E+9 N/ m^2

Poisson ratio = 0.3

FIGURE 1 The imperfection masses and the generated imperfections:

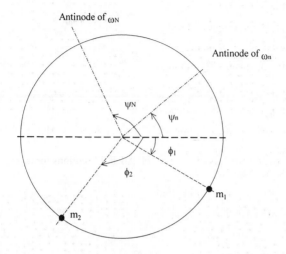

Figures (2) to (7) show the complete set of angular solutions to equations (18) and (19) for the specified modes. Figure (8) shows equations (18) and (19) graphically for the (n=2, N=3) case to indicate that the solutions shown in figure (2) occur when the curves intersect. Figure (9) is a modified form of equation (18) in which the x-axis represents $tan(N-n)(\phi_2+\delta)$ and the y-axis represents $tan(N+n)(\phi_1+\beta)$.

FIGURE 2 Solutions for (n=2, N=3);

FIGURE 3 Solutions for (n=2, N=4);

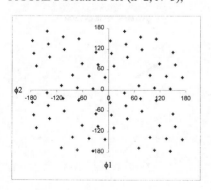

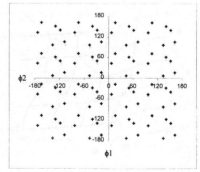

FIGURE 4 Solutions for (n=2, N=5)   FIGURE 5 Solutions for (n=3, N=4)

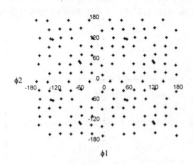

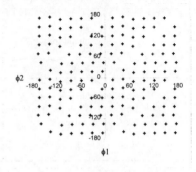

FIGURE 6 Solutions for (n=3, N=5)   FIGURE 7 Solutions for (n=4, N=5)

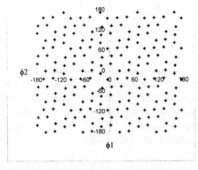

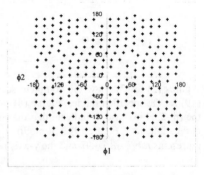

FIGURE 8 Solutions for (n=2, N=3)   FIGURE 9 Solutions for (n=2, N=3)

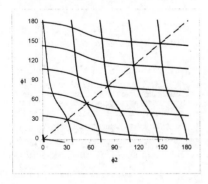

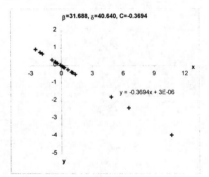

372

ANALYSIS OF THE MULTIPLE-SOLUTION RESPONSE OF A FLEXIBLE ROTOR SUPPORTED ON SQUEEZE FILM DAMPERS

Changsheng, Zhu*, D.A. Robb* and D. J. Ewins*

The multiple-solution response in a flexible rotor supported on squeeze film dampers is one of typical non-linear phenomena. The behaviour of the multiple-solution response in a flexible rotor supported on two identical squeeze film dampers with centralising springs is studied by three methods: iteration method of synchronous circular centred orbit motion, numerical integration method and slow acceleration method using the assumption of the short bearing and cavitation oil film; the differences of computational results obtained by the three different methods are compared in this paper. It is shown that there are three basic forms for the multiple-solution response in the flexible rotor-squeeze film damper system, which are the resonant, isolated bifurcation and swallowtail bifurcation multiple-solutions. In the multiple-solution speed regions, the rotor motion may be sub-synchronous, sub-super-synchronous, almost-periodic and even chaotic, besides synchronous circular centred, even if the gravity effect is not considered. The assumption of synchronous circular centred orbit motion for the journal can be used only in some special cases; the steady state numerical integration method is very useful, but time-consuming. Not only can the multiple-solution speed regions be detected by the slow acceleration method, but also the non-synchronous response regions.

1. INTRODUCTION

It is well known that a squeeze film damper(SFD), which has been used in the rotor structures of aero-engines to control rotor vibration, behaves with a non-linearity in the region of the high journal eccentricity ratios. Various non-linear phenomena can be experimentally observed in the rotor system supported on the SFDs, the multiple-solution in the unbalance response curves is one of typical non-linear phenomena. Generally, the largest and the smallest solutions are stable, this phenomenon is often called bistable operation. Since the largest solution of the bistable operation, characterised by the large vibrational amplitude and transmitted force, has a great influence on the reliability of the damper, therefore, a very important problem in the design of the SFD is to determine the regions and locations of the multiple-solution and to analyse its behaviour.

* Centre of Vibration Engineering, Department of Mechanical Engineering, Imperial College, London SW7 2BX, U.K.

Many numerical methods, for example, the iteration method of synchronous circular centred orbit motion (Radinowitz and Hahn[1], Greenhill and Nelson[2] and Taylor and Kumar[3]), harmonic balance method(Shiau and Hwang[5], Levesley and Holmes[6]), trigonometric collocation method(Jean and Nelson[7]), generalised polynomial expansion method(Hwang and Shian[8]), numerical integration method etc, can be used to analyse the behaviour of the multiple-solution, but there are some weaknesses for every analysis method mentioned above. In this paper, we analyse the behaviour of the multiple-solution in a flexible rotor-SFD by iteration method of synchronous circular centred orbit motion, numerical integration method and slow acceleration method and compare the difference of the computational results from the three different methods. In order to avoid the complex mathematical problems in getting all solutions of multiple-variable non-linear equations, we chose a symmetrical Jeffcott rotor supported on two identical SFDs with the centralising springs and assume that the short bearing and cavitation oil film model are applicable.

2. ROTOR MODEL AND ANALYSING METHODS

2.1 Rotor model

The rotor system to be investigated is a Jeffcott rotor symmetrically supported on two identical SFDs with the centralising springs as shown in Figure 1. In order to simplify the analysis, the following assumptions are made: (a) The imbalance of the rotor system is defined at the mid-span of the rotor and the rotor mass is lumped at the rotor mid-plan and at the two damper stations; (b) The rotor stiffness and the centralising spring stiffness are radially symmetric and the damping at the mid-span disk due to the air dynamics is viscous. (c) The gyroscopic effect of the disc on the rotor system is neglected; (d) The axial and torsion vibrations of the rotor system and the influence of the rolling bearings are negligible; (e) The oil-film forces of the damper are determined by the Reynolds equation with an incompressible lubricant and the short bearing and cavitation π-film are applicable.

Since the rotor system is symmetric about its mid-span, it is sufficient to consider one half of the system only. Thus, the equations of the motion of the rotor system in Cartesian co-ordinates can be expressed by the complex variables in varying speed operation as the following form:

$$m_D \ddot{Z}_D + c_D \dot{Z}_D + k_s \left(Z_D - Z_B \right) = m_D g + m_D e_\mu \dot{\varphi}^2 e^{i\varphi} - m_D e_\mu \ddot{\varphi} e^{-i\varphi} \tag{1}$$

$$m_B \ddot{Z}_B + \frac{k_s}{2} \left(Z_B - Z_D \right) + \frac{k_a}{2} Z_B = m_B g + \left(F_x + i F_y \right) \tag{2}$$

Dividing by $m_D \omega_r^2 C$ and $m_B \omega_r^2 C$ respectively, the non-dimensional equations of the motion of the rotor system are given by:

$$Z_D'' + \frac{2\xi\Omega_r}{\Omega} Z_D' + \frac{\Omega_r^2}{\Omega^2}(Z_D - Z_B) = \frac{\Omega_r^2}{\Omega^2} W + U(\varphi'^2 e^{i\Omega_r t} - i\varphi'' e^{-i\Omega_r t}) \tag{3}$$

$$Z_B'' + \frac{\Omega_r^2}{2\alpha\Omega}(Z_B - Z_D) + \frac{k\Omega_r^2}{2\alpha\Omega^2} Z_B = \frac{\Omega_r^2}{\Omega^2} W + \frac{\Omega_r}{\Omega}(\overline{F}_x + i\overline{F}_y) \tag{4}$$

$\overline{F}_x$ and $\overline{F}_y$ are the non-dimensional oil-film force components of the SFD in x and y directions, respectively, which depend on the oil film model used in the theoretical analysis. For the SFD without side-seals and $L/D < 0.25$, the short bearing approximation solution and half cavitated film model are valuable. In this case, the non-dimensional oil film force components in the XY co-ordinate system are given by(Holmes[9]):

$$\overline{F}_X = -\frac{2B}{\sqrt{(X_B^2 + Y_B^2)}}\left[X_B\left(\varepsilon_B\varphi_B' I^{11} + \varepsilon_B' I^{02}\right) - Y_B\left(\varepsilon_B\varphi_B' I^{11} + \varepsilon_B' I^{02}\right)\right] = -2Bf_x \tag{5}$$

$$\overline{F}_Y = -\frac{2B}{\sqrt{(X_B^2 + Y_B^2)}}\left[-Y_B\left(\varepsilon_B\varphi_B' I^{11} + \varepsilon_B' I^{02}\right) + X_B\left(\varepsilon_B\varphi_B' I^{11} + \varepsilon_B' I^{02}\right)\right] = -2Bf_y \tag{6}$$

Where, $\varepsilon_B = \sqrt{x_B^2 + y_B^2}$, $\varphi_B = tg^{-1}\left(\frac{Y_B}{X_B}\right)$, $I^{mn} = \int_{\theta_1}^{+\theta_1} \frac{\sin^m \theta \cos^n \theta}{(1 + \varepsilon_B \cos\theta)^3} d\theta$, $\theta_1 = tg^{-1}\left(\frac{-\varepsilon_B'}{\varepsilon_B\varphi_B'}\right)$.

2.2 Analysis methods

2.2.1 Iteration method of circular centred orbit motion

Generally, if there is a centralising spring in the SFD, the effect of the weight on the rotor system is not considered due to the centralised function of the centralising spring, we can set $W=0$ in Eqs. (3)-(4). In this case, the assumption of the synchronous circular centred orbit (CCO) motion of the journal around the centre of the bearing is often used[1,2,3]. Under the synchronous CCO motion, let $Z_b = \varepsilon_B e^{i\varphi_B}$ and $Z_D = \varepsilon_D e^{i\varphi_D}$, where $\varepsilon_D, \varepsilon_B, \varphi_B$ and φ_D are constants, Eqs. (3)-(4) can be transmitted to a set of non-linear algebraic equations.

$$\left\{\frac{1+k}{2\alpha\Omega^2} - 1 - \frac{1-\Omega^2}{2\alpha\Omega^2[(1-\alpha^2)^2 + (2\xi\Omega)^2]} + \frac{4B}{\Omega}\frac{\varepsilon_{BO}}{(1-\varepsilon_{BO}^2)^2}\right\}^2 \varepsilon_{BO}^2$$

$$+ \left\{\frac{2\xi\Omega}{2\alpha\Omega^2[(1-\alpha^2)^2 + (2\xi\Omega)^2]} + \frac{B\pi}{\Omega}\frac{1}{(1-\varepsilon_{BO}^2)^{1/2}}\right\}^2 \varepsilon_{BO}^2 = \frac{U^2}{2\alpha^2[(1-\Omega^2)^2 + (2\xi\Omega)^2]} \tag{7}$$

$$tg\,\varphi_{BO} = \frac{2\xi\Omega\left[\dfrac{1+k}{2\alpha\Omega^2} - 1 + \dfrac{4B}{\Omega}\dfrac{\varepsilon_{BO}}{(1-\varepsilon_{BO}^2)^2} + \dfrac{\pi B}{\Omega}\dfrac{1-\Omega^2}{(1-\varepsilon_{BO}^2)^{1/2}}\right]}{\left[\dfrac{1+k}{2\alpha\Omega^2} - 1 + \dfrac{4B}{\Omega}\dfrac{\varepsilon_{BO}}{(1-\varepsilon_{BO}^2)^2}\right](1-\Omega^2) - 2\xi\Omega\dfrac{\pi B}{\Omega}\dfrac{1}{(1-\varepsilon_{BO}^2)^{1/2}} - \dfrac{1}{2\alpha\Omega^2}} \tag{8}$$

375

$$\varepsilon_{DO}^{2} = \frac{\left[\varepsilon_{BO}^{2}\cos\varphi_{BO} + U\Omega^{2}\right]^{2} + \left(\varepsilon_{BO}\sin\varphi_{BO}\right)^{2}}{\left(1 - \Omega^{2}\right)^{2} + \left(2\xi\Omega\right)^{2}} \tag{9}$$

$$tg\varphi_{DO} = \frac{2\xi\Omega\left[\varepsilon_{BO}\cos\varphi_{BO} + U\Omega^{2}\right]^{2} + \left(1 - \Omega^{2}\right)\varepsilon_{BO}\sin\varphi_{BO}}{\left(1 - \Omega^{2}\right)\left[\varepsilon_{BO}\cos\varphi_{BO} + U\Omega^{2}\right] - 2\xi\Omega\varepsilon_{BO}\sin\varphi_{BO}} \tag{10}$$

From Eq.(7), we can easily determine all the solutions of the journal eccentricity ε_{B} by any iterative method in the region of $0 \le \varepsilon_{B} < 1.0$, then obtain φ_{B}, ε_{D} and φ_{D} from Eqs.(8)-(10). Therefore it is very efficient to analyse the non-linear behaviour of the rotor system with the SFD and to study the effect of the system parameters of the SFD on the dynamic behaviour of the rotor system.

2.2.2 Numerical integration method

Even if the rotor is mounted vertically or the centralising spring provides a static load capability to centralise the journal within the radial clearance of the damper in the static state, this does not guarantee the motion of the journal is always a synchronous CCO motion around the centre of the bearing in the dynamic state. In order to investigate the non-linear behaviour of the rotor system, the most general method is to numerically integrate the equations of the motion of the system for a given rotating speed. It takes a longer computing time, but does not make any assumption about the motion of the journal. Under a steady state rotating speed, letting $\omega_{s} = \omega$ in Eqs.(3)-(4), we have the non-dimensional equations of the motion of the rotor system as follows:

$$Z_{D}'' + \frac{2\xi}{\Omega}Z_{D}' + \frac{1}{\Omega^{2}}\left(Z_{D} - Z_{B}\right) = W + U_{a}e^{ir} \tag{11}$$

$$Z_{B}'' + \frac{1}{2a\Omega^{2}}\left(Z_{B} - Z_{D}\right) + \frac{k}{2a\Omega^{2}}Z_{B} = W + \frac{2B}{\Omega}\left(f_{x} + if_{y}\right) \tag{12}$$

Although some fast convergence integration methods can be used(Chu and Holmes[10]), no one method is always fast for every speed. Therefore, a fourth-order Runge-Kutta method with a constant time step is used here. The time step generally is $2\pi/400$ or $2\pi/800$, which is so small that there is no truncation error even if the step size decreases further. After integrating 100 cycles at each steady state rotating speed and ensuring that all transient motion caused by the initial conditions has died away, the integrating results in the next 50 integrating cycles are output as the steady state response of the rotor system at this rotating speed. If the motion of the rotor system is synchronous, the integration results in the next 5 integrating cycles will be the steady state response. This is automatically checked in the program by analysing the motion orbit of the rotor system.

2.2.3 Slow acceleration method

When the rotor is accelerated with a constant acceleration, letting $\omega_r = \omega_{cr}$ in Eqs.(3)-(4), we also have the equations of the motion of the rotor system.

$$Z''_D + 2\xi Z'_D + (Z_D - Z_B) = W + U\varphi'^2_D e^{i\varphi_D} - iU\varphi''_D e^{-i\varphi_D} \tag{13}$$

$$Z''_B + \frac{1}{2\alpha}(Z_B - Z_D) + \frac{k}{2a}Z_B = W + 2B(f_x + if_y) \tag{14}$$

Where $\varphi'' = \lambda = $ constant, $\varphi' = \varphi''\tau + \Omega_0$ and $\varphi = \frac{1}{2}\varphi''\tau^2 + \Omega_0\tau + \varphi_0$. Ω_0 and φ_0 are respectively steady state initial rotating speed ratio and attitude angle of starting to accelerate.

The equations (13) and (14) are numerically integrated in time using the fourth order Runge-Kutta integration method with a constant step, the transient response in the acceleration process can be obtained with different parameters of the SFD and different rotor angular acceleration ratios λ. In order to avoid the numerical divergence in the calculation due to $\varepsilon_B > 1.0$ which is caused by a larger integration time step, the variable time step in the integration (Zhu[11]) is used and controlled by keeping a constant angular increment for each time step. The angular increment used in the calculation generally is 1/500 revolution per step in which the numerical divergence does not appear. The effect of the time step on calculated results was checked by varying the angular increment to as small as 1/1000 revolution in order to reduce the effect of the rotor acceleration on the results.

The steady state response for the rotating speed in which the rotor will start to accelerate is taken as the initial conditions for the integration procedure. The integration procedure continues up to the given maximum rotating speed.

3. NUMERICAL RESULTS AND DISCUSSION

3.1 Solution of synchronous circular centred orbit motion

There are many kinds of response curve with multiple-solution in the steady state synchronous CCO motion, but they all consist of basic forms of the multiple-solution shown in Figure 2.

The multiple-solution in Figure 2a and 2b is called the resonant multiple-solution, which appears between the flexible critical speed and the rigid critical speed of the flexible rotor system. The largest and smallest solutions are stable and the medium one is unstable. If the end speed of the resonant multiple-solution speed region is very close to the rigid critical speed, the vibration amplitudes of the disk will dramatically increase, and the rotor has difficulty in passing through the critical speed. When the rotating speed is above the rigid critical speed, the resonant multiple-solution will disappear.

The multiple-solution shown in Figure 2c is called the isolated bifurcation multiple-solution. The isolated bifurcation multiple-solution also appears in the range of rotating speeds between the flexible critical speed and the rigid critical speed of the flexible rotor system. The reason is that the dynamic characteristics of the oil film force of SFD behave with a high non-linearity with a hardening characteristic in the region of high journal eccentricity ratios and the exciting force is directly proportional to the square of the exciting frequency.

The variation of the rotor vibration both in the journal and the disk position with the rotating speed for the resonant and the isolated bifurcation multiple-solutions is very similar, both jump from a larger solution to a smaller one or reverse. However, there is another multiple-solution shown in Figure 2d, which is called here the swallowtail bifurcation multiple-solution and occurs near the second rigid critical speed. The variation of the journal vibration shown in the top is the same as that of the resonant multiple-solution, the variation of the disk vibration shown in the bottom is completely different. The largest solution of the swallowtail bifurcation multiple-solution in the disk response curve is always unstable, the smallest and middle solutions are stable. Therefore, the journal amplitude will jump down from a larger solution to a smaller one in increasing rotating speed and jump up from a smaller one to a larger one in decreasing rotating speed, but the disk vibration is almost unchanging in the increasing rotating speed and jump down from a larger solution to a smaller one in the decreasing rotating speed.

The resonant and the swallowtail bifurcation multiple-solution have been observed in experiments(Zhu[12]), however most research work has been focused on the former since the resonant multiple-solution has a great effect on the rotor vibration and reliability of the damper.

Generally, the unbalance responses with multiple-solution are a combination of basic types shown above. Some typical unbalance response curves with multiple-solution are shown in Figure 3.

For rotor systems with many degrees of freedom and the complex oil film model, the main problems for this method are how to translate the motion equation of the rotor system to a set of non-linear algebraic equations when a complex oil film model is used and how to find the complete solution of the multiple-variable algebraic equations, even if the set of non-linear algebraic equations can be obtained.

3.2. Steady state solution by numerical integration method

In order to compare with the solution of the synchronous CCO motion, the effect of the gravity parameter W is not considered in the following sections. The steady state unbalance responses by the numerical integration method in increasing and decreasing rotating speed for the same parameters as in Figure 2 are shown in Figure 4. It should be noted that the increasing or decreasing rotating speed just means the rotating speed varies step by step, the changing ratio of the rotating speed is zero. In Figure 4, the dashed line stands for the increasing rotating speed and the solid line for the decreasing rotating speed.

Many numerical results show that it is very difficult to obtain all possible solutions for a given speed by the numerical integration method, even if the region of the initial conditions are known(Taylor and Kumar[4]). In fact, the regions of the displacement and the attitude angle of the journal are known, but the regions of the velocity of the journal and the whirling speed of the journal are unknown. Therefore, several techniques should be used in order to make the integration result converge for different solutions. A lot of numerical analyses show that when the rotating speed is increased or deceased step by step, the final steady state variables at a given rotating speed were used as initial conditions of the integration at the next rotating speed, which is a very efficient method to get multiple-solution and to save computing-time. There probably exist more multiple-solution speed regions but when the multiple-solution is found by the numerical integration method, the multiple-solution at least exists in these rotating speed regions.

If the motion of the rotor system is synchronous CCO, there is no difference between the solution of the synchronous CCO motion and the steady state solution obtained by the numerical integration method.

It is very obvious that there exist two different motion states at the same rotating speed, by comparing the unbalance responses in increasing and the decreasing rotating speed in Figure 4. The orbits of the rotor system in the multiple-solution speed regions are not always synchronous, but the sub-synchronous and sub-super-synchronous or almost-periodic orbits may exist. Within the multiple-solution rotating speed regions, the rotor system could run in the larger orbit or the small one, depending on whether the speed of the rotor system is increased or decreased. The unstable motion state that exists between the two stable orbits and is found by the synchronous CCO motion was not determined by the numerical integration method here. The multiple-solution regions predicted by the solution of synchronous CCO motion can also be obtained by the numerical integration method except the isolated bifurcation multiple-solution, but the numerical integration method can also obtain the region of the multiple-solution in which the motion of the rotor is non-synchronous. The numerical integration method is also able to analyse the non-synchronous, almost-periodic and even chaotic motions besides the synchronous CCO motion and the effect of any SFD structure parameter, such gravity parameter, initial eccentricity or misalignment of the journal, seals and the different oil film models.

In a word, the solution of the synchronous CCO motion is only very efficient to predict the steady state synchronous CCO response, but the solution of the synchronous CCO motion is not always reliable even if the effect of the gravity parameter is not considered since there are non-synchronous motions in some regions of the rotating speeds.

Figure 5 shows some orbits of the rotor system in the multiple-solution region and corresponding power spectrums of the vibration response. In increasing rotating speed, the motions of the rotor system shown in the top of every sub-figure are synchronous, synchronous, almost 1/11 sub-synchronous (maybe almost-periodic) and almost 1/8-order sub-synchronous at $\Omega=1.5$, 2.0 and 2.5 and 3.5, respectively, but at the same rotating speeds, the orbits of the rotor system in the decreasing rotating speed shown in the bottom of every sub-figure are almost 1/3-order sub-synchronous, almost 1/15-order sub-synchronous, almost 1/11-order sub-synchronous and synchronous, respectively. If we find the whirling frequency and the rotating frequency and determine the rational approximation between these two frequencies by using MATLAB tool, the ratio of the whirling frequency to the rotating frequency in Figure 5 are 1, 1, 6/25 and 3/25 in the increasing rotating speed, 17/50, 6/25, 6/25 and 1 in the decreasing rotating speed, respectively. In fact, the frequency ratio obtained by rational approximation cannot express the whole behaviour of the rotor motion, since the motions of the rotor system with same rational approximation at $\Omega=2.0$ and 2.5 are completely different. The orbit in Figure 5a is formed by whirling the 1/3-order sub-synchronous orbit at a very slow frequency. The whirling frequency is so slow that only the 1/3-order sub-synchronous orbit can be observed using a oscilloscope in many real experiments. The reason for the multiple-solution occurring and the non-synchronous motion is that the oil film forces produced by the squeeze film damper are highly non-linear in the region of the high journal eccentricity ratios; the static initial eccentricity or the misalignment of the journal discussed by Zhao et al[13,14] make the non-linearity more serious but not the real reason.

Generally speaking, the orbits of the rotor motion are very complex almost-periodic, and the sub-synchronous or sub-super-synchronous orbits can only appear in special rotating speed points. In most cases, the whirling speed of the rotor motion in the non-synchronous regions is neither a fraction nor an integer multiple of the rotating speed. The ratio of the whirling frequency to the rotating frequency is an irrational number. There are many frequency components in the spectrum due to non-circular motion orbit and the interaction between the rotor rotating motion and the rotor whirling motion. A Poincarè map, which is often used in non-linear dynamics, is used to reduce the influence of the rotor's motion [Zhao et al.[13,14] and Zhu and Ulbrich[15]). When the sampling period of the Poincarè map equals the period of the rotating, the return points of the Poincarè map do not always consist of a finite set of fixed points, but form a closed curve, several closed (or unclosed) curves or a geometrically fuzzy structure. The closed curve, several closed (or unclosed) curves or a geometrically fuzzy structure in the Poincarè map mean there are two or more dominate incommensurable frequencies in the motion of the rotor system or that the motion of the rotor system is chaotic. It is very difficult to know the order of the sub-synchronous or sub-super-synchronous orbits in advance and where the sub-synchronous or sub-super-synchronous orbit occurs and which frequency components should be considered in the harmonic balance method. Especially if the motion of the rotor system is often almost-periodic, the harmonic balance method will fail. This is the reason that the harmonic balance method is not widely used to predict the multiple-solution in the rotor systems with the SFDs.

3.3. Slow acceleration solution

In the cases without gravity effect, the vibration amplitudes both in journal and the disk positions in the slow acceleration process can be expressed by the journal and disk eccentricity.

The unbalance responses by the slow acceleration method both in the acceleration and deceleration processes for the same parameters as in Figure 2 are shown in Figure 6. In Figure 6, the dashed line stands for the increasing rotating speed and the solid line for the decreasing rotating speed.

The unbalance response curves in Figure 6 show that the slow acceleration method can not only predict the synchronous multiple-solution regions, but also the non-synchronous multiple-solution regions. Due to the rotor acceleration effect, the starting and the end speeds of the multiple-solution speed region will slightly move towards the high rotating speed, which can be minimised by slowing the angular acceleration ratio used in the slow acceleration calculation.

Figure 7 compares the results by the numerical integration method with dotted line and the slow acceleration method with the solid line. It is shown that the results from the slow acceleration method are in very good agreement with the steady state solution obtained by the numerical integration method and those obtained by the solution of the synchronous CCO motion in the speed regions of synchronous motion.

Since the motion during acceleration or deceleration is a non-stationary process with time varying frequency content, the short-time Fourier transform (STFT) will be useful to analyse the frequency content of the non-stationary motion. Using STFT and directional spectrogram, we can locate where the non-synchronous motion occurs and what frequencies there are in the rotor motion and get almost the same power spectrum as in Figure 5.

Similarly, the slow acceleration method can also be used to consider many effects, such as the gravity parameter, oil film models and supply pressure etc. Another advantage of this method is that it can save more computing-time in comparison with the numerical integration method. For rotor systems with many degrees of freedom, the transient properties transfer approach(TPTA)(Subbiah et al.[16]), successive merging and condensation(SMAC) (Ratan and Rodrigue[17]) and others can be used to develop an efficient and less computing-time method for the acceleration process.

CONCLUSION

The behaviour of the multiple-solution response in a flexible rotor supported on two identical SFDs with a centralising spring is studied by the iteration method of circular concentric motion, numerical integration and the slow acceleration method using the assumption of the short bearing and cavitation oil film, and the differences of computational results by the three methods are compared with each other. It is shown that there are many non-linear phenomena in the rotor system with the SFDs. The reason for this is that the oil film forces produced by the SFDs are highly non-linear in the region of the high journal eccentricity ratios. There are three basic forms for the multiple-solution response in the flexible rotor-SFD system, which are resonant multiple-solution, isolated bifurcation multiple-solution and the swallowtail bifurcation multiple-solution. In the multiple-solution speed regions, the rotor motion may be sub-synchronous, sub-super-synchronous and almost-periodic, besides synchronous motion. Therefore, the assumption of synchronous circular centred orbit motion for the journal can be used in some special cases even if the effect of the gravity on the system is not included. The steady state numerical integration method is very useful, but time-consuming. Not only can the multiple-solution speed regions be detected by the slow acceleration method, but also the non-synchronous response regions. Both the numerical integration method and the slow acceleration method can consider the effect of other parameters, such as the seals, supply groove and oil film models. The best process to use is to first determine the basic regions of the multiple-solution and the non-synchronous motion by using the slow acceleration method, then to analyse in detail the non-linear behaviour of the system using the numerical integration method.

ACKNOWLEDGEMENTS

The authors gratefully acknowledge the part support of the European Community in the scope of the BRITE/EURAM program under contract BRPR-CT97-0544 IMPACT project.

NOTATION

B Bearing parameter, $B = \mu R L^3 / m_B \omega_\alpha^2 C^3$

C, L, R radial clearance, land length and housing radius of the SFD

C_d external damping coefficient at the mid-plan disk

e, e_u eccentricity and unbalance eccentricity of the disk

F_x, F_y oil film force

f_x, f_y non-dimensional oil film force

k_a, k_s retainer spring stiffness and shaft stiffness

K stiffness ratio, $k = k_a/k_s$

m_B , m_D lumped mass at journal and mid-plan disk station, respectively

U unbalance parameter of the rotor system, $U = e_\mu / C$

W gravity parameter, $W = g / C\omega_{cr}^2$

x, y, r, φ Cartesian and polar co-ordinates

X, Y $X = x/C,\ Y = y/C$

Z nondimensional complex variable, $Z = X + iY$

α mass ratio of the rotor system, $\alpha = m_B / m_D$

ε non-dimensional eccentricity ratio with C

φ attitude angle

λ acceleration ratio

μ oil viscosity

τ non-dimensional time, $\tau = \omega_r t$

ω_r reference rotating speed

ω, ω_r rotating speed, first pin-pin critical speed of the flexible rotor mounted rigidly, $\omega_{cr} = \sqrt{k_s / m_D}$.

Ω rotating speed ratio, $\Omega = \omega / \omega_{cr}$

Ω_r reference rotating speed ratio, $\Omega_r = \omega / \omega_r$

ξ linear air damping ratio, $\xi = C_d / 2m_D\omega_{cr}$

$'$ $d/d\tau$

Subscripts

B   Bearing

D   Disk

REFERENCES

1. Radinowitz,M.D. and Hahn,E.J., *J. of Engrg. for Power*, 99(4), 1977, pp:552-558.

2. Greenhill,L.M. and Nelson,H.D., *J. of Mech. Design*, 104(2), 1982, pp:334-338

3. Taylor,D.L. and Kumar,B.R.K., *J. of Engrg for Power*, 105(3), 1983, pp:551-559.

4. Taylor,D.L. and Kumar,B.R.K., *J. of Lubrication Tech.*, 102(1), 1980, pp:51-58.

5. Shiau,T.N. and Hwang,J.L., *J. of Engrg. for Gas Turbines and Power*, 115(2), 1993, pp:218-226

6. Levesley,M.C. and Holmes,R., *Proc. Instn. Mech. Emgrs, Part.G*, 208(1), 1994, pp:41-51

7. Jean,A.N. and Nelson,H.D., *J. of Vibration and Sound*, 143(2),1990, pp:473-489

8. Hwang, J.L., and Shiau,T.N., *J. of Vibration and Acoustics*, 113(2),1991, pp:299-308

9. Holmes,R. *J. of Mech. Engrg. Sci*, 14(1), 1972, pp:74-77

10. Chu,F.L., and Holmes,R., *Comput. Methods Appl. Mech. and Engrg.*, 164, 1998, pp:363-373

11. Zhu,C.S., Acceleration characteristics of a flexible rotor system supported on non-linear squeeze film damper, *Proceedings of the 5th International Symposium on Transient Phenomena and Dynamics of Rotating Machinery*, Edited by W.J.Yang, pp:210-221.

12. Zhu,C.S., *J. of Zhejiang University*, Vol:28,1994,pp:132-140(in Chinese)

13. Zhao,J.Y. and Hahn,E.J., *Proc. Inst. Mech. Engrs, Part C*, 207, 1993, pp:383-392.

14. Zhao,J.Y., Hahn,E.J. and McLean,L.J., *J. of Tribology*, 116(2),1994, pp:361-368.

15. Zhu,C.S. and Ulbrich, H., *Int. J. of Rotating Machinery*, 1999, No:1, pp:125-139.

16. Subbiah,R., Kumar,A.S. and Sanhar,T.S., *J. of Appl. Mech.*, Vol:55, 1988, pp448-452.

17. Ratan,S., and Rodrigue,J., *J. of Vibration and Acoustics*, 114(3),1992,pp:477-488

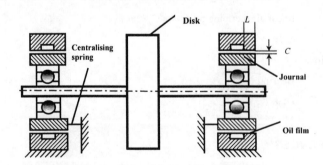

FIGURE 1. Flexible rotor –SFD model

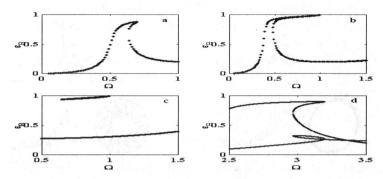

FIGURE 2. The basic forms of the multiple-solution in the rotor SFD system

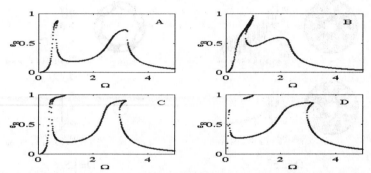

FIGURE 3. Typical combination of the basic forms of the multiple-solution

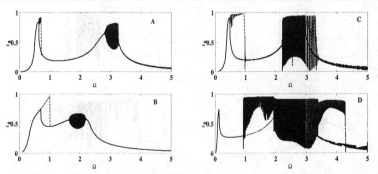

FIGURE 4. Steady state responses obtained by numerical integration method
(The dashed line for the increasing speed and the solid line for the decreasing speed)

385

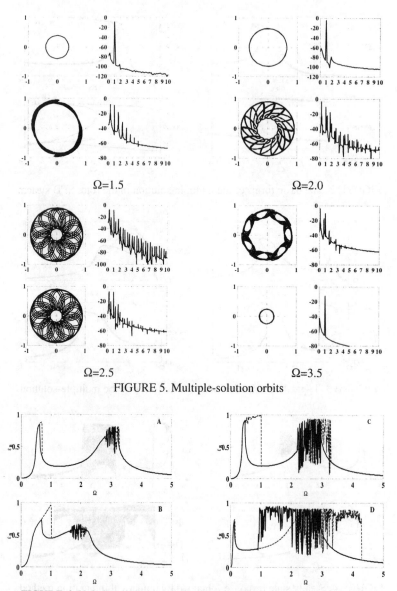

FIGURE 5. Multiple-solution orbits

FIGURE 6. Unbalance responses obtained by the slow acceleration method
(The dashed line for the acceleration and the solid line for the deceleration)

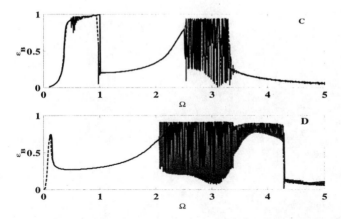

FIGURE 7. The comparison of the unbalance responses calculated by numerical integration method(dashed line) and slow acceleration method(solid line)

NON-LINEAR FINITE ELEMENT ANALYSIS OF JOURNAL BEARINGS

H. Bahai[*]

This paper presents a method by which an elasto-hydrodynamic (EHD) analysis is combined with a full elasto-plastic finite element (FE) stress analysis using a particular Fourier type of element which enables the application of non-uniform, non-axisymmetric hydrodynamic pressure loading to an axisymmetric bearing geometry. This approach is adopted to conduct an analysis which accounts for the effect of the initial interference fit and the three dimensional pressure distribution which is obtained from the EHD analysis. Plasticity is incorporated into the analysis using the Mises yield surface hardening rule. The analysis predicts the variation of cyclic stress and strain values in the lining material across the bearing width. It is seen from the results that a hoop strain variation changing from tensile in the loaded condition to compressive in the unloaded condition is responsible for the initiation of cracks at the surface of the bearing lining material.

INTRODUCTION

A predominant mode of bearing fatigue is usually characterized by small cracks initiating from the bearing surface and penetrating through the lining material. The cracks subsequently propagate almost parallel to the bonding surface and coalesce with other cracks. It is widely believed [1,2,3] that the surface cracks are induced by the presence of circumferential stresses in the lining material. The circumferential location of the cracks was observed [4] to occur mainly in the region of the bearing corresponding to the peak of the cyclic hydrodynamic pressure. The cracks also tend to occur towards the edge of the bearing, although this is not universal.

A number of investigators such as [5] have carried out finite element analyses to determine the stress distribution in the bearing lining layer. The results reported by these papers are, however, based on elastic analyses, usually of two dimensional models. The results from such analyses are inherently inaccurate as under the real service loading the bearing lining layer yields at a very early stage. Moreover, the load is distributed in such a way that it exhibits a non-uniform distribution in both circumferential and axial directions and therefore a two-dimensional model cannot be

Department of Systems Engineering, Brunel University, Uxbridge, Middlesex, UB8 3PH, UK

representative of the actual bearing behaviour. Many of the investigators also consider the bearing housing to be rigid which again introduces another source of inaccuracy in the analysis, as it is now known [6] that the housing compliance has a significant effect on the pressure distribution in the bearing.

An accurate calculation of stress and strain values in the bearing requires a reasonably fine finite element mesh in the region of interest. The ratio of the thickness of the bearing lining to other dimensions of the bearing and housing is, however, so small that a full three dimensional analysis would be very expensive. Such an analysis would be further complicated by the presence of a geometrical non-linearity which results from modeling the contact behaviour between the bearing steel backing and the housing.

The availability of a reasonably accurate pressure distribution is also fundamental to such an analysis as any variation in the way that the load is applied to the surface of the bearing can have a significant effect on the stresses resulting from such loads.

Most of the above problems are addressed in the analysis described in this paper. This is achieved by adopting an efficient finite element analysis technique which uses a special type of Fourier element. These elements allow the analysis of axisymmetric models combined with non-axisymmetric loading and displacement behaviour. The loading boundary condition on the bearing surface is simulated in the model using a pressure distributions obtained from an elasto-hydrodynamic analysis [7]. The analysis also deals with the material non-linear behaviour due to plastic straining of the aluminum bearing lining.

THEORETICAL BACKGROUND

Finite Element Analysis
The finite element analysis which is conducted using the ABAQUS program is based on a particular element formulation used for the non-linear analysis of structures which are initially axisymmetric but which undergo non-linear, non-axisymmetric deformation. The elements use standard isoparametric interpolation with respect to the radial, R, and axial, Z, directions combined with Fourier interpolation with respect to the circumferential direction, θ (Fig. 1). The original geometry of the elements is assumed to be axisymmetric with respect to the R and Z axes of the co-ordinate system corresponding to X and Y co-ordinates in axisymmetric models and thus independent of θ. Let e_r, e_z and e_θ be unit vectors in the radial, axial and circumferential directions at a point in the undeformed state. The displacement u of a point in terms of component displacements with respect to the same vectors at the original position of the point can be written as:

$$u = u_r \; e_r + u_z \; e_z + u_\theta \; e_\theta \tag{1}$$

The interpolation scheme for u using Fourier terms with respect to θ is:

$$\begin{Bmatrix} u_x \\ u_r \\ u_\theta \end{Bmatrix} = \sum_{m=1}^{M} H^m(g,h) \left(\begin{Bmatrix} u_r^{m0} \\ u_z^{m0} \\ 0 \end{Bmatrix} + \sum_{p=1}^{P} \cos p\theta \begin{Bmatrix} u_{rc}^{mp} \\ u_{zc}^{mp} \\ 0 \end{Bmatrix} + \sum_{p=1}^{P} \sin p\theta \begin{Bmatrix} 0 \\ 0 \\ u_\theta^{mp} \end{Bmatrix} \right) \tag{2}$$

where g and h are isoparametric co-ordinates in the R and Z plane. H^m is the polynomial interpolation function and U_r^{m0}, U_z^{m0}, U_{rc}^{mp}, U_{zc}^{mp} and U_θ^{mp} are solution amplitude values for various displacement components. M is the number of terms used for interpolation with respect to g and h. P is the number of terms used in the Fourier interpolation with respect to θ. For the pure axisymmetric situation, $\theta = 0$.

To allow the Fourier elements to be used in conjunction with interface elements, it is more convenient to use values of U_r and U_z displacement components at specific locations around the model between $\theta=0$ and $\theta= \pi$ instead of the Fourier amplitudes. This is only accurate if it is assumed that the relative displacement in the θ- direction is small, so that the interface condition can be considered with respect to U_r and U_z alone that is in the planes of constant θ. Equation 2 is therefore rewritten as:

$$\begin{Bmatrix} u_x \\ u_r \\ u_\theta \end{Bmatrix} = \sum_{m=1}^{M} H^m(g,h) \left(\begin{Bmatrix} u_r^{m0} \\ u_z^{m0} \\ 0 \end{Bmatrix} + \sum_{p=1}^{P+1} R^p(\theta) \begin{Bmatrix} u_r^{mp} \\ u_z^{mp} \\ 0 \end{Bmatrix} + \sum_{p=1}^{P} \sin p\theta \begin{Bmatrix} 0 \\ 0 \\ u_\theta^{mp} \end{Bmatrix} \right) \tag{3}$$

where $R^p(\theta)$ are trigonometric interpolation functions, and , u_r^{mp} and u_z^{mp} are physical radial and axial displacement components at $\theta = \pi(p - 1/P)$ plane.

The R^p interpolators at the associated positions θ_p for $P = 4$ which are used in this analysis are taken as:

$$R^1 = 1/8 \; (1+ 2\cos \theta + 2\cos 2\theta + 2\cos 3\theta + 2\cos 4\theta) \tag{4}$$

$$R^2 = 1/4 \; (1+ \sqrt{2}\cos \theta - \sqrt{2} \cos 3\theta - \cos 4\theta) \tag{5}$$

$$R^3 = 1/4 \; (1- 2\cos 2\theta + 2\cos 4\theta) \tag{6}$$

$$R^4 = 1/4 \; (1- \sqrt{2}\cos \theta - \sqrt{2} \; co \; 4\theta) \tag{7}$$

$$R^5 = 1/8 \; (1- 2\cos \theta + 2\cos 2\theta + 2\cos 3\theta + 2\cos 4\theta) \tag{8}$$

and:

$$\theta^1 = 0, \; \theta^2 = (1/4) \; \pi, \; \theta^3 = (1/2) \; \pi, \; \theta^4 = (3/4) \; \pi, \; \theta^5 = \pi$$

At present ABAQUS allows up to four Fourier modes. The deformation is assumed to be symmetric with respect to $\theta =0$. These elements use a set of nodes in each of several R-Z planes. For the case of a cylinder subjected to bending load these elements have been verified [9] to have an accuracy within 10% of the exact solution.

Elasto-Hydrodynamic Analysis

The lubrication of journal bearings is enabled by the presence of a viscous fluid (lubricant) and a converging clearance between the bearing and journal surface. During operation, the hydrodynamically pressurised lubricant acts to separate the two opposing surfaces. In recent years, higher specific loads have been applied to engine bearings, which leads to increased hydrodynamics pressures being generated in the oil film. Such high pressures are capable of inducing significant deformation of the bearing/housing structure, which in turn can affect the hydrodynamics of the lubricant. To understand such a phenomenon, an elasto-hydrodynamic analysis is required.

The lubricant of a finite width bearing is generally governed by the 2D Reynolds equation. For an incompressible Newtonian fluid, it is given as:

$$\nabla(\frac{h^3}{12\eta}\nabla p) - \frac{U}{R}\frac{\partial h}{\partial \theta} - \frac{\partial h}{\partial t} = 0 \tag{9}$$

In the above equation, (p), (h) and (η) are the oil film pressure, film thickness and lubricant viscosity at any given point on the bearing surface, which are functions of the position of the point and time. The entraining velocity (U) is a function of time only and the bearing radius (R) is a geometrical constant by design. The entraining velocity is conventionally defined as the average of the velocities of the bearing and shaft surfaces.

The oil film thickness (h) is given by:

$$h = h_0 + \delta \tag{10}$$

where (h_0) is the oil film thickness between the undeformed bearing and journal surfaces with the journal centre located at a certain position and (δ) is the elastic deflection of the bearing surface induced by hydrodynamic pressures. The elastic deformation of the bearing surface is calculated from the surface deflection coefficients, which are defined in the bearing radial direction only.

Rheologically, the viscosity of a mineral oil increases with the pressure exerted on it. The Barus expression assumes that the viscosity increases exponentially with the hydrodynamic pressure. The relationship can be expressed as follows:

$$\eta = \eta_o\, e^{\alpha p} \tag{11}$$

In order to incorporate the elastic deflection of the bearing surface into the lubrication analysis, the stiffness coefficient of the bearing surface is required. The generation of the stiffness coefficient can be achieved by the FE analysis. The stiffness matrix can then be inverted and modified to a compliance matrix $[C]$, which relates the nodal deformation to the hydrodynamic pressures over the bearing surface. Thus:

$$\{\delta\} = [C]\{P\} \tag{12}$$

In a dynamically loaded journal bearing, such as an engine bearing, it is advantageous to include the journal centre position (e_x, e_y) as a part of the simultaneous solutions. To do so, the equilibrium of the oil film pressure with the applied load needs to be always satisfied. That is:

$$\oint P\cos\theta R d\theta dz = w_x \tag{13}$$

$$\oint P\sin\theta R d\theta dz = w_y \tag{14}$$

The integration is carried out over the whole bearing surface.

Equations (10-14) form a non-linear system in terms of hydrodynamic pressure (p) and journal centre eccentricity (e). The Newton-Raphson method has proven to be highly robust and efficient for this type of problem and is therefore adopted for the numerical analysis. Murty's algorithm for the determination of cavitation boundaries is used. For a given load, the unknown variables, (p) and (e), can be solved for iteratively. The convergence of the dynamical solution is achieved by employing a marching algorithm.

CASE STUDY

The analysis method described in the foregoing sections was applied to a commonly used fatigue rig engine bearing, the Sapphire rig. Details of the con-rod dimensions of the Sapphire rig can be found in Reference [6]. The dimensions of the particular type of bearing / housing modelled in the analysis are shown in Figure 1. In the current analysis, some modifications were made to the shape of the big-end of the con-rod in order to make it suitable for the application of Fourier elements. The overall mesh used in the finite element axisymmetric model is shown in Figures 2. Figure 3 shows a more detailed view of the mesh at the location of interest. i.e. the aluminum layer near the edge of the bearing shell. A second plane of symmetry is also assumed about the centre line in the circumferential direction (Z=0 plane) of the bearing so only half of the bearing and housing is modelled. The third plane of symmetry assumed is the middle plane through the con-rod line of centres and the journal axis. Only half of the bearing with respect to these two planes of symmetry is, therefore, modelled.

The contact between the bearing and the housing is modelled using INT2A interface elements which are compatible with the Fourier elements used in the rest of the model. A set of interface elements had to be modelled at each of the R-Z planes in order to model the geometrically non-linear behaviour of the model at various positions around the circumference.

Another non-linearity introduced in the analysis is the material plastic behaviour. The stress-strain curve input into the model was obtained from uniaxial tensile tests on aluminum alloy specimens. The yield stress for the alloy material from this test is 29.5 MPa. An isotropic hardening rule based on Mises' yield surface criteria is adopted in the analysis. The plastic stress - strain curve used in the model is shown in Figure 4.

The isometric pressure distribution on the bearing surface obtained from the EHD analysis is shown in Figure 5. This corresponds to a crank angle of 360° when the applied load reaches its maximum value. It should be noted that the pressure dip at the centre line of the bearing occurs due to the presence of an oil feed hole at a position near to one end of the high pressure zone. At the other end of the high pressure zone, the dip at the center-line of the bearing is due to the fact that there is a much thicker oil film at the bearing centre which reduces the hydrodynamics effect locally and leads to a drop in the load pressure values. This data is then mapped onto the finite element model used in this analysis via a subroutine which performs a parabolic interpolation of nodal pressures obtained from the EHD analysis onto element integration points on the elements where the pressure is applied. A Fourier interpolation of this load is then carried out around the circumference of the bearing. Due to a sharp change in the gradient of the pressure near the edge of the bearing, a slight pressure peak occurs at that position as a result of the interpolation as seen in Figure 6, which shows radial stress distribution at the bearing surface resulting from the application of this load. The formulation of the Fourier elements used in this analysis is based on the assumption that a plane of symmetry exists at $\theta = 0$ position. In the case of the bearing analysis this would imply that the same pressure load is applied to the upper half of the bearing shell which is clearly not consistent with the real crank load situation. In order to overcome this problem the pressure load application position was shifted through an angle of 90 degrees to the $\theta = 0$ position. The pressure loading is therefore applied to only one half of the bearing shell. This, however, was achieved at the cost of neglecting a slight skew in the pressure distribution which exists about the z direction. The resulting radial stress distribution after the transformation of the load to the $\theta = 0$ position is shown in the form of the contour plot in Figure 7.

The first load case in the analysis modelled the effect of the initial interface fit of the bearing into the housing. This was simulated by assuming an initial overclosure at the beginning of the ABAQUS loading step. This gap is then reduced gradually to zero through several increments of displacement. To study the effect of the pressure loading, the hydrodynamic pressures are then applied and removed in the subsequent loading steps.

RESULTS

Figure 8 shows the stress - strain behaviour at one node on the surface of the aluminum lining during the first loading step through increments. The stresses and strains plotted in this graph are the Von Mises stresses against equivalent plastic strains. The shape of this curve is similar to that of Figure 4. Both diagrams show that the plastic yielding occurs at about 29.5 MPa. The strain values from the two curves can also be compared directly since strains plotted in Figure 8 are the accumulative equivalent plastic strain which will be defined later. It should also be noted that the stress values shown in Figure 8 and all the subsequent figures are values which are obtained by averaging the stresses at elemental integration points. Figure 9 shows the hoop stress distribution in the bearing due to the initial interference fit and the subsequent pressure loading and unloading. It is seen from this figure that the hoop stresses in the bearing are compressive in both loaded and unloaded conditions ranging from a value of approximately -170 MPa to -65 MPa respectively. As it is seen from this figure these values vary along the bearing width and have their maximum magnitude near the edge of the bearing. Figure 10 shows the variation of hoop strain along the bearing width in both loaded and unloaded conditions. It is interesting to note that whilst the hoop stresses vary between compressive ranges, the hoop strains fluctuate between tensile and compressive strains under loaded and unloaded conditions, respectively.

The application of the pressure loading causes the whole of the aluminum lining surface to yield plastically as shown in Figure 11. This Figure shows the variation of Von Mises stresses along the bearing width under the loaded and unloaded conditions. It should be noted that after the completion of the unloading step, the Von Mises stresses, being a scalar variable, will increase. It is possible to examine the variation of Von Mises stresses through the loading and unloading process by closely investigating the variation of component stresses on a node near the bearing edge at the surface of the aluminum alloy through the loading and unloading increments. Figure 12 shows this variation. It should be noted that the three principal stresses are in this case equal to the three component stresses i.e. there is no shear on the surface. It should further be noted that the hoop and axial stresses are causes by the Poisson effect from the radial stresses due to pressure loading. Some initial hoop stresses are, however, present due to the interference fit. It is seen from Figure 12 that the difference between the radial stress and the other two component of stresses i.e.

$(\sigma_{11} - \sigma_{22})$ and $(\sigma_{11} - \sigma_{33})$ are dominant through the loading and unloading cycle and there is little contribution from $(\sigma_{22} - \sigma_{33})$.

Figure 13 shows the variation of plastic equivalent strain which is defined [8] as:

$$\int \sqrt{\frac{2}{3}} d\varepsilon : d\varepsilon^{pl} \tag{15}$$

where $d\varepsilon^{pl}$ is the incremental plastic strain and the colon indicates matrix scalar multiplication.

It should be noted that these strains are accumulative plastic strains which are again scalar quantities. This implies that the unloading curve is at a higher strain level than the loading curve. The variation of plastic strain along the bearing width also follows a similar pattern to other variables considered so far with a maximum occurring about 6 mm from the bearing edge.

In a plastic analysis it is usually more appropriate to consider stresses with reference to *hydrostatic* stresses. This is the stress which acts equally in all directions and produces only a change in volume. It is defined in terms of component stresses as follows:

$$\sigma_m = \frac{1}{3}(\sigma_{xx} + \sigma_{yy} + \sigma_{zz}) \tag{16}$$

It is generally assumed that the hydrostatic stress component does not cause yielding of the material and that it does not influence the point at which yielding occurs. It is, therefore, the difference between the hydrostatic stress and the principal stress i.e. the *deviatoric* stress which must govern the yield behaviour of the bearing aluminum alloy. This is supported by the accuracy of the distortion energy theory in predicting the yielding of ductile materials.

In the case of the bearing, only the deviatoric hoop stresses are considered. This is defined as:

$$\sigma_\theta = \frac{1}{3}(2\sigma_{xx} - \sigma_{yy} - \sigma_{zz}) \tag{17}$$

The deviatoric strains are also defined in a similar manner. Figures 14 and 15 respectively show the variation of deviatoric stresses and strain along the bearing width under loaded and unloaded conditions. It can be seen from these figures that under loaded condition both stresses and strains are tensile.

DISCUSSION

The above analysis has demonstrated that the hoop component of stresses in the aluminum alloy lining are essentially compressive in both loaded and unloaded bearing condition. This is due to the fact that the steel backing and the housing, being made of stiffer material, constrain the aluminum alloy lining from deforming beyond the aluminum-steel inter-layer by any significant amount. Therefore, there remains a considerable bulk of elastic material surrounding the yielded area which contains the resulting strains within limits. On the release of the pressure loading the elastic outer zone attempts to return to its original dimensions but is prevented from doing so by the permanent deformation of the yielded material. The result is that the elastic material is held in a state of residual tension whilst the inside is brought into residual compression. This mechanism is similar to a process called *auto-frettage*. On the subsequent loading cycles the bearing is able to withstand a higher load without further plastic deformation, since the compressive residual stress at the inside surface has to be overcome before the region begins to experience tensile stresses. The plastic zone is also constrained in the circumferential direction within the elastic material as the yielding occurs in the central region of the bearing where the load is concentrated.

Despite the fact that most research work on the crack propagation phase in fatigue has been performed at a stress ratio equal or greater than zero, and deals with the effect of tensile stress, some attention has in the past decade been paid to compressive loading stress range situations. For example, Yu et al [10] conducted a series of fully compressive loading tests in notched steel and aluminum specimens. They observed that in the case of the aluminum specimen, compression - compression cycling could initiate a crack as the compressive peak stress increased. For an aluminum alloy specimen under compression cycles of -207 to -25 MPa, they reported a crack of 2.64 mm to have initiated after 4.36×10^5 cycles. A further 1.25×10^6 produced a detectable growth. Increasing the maximum stress from -25 to -12 Mpa made the crack to grow to 3.45 mm in 6.77×10^5. They concluded from their experimental work that a residual tensile strain was responsible for the crack growth.

In the case of the aluminum alloy lining in the bearing under the initial interference and subsequent pressure loading and unloading described above, the peak hoop strain change between -0.04% and 0.015%. The tensile strains in the loaded condition are created due to the Poisson effect from the radial component which is always compressive. In considering the fatigue behaviour of the bearings it is, therefore, more appropriate to consider the strain range within which the strains in the aluminum alloy change. This is also consistent with the local strain approach to estimate the fatigue life of the bearings.

The positions of maximum hoop strain in this analysis was consistent with the location of surface cracks in the experimental Sapphire fatigue tests carried out in-house where it was observed that surface cracks initiated usually at a location about 5 mm from the bearing edge.

CONCLUSION

In order to understand the stress and strain distributions which result in fatigue failure of journal bearings a method based on a mixture of EHD analysis of a dynamically loaded bearing, and a Fourier elasto-plastic stress analysis of the con-rod bearing has been proposed, and a case study of a bearing from the Sapphire fatigue test rig has been conducted. Based on this study the following conclusions are made:

(i)   the loaded part of the bearing aluminum lining goes entirely plastic almost from the onset of the pressure loading.

(ii)   the hoop stress component is compressive in both loaded and unloaded conditions.

(iii)   the hoop strain changes from compressive to tensile respectively in the loaded and unloaded conditions.

(iv)   the deviatoric hoop stresses and strains are tensile in both loaded and unloaded conditions.

(v)   the maximum hoop stresses and strains usually occur at about 5 to 7 mm away from the edge of the bearing. This position is consistent with the location of cracks occurring in the Sapphire bearing fatigue tests.

ACKNOWLEDGMENT

Financial support from the T&N Bearing Group companies which has enabled this project and the permission by the T&N Plc. to publish the results presented in this paper is gratefully acknowledged.

Nomenclature

R, Z, θ cylindrical co-ordinate in radial, axial and circumferential directions

e_r , e_z, e_θ unit vectors in the radial, axial and circumferential directions

u_r , u_z displacement vectors in the radial and axial directions

g, h isoparametric co-ordinates in the R and Z planes

H^m polynomial interpolation function

$u_r^{mo}, u_z^{mo}, u_{rc}^{mp}, u_{zc}^{mp}, u_\theta^{mp}$ solution amplitude values for various displacement components

P number of terms used in the Fourier interpolations

$R^p (\theta)$ trigonometric interpolation function

u_r^{mp}, u_z^{mp} physical radial and axial displacements at $\theta = \pi (p-1)p$

R^P displacement interpolators for P=1, 2, 3, 4 & 5 modes

p oil film pressure

h film thickness

η lubricant viscosity

U entraining velocity

h_o oil film thickness in the undeformed bearing & journal surfaces

δ elastic deflection of the bearing surface

e journal centre eccentricity

η_o lubricant viscosity at room temperature

α viscosity pressure index

e_x, e_y journal centre position

$[C]$ compliance matrix

$\sigma_{11}, \sigma_{22}, \sigma_{33}$ principal stresses

$\sigma_{xx}, \sigma_{yy}, \sigma_{xx}$ component stresses

$peeq$ equivalent plastic strain

$d\varepsilon^{pl}$ incremental plastic strain

σ_m hydrostatic stress

σ'_{xx} deviatoric stress

REFERENCES

(1) Lang, O. R., 'Surface Fatigue of Plain Bearings', *Wear*, 43, p25-30, 1973

(2) Kollman, K. and Harbordt, J., 'Criteria For the Material Fatigue of Dynamically Loaded Journal Bearings', *HOPE International Symposium, JSME,* Tokyo, p317-324, 1977.

(3) Blundell, J. K., 'Fatigue Initiation in Thin Walled Journal Bearings', *ASLE Trans.,* 33,2, p131-140, 1978.

(4) Glyde, N, 'Fatigue Fracture in Babbit Lined Journal Bearings', PhD Thesis, Technical University of Denmark, Copenhagen, 1969.

(5) Peeken, H., 'Operational Life of Journal Bearing's Combination Material Under the Influence of Pressure Oil on the Surface', *Proceedings of the JSLE International Tribiology Conference,* 1985, Tokyo.

(6) Fenner, D. N., McIvor, J. D. C., Conway-Jones, J. M. and Xu, H., 'The Effect of Compliance on Peak Oil Film Pressure in Connecting Rod Bearings', *19th Leeds-Lyon Symposium on Tribology, Leeds, September 1992.*

(7) McIvor, J. D. C. and Fenner, D. N., 'Finite Element Analysis of Dynamically Loaded Flexible Journal Bearings: A Fast Newton-Raphson Method', *ASME J. Tribology,* 111, 597-604, 1989.

(8) ABAQUS Standard Manual, Version 5.4, HKS, 1995.

(9) ABAQUS Verification Manual, Version 5.4, HKS, 1995.

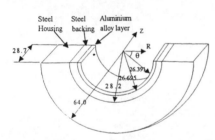

Fig. 1 Bearing and housing dimensions and coordinate system

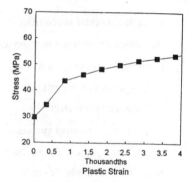

Fig. 4 Aluminium plastic stress–strain input curve

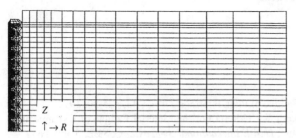

Fig. 2 Axisymmetric mesh of the bearing and housing full FE model

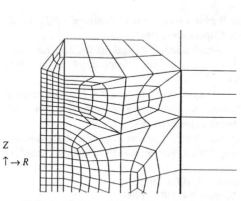

Fig. 3 Detailed view of the mesh in the bearing region

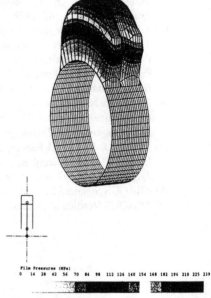

Fig. 5 Pressure distribution obtained from the EHD analysis

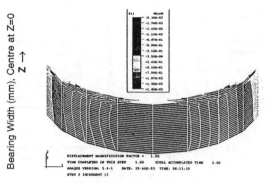

Fig. 6 Radial stress distribution

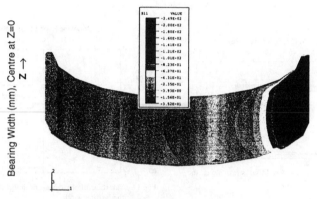

Fig. 7 Radial stress distribution (shifted through 90°)

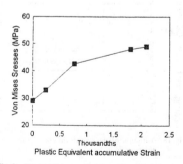

Fig. 8 Bearing lining material stress–strain behaviour

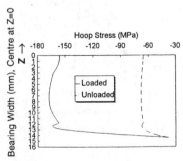

Fig. 9 Variation of the hoop stress along the bearing width

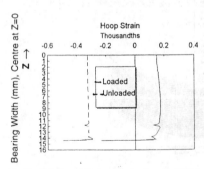

Fig. 10 Variation of the hoop strain along the bearing width

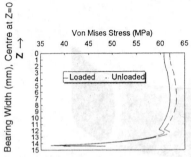

Fig. 11 Variation of the von Mises stress along the bearing width

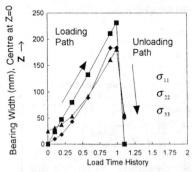

Fig. 12 Variation of component stresses through the load history

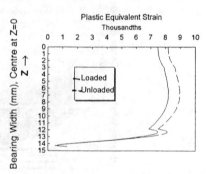

Fig. 13 Variation of the plastic equivalent strain along the bearing width

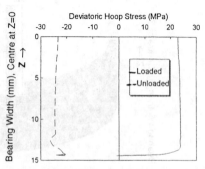

Fig. 14 Variation of the deviatoric hoop stress along the bearing width

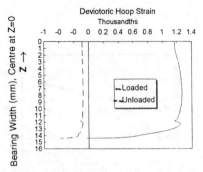

Fig. 15 Variation of the deviatoric hoop strain along the bearing width

DESIGN OF THE STATE OBSERVERS FOR THE VEHICLE DISC BRAKE

I.L.M. Ahmed*, P.S. Leung *, and P.K. Datta*

The brake squeal noise generated during the duty of brake is a common problem that has not been solved till now. Generally, contact of two bodies with each other with unstable oscillation generates the squeal noise. Minimizing this brake squeal noise during the duty of the brake is very important for the comfort of the passengers and stability of the car. A multi-degree-of-freedom mathematical model has been built to study the effect of the different parameters on the brake squeal noise. The state-space equations developed have been solved using the program MATLAB. The program has been used in this study to calculate the complex eigenvalues, which indicate the natural frequencies and the instability of the system. It is evident from the analysis that the squeal noise of the brake is a self-induced vibration and generally divided into two groups, the first group is the low frequency vibration less than 1 kHz and the second group is the high frequency vibration more than 1 kHz till 15 kHz that is included in the paper. The system is considered to be completely state controllable and hence it will be "observable", then poles of the closed-loop system will be placed at a desired location by means of state feedback through the state feedback gain matrix.

1. INTRODUCTION

The theory of the brake squeal noise has attracted attention many years ago. Cancellation of the squeal is very important for the braking system but it would never happen. Reducing this squeal will be important for the developer of the braking system. Murakami et al. [1] combined both theories of decreasing μ -velocity characteristic and kinematics constraint instability to analyze brake squeal. The parameters influencing the squeal were categorized into two groups to generalize rules for designers to deal with instability problems. This squeal was also studied experimentally and theoretically by Nishiwaki et al. [2] who modified the disc to eliminate brake squeal that occurred by self-excited vibration. The conventional disc vibrates at the maximum amplitude in the area excited artificially. Millner [3] dealt with the squeal theoretically by studying the first eight disc mode instabilities for $\mu <$

*University of Northumbria , School of Engineering , Camden Street Newcastle Upon Tyne NE2 1XE, UK

0.5. The least value of linear stiffness of the caliper 318 MNm^{-1} to give instability was obtained with the third mode. Nishiwaki [4] concluded that the disc brake squeal and the disc brake groan are not independent problems despite the difference of noise frequencies or structures. These brake squeals and brake groan noises are generated by the same cause of dynamic instability in friction force that acts as non-conservative forces.

A number of issues dealt with the disc brake squeal by using the finite element model (FEM). Mottershead and Chan [5] analyzed the instability of brakes based on a multi-degree-of-freedom using FEM with the assumption of simple coulomb friction. It was realized that the disc was prone to flutter at doublet mode frequencies even when the pressure load was very small. The same phenomena was also studied using FEM by Gregory [6] who realized that increasing the squeal propensity with the higher coefficient of friction and decreasing the lining length also decreased the degree of instability in the brake system.

Dihua and Dongying [7] constructed FEM for the components of the disc brake and found an unstable mode below 4 kHz was at 2.3 kHz and seven unstable modes from 4 kHz to 10 kHz. The effect of negative friction-speed slope on the brake squeal was analyzed by Yuan [8] who found that the brake squeal occurred due to the coupled vibrations of the brake system even if the negative μ-speed slope does not exist. The squeal propensity increased with the friction level when the negative μ-speed slope was absent. It was also noted that increasing the steel back-plate thickness and also lining thickness might reduce the squeal propensity. Thomas and Clark [9] studied the effect of the support stiffness and damping conditions on the measured modal parameters like frequencies and damping ratios. It was realized that the increase of the measured frequency of the supported system was related to the square of the frequency ratio of the rigid body mode and the elastic mode as well.

It is clear then from those issues that there were no recommendations for reducing the squeal of the disc brake. There was no recommendation about the disc brake squeal from the point of view of the control system dynamics. In the following model of the disc brake the relevant parts of these theories are incorporated according to the theory of system dynamics.

2. MATHEMATICAL MODEL OF THE DISC BRAKE SQUEAL NOISE

It is well known for the floating caliper disc brake type that the piston of the caliper presses on the inner pad towards the rotor and the supporting bolts of the caliper push the outer pad towards the rotor as a reaction force. Therefore, there is a lag between the two pads to press on the rotor and it is assumed that the forces occurred at the same time and it is fully in contact between the pads and the rotor during this application. A theoretical 8-degree of freedom mathematical model has been developed in this study depending on the theoretical model of North [10] and Millner [3]. Other assumptions have been made in the model including:

1- The system is state controllable.

2- The disc has two degrees of freedom, one in the x-axis direction and the other around the y-axis direction.

3- The pads have two degrees of freedom, the first one in the x-axis direction and the other one around the y-axis direction.

4- The piston moves in the x-axis direction to the caliper.

5- The contact forces *F1* and *F2* are parallel to the face of the rotor and will be activated during the contact between the pads and the rotor.

6- It is also assumed that the rotor and the pads vibrate in the same mode.

Based on Newton's second law, the equations of motion of the disc brake in figure (1) can be written as:

$$M_d.\ddot{x}_d + C_{PL1}.(\dot{x}_d - \dot{x}_{P1}) + K_{PL1}.(x_d - x_{P1}) + K_d.x_d + C_d.\dot{x}_d$$
$$+ C_{PL2}.(\dot{x}_d - \dot{x}_{P2}) + K_{PL2}.(x_d - x_{P2}) + F1.\theta_d + F2.\theta_d = 0 \tag{1}$$

$$I_d.\ddot{\theta}_d + C_{PR1}.(\dot{\theta}_d - \dot{\theta}_{P1}) + K_{PR1}.(\theta_d - \theta_{P1}) + K_{dR}.\theta_d + C_{dR}.\dot{\theta}_d$$
$$+ C_{PR2}.(\dot{\theta}_d - \dot{\theta}_{P2}) + K_{PR2}.(\theta_d - \theta_{P2}) + F2.h + F1.h = 0 \tag{2}$$

$$M_{P1}.\ddot{x}_{P1} + C_{PL1}.(\dot{x}_{P1} - \dot{x}_d) + K_{PL1}.(x_{P1} - x_d) + C_{CL1}.(\dot{x}_{P1} - \dot{x}_c)$$
$$+ K_{CL1}.(x_{P1} - x_c) = 0 \tag{3}$$

$$I_{P1}.\ddot{\theta}_{P1} + C_{PR1}.(\dot{\theta}_{P1} - \dot{\theta}_d) + K_{PR1}.(\theta_{P1} - \theta_d) + C_{CR1}.(\dot{\theta}_{P1} - \dot{\theta}_c)$$
$$+ K_{CR1}.(\theta_{P1} - \theta_C) - F1.d + F3.d = 0 \tag{4}$$

$$M_{P2}.\ddot{x}_{P2} + C_{PL2}.(\dot{x}_{P2} - \dot{x}_d) + K_{PL2}.(x_{P2} - x_d) + C_{CL2}.(\dot{x}_{P2} - \dot{x}_C)$$
$$+ K_{CL2}.(x_{P2} - x_C) = 0 \tag{5}$$

$$I_{P2}.\ddot{\theta}_{P2} + C_{PR2}.(\dot{\theta}_{P2} - \dot{\theta}_d) + K_{PR2}.(\theta_{P2} - \theta_d) + C_{CR2}.(\dot{\theta}_{P2} - \dot{\theta}_C)$$
$$+ K_{CR2}.(\theta_{P2} - \theta_C) + F2.d = 0 \tag{6}$$

$$M_C.\ddot{x}_C + C_{CL1}.(\dot{x}_C - \dot{x}_{P1}) + K_{CL1}.(x_C - x_{P1}) + K_{CL}.x_C + C_{CL}.\dot{x}_C$$
$$+ C_{CL2}.(\dot{x}_C - \dot{x}_{P2}) + K_{CL2}.(x_C - x_{P2}) - F = 0 \tag{7}$$

$$I_C.\ddot{\theta}_C + C_{PR1}.(\dot{\theta}_C - \dot{\theta}_{P1}) + K_{PR1}.(\theta_C - \theta_{P1}) + K_{CR}.\theta_C + C_{CR}.\dot{\theta}_C + F3.b = 0 \tag{8}$$

where

$$F1 = \mu.R1 = \mu.[F_{st} + C_{PL1}.(\dot{x}_d - \dot{x}_{P1}) + K_{PL1}.(x_d - x_{P1})] \tag{9}$$

$$F2 = \mu.R2 = \mu.[F_{st} + C_{PL2}.(\dot{x}_d - \dot{x}_{P2}) + K_{PL2}.(x_d - x_{P2})] \tag{10}$$

$$F3 = \mu_b.R3 = \mu_b.[F_{st} + C_{CL1}.(\dot{x}_C - \dot{x}_{P1}) + K_{CL1}.(x_C - x_{P1})] \tag{11}$$

The equations from (1) to (8) can be rewritten in the form of:

$$\ddot{x} + c/m.\dot{x} + k/m.x = 0 \tag{12}$$

$$\ddot{x} + 2.\zeta.\omega_n.\dot{x} + \omega_n^2.x = 0 \tag{13}$$

where ω_n is the natural frequency of the system, and ζ is the damping ratio or viscous damping factor and equal to $\zeta = c/2m.\omega_n$

We assume the solutions of the form

$x_d = A_d.e^{\lambda t}$ $\qquad \theta_d = B_d.e^{\lambda t}$ $\qquad x_{pl} = C_{pl}.e^{\lambda t}$ $\qquad \theta_{pl} = D_{pl}.e^{\lambda t}$

$x_{p2} = E_{p2}.e^{\lambda t}$ $\qquad \theta_{p2} = F_{p2}.e^{\lambda t}$ $\qquad x_c = G_c.e^{\lambda t}$ $\qquad \theta_c = H_c.e^{\lambda t}$

and by substitution in the main equations, we will get the characteristic equation that in the form of:

$$\lambda^2 + 2.\zeta.\omega_n.\lambda + \omega_n^2 = 0 \tag{14}$$

The roots of this equation are

$$\lambda 1 = \omega_n.(-\zeta + \sqrt{(\zeta^2 - 1)}.) \qquad \text{and} \qquad \lambda 2 = \omega_n.(-\zeta - \sqrt{(\zeta^2 - 1)}.)$$

Three categories of damped motion are considered:

1- If $\zeta > 1$ (over-damped) the roots will be negative numbers and the system will decay without oscillation for a long period.

2- If $\zeta = 1$ (critically damped) the roots will be negative numbers equal to $-\omega_n$ and the solution will be in the form $x = (A1 + A2t).e^{-\omega t}$. The system will decay in a large time and the motion will be non-periodic.

3- If $\zeta < 1$ (under-damped) the system will decay in a short time and the solution will be in the form of $x_d = A_d\,e^{-\zeta \omega t} \sin(\omega_d t + \psi)$

where $\omega_d = \omega_n.(1-\zeta^2)^{1/2}$

3. RESULTS AND DISCUSSION:

Brake squeal noise

Generally, the disc brake squeal is caused by the unstable vibrations of the brake system and to know if the brake system will squeal or not, the stability has to be checked by applying the Matlab program. This program has the ability to perform the eigenvalue analysis that can take the instability level and the natural frequency, for which the corresponding eigenvalue problem will be in the form of det $([A]-\lambda[I]) = 0$.

Each eigenvalue λ is a complex number that contains two parts; the first part is real and the second part is imaginary. If the real part is negative, this indicates that the mode is damping and stable, but in some cases the real part will be positive, which means that the mode is not stable and the damping is negative or the system is oscillating. From the eigenvalues, the instability levels and the eigenfrequencies are calculated. The instability level is defined as the real part of the eigenvalue $\alpha=\text{Re}[\lambda]$ and the eigenfrequency is defined as the imaginary part of the eigenvalue $\omega=\text{Im}[\lambda]$ rad/sec. Some authors take the instability level as a squeal propensity while others do not. In this work the squeal propensity (σ) will be taken as $\sigma = \left(\alpha^2 + \omega^2\right)^{1/4} \cdot \sin(\delta/2)$ and this agrees with Milliner's [3] calculations and the eigen frequencies will be taken as $\omega/2\pi$ Hz, where δ is the phase angle and equal to arctan (ω/α).

System control design

The dynamic behaviour of the closed-loop system is predicted by means of the open-loop frequency response. Generally, the dynamic behaviour of any complex system can be improved through inserting a simple lead or a compensator. The techniques of conventional control theory are conceptually simple and require only a reasonable amount of computation; the input, the output, and error signals are considered important in the control theory. The system designed by conventional control theory depends on trial and error procedures that will not yield optimal control systems. On the other hand, the system designed by the modern control theory particularly by state-space enables designing such systems having desired closed-loop poles or optimal control systems with respect to given performance index. However, the design by modern control theory through state-space methods requires accurate mathematical description of the system dynamics. The performance index is a function whose value indicates how well the actual performance of the system matches the desired performance. In most cases, the control vector which is in the form of $u=-Kx$ (where u is unconstrained) is chosen in such a way that the performance index is minimized or maximized to optimise the system behaviour. In this case the performance index will be taken as Performance Index $= \sum_{i=1}^{n}\left(\mu_i - s_i\right)^2$

as mentioned by Ogata [11], where μ_i's are the desired eigenvalues of the error dynamics of the system and the s_i's are the actual eigenvalues of the error dynamics of the designed system.

The data of the disc brake used in the numerical work is

	Mass (kg)	Density (kg/m^3)	Outer radius (m)	Inner radius (m)	Poisson's ratio	Thickness (m)	Width (m)	μ
Rotor	3.4	7800	0.107	0.063	0.27	0.012	-	-
Friction material	0.194	3000	-	-	0.23	0.0154	0.031	0.42

The equations of motion (1-8) can be rearranged into a matrix form. The solution in the state space method will be in the form of:

$$\dot{x} = Ax + Bu \tag{15}$$

$$y = Cx + Du \tag{16}$$

where

A is the System 16×16 matrix.

B is the Input 16×1 matrix.

C is the Output 8×16 matrix.

x is the System State 16-vector.

Design through pole placement

The state space is concerned with three types of variables that are involved generally in the dynamic systems, which are input variables, output variables, and state variables. Generally, if the dynamic system is linear and time invariant the state-space equations will be in the form mentioned in equations (15) and (16).

The state feedback control scheme, which is the relationship between the output and reference input can be obtained by comparing them and using the difference as a means of control is called feedback control system, is given by

$$u = -Kx \tag{17}$$

Where u is the control signal (control vector).

The system is assumed to be completely state controllable. This means that, the control signal is determined as an instantaneous state and the 1×n matrix K is called the state feedback gain matrix. In the closed-loop control system as in figure (2), the actuating error signal, which is the difference between the input signal and the feedback signal is fed to the controller to reduce the error and bring the output of the system to a desired value.

Substitution of equation (17) in equation (15) gives

$$\dot{x}(t) = (A - BK).x(t) \tag{18}$$

and the solution of this equation will be in the form of

$$x(t) = e^{(A-BK)}.x(0) \tag{19}$$

where $x(0)$ is the initial state caused by external disturbances. The stability and transient response characteristics are determined by the eigenvalues of matrix $(A-BK)$. The eigenvalues of the matrix $(A-BK)$ are called the regulator poles. If these regulator poles are located in the left-half plane (negative plane), then $x(t)$ approaches zero while t approaches infinity. Placing the closed-loop poles at the desired location is called a pole placement method.

It is possible to transform the state equation given by equation (15) into the controllable canonical form. The transformation matrix T is given in the form of

$$T = M.W \tag{20}$$

where M is the controllability matrix and given by

$$M = \begin{bmatrix} B & AB & A^2 B & A^3 B & \dots\dots & A^{15} B \end{bmatrix} \tag{21}$$

and W is given in the form of

$$W = \begin{bmatrix} a_{15} & a_{14} & a_{13} & \dots\dots\dots & a_1 & 1 \\ a_{14} & a_{13} & a_{12} & \dots\dots\dots & 1 & 0 \\ a_{13} & a_{12} & a_{11} & \dots\dots\dots & 0 & 0 \\ . & . & . & \dots\dots\dots\dots & & \\ . & . & . & \dots\dots\dots\dots & & \\ a_1 & 1 & 0 & \dots\dots\dots\dots & & \\ 1 & 0 & 0 & \dots\dots\dots & 0 & 0 \end{bmatrix} \tag{22}$$

where a_i's are the coefficients of the characteristic polynomial equation which is

$$|SI - A| = S^{16} + a_1 S^{15} + a S^{14} + \dots\dots\dots + a_{15}.S + a_{16} \tag{23}$$

where I is the unity matrix, and by substitution of I and A the coefficients can be calculated from the characteristic equation.

A new state vector is then given by

$$x = T.\hat{x} \tag{24}$$

Substitution in equation (15) gives

$$\dot{\hat{x}} = T^{-1}AT\,\hat{x} + T^{-1}Bu \quad \text{(the canonical form)} \tag{25}$$

where

$$T^{-1}AT = \begin{bmatrix} 0 & 1 & 0 & 0............0 \\ 0 & 0 & 1 & 0............0 \\ 0... & & & ....0 \\ .. & . & . & .... \\ 0 & 0 & & ....1 \\ -a_{16} & -a_{15} & & ....-a_{1} \end{bmatrix} \tag{26}$$

and

$$T^{-1}B = \begin{bmatrix} 0 \\ 0 \\ . \\ . \\ 0 \\ 1 \end{bmatrix} \tag{27}$$

Thus, equation (23) has been transformed to the controllable canonical form taking into consideration that the system is completely state controllable. Then, a set of the desired eigenvalues as μ_1, μ_2, μ_3, μ_4 .... and μ_{16} are chosen.

By substitution, the characteristic equation will be in the form

$$(S - \mu_1)(S - \mu_2).......(S - \mu_{16}) = S^{16} + \alpha_1.S^{15} + \alpha_2.S^{14} + ... + \alpha_{15}.S + \alpha_{16} = 0 \tag{28}$$

where, $\alpha_1, \alpha_2 ....\alpha_{16}$ are the coefficients of the desired equation.

Finally, the desired feedback gain matrix becomes

$$K = [(\alpha_{16} - a_{16})(\alpha_{15} - a_{15})(\alpha_{14} - a_{14}) ....(\alpha_1 - a_1)]T^{-1} \tag{29}$$

where T^{-1} is the inverse of the transformation matrix.

$$K = [K1 \quad K2 \quad K3 \quad K4 \quad K5 .... K16] \tag{30}$$

where $K1 = \alpha_{16}\text{-}a_{16}$, $K2 = \alpha_{15}\text{-}a_{15}$ and $K16 = \alpha_1\text{-}a_1$

4. DISCUSSION OF THE RESULTS

Effect of the Young's modulus of the rotor

Figures (3) and (4) indicate the effect of the Young's modulus of the rotor on the brake squeal noise and the instability of the disc brake. The modulus of elasticity of the brake rotor was increased from 50 to 200 GN/m^2. It is realized from the figure that as the young's modulus of the rotor increases the squeal index decreases till a certain limit then increases again with the increase in the modulus of elasticity of the rotor to give the best value between 80 and 120 GN/m^2. Further increase of Young's modulus to 210 GN/m^2 only increases the squeal index slightly. The maximum squeal 141 sec^{-1} occurred at a low modulus of elasticity and the best value of squeal was between 90 and 92 sec^{-1} between 80 and 120 MN/m^2 and the maximum frequency reached in this case was 6308 Hz with the maximum instability of 150 (Real Part).

Effect of the Young's modulus of the friction material

Figures (5) and (6) indicate the effect of the Young's modulus (50-1200 GN/m^2) of the friction material on the squeal noise and also the instability of the disc brake. The figures show that as the young's modulus of the friction material increases the squeal index increases. The maximum squeal 243 sec^{-1} occurred at a high modulus of elasticity of 1200 MN/m^2 and the best value of squeal was at 199 sec^{-1} with a low modulus of elasticity of 100 MN/m^2. The maximum frequency reached in this case was 18948 Hz with the maximum instability of 64 (Real Part).

Effect of the control signal

The response of the system was obtained by using Simulink in the Matlab program. The figures (7-14) indicate the response of the system with time. It was clear that, by doing feedback control to the system state (the system assumed to be state controllable), the settling time for all states ranging from 1.5 to 2 seconds is determined depending on the desired poles for the system. Also, the gain matrix K is not one for any system but depends mainly on the desired closed-loop poles locations, which determine the damping of the system and also the speed. By choosing these poles, the system has quite acceptable response characteristics. Because the system is a 16× 16 matrix, it was very difficult to determine the poles so, the response characteristics of the system has been checked a lot of times with several different gain matrix K to give the acceptable response.

5. CONCLUSIONS

It is clear from this study that the brake squeal noise is an important problem in cars particularly regarding the comfort of the passengers in the vehicle. The conclusions derived from the investigation concerning the effect of some important parameters are:

1- Increasing the Young's modulus of the rotor will affect the system behavior and the best value of the Young's modulus between 80 and 120 GN/m^2, which give the lowest value of the squeal noise and frequency.

2- Increasing the Young's modulus of the friction material will increase the squeal index noise of the brake system.

3- Controlling the output signal of the system by using the pole placement gives a better response to the system depending on the desired poles which determine the damping and the speed of the response.

6. NOMENCLATURE

r_i, r_o	Inner and outer radius of the disc respectively.
h	Semi-thickness of the disc.
ρ, ρ_p	Density of the disc and the pad respectively.
E_d, E_P	Young's modulus of the disc and the pad.
M_d, M_C, M_P	Mass of the disc, caliper, and the pad respectively.
I_d, I_C, I_P	Moment of inertia of the disc, caliper and the pad respectively.
X_d, X_c, X_p	Displacement of the disc, caliper and the pad respectively.
$\theta_d, \theta_c, \theta_p$	Angle of rotation of the disc, caliper and the pad respectively.
K_{dL}, K_{CL}, K_{PL}	Linear stiffness of the disc, calliper and the pad respectively.
K_{dR}, K_{CR}, K_{PR}	Rotary stiffness of the disc, caliper and the pad respectively.
C_{dL}, C_{CL}, C_{PL}	Linear damping of the disc, caliper and the pad respectively..
C_{dR}, C_{CR}, C_{PR}	Rotary damping of the disc, caliper and the pad respectively.
$1,2$	The inner pad and the outer pad respectively.

REFERENCES

(1) Murakami, H., Tsunada, N., and Kitamura, T., *A Study Concerned with a Mechanism of Disc-Brake Squeal,* SAE, No. 841233, 1984, pp 5.604-5.616.

(2) Nishiwaki, M., Harada, H., Okamura, H., and Ikeuchi, T., *Study on Disc Brake Squeal*, SAE, No. 890864, 1989, pp 980-989.

(3) Millner, N., *An Analysis of Disc Brake Squeal*, SAE, No. 780332, 1978.

(4) Nishiwaki M., *Generalized Theory of Brake Noise*, Proc. Instn Mech Engrs Vol. 207, 1993, pp 195-202.

(5) Mottershead, J., and Chan, S., *Brake Squeal- an Analysis of Symmetry and Flutter Instability*, ASME, DE-Vol. 49, Friction-Induced Vibration, Chatter, Squeal, and Chaos, 1992, pp 87-97.

(6) Gregory, D., *Analysis of Disc Brake Squeal Using Finite Element Methods*, SAE, No. 981150, 1989, pp 11381146.

(7) Dihua, G., and Dongying, J., *A Study on Disc Brake Using Finite Element Methods*, SAE, No. 980597, 1998, pp 157-163.

(8) Yuan, Y., *A Study of the Effects of Negative Friction-Speed Slope on Brake Squeal*, ASME, DE-Vol. 84-1, Design Engineering Technical Conferences, Volume 3- Part A, 1995.

(9) Thomas, G., and Clark, R., *Support Conditions, Their Effect on Measured Modal Parameters*, Proceedings of the 16th International Modal Analysis Conference- Santa Barbara-California IMAC-1998 volume I.

(10) North M., *Disc Brake Squeal- A Theoretical Model*, MIRA Report, No. 1972/5.

(11) Ogata K., *System Dynamics*, third edition, Prentice-Hall International Limited, London, UK, 1998.

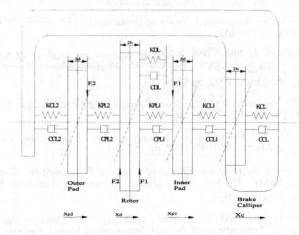

FIGURE 1   Theoretical 8-degree of freedom mathematical model.

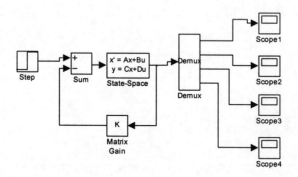

FIGURE 2   State-space of the disc brake with feedback control.

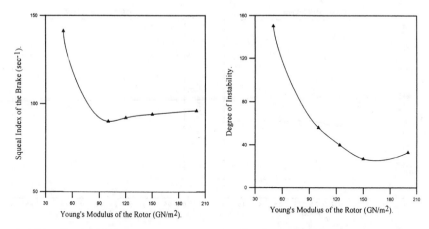

FIGURE 3 The effect of the young's modulus of the brake rotor on the brake squeal noise.

FIGURE 4 The effect of the young's modulus of the brake rotor on the degree of instability.

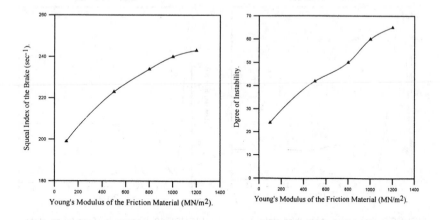

FIGURE 5 The effect of the young's modulus of the pad on the brake squeal noise.

FIGURE 6 The effect of the young's modulus of the pad on the degree of instability.

415

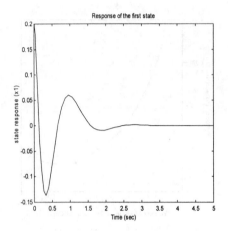

FIGURE 7 Response of the first state.

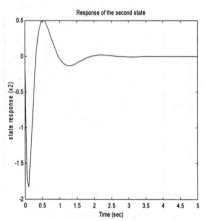

FIGURE 8 Response of the second state.

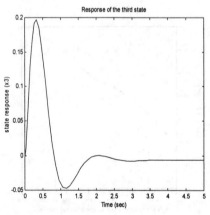

FIGURE 9 Response of the third state.

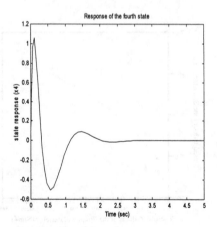

FIGURE 10 Response of the fourth state.

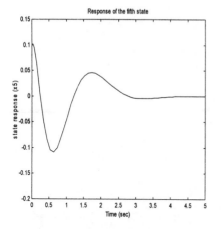

FIGURE 11 Response of the fifth state.

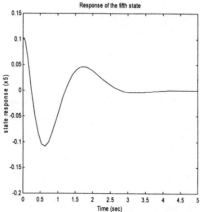

FIGURE 12 Response of the sixth state.

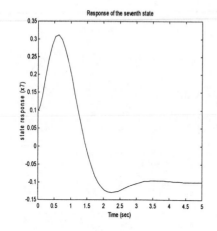

FIGURE 13 Response of the seventh state.

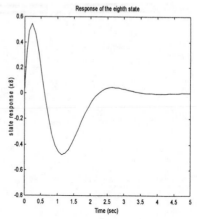

FIGURE 14 Response of the eighth state.

VIBRATIONAL RESPONSE OF A THREE DIMENSIONAL FRAMEWORK DUE TO TRANSVERSE AND LONGITUDINAL MOTION OF A TWO DIMENSIONAL SUBSTRUCTURE

J.J. Wu[*], A.R. Whittaker[*] and M.P. Cartmell[*]

This paper presents the finite element modelling and experimental modal testing of a 1/10 scale crane rig in the laboratory and the approach used for improving this model by including flexible members. A novel technique is then presented which uses the free vibration results of the validated finite element model to calculate the response to moving trolley loads.

1. INTRODUCTION

The motivation for the work described in this paper is the improved design of a mobile gantry crane, as used in various types of freight handling locations all over the world. In order to simulate the dynamic response characteristics of the full-size crane, a 1/10 scale model has been built in the laboratory [1]. Unlike the actual crane, which is on wheels, the laboratory model is fixed to the floor. The spreader is moved in a horizontal plane by allowing a trolley to move on two sets of rails which are fastened to the top of the fixed structure. Cartmell *et al.* [2] developed a mathematical model of the moving parts of this laboratory rig and used this model to design a nonlinear control system. Rigid structural members were assumed for the experimental model, however the current work aims to improve on the mathematical model of this system by including flexible members. This paper describes the approach used and highlights some of the lessons learned, which may be of general interest.

Dealing with moving loads is not a standard procedure in I-DEAS [3], which was the Finite Element package used for this work. Indeed it appears not to be a standard procedure in any FE packages. As part of the current work, a technique of dealing with these moving loads has been developed and is reported elsewhere [4]. It is based on the idea that the crane can be divided into a fixed substructure that is excited by the effects of a moving trolley. Earlier work on this type of problem has been mainly

[*] Department of Mechanical Engineering, University of Glasgow, Glasgow, G12 8QQ, Scotland, UK

restricted to beams subjected to either moving masses or moving loads [5,6]. This work is broadly based on classical solutions to the problem [7] where the difference between moving mass (including inertia effects of the moving body) and moving load (ignoring inertia effects) is highlighted.

Before the forced response calculations are performed, it is first necessary to have accurate predictions of natural frequencies and mode shapes. This is not a trivial problem and a large proportion of this paper is concerned with model validation and model improvement, looking in particular at the modelling aspects of the joints and the foundation stiffness.

2. FINITE ELEMENT MODELLING OF AN EXPERIMENTAL CRANE RIG

To simulate the dynamic behaviour of the full-sized crane in the laboratory, a 1/10 scale crane model, shown schematically in Figure 1(a), has already been built [1]. The assumption in the original model was that the structural members should be rigid. In order to improve the mathematical model of the crane by including flexible members, the approach discussed in this paper is to divide the whole structure into two sections: a fixed framework, as shown in Figure 1(b) and a moving sub-structure, as shown in Figure 1(c).

I-DEAS [3] was used to provide a free vibration analysis of the fixed framework, as shown in Figure 2, with 73 nodes and 99 linear beam elements. The first mode shape is shown in Figure 3 with its associated natural frequency at 11.75 Hz. It manifests as a horizontal oscillation of the static framework along the z-axis: one of the most important mode shapes.

3. EXPERIMENTAL MODAL ANALYSIS OF THE LABORATORY CRANE RIG

An LMS modal testing system [8] is used for the experimental validation. Figure4 shows the modal testing arrangement. Two shakers simultaneously supply excitations on two different nodes, node 10 and node 18 in the positive z and positive x directions respectively. Each shaker is connected through a load cell which is used for detecting the magnitude of exciting force. An accelerometer is used for measuring the response at each nodal position. The modal parameters of the experimental crane rig were determined once the measurements and analysis had been done. Figure 5 shows the first measured mode shape with associated natural frequency, 9.01 Hz.

Two kinds of connector are used to connect the load cell and the tested structure (the scale crane model). Figure 6(a) shows the tubular type and Figure 6(b) the double-sided screw type. Figure 7 shows the FRF graphs of node 18 vibrating in x direction for different load cell attachments. It can be found that the connecting mechanism between the load cell and the tested model significantly affects the

420

experimental results. The response amplitudes using double-sided screw connector (the dashed curve shown in Figure 7) are greater than the corresponding ones using the tubular connector (the solid curve in Figure 7). The double-side screw connector will give better results because it is less dissipative than the flexible tubular connector.

4. COMPARISON OF THE NATURAL FREQUENCIES AND ASSOCIATED MODE SHAPES

The comparison between the first five main calculated and measured natural frequencies is listed in Table 1, along with the percent difference between the natural frequencies for the finite element modelling and the modal testing. It can be seen that the difference between the predicted and measured natural frequencies is not small enough, being up to 29.89% in one case. Therefore, the finite element modelling of the crane rig as discussed in section 2 is not completely correct. It is noted that the comparison between the measured and calculated natural frequencies should only be made on the basis of corresponding mode shapes.

TABLE 1. A comparison of the first five main natural frequencies

Mode No.	Natural Frequencies from I-DEAS (Hz)	Natural Frequencies from LMS (Hz)	Difference (%)
1st	11.75	9.01	23.32
2nd	14.92	10.46	29.89
3rd	19.80	14.85	25.00
4th	26.89	20.07	25.36
5th	38.34	31.52	17.79

5. MODIFICATIONS OF THE ORIGINAL FINITE ELEMENT MODEL OF CRANE RIG

It is not always easy to simplify a real structure as a finite element model and still retain all the necessary phenomena. Referring to Table 1, it can be seen that modifications must be made in order to obtain a more accurate finite element model of the crane rig. Figure 8(a) shows the beam connection at each node for the finite element model. Figure 8(b) shows most of the joints of the crane's fixed framework and Figure 8(c) shows the special joints. The original finite element model was modified by including extra beam elements (i.e., by replacing the joints shown in

Figures 8(b) and (c) with (d) and (e)), but no satisfactory results were obtained. It was also felt to be worth moving the accelerometer, as shown in Figure 4, to more accurate positions in careful alignment with the nodes of the finite element model. Reasonable agreement was still not achieved.

Considering the location of the experimental crane rig, on the second floor of a building and attached to a wooden tile floor, several ground-node spring elements were then included into the ground-fixed nodes of the finite element model, as shown in Figure 9. Using a spring stiffness of 2000 *N/mm* gave the closest natural frequencies to the ones from experimental modal testing. The first five main natural frequencies of this new finite element model are listed in the second column of table 2. The maximum percent difference between the natural frequencies is 7.02, and the average is 3.61, which was considered acceptable. Though time was not available to use sophisticated model updating and mode shape correlation techniques, visual inspection of the mode shapes also showed reasonable agreement. This new finite element model has therefore been used for further, forced vibration, analysis.

It is also worthy of mention that the variation of the spring stiffness causes the change of the natural frequencies of this finite element model. From Table 3, one may see that the variation of the spring stiffness, from 500 *N/mm* to 3500 *N/mm*, does change the natural frequencies of this finite element model. Figure 10 shows the percent difference against the variation of spring stiffness for first five modes. The solid line with star (—★—) represents the average percent difference of first five modes due to the variation of spring stiffness. The lowest percent value appears at the value of 2000 *N/mm* for spring stiffness. This is the value used for further analysis in this paper. It should also be noted that the use of single spring stiffness value for all three directions may not reflect the reality. However, the satisfactory agreement between the natural frequencies obtained from new finite element model and LMS modal testing system has been achieved. Therefore, the use of different spring stiffness values for all three directions is not studied in this paper.

TABLE 2 The first five main natural frequencies of new finite element model and the ones of modal testing

Mode	Natural Frequency of New finite element model (Hz)	Natural Frequency from LMS (Hz)	Difference	Percentage (%)
1st	9.05	9.01	0.04	0.48
2nd	10.05	10.46	0.41	3.93
3rd	15.89	14.85	1.04	7.02
4th	20.51	20.07	0.44	2.17
5th	30.11	31.52	1.41	4.46
Average	--------	------	------	3.61

TABLE 3 The first five main natural frequencies of new finite element model with different spring stiffness

Mode	Natural frequencies (Hz)							
	Spring Stiffness 500 N/mm	Spring Stiffness 1300 N/mm	Spring Stiffness 1800 N/mm	Spring Stiffness 1900 N/mm	Spring Stiffness 2000 N/mm	Spring Stiffness 2100 N/mm	Spring Stiffness 2500 N/mm	Spring Stiffness 3500 N/mm
1st	6.480	8.359	8.896	8.898	9.053	9.123	9.358	9.745
2nd	8.486	9.631	9.954	10.003	10.049	10.091	10.233	10.468
3rd	13.345	15.392	15.789	15.843	15.893	15.938	16.082	16.299
4th	17.712	19.942	20.387	20.449	20.506	20.557	20.723	20.975
5th	27.086	29.550	29.995	30.058	30.114	30.165	30.326	30.566

6. MOVING LOADS PROBLEM USING NEW FINITE ELEMENT MODEL

As mentioned in section 2 the whole crane structure has been divided into two sections: the fixed framework, as shown in Figure 1(b) and the moving sub-structure, as shown in Figure 1(c). The relationship between the fixed framework and the moving sub-structure has been simplified to four time-variant moving point loads [4], as shown in Figure 11. The problem could then be solved by applying forces and moments, being functions of time, to all the nodes of the finite element model of the whole structure. Shape functions [5,6] were used for calculating the equivalent nodal forces due to the concentrated moving point load. This technique was initially applied using a simply supported beam with a single point load and validated with the analytical method proposed for the same simple beam problem as proposed by Rogers [7]. The technique was then applied to a beam with two moving point loads and subsequently extended to the crane problem in the form of a pair of parallel beams, each being subjected to two time-variant moving concentrated forces [4].

7. RESULTS

This section shows a few typical results for a representative node: node 60. Node 60 is a quarter of the way along rail Q, as shown in Figure 11. The trolley moves on the moving sub-structure along $\bar{x}$-axis and the moving sub-structure moves on the two fixed rails along the $\bar{y}$-axis. The trolley accelerates from $\bar{x}$ = -0.49 m, $\bar{y}$ = -0.6 m to the maximum $\bar{x}$ and $\bar{y}$ velocities (0.3124 m/sec and 0.5236 m/sec respectively) in 1 s. The final $\bar{y}$ position of 0.709 m is reached in 3.5 s, with a constant velocity period of 1.5 s followed by a deceleration period of 1 s. After 3.5 s, there is no further $\bar{y}$ movement of the trolley. The final $\bar{x}$ position of 0.4472 m is reached in 4 s, with a constant velocity period of 2 s and a deceleration period of 1 s. For the remainder of the 10 s simulation time, the trolley remains stationary at $\bar{x}$ = 0.4472 m, $\bar{y}$ = 0.709 m. Figure 12 shows the vertical ($\bar{z}$) displacement of node 60. The curve marked Δ is the result of the $\bar{x}$, $\bar{y}$ trolley movement as described above. To create this curve, the damping factor ζ for all modes is chosen as 0.003. The solid line with circle (—O—) is the results for the same $\bar{x}$, $\bar{y}$ motion, but with the higher damping factor, 0.01. These two curves are identical. This is to be expected, since the dynamic effects are insignificant under these loading conditions. After 3.5 s, the vertical displacement remains constant, since at this time the trolley reaches the end of the specified travel. The dashed line (– – –) represents the deflections while the trolley follows the same path, but at half speed. As expected, this curve is similar to the previous two, except that the time taken to reach the final position is twice as long. Figure 12 also shows one curve, the solid line with a cross (—×—), for the same $\bar{x}$ motion, but zero $\bar{y}$ motion and another curve, the solid line with star (—*—), for the same $\bar{y}$ motion, but zero $\bar{x}$ motion. It can be seen that the structure appears stiffer when the trolley moves in the $\bar{x}$ direction than when it moves in the $\bar{y}$ direction. In fact, most of the deformation corresponding to the simultaneous $\bar{x}$, $\bar{y}$ motion is as a result of $\bar{y}$ movement. It is also worthy of mention that the reason why the displacements do not start at zero is due to the static equilibrium offset effect (i.e., the moving sub-structure is stationary on the top of the fixed framework at time t = 0).

It is also interesting that the inclusion of the spring elements into the original finite element model of the crane rig causes the different responses. As shown in Figure 13, the solid line (——) represents the vertical ($\bar{z}$) deflections of node 60 while the trolley only moves along the $\bar{y}$-axis at full speed using the original finite element model (without spring elements) and the dashed line (-----) represents the ones using the new finite element model (with spring elements). Significant differences can be found, indicating that the original forced response, based on the rigid supports does not give adequate accuracy.

8. CONCLUSIONS

Accuracy of finite element modelling of a real structure should always questioned and experimental modal analysis is a valuable tool for the purpose of validation. In this paper it has been shown that an initial Finite Element analysis did not provide accurate results. After comparison with experimental results it was shown that a better model for the support structure was required. As a result of this modification, the new FE model gave much more acceptable results. The accuracy of the results from modal testing is also questioned. The set-up of the modal testing should also be carefully considered, in particular the connection of the shaker to the structure via the load cell.

To solve the problem of moving loads, a technique has been developed for applying time variant forces and moments to all the nodes of the whole structure. This technique has only been applied to beam elements so far, but in principle, it is general and can be adapted to any element type.

9. REFERENCES

(1) Huang, KC., Integrated Sensing, Dynamics and Control of a Mobile Gantry Crane. PhD thesis, University of Edinburgh, 1997.

(2) Cartmell, MP., and Morrish, L., and Taylor, AJ., Dynamics of spreader motion in a gantry crane. Proc. Instn. Mech. Engrs. 1998, Vol. 212(Part C), pp. 85-105.

(3) SDRC. I-DEAS Master Series 6 FINITE ELEMENT MODELING. Structural Dynamics Research Corporation, 1998.

(4) Wu, JJ., and Whittaker, AR., and Cartmell, MP., The use of finite element techniques for calculating the dynamic response of structures to moving loads. Submitted to Computers & Structures.

(5) Trethewey, YH., and Trethewey, MW., Finite element analysis of elastic beams subjected to moving dynamic loads. Journal of Sound and Vibration 1990, Vol. 136(2), pp. 323-342.

(6) Clough, RW., and Penzien, J., Dynamics of Structures. McGRAW-HILL BOOK COMPANY, INC. New York. 1993.

(7) Rogers, GL., Dynamics of framed structures. John Wiley & Sons, Inc. New York, 1959.

(8) LMS International. LMS CADA-X USER MANUAL. LMS International, 1992.

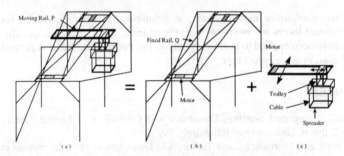

FIGURE 1 The 1/10 scale crane model: (a) complete, (b) static framework, (c) moving sub-structure (rotational and hoisting motors are not in the figure).

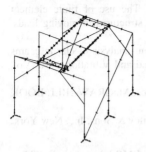

FIGURE 2 The orthographic view of the finite element model of the fixed framework of the experimental crane rig.

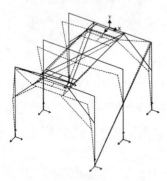

FIGURE 3 The first mode shape with associated natural frequency, 11.75 Hz, of the finite element model of the crane rig.

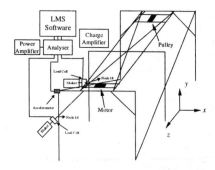

FIGURE 4 The setup of the modal testing for experimental crane rig.

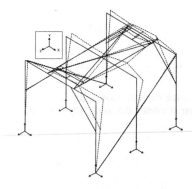

FIGURE 5 The first mode shape with associated natural frequency, 9.01 Hz, of the experimental crane rig using modal testing.

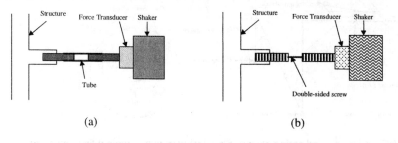

FIGURE 6 The connection between bolt and force transducer using (a) tube, (b) double-side screw.

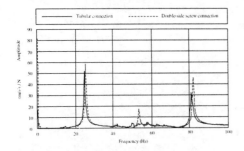

FIGURE 7 FRF graphs for different load cell attachments.

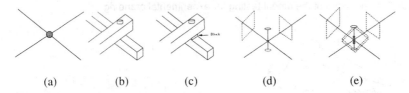

(a)   (b)   (c)   (d)   (e)

FIGURE 8 The connections between beams of (a) finite element model, (b) experimental crane rig, (c) some special joints of experimental crane rig, (d) modified joint of (b), (e) modified joint of (c).

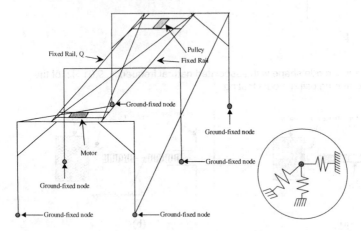

FIGURE 9 Node-ground spring elements are included to the original finite element model.

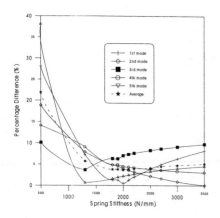

FIGURE 10 Error percentage – Spring stiffness graph for first five mode.

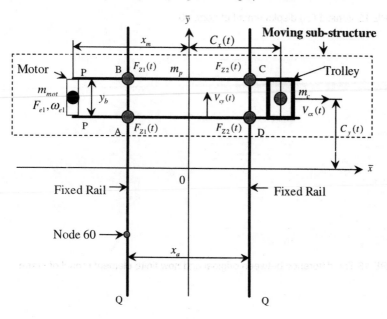

FIGURE 11 Top view of the crane model structure.

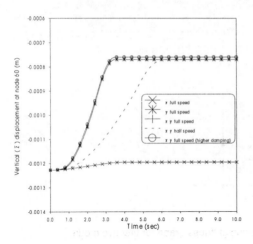

FIGURE 12 Vertical ($\bar{z}$) displacement of node 60.

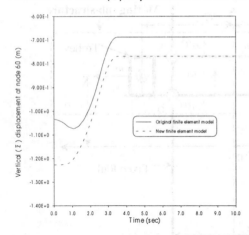

FIGURE 13 The difference between original and new finite element model of crane rig.

NATURAL FREQUENCIES OF CIRCULAR RINGS MADE FROM CRYSTALLINE SILICON

*R. Eley, *C.H.J. Fox and *S. McWilliam

The effects of the elastic anisotropy of crystalline silicon on the vibrational behaviour of a circular ring are investigated. Crystalline silicon has three principal planes and the precise cut of silicon with respect to these planes determines the form and degree of anisotropy. Expressions are derived for the anisotropic material properties on a number of different planes. The effects of anisotropy on the natural frequencies of flexural modes of vibration with different numbers of nodal diameters are then quantified. Frequency splitting is predicted between pairs of modes that would be degenerate if the material were isotropic. The relationship between frequency splitting and the number of nodal diameters is explained using a Fourier analysis of the material property variations.

INTRODUCTION

Due to its excellent mechanical properties, crystalline silicon is a material of rapidly increasing importance for micro-mechanical structures, manufactured using micro-machining techniques. Typical applications of such microstructures include the sensing elements in a range of transducers, [1] and micro-pumps for medical applications. However, the fact that crystalline silicon is anisotropic means that particular care must be taken when designing components from this material, particularly when precise control of the component's natural frequencies is required, typically 1Hz in 10kHz.

ANISOTROPY IN SINGLE CRYSTAL SILICON

It is well known that crystalline silicon exhibits significant anisotropy [2]. Silicon has three principal planes, denoted as (100), (110) and (111) in Miller indices, see Figure 1. The cut of a silicon wafer with respect to these principal planes determines the extent of anisotropy and the variations in the material properties in devices made from the wafer. Generally, the directional variations of the Young's and shear moduli are given by equations (1) and (2) respectively [3].

$$\frac{1}{E(\theta)} = S_{11} - 2\left(S_{11} - S_{12} - \frac{S_{44}}{2}\right)F(\theta) \tag{1}$$

*School of Mechanical, Materials, Manufacturing Engineering & Management, University of Nottingham, University Park, Nottingham NG7 2RD

$$\frac{1}{G(\theta)} = S_{44} + 4\left(S_{11} - S_{12} - \frac{S_{44}}{2}\right)F(\theta) \qquad (2)$$

where

$$F(\theta) = l_s^2 m_s^2 + l_s^2 n_s^2 + m_s^2 n_s^2 \qquad (3)$$

and l_s, m_s and n_s are the direction cosines of a line of applied stress with respect to the material axes X, Y, Z, respectively. The elastic compliance constants, S_{11}, S_{12}, S_{44} for crystalline silicon have the values $7.6442\times10^{-12}\text{Pa}^{-1}$, $-2.1434\times10^{-12}\text{Pa}^{-1}$ and $1.2564\times10^{-11}\text{Pa}^{-1}$ respectively [3]. The argument (θ) simply denotes that the line of applied stress lies at angle θ from a suitable reference direction in a plane which, for the moment, is arbitrary. Relevant particular cases will be defined later.

MATERIAL PROPERTIES ON THE PRINCIPAL PLANES AND CLOSE TO THE (111) AND (100) PLANES

Devices are more commonly manufactured from silicon wafers that are nominally cut in the (111) and (100) planes than the (110) plane. This is due to the capabilities of etching processes used in micro-machining [4]. The general equations, (1) and (2), for the material properties can be used to calculate the variations in moduli for any plane. A convenient way to achieve this is to manipulate expression (3) to find the direction cosines of lines of applied stress in planes which lie at some known angle relative to the principal planes.

ELASTIC CONSTANTS ON PLANES TILTED FROM THE (111) PLANE

Refer to Figure 2 and consider the (111) plane, the normal to which has equal direction cosines relative to the material axes. By varying one direction cosine, say l_p, and keeping the other two equal, ($m_p = n_p$), a new tilted plane is made, which makes angle δ with the (111) plane [5]. In the tilted plane the angular variations of the Young's and shear moduli are calculated by considering a line of applied stress which lies in the plane at angle θ relative to a given reference line. To simplify the analysis, without loss of generality, the reference line is chosen to lie in the y-z plane so that the direction cosine, l_r=0 (See Figure 2).

The following equations apply for an angle θ between two lines with direction cosines (l_1,m_1,n_1) and (l_2,m_2,n_2) and for any line with direction cosines (l, m, n) [6]

$$l_1 l_2 + m_1 m_2 + n_1 n_2 = \cos\theta \qquad l^2 + m^2 + n^2 = 1 \qquad (4)$$

Equations (4) and (3) can be manipulated for the case considered to give the following expression for $F(\theta)$

$$F_{(\delta,111)}(\theta) = \left(1 - \frac{3}{2}l_p^2\right)\sin^2\theta\cos^2\theta + l_p^2\left(1 - \frac{3}{4}l_p^2\right)\sin^4\theta + \frac{\cos^4\theta}{4} \qquad (5)$$

where

$$l_p = \cos(\alpha_0 + \delta) \qquad (6)$$

and α_0 is the angle subtended by the (111) plane with respect to the material axes. Note that, due to the symmetry associated with the (111) plane, the effect would be the same if we chose to define δ about any line in the (111) plane. The particular reference direction chosen here is simply convenient for the analysis.

It follows from equations (5), (6), (1) and (2) that, for the (111) plane, ($\delta = 0$), the Young's and shear moduli values are 1.7×10^{11}Pa and 6.22×10^{10}Pa respectively and are independent of θ. Other values of δ can be substituted into equations (6), (5), (1) and (2) to find the appropriate elastic moduli.

Assuming that δ is a small angle, equations (6) and (5) can be used to derive approximate expressions for $F_{(111)}$. This expression can be substituted into equations (1) and (2) and binomially expanded. Neglecting terms of second order and higher in δ leads to linear expressions for the moduli. The utility of such an approximation will be discussed later.

ELASTIC CONSTANTS ON PLANES TILTED FROM THE (100) PLANE

The orientation of a plane which is tilted relative to the (100) plane can be described by means of a rotation about any two of the principal crystal axes or a combination of rotations as shown in Figure 3. The reference line from which the direction of loading is defined is conveniently taken to be OY_2 since this line lies in both plane-1 and plane-2. Equations (4) and (3) can be manipulated to give the following expression for $F(\theta)$, valid for small deviations from the (100) plane, in which terms in γ_1, γ_2 of third and higher order have been neglected.

$$F_{(\gamma,100)}(\theta) = \left(1 + 3\gamma_1^2 + 3\gamma_2^2\right)\sin^2\theta\cos^2\theta + \gamma_1^2\cos^4\theta + \gamma_2^2\sin^4\theta + 2\gamma_1\gamma_2\cos^3\theta\sin\theta \qquad (7)$$

Substitution of equation (7) into equations (1) and (2) gives the required expressions for $E(\theta)$ and $G(\theta)$. For the (100) plane ($\gamma_1 = \gamma_2 = 0$), equation (7) can be rearranged as

$$F_{(100)}(\theta) = \frac{1}{8}(1 - \cos 4\theta)$$

showing that there will be a strong 4θ periodicity to the (100) plane moduli.

ELASTIC CONSTANTS ON THE (110) PLANE

The following analysis shows the extent of anisotropy on the (110) plane, however, deviations from this plane are not considered. The analysis presented for deviations from the (111) plane can be manipulated to give the corresponding moduli expressions for the (110) plane. To transform the (111) plane to the (110) plane, the corresponding angle of misalignment from the (111) plane, δ, is given by

$$\delta = 90 - \alpha_0 \tag{8}$$

Substituting equation (8) into equations (6) and (5) gives the direction cosine expression, $F(\theta)$, for the (110) plane as

$$F_{(110)}(\theta) = \frac{1}{32}(7 + 4\cos 2\theta - 3\cos 4\theta) \tag{9}$$

Equation (9) can be substituted into equations (1) and (2) to give the directional variations of Young's and shear moduli on the (110) plane respectively. Equation (9) shows that there is a strong 2θ and 4θ periodicity to the (110) plane moduli.

NATURAL FREQUENCIES OF SMALL AMPLITUDE VIBRATION

The expressions for the elastic moduli derived above can be used in conjunction with an energy method to predict the effects of material anisotropy on the natural frequencies of flexural modes of vibration of circular rings with rectangular cross section. For a circular ring made from isotropic material, in-plane and out-of-plane modes of vibration with a given harmonic number appear as degenerate pairs with equal natural frequencies at an arbitrary circumferential position. The displacement of the ring is represented using generalised coordinates based on the eigenfunctions of a circular isotropic ring. Lagrange's equation is used to set up equations of motion from which the natural frequencies and the circumferential positions of the corresponding modes can be found for the anisotropic ring.

IN-PLANE MODES

For a pair of in-plane modes of vibration with n nodal diameters, the radial and tangential displacements, w, v, at some angular position θ, (see Figure 4) can be expressed in terms of generalised coordinates $Q_{11}(t)$ and $Q_{12}(t)$ as follows [7].

$$\begin{Bmatrix} w \\ v \end{Bmatrix} = Q_{11}(t) \begin{Bmatrix} n\sin n\theta \\ \cos n\theta \end{Bmatrix} + Q_{12}(t) \begin{Bmatrix} n\cos n\theta \\ -\sin n\theta \end{Bmatrix} \tag{10}$$

Here, $\theta = 0$ is assumed to coincide with the reference direction for θ used in the expressions for the material properties presented in Section 3. Equation (10) can be

434

used to determine the appropriate expression for the kinetic and strain energies of the ring. For in-plane modes the kinetic energy due to bending [8] is given by

$$T_{IP} = \int_0^{2\pi} \frac{1}{2} \rho A a \left(\dot{v}^2 + \dot{w}^2 \right) d\theta \quad = \quad \frac{\rho A a \pi \left(n^2 + 1 \right)}{2} \left(\dot{Q}_{I1}^2 + \dot{Q}_{I2}^2 \right) \tag{11}$$

where ρ, A and a are the density, cross-sectional area and mean radius of the ring respectively. In general terms, assuming the ring to be thin, the strain energy due to in-plane bending, U_{IP}, can expressed as [8]

$$U_{IP} = \frac{I_z}{2a^3} \int_0^{2\pi} E \left(\theta - \frac{\pi}{2} \right) \left[\frac{\partial^2 w}{\partial \theta^2} + w \right]^2 d\theta \tag{12}$$

where I_z is the second moment of area of the ring. The variable Young's modulus, $E(\theta - \pi/2)$, can be expressed in a number of different ways as described above. The argument $(\theta - \pi/2)$ accounts for the fact that the bending stresses in the ring at position θ are directed at $\pi/2$ to the radius vector at that point. The reciprocal form of equation (1), which defines $E(\theta)$, makes a general analytical evaluation of the integral in equation (12) difficult, if not impossible and therefore, equation (12) will be evaluated numerically for particular cases.

The energy equations, (11) and (12) are substituted into Lagrange's equation [9] to give the equations of motion for free undamped vibration in the following form.

$$\ddot{Q}_{I1} + \Omega_{I1}^2 Q_{I1} \quad = \quad 0 \; ; \qquad \ddot{Q}_{I2} + \Omega_{I2}^2 Q_{I2} \quad = \quad 0 \tag{13}$$

where Ω_{I1} and Ω_{I2} are the non-dimensional natural frequencies. The fact that the equations of motion, equations (13), occur as an uncoupled pair indicates that the mode shapes of the orthotropic ring are aligned with the original displacement patterns associated with the relevant generalised coordinate. This is a consequence of the choice of datum for θ for the generalised coordinates and for the anisotropy description, and of the symmetry of the anisotropy about $\theta = 0$.

OUT-OF-PLANE MODES

For out-of-plane modes of vibration with i nodal diameters, the translation, u, and rotation, ϕ, of the ring (see Figure 4) can be described in terms of generalised coordinates, Q_{O1} and Q_{O2}, as follows [7],

$$\begin{Bmatrix} u \\ \phi \end{Bmatrix} = Q_{O1}(t) \begin{Bmatrix} 1 \\ -i^2 \xi \end{Bmatrix} \cos i\theta + Q_{O2}(t) \begin{Bmatrix} -1 \\ i^2 \xi \end{Bmatrix} \sin i\theta \tag{14}$$

in which $\xi = \dfrac{1}{a}\left[\dfrac{1+\mu}{1+i^2\mu}\right]$, where $\mu = \dfrac{\widetilde{G}C}{\widetilde{E}I_x}$ and $C = \dfrac{cr_t^3 a_l^3}{r_t^2 + a_l^2}$

In the above r_t and a_l are the radial thickness and axial length of the ring respectively and c is a coefficient with numerical value in the range 0.28–0.33 [7], which depends on the ratio r_t/a_l. I_x is the second moment of area of the ring section for out-of-plane bending. In the present analysis, the assumed displacements associated with the generalised co-ordinates are based on the mode shapes of isotropic rings. It is therefore reasonable to use the (111)-plane values, $\widetilde{E}$ and $\widetilde{G}$, of the elastic moduli to define the stiffness ratio, μ. The displacements are used to find the kinetic and strain energies as follows. The kinetic energy, due to bending and twisting, is given by

$$T_{OP} = \int_0^{2\pi} \frac{1}{2}\rho A a \dot{u}^2 d\theta + \int_0^{2\pi} \frac{1}{2}\rho J a \dot{\phi}^2\, d\theta = \frac{\rho a \pi}{2}\left\{ A + \frac{J\, i^4}{a^2}\left[\frac{1+\mu}{1+i^2\mu}\right]^2\right\}\left(\dot{Q}_{o1}^2 + \dot{Q}_{o2}^2\right) \quad (15)$$

where J is the polar second moment of area of the ring section. The strain energy due to bending and twisting [10] can be expressed as

$$U_{OP} = \frac{I_x a}{2}\int_0^{2\pi} E\left(\theta - \frac{\pi}{2}\right)K_1^2 d\theta + \frac{Ca}{2}\int_0^{2\pi} G\left(\theta - \frac{\pi}{2}\right)K_2^2 d\theta \quad (16)$$

where

$$K_1 = \frac{1}{a}\left(\frac{1}{a}\frac{\partial^2 u}{\partial \theta^2} - \phi\right); \qquad K_2 = \frac{1}{a}\left(\frac{\partial \phi}{\partial \theta} + \frac{1}{a}\frac{\partial u}{\partial \theta}\right) \quad (17)$$

In general, equation (16) can be evaluated numerically for any $E(\theta)$ and $G(\theta)$. Substituting equations (15) and (16) for a particular case into Lagrange's equation gives the equations of motion for free, undamped vibration in the following form

$$\ddot{Q}_{o1} + \Omega_{o1}^2 Q_{o1} = 0 ; \qquad \ddot{Q}_{o2} + \Omega_{o2}^2 Q_{o2} = 0 \quad (18)$$

where Ω_{o1} and Ω_{o2} are the non-dimensional natural frequencies.

NUMERICAL EXAMPLES

FREQUENCY SPLITS IN RINGS CLOSE TO THE (111) PLANE

The natural frequencies have been calculated using the expressions for the elastic moduli given by equations (1) and (2) and the appropriate expression for $F(\theta)$, equation (5). These have been substituted into the strain energy expressions, equations (12) and (16) respectively, for in-plane and out-of-plane modes. Numerical results are shown for small deviations in the range 0° to 4°, from the (111) plane and for modes with 2, 3 and 4 nodal diameters.

Fourier analysis of elastic moduli

To explain the natural frequency predictions, it is useful to consider the harmonic content of the elastic modulus variations with respect to θ, which defines the direction of the line of applied stress. The form of equations (1), (2), (5) and (6) precludes a simple analytical determination of the Fourier coefficients when $\delta \neq 0$ and they have been calculated numerically so that $E(\theta)$ can be expressed in the form

$$E(\theta) = E_O + \sum_{m=1}^{M} [E_{mC} \cos m\theta + E_{mS} \sin m\theta] \qquad (19)$$

The shear modulus $G(\theta)$ can be treated in the same way. The Fourier analysis shows that, on the (111) plane ($\delta=0$) only the constant term, E_0, is non-zero. For non-zero values of δ, the Fourier analysis shows a constant component together with even-order harmonic, cosine components, E_{2C}, E_{4C}... The sine components are all zero, due to the choice of reference direction for θ. For the range of values of δ considered, the E_{2C} and E_{4C} cosine components are generally two orders of magnitude smaller than the constant value. The magnitude of each harmonic increases as δ increases. Higher order harmonics, E_{6C}, E_{8C} etc. are also present, but at a much reduced magnitude.

To see how the spatial harmonic content of the elastic moduli influences the pattern of frequency splitting between modes we note that the integral for the in-plane strain energy, equation (12), can be written in the following form

$$U_{IP} = \frac{I_z}{2a^3} \int_0^{2\pi} \left(E_o + \sum_{m=2}^{4,6,8,10} [E_{mC} \cos m\theta] \right) (W_1 \sin n\theta + W_2 \cos n\theta)^2 d\theta \qquad (20)$$

where W_1 and W_2 are the amplitudes of the displacement components. When integral (20) is evaluated, the constant part of the elastic modulus, E_0, gives rise to non-zero contributions to the strain energy which depend only on W_1^2 and W_2^2 but not on $W_1 W_2$. The terms involving E_{mC} give rise to integrals which are zero for $m \neq 2n$ but non-zero when $m=2n$, in which case the sign of W will be different depending on whether the integral involves W_1 or W_2. This implies that the natural frequencies of pairs of modes with n nodal diameters will be split when $m=2n$. Thus, the Fourier analysis predicts that for non-zero values of δ, the frequencies will be split for modes where $n=2,3,4,5...$ On the (111) plane the absence of any harmonics means that the natural frequencies of a pair of modes will be equal for a given value of n.

A linear approximation of equation (5) can be derived where only terms in δ are retained. For this case, Fourier analysis shows a large constant term, E_0, and E_{2C} and

E_{4C} components which are within ~4% and ~1.8% of the values obtained using equation (5) respectively. Therefore, a linear expression gives good approximations for frequency splits between modes with 2 nodal diameters. If an approximation of equation (5) is used where terms in δ^2 are retained then a Fourier analysis gives E_0, E_{2C}, E_{4C}, E_{6C}, E_{8C}...The coefficients, E_{6C} and E_{8C} are found to be in error by ~50% and this leads to discrepancies in the predicted natural frequencies for modes with 3 and 4 nodal diameters. Therefore, the full expression must be used for modes with more than 2 nodal diameters.

In-plane and out-of-plane modes with 2,3,4 nodal diameters

Figure 5 shows the variation in non-dimensional natural frequencies obtained numerically for in-plane and out-of-plane modes with 2 nodal diameters. As expected the frequency values are equal on the (111) plane where the material properties are isotropic. A deviation of 4° produces frequency splits of 0.97% and 0.92% for the in-plane and out-of-plane modes respectively. Figures 6 and 7 show the variation of the natural frequencies of in-plane and out-of-plane modes with 3 and 4 nodal diameters. A deviation of 4° produces frequency splits of 0.02% and 0.01% of the (111) plane value for modes where $n=i=3$ and $n=i=4$ respectively. Therefore as expected when $n=i=2$ the frequencies are affected greatest and for higher values of nodal diameter the effects of anisotropy are reduced.

FREQUENCY SPLITS IN RINGS CLOSE TO THE (100) PLANE

The analysis presented for planes tilted from the (100) plane allows deviations about one crystal axis or a combined rotation to be examined. The variations in elastic moduli are similar if either γ_1 or γ_2 is equal to zero. A Fourier analysis using equations (1) and (7) which define the elastic moduli on planes at small angular deviations from the (100) plane allow predictions for frequency splitting to be obtained. On the (100) plane there is a large constant term, E_0, together with E_{4C}, E_{8C}, E_{12C} ...etc. harmonics of relatively smaller magnitude. This would be expected to give rise to frequency splits only in modes with even numbers of nodal diameters. On planes tilted about one principal axis from the (100) plane, the Fourier analysis shows additional E_{2C}, E_{6C}, E_{10C}... components, but these are much smaller in magnitude compared to the E_{4C} and E_{8C} components and these would give rise to split frequencies for flexural modes with odd numbers of nodal diameters.

Deviations About One Axis

Figure 8 shows the frequency variations for modes with 2 nodal diameters. The in-plane and out-of-plane modes are split on the (100) plane by 6.51% and 6.42% respectively. All frequencies increase slightly with angle of deviation to give splits of 6.6% and 6.5% for in-plane and out-of-plane modes respectively when the angle rotated is 4°. Figure 9 shows that for modes with 3 nodal diameters, the natural frequencies for a given pair are not split on the (100) plane. As the angle of deviation from the (100) plane is increased, all frequencies increase and separate to give splits of 0.02% and 0.01% for in-plane and out-of-plane modes respectively at an angle of 4°. For in-plane and out-of-plane modes with 4 nodal diameters, Figure 10 shows that the natural frequencies are split by 0.42% and 0.37% respectively on the (100) plane. All frequencies increase with angle of deviation to give splits of 0.43% and 0.38% respectively at an angle of deviation of 4°. The percentage splits reflects the magnitude of the relevant harmonic components.

Combined Rotations

Combinations of γ_1 and γ_2 which give resultant misalignments of 1°, 2°, 3° and 4° have also been investigated. For a given *resultant* misalignment angle, there are no practically significant variations in the frequency values for different combinations of γ_1 and γ_2. To 5 significant figures, the values are the same as those obtained when a 1° rotation is applied about a single principal axis. The reason for this is illustrated by examining the reciprocal of equation (7) with varying values for γ_1 and γ_2. The amplitudes of the variations are several orders of magnitude smaller than the moduli values and hence are negligible.

Frequency Splits In Rings On The (110) Plane

Equations (9), (1) and (2) which define the elastic moduli on the (110) plane are substituted into the strain energy equations, (12) and (16) for in-plane and out-of-plane modes respectively to show the effects on the natural frequencies. A Fourier analysis on the material properties for the (110) plane show that there is a large constant term, E_0, together with E_{2C}, E_{4C}, E_{6C}, ...etc. This would be expected to give rise to frequency splits in modes with 2, 3, 4.... nodal diameters. The higher order harmonics have relatively smaller magnitude. Therefore as the number of nodal diameters is increased a smaller frequency split is predicted.

For modes with 2 nodal diameters, the non-dimensional frequencies are split by ~5%. For in-plane and out-of-plane modes with 3 nodal diameters, the frequencies are split by ~3% and ~0.6% respectively and for modes with 4 nodal diameters, the frequencies are split by ~0.2%. The percentage split is reduced at higher numbers of nodal diameters due to the reduced magnitude of the Fourier components.

CONCLUSION

The Fourier analysis results show that an $m\theta$ variation in the material properties will lead to frequency splits for modes with $m/2$ nodal diameters. Therefore, on the (111) plane, the absence of any harmonics leads to no frequency splitting. On planes at a small angular deviation from the (111) plane and on the (110) plane the presence of $m=2,4,6,8$...harmonics lead to frequency splits between modes with 2,3,4... nodal diameters. For the (100) plane, the presence of $m=4,8,12...$harmonics lead to frequency splitting between modes with an even number of nodal diameters. Misalignment from the (100) plane introduces additional harmonic components which will split modes with an odd number of nodal diameters. The magnitude of higher order harmonics is relatively less and therefore, modes with 2 nodal diameters experience the greatest effect from material anisotropy.

REFERENCES

(1) Hopkin, I., Performance and design of a silicon micro-machined gyro *Proc. DGON Symposium on Gyro Technology,* 1997

(2) Runyan, W., *Silicon Semiconductor Technology,* McGraw-Hill, 1965

(3) Menzel, D. *Fundamental Formulas of Physics Vol 1,* Dover, 1960

(4) Ristic, L. *Sensor Technology and Devices,* Artech House, 1994

(5) *Private Communication* (British Aerospace)

(6) Heading, J., *Mathematical Methods in Science and Engineering,* Edward Arnold, 1970

(7) Blevins, R., *Formulas for Natural Frequencies and Mode Shapes,* Krieger, 1995

(8) Kirkhope, J., *J. Sound and Vibration* Vol. **50**(2), 1977, pp.219-247

(9) Warburton, G., *The Dynamical Behaviour of Structures,* Pergamon, 1976

(10) Kirkhope, J., *ASCE J. Engineering Mechanics Division,* 1976, pp239-247

FIGURE 1 The principal planes of a cubic crystal

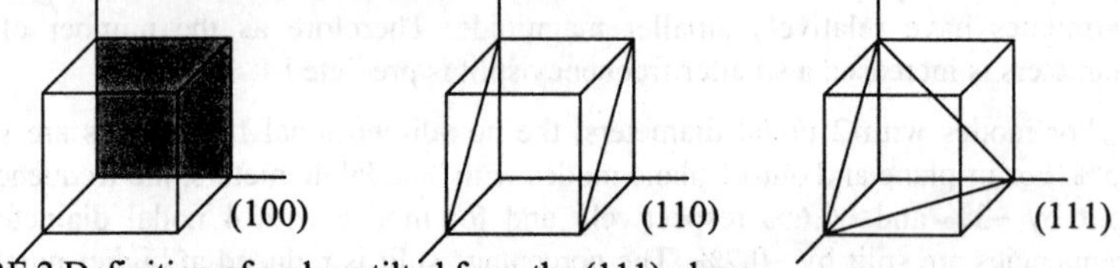

(100)   (110)   (111)

FIGURE 2 Definition of a plane tilted from the (111) plane

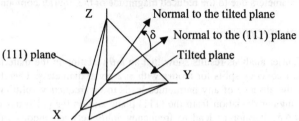

Z
Normal to the tilted plane
δ
Normal to the (111) plane
(111) plane
Tilted plane
Y
X

FIGURE 3 Definition of planes tilted from the (100) plane

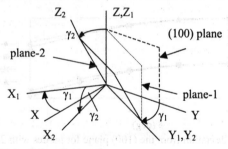

FIGURE 4 Definition of ring displacement components

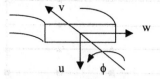

FIGURE 5 Effect of deviation from the (111) plane for modes with 2 nodal diameters

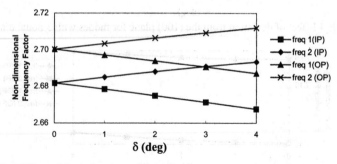

FIGURE 6 Effect of deviation from the (111) plane for modes with 3 nodal diameters

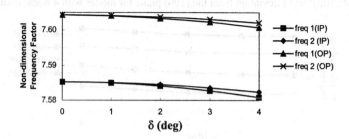

FIGURE 7 Effect of deviation from the (111) plane for modes with 3 nodal diameters

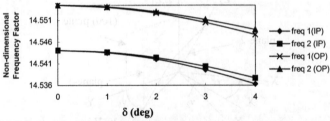

FIGURE 8 Effect of deviation from the (100) plane for modes with 2 nodal diameters

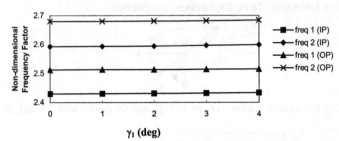

FIGURE 9 Effect of deviation from the (100) plane for modes with 3 nodal diameters

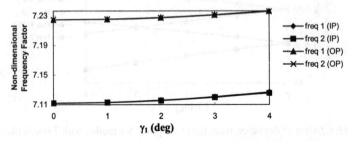

FIGURE10Effect of deviation from the (100) plane for modes with 4 nodal diameters

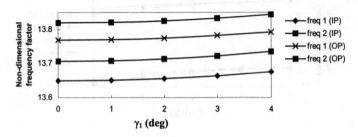

7. MATERIAL AND GEOMETRIC NON-LINEARITY

2. MATERIAL AND GEOMETRIC NON-LINEARITY

MODELLING PLASTICITY USING STRAIN NUCLEI

D. A. Hills* and L. Limmer †

Severely loaded components, particularly those at elevated temperature where the yield stress is suppressed, may show local regions of plasticity at stress raising features. The object of the paper is to present a novel way of describing plastic flow in the neighourhood of such features, making full use of the underlying elasticity solution, but correctly obeying the plastic flow rules. The technique relies on distributing glide dislocations over the plastic region so as to represent plastic flow, whilst maintaining the boundary conditions. The approach described is implemented and several example problems are solved. Each shows a substantial saving in computational effort over a solution of equivalent accuracy found by finite element methods, and the approach is advocated as one which shows great promise in carrying out lifing calculations, where detailed information on constrained plastic flow is needed, and the strains developed are controlled by an elastic hinterland.

INTRODUCTION

Severely loaded components, particularly those experiencing elevated temperature, may suffer local regions of plasticity in the neighbourhood of stress-raising features. Examples occur in gas turbine blades and within many components in a steam turbine power plant. The conventional way of analysing such problems is to use the finite element procedure, but the difficulty with this is that it is computationally expensive, mainly because of the incremental nature of the problem. There is clearly no getting away from the fact that all plasticity problems are incremental in nature, and attempts to circumvent this, for example by an equivalence of strain energy between an extended elastic solution and the solution for an elastic- plastic material, proposed by Neuber [1], are limited in accuracy. At best, they represent a deformation plasticity approach to something which is experiencing very far from proportional loading.

An area where plasticity modelling, using ingenious modifications of elasticity solutions, has enabled good progress with only moderate amounts of computational effort, and yet showing respectable accuracy, is in analysing yielding of crack tips.

* Department of Engineering Science, Oxford University, Parks Road, Oxford, OX1 3PJ

† Rolls Royce plc., P.O. Box 31, Derby DE24 8BJ

Early solutions of this kind include the celebrated BCS solution, originally for mode III crack tip loading [2], and integral equation forms of the Dugdale-Barenblatt solution [3], giving an estimate of the plane stress mode I crack tip plastic stress field. The success of the latter solution was that, whilst it collapsed what should, in theory, be an area of plasticity onto a line, the region of violation of the yield criterion is very small, and the solution is therefore accurate. Results from the calculation are displayed in summary form in Figure 1. The crack is present along the y = 0 line, and extends from x = -a to x = +a. It is subjected to a uniform remote tension (1, and the yield stress of the material is σ_y. The figure shows contours of the normalised Tresca yield parameter, when the solution has been found, and it may be seen that the region in which the yield criterion is exceeded is very modest.

Further, the direction of plastic flow on the plane of symmetry (y = 0, Figure 1) is clearly defined by symmetry: the x-direction stress is intermediate between the x- and z- values, so that material flows into the plane of analysis by thinning of adjacent material, along planes at ± 45° to the x-z axes. Material added to the plane is therefore represented by the Burgers vector of the dislocations inserted within this region which are therefore of the climb type. Because the loading is proportional, and there is no rotation of axes, it is possible to jump from the elastic solution to the final load without incurring the penalty of an incremental formulation.

Cracks under transverse Plane Strain

Practical plane stress problems are rare, and the plane strain limiting solution is almost always of greater practical relevance. For almost every realistic stress distribution, and certainly ahead of a crack tip, practically encountered values of Poisson's ratio give rise to a stress state where the through-thickness principal stress is intermediate between the two in-plane ones. Thus, from the plastic flow rules, it is clear that flow must occur *within* the plane of analysis. Furthermore, in the case of the crack tip, the regions in which the state of stress is severest are along two 'wings', at approximately ± 67° to the x-axis, Figure 2. Plastic flow can still be modelled using distributions of dislocations for this case, but the nature of the plastic flow is completely different. Instead of material flowing into the plane, it is merely re-arranged within it, and the function of the dislocation is now to permit slip displacement to occur, whilst preserving continuity of the material in other directions. Thus *glide* dislocations need to be employed, rather than the climb dislocations used under plane stress conditions.

At this point, it is worth, as an aside, noting that a Volterra edge dislocation is formed by taking a path cut from what is to the core of the dislocation to infinity, and imposing a constant displacement (the Burgers vector) across the cut before joining the material back together. If the Burgers vector is parallel with the cut it is conventional to think of the dislocation as being of the glide type, whilst if it is normal to the cut the dislocation is normally thought of as climb in character. However, the two dislocations are, in fact, the same, and the only distinction between the two is the chosen trajectory of the path cut, and hence the line across which the displacement discontinuity occurs [4].

Returning to the question of plane strain crack tip plasticity, we note that earlier solutions to the problem employed arrays of dislocations in which the Burgers vector was made parallel with the direction of the ray along which the severest state of stress, as measured by the yield parameter, arose. Hence, for a Tresca material the ray direction is simply the one along which the maximum shear stress occurs. However, if the dislocation Burgers vector is given this orientation the dislocation is acting as nothing more than a general strain nucleus, and there is no direct physical interpretation of the Burgers vector. A much better way to proceed would seem to be to align the Burgers vector with the direction in which slip occurs, to satisfy the normality condition in plasticity. For the crack tip problem shown in Figure 2, if the elasticity solution is taken to be that associated with the stress intensity factor, i.e. the singular term relating to a semi-infinite crack, the direction of maximum shear is constant along the ray, because the form of the stress field is uncoupled in (r,θ). The simplest way to consider this problem is to look at the resultant shear stress $S(x')$, acting along one of the rays, where x' is measured along the ray. The shear is taken as the superposition of the nominal elastic stress $\tau_{x'y'}(x')$, and the effect of an unknown dislocation density, $B_{x'}(\xi)$, which may be written as

$$S(x') = \overline{\tau}_{x'y'}(x') + \frac{\mu}{\pi(\kappa+1)} \int_0^\rho B_{x'}(\xi) \, K(x',\xi) \, d\xi \qquad (1)$$

where μ is the modulus of rigidity and κ is Kolosov's constant. The kernel, $K(x',\xi)$, represents the effect of a dislocation located at point ξ, and three symmetrically positioned and oriented dislocations on the other three rays. If, for simplicity, Tresca's yield criterion is assumed, the yield condition may be written down as

$$S(x') = k \qquad 0 \le x' \le \rho \qquad (2)$$

where k is the yield stress in pure shear, and the unknown extent of the plastic zone, ρ, is determined as part of the solution, from the side condition which demands bounded behaviour at the elastic/plastic transition point. A comparison of the region in which the yield criterion is exceeded, using this simple line array model, is shown in Figure 3(a). The solution is in error for two reasons; first, because a region of plasticity has been collapsed onto a line, and secondly because the Burgers vector has not been aligned with the local direction of maximum shear stress, as required by the normality rule, for a Tresca material. If the calculation is repeated, but leaving the orientation of the Burgers vector as a parameter, to be chosen so that it *does* lie along

447

the slip direction, the quality of the solution is improved. Figure 3(b) shows the region in which the yield criterion is violated, and it is now seen to be smaller than that for the arbitrarily oriented dislocation.

This extensive preamble has sought to show that the procedure of starting off with an elasticity solution and using a distributed strain nucleus, in the form of a dislocation, to model plasticity, has considerable potential. In the problems discussed so far plasticity has been collapsed from an area onto a line, but this is a gross and unnecessary idealisation. Also, the solution has the feature that, because the notional elastic stress field is self-similar, the stress state does not rotate, i.e. it remains proportional, and hence an incremental formulation is not needed. This will not be true in general. There is one further feature of the procedure which merits a remark at this stage. This is the interaction between the dislocation and the boundaries of the component. In the problem described above an explicit expression is available for the state of stress induced by a dislocation in the neighbourhood of a crack [5]. Solutions are also known for dislocations in the neighbourhood of many stress-raising features, and hence any number may be deployed, to satisfy the plastic flow conditions, whilst leaving the boundary conditions satisfied [6]. If a solution is not known in the relevant domain it is still possible to use the procedure to be developed, but the boundary element technique will be needed in order to restore traction-free conditions along free edges [7]. A boundary element may be developed by using two dislocations, of equal magnitude but opposite sign, at a small but finite distance apart. Many elements so formed are arranged along the line which is to form the free boundary of the component. The influence of each boundary element on the traction components of stress arising at the centre of each element is determined, and the strength of each element (the Burgers vector of the dislocations) adjusted so that the resultant traction, including the influence of the nominal stress field, vanishes. This technique is particularly attractive to use with the method being described, as the same dislocation influence function may be used as a kernel for each.

GENERAL PRINCIPLES BEHIND FORMULATION

The above calculations suggest that a method might be developed for limited plastic flow, present in the neighbourhood of a stress-raising feature, which is numerically very efficient. Full use will be made of the information contained in the elasticity solution, on which a perturbation is developed. In general, the solution must proceed incrementally, in order for the plastic flow rules to be satisfied, and, at each loading step, consistency between the yield function normal and the flow direction (as manifested by the Burgers vector direction) ensured. A flow chart indicating the procedure to be followed is shown in Figure 4. The starting ingredients are; (a) a solution for the elastic stress state in the body induced by the far field loads under consideration, and (b) a solution for the dislocation in a body of the same geometry. Ready-made solutions are available for dislocations in the neighbourhood of circular or elliptical holes, in half-planes, near semi-infinite or finite cracks, or in layered geoemtries. These are precisely the kind of feature which produce local stress concentrations, and hence which give rise to localised plasticity, and they therefore form a useful starting point for many solutions. If remote boundaries are to be included this may be done using the boundary element method, in an approximate way, which is usually sufficient, as remote boundaries will have only a moderate influence on the local stress state.

The next decision to be taken in formulating the problem is the way in which the dislocations are to be distributed. In our first attempts to explore the approach, discrete dislocations were installed at fixed points, and their strengths found by carrying out a collocation at the mid-points of the grid [8]. This is a computationally attractive and direct method, but it clearly provides no more than an averaged solution to the problem, and what is needed is some kind of continuous distribution. The next step in the solution is to divide the region of potential plasticity up into finite cells, and, within each, to define a Burgers vector density (in two orthogonal directions), whose values are the primary unknowns in the problem. The simplest form of the dislocation density which can be assumed (the shape function in finite element nomenclature) is a piecewise constant one. Solution then proceeds in the following way:

1. The elastic solution to the problem under consideration is determined, and the elastic limit found.

2. An array of elements is set up over the potential (final) extent of the region of plastic flow.

3. The load is increased to the point of first yield, and then by a small but finite amount. A region will now exist in which the yield condition is exceeded.

4. Elements within the first estimate of the yielded region are 'activated'. The direction of the Burgers vector in each element is set equal to the direction in which plastic flow is judged to occur (maximum shear stress direction if Tresca's yield criterion is employed), and the magnitude of the Burgers vectors chosen. This is done by determining the influence functions for each element on both itself and every other element, forming a matrix, and solving.

5. The state of stress is now found everywhere. Because of the redistribution of stress associated with plastic flow, it will be found that the zone of plastic flow is now greater than that initially found. It may therefore now be the case that further elements, previously in the marginal elastic domain, have become plastic. Further elements are therefore activated, and the problem re-solved.

6. The loop formed by steps 4 & 5 is circulated until stability occurs. It is now necessary to ensure that the flow normality condition is correctly satisfied. As a first step, the flow direction was set to that implied by the elastic solution. This must now be refined, so that it takes into amount the modification of the stress state by the dislocation elements themselves.

7. Convergence requires that a self-consistent solution be present, where the flow direction is normal to the yield surface. For a Tresca material this is the direction of maximum shear stress. When this is achieved the load may be incremented.

These steps are shown diagrammatically in Figure 4.

ELEMENT FORMULATION

A solitary dislocation present in an infinite plane produces a state of stress which varies like $1/r$, where r is measured from the dislocation core, and is also a complicated function of the polar angle, θ. If finite boundaries are included they modify the stress state, but do so in a way which is bounded. Thus, when the influence functions associated with a particular element of dislocations is found, a singular term and a regular term appear within the integral. Further, the singular term is not Cauchy if the observation point is exterior to the element. Attention has been focused on the evaluation of the singular term, as there are some features of this which are of interest. Suppose that a single dislocation, having Burgers vector components (b_x, b_y), is located at (x,y), and that we require the state of stress at point (x_0, y_0). The functional connection in terms of real arithmetic was given by Dundurs, but a compact way of writing these quantities in terms of complex invariants is

$$\sigma_{xx} + \sigma_{yy}\,(x_0, y_0) \;=\; \frac{\mu}{\pi\,(\kappa + 1)}\;\Re e\left[\frac{4}{i}\,\frac{b_x + i b_y}{(x_0 - x) + i(y_0 - y)}\right]$$

$$(3)$$

$$\sigma_{yy} - \sigma_{xx} + 2\,i\,\sigma_{xy} \;=\; \frac{2\mu}{\pi\,(\kappa + 1)}\left[\frac{2i\,(x_0 - x)\,b_x}{[(x_0 - x) + i(y_0 - y)]^2} + \frac{2i\,(y_0 - y)\,b_y}{[(x_0 - x) + i(y_0 - y)]^2}\right]$$

This form of the stress distribution is then conveniently re-cast in terms of the Muskhelishvili potential as

$$\phi(z_0\text{-}z) \;=\; \frac{\mu}{\pi\,i(\kappa + 1)}\,\frac{b_x + i b_y}{z_0 - z}$$

$$\phi'(z_0\text{-}z) \;=\; \frac{\partial \phi}{\partial z_0} \;=\; -\,\frac{\mu}{\pi\,i(\kappa + 1)}\,\frac{b_x + i b_y}{(z_0 - z)^2}$$

$$(4)$$

$$\Psi(z_0\text{-}z) = -\frac{\mu}{\pi\, i(\kappa+1)}\,\frac{b_x-ib_y}{z_0-z} = -\frac{b_x-ib_y}{b_x+ib_y}\,\phi(z_0\text{-}z)$$

$$z = x + iy$$

We now require to distribute dislocations over a domain, S, which will usually be a triangle, and here the dislocation density will be taken as uniform. Note, from equations (4), that the effect of a dislocation can now be encapsulated by a single potential, Ψ. The next step is to introduce two further potentials, $\Phi(z_0)$, $\Omega(z_0)$ which represent the resultant influence of the element. These are given by

$$\Phi(z_0) = \iint_S \phi\,(z_0-z)\,dS$$

$$\Omega(z_0) = \iint_S (\bar{z}_0-\bar{z})\,\phi'(z_0-z)\,dS \tag{5}$$

Which are related to the stress components by

$$\sigma_{xx} + \sigma_{yy} = 4\,\Re e\,[\,\Phi(z_0)\,]$$

$$\sigma_{yy} - \sigma_{xx} + 2\,i\,\sigma_{xy} = 2\left[\Omega(z_0) - \frac{b_x-ib_y}{b_x+ib_y}\,\Phi(z_0)\right] \tag{6}$$

And it turns out that the integrals of equations (5) take on a particularly simple form, viz.

$$\Phi(z_0) = -\frac{\mu\,(b_x+ib_y)}{\pi\,i(\kappa+1)}\iint_S e^{i\theta}\,r\,dr\,d\theta$$

$$\Omega(z_0) = \frac{\mu\,(b_x+ib_y)}{\pi\,i(\kappa+1)}\iint_S e^{-3i\theta}\,dr\,d\theta \tag{7}$$

These integrals are straightforward to integrate over the element, and are much more compact and convenient than a direct evaluation of the influence functions of a single dislocation themselves.

EXAMPLE PROBLEM

An illuminating example to display the proposed method is afforded by the problem of a large plate containing a circular hole, subject to uniform remote tension. The underlying elasticity solution is well known, and given in Timoshenko and Goodier [9]. The solution for a dislocation near a circular hole in an infinite plate is also well known, and was derived by Dundurs and Mura [10]. Orthogonal families of slip lines in the neighbourhood of the hole are shown in Figure 5(a), and a related grid of triangular elements is shown in Figure 5(b). The inherent symmetry in the problem about two axes is exploited, and a solution found for the first quadrant.

Figure 6 displays the output found, by giving contour plots of the Tresca yield parameter, evaluated by (a) the present method, and (b) ABAQUS finite element package. The model for one quarter of the problem consisted of 400 8-noded isoparametric elements and had 1280 nodes. Also shown on each figure is an estimate of the plastic zone size found by taking the elastic solution and noting the zone in which the yield criterion is exceeded; this does not take plastic flow into account, and hence does not allow for the redistribution of the stress. The maximum load applied was 2.4 × elastic limit, and, up to this point, 15 load increments had been used. The closeness of the FEM and present results is encouraging, and indicates the precision of the approach. Needless to say, the computation time using the present method was less than 1/10 of that needed for ABAQUS.

CONCLUSIONS

Distributing point singularities in the form of dislocations is a promising way of solving problems involving limited plastic flow, where strains are controlled by an elastic hinterland. The method derived exploits fully the properties of the singularity as a vector, enabling the flow rules to be tracked in a physically correct way. So far, the problems treated have related to elastic ideally plastic materials, but the technique could readily be extended to work hardening materials, by specifying the material connection between the strain components and instantaneous flow stress. The strain present at any point is that due to both the notional elastic stress field, and the **instantaneous dislocation distribution. There are many points where numerical** efficiencies are developed over a finite element formulation in the classical sense, so that, overall, the solution is much more rapid. It therefore lends itself to problems of cyclic loading.

REFERENCE LIST

(1) Neuber, H. *ASME J. Appl. Mech.*, Vol. 28, No. 4, 1961, pp. 554-560.

(2) Bilby, B. A., Cottrell, A. H. and Swinden, K. H. *Proc. Roy. Soc. London*, Vol. 272, 1963, pp. 304-314.

(3) Dugdale, D. S. J. *Mech. Phys. Solids*, Vol. 8, pp. 100-108.

(4) Dundurs, J. *Mathematical theory of dislocations*. Pub ASME, New York, 1969, pp. 70-114.

(5) Lakshmanan, V. and Li, *J. Mater. Sci. and Eng.*, Vol. A104, 1988, 95-104.

(6) Hills, D. A., Kelly, P. A., Dai, D. N., and Korsunsky, A. *Solution of Crack problems: the distributed dislocation technique*. Pub. Kluwer Academic Publishers, Dordrecht, 1996.

(7) Blomerus, P. and Hills, D. A. *J. Strain Anal.*, Vol. 33, No.4, 1998, pp.315-326.

(8) Blomerus, P. M. and Hills, D. A. *Proc. I. Mech. E. Part C*, Vol. 212, 1998, pp. 731-740.

(9) Timoshenko, S. P. and Goodier, J. N. *Theory of Elasticity*. Pub. McGraw-Hill, New York, 1964, p.91.

(10) Dundurs, J. and Mura, T. *J. Mech. Phys. Solids*. Vol. 12, 1964, pp. 177-189.

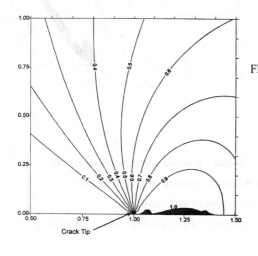

FIGURE 1   Plane stress Mode I crack tip plastic stress field based on the Dugdale-Barenblatt solution [3]. Contours of Tresca's yield parameter normalised with respect to the yield stress in tension.

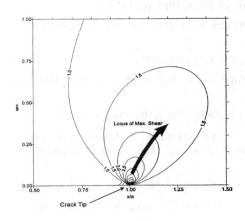

FIGURE 2 Plane strain Mode I crack tip stress field displaying state of severest stress at approximately $\pm 67^0$ to x-axis. Elasticity solution contours of Tresca's yield parameter.

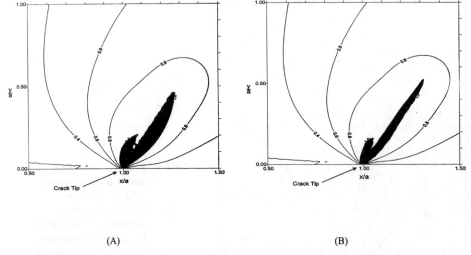

(A)   (B)

FIGURE 3   Plane strain Mode I crack. Tresca's yield parameter normalised with respect to the yield stress in tension. Inclined strip yield model.

A. Dislocation Burgers vector aligned with plastic ray.

B. Dislocation Burgers vector aligned with direction of maximum shear stress.

454

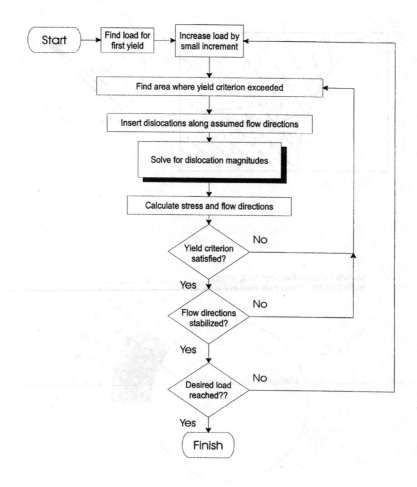

FIGURE 4   Solution procedure for modelling plane strain crack tip plasticity using distributed strain nuclei.

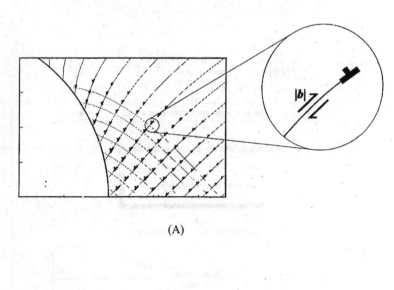

(A)

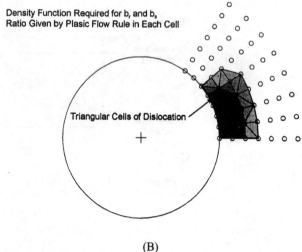

Density Function Required for b_r and b_θ
Ratio Given by Plasic Flow Rule in Each Cell

Triangular Cells of Dislocation

(B)

FIGURE 5   Modelling plasticity near a circular hole in an infinite plate using distibuted dislocations.

A. Orthogonal families of slip lines in the neighbourhood of the hole.

B. Division of expected plastic domain into finite cells using triangular Cells of dislocations.

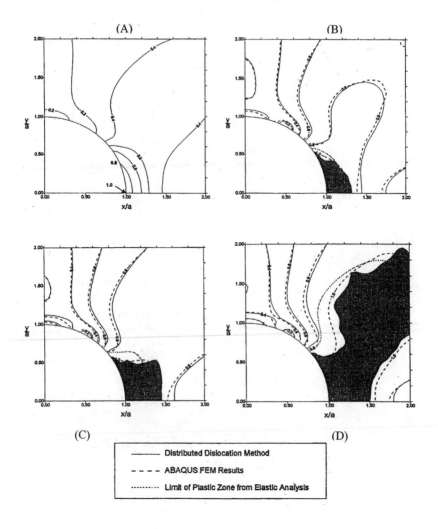

FIGURE 6   Distribution of normalised Tresca yield parameter in a large plate containing a circular hole, under uniaxial tension, σ_0 transverse plane strain.

   A.   At elastic limit. $\sigma_0/\sigma_y = 1/3$.

   B.   At 180% of elastic limit. $\sigma_0/\sigma_y = 0.6$.

   C.   At 210% of elastic limit. $\sigma_0/\sigma_y = 0.7$.

   D.   At 240% of elastic limit. $\sigma_0/\sigma_y = 0.8$.

Prediction of Elastic-Plastic Response of a Spoke-Type Structure Using Approximate and FE Methods

T.H. Hyde [*], H. Ou [†] and J.W. Taylor [‡]

Local stress and strain concentrations and elastic-plastic deformations are a major concern in the design of aeroengine casing structures. Such localised behaviour could result in load path redistribution, crack initiation and growth. They are also important factors in the assessment of the service life of an entire engine. This paper is concerned with the prediction of the elastic-plastic response of spoke-type structures using a combination of approximate and FE methods. The calculation of elastic-plastic stress and strain components was carried out using Neuber's rule and the Glinka method. The accuracy of these predictions was then assessed by comparing them with elastic-plastic FE results. The results obtained for the elastic-plastic response of a simplified spoked structure showed reasonable agreement when compared with nonlinear FE solutions.

Notation

E	Young's modulus
e	elastic strain due to the nominal stress
K	material strength coefficient
K_t	stress concentration factor
P	applied load
S	nominal stress
T	thickness of semi-circularly notched specimen
W	strain energy density
ε	local elastic-plastic strain
ν	Poisson's ratio
σ	local elastic-plastic stress

subscript

$1,2,3$	principal stresses and strains
e	elastic deformation
p	plastic deformation
q	equivalent stress and strain
s	nominal stress and strain
u	ultimate
y	yield condition

superscript

n	strain hardening exponent

1 INTRODUCTION

In the current civil and military aeroengine applications there is a constant need to improve strength to weight ratio and reduce cost without compromising safety. This consequently places greater demands on the components that form the structure of an aeroengine. An improved understanding is needed of structural behaviour under extreme load conditions where localised plastic strain may occur in some cases, or may need to be designed against.

[*] School of Mechanical, Manufacturing and Material Engineering, University of Nottingham, Nottingham, NG7 2RD, UK; [†] School of Mechanical and Manufacturing Engineering, The Queen's University of Belfast, Belfast, BT9 5AH, UK; [‡] Aerospace Group, Rolls-Royce plc, Derby, DE24 8BJ, UK

A typical structure to be considered consists of an outer casing, an inner hub and vanes or spokes in between. The difficulty under ultimate load conditions is to predict the plastic strains and the subsequent effect on the load distribution throughout the structure and hence the real failure load of the structure. Current approaches are conservative as proven by component rig testing prior to engine certification. The objective of this work is to investigate ways of achieving a more realistic analytical prediction of the ultimate load carrying capability of a complex spoked structure under extreme loads.

To understand structural behaviour and capability at the design stage, it is important to predict the elastic-plastic deformation and local stress-strain concentrations. By incorporating the stress-strain behaviour of engine materials, the crack initiation and growth, and the service life of the structures can be estimated using appropriate prediction criteria. However, the local elastic-plastic stress and strain concentration in spoked casing structures is usually under multiaxial conditions and elastic-plastic FE analysis is often impractical due to the large number of elements and resulting long computing times that are required because of the geometric complexity of this type of structure. As an alternative to elastic-plastic FE analysis, attempts have been made to predict local elastic-plastic stresses and strains using approximate methods such as Neuber's rule (Neuber [1]) and the Glinka method (Molski et al [2] and Glinka [3]). These approaches relate the local elastic-plastic stress and strain in a notched specimen to the nominal stress and strain in plane-stress or plane-strain conditions (Sharpe et al [4, 5]). Generalised methods for predicting the multiaxial elastic-plastic stress and strain, and fatigue behaviours of notched specimens were also proposed (Hoffmann et al [6, 7] and Walker [8]). However, the applicability of these approximate methods to aeroengine casing structures, which have complex configurations and several positions which may experience plasticity at the same time, has yet to be established.

The paper studies the local elastic-plastic stresses and strains in the stress concentration regions of a semi-circular notch in a specimen, using approximate methods and nonlinear FE analysis. Based on Neuber's rule and the Glinka method, an approximate approach for predicting local multiaxial elastic-plastic stress and strain components, under proportional load conditions, was established. The elastic-plastic response of a simplified spoked structure subjected to axial loading was then determined using the approximate method and nonlinear FE analysis. It was found that the local elastic-plastic stress and strain components, obtained by using the approximate methods, bounded the results from the nonlinear FE analysis. By using a combination of the approximate methods and the results of elastic FE analyses, the same method should be capable of predicting the elastic-plastic behaviour of aeroengine spoked structures, with reasonable accuracy.

2 APPROXIMATE METHODS

2.1 Neuber's Rule and the Glinka Method

Local elastic-plastic stress and strain concentrations in a complex structure often occur due to the notch effects when other parts of the structure are still in an elastic state. As illustrated in Figure 1, the peak elastic-plastic stresses and strains in a semi-circularly notched specimen can be estimated by approximate methods. Two of the most commonly used approximate methods are Neuber's rule and the Glinka method [1 to 5]. Neuber's rule states that the product of local peak stress and strain in the notch is constant for a known material, geometry and applied load, which can be written as

$$\frac{(K_t S)^2}{E} = \sigma \varepsilon \tag{1}$$

Since local stresses and strains are prescribed by the stress-strain relationship of the material, the local stress σ and strain ε can be predicted using equation (1) and the material stress-strain curves. Based on the assumption that the strain energy density at the notch root is the same whether elastic or elastic-plastic conditions exist, provided local plastic zones are surrounded by predominantly elastic material, the Glinka method, illustrated in Figure 1(b), may be expressed as

$$W_p = W_e = K_t^2 W_s \tag{2}$$

where $W_e = \sigma_e^2/2E$ and $W_s = S^2/2E$

For plane-stress conditions, a uniaxial stress state exists in the notch root. Therefore, the elastic-plastic notch stresses and strains can be estimated using either Neuber's rule or the Glinka method with the uniaxial tensile stress-strain curve of the materials. As shown in Table 1, closed-form solutions for plane-stress conditions can be derived for elastic perfectly plastic and elastic power hardening materials, while a trial and error approach is required for a Ramberg-Osgood material. In plane-strain conditions, the uniaxial stress-strain curve needs to be related to the biaxial stress state, which is achieved by using Hooke's law and the von Mises's criterion for multiaxial stresses [3].

2.2 Multiaxial load conditions

Under conditions of proportional loading and with certain strain constraints, an estimate for multiaxial elastic-plastic stress and strain components may also be carried out [6 to 8]. By introducing stress concentration factors K_t and K_{tq}, which correspond to elastic maximum principal stress σ_1, and elastic equivalent stress σ_q, respectively, the elastic-plastic equivalent stress and strain components may be approximated with Neuber's rule as follows

TABLE 1   Formulae of Neuber's rule and Glinka method

Material type	Neuber's rule	Glinka method
Elastic, perfectly plastic $\sigma = E\varepsilon \ (\sigma \le \sigma_y)$ $\sigma = \sigma_y \ (\sigma \ge \sigma_y)$	$\varepsilon = \dfrac{(K_t S)^2}{\sigma_y E}$	$\varepsilon = \dfrac{(K_t S)^2}{2\sigma_y E} + \dfrac{\sigma_y}{2E}$
Elastic, power-hardening $\sigma = E\varepsilon \ (\sigma \le \sigma_y)$ $\sigma = K'\varepsilon^{n'} \ (\sigma \ge \sigma_y)$	$\varepsilon = \left[\dfrac{(K_t S)^2}{EK'}\right]^{\frac{1}{n'+1}},$ $\sigma = K'\left[\dfrac{(K_t S)^2}{EK'}\right]^{\frac{n'}{n'+1}}$	$\varepsilon = \left[\dfrac{(n'+1)(K_t S)^2}{2EK'}\right]^{\frac{1}{n'+1}},$ $\sigma = K'\left[\dfrac{(n'+1)(K_t S)^2}{2EK'}\right]^{\frac{n'}{n'+1}}$
Ramberg-Osgood $\varepsilon = \dfrac{\sigma}{E} + \left(\dfrac{\sigma}{K}\right)^{\frac{1}{n}}$	$(K_t S)^2 = \sigma^2 + \sigma E \left(\dfrac{\sigma}{K}\right)^{\frac{1}{n}}$	$(K_t S)^2 = \sigma^2 + \dfrac{2}{n+1}\sigma E \left(\dfrac{\sigma}{K}\right)^{\frac{1}{n}}$

$$\frac{(K_{tq} S)^2}{E} = \sigma_q \, \varepsilon_q \tag{3}$$

where, using the von Mises Yield criterion,

$$K_{tq} = \frac{K_t}{\sqrt{2}}\left[\left(1 - \frac{\sigma_2}{\sigma_1}\right)^2 + \left(1 - \frac{\sigma_3}{\sigma_1}\right)^2 + \left(\frac{\sigma_2}{\sigma_1} - \frac{\sigma_3}{\sigma_1}\right)^2\right]^{\frac{1}{2}} \tag{4}$$

$$K_t = \frac{\sigma_1}{S} \quad \text{and} \quad K_{tq} = \frac{\sigma_q}{S} \tag{5}$$

The total maximum strain components can then be obtained according to the Prandtl-Reuss flow rule [6]

$$\varepsilon_1 = \frac{\varepsilon_q}{\sigma_q}\left[\sigma_1 - \nu'(\sigma_2 + \sigma_3)\right] \tag{6}$$

$$\varepsilon_2 = \frac{\varepsilon_q}{\sigma_q}\left[\sigma_2 - \nu'(\sigma_1 + \sigma_3)\right] \tag{7}$$

$$\varepsilon_3 = \frac{\varepsilon_q}{\sigma_q}\left[\sigma_3 - \nu'(\sigma_1 + \sigma_2)\right] \tag{8}$$

where $\nu' = \dfrac{1}{2} - \left(\dfrac{1}{2} - \nu\right)\dfrac{\sigma_q}{E\varepsilon_q}$

2.3 Elastic-plastic response of semi-circular notch specimen

To assess the validity of the approximate methods for predicting the elastic-plastic stresses and strains, a semi-circular notch specimen was studied. The results were compared with the results from nonlinear FE analysis. An elastic perfectly plastic material behaviour model was assumed with Young's modulus $E=202$GPa, Poisson's ratio $\nu=0.3$ and a yield stress $\sigma_y=830$MPa. For a semi-circular notch specimen, the stress concentration factor, K_t is 1.6 (Peterson [9]). To evaluate the effect of strain constraints on the local stress components, FE results for plane-stress and plane-strain conditions as well as for 3D models with different thicknesses were obtained. Figure 2 shows 2D and 3D FE meshes of the semi-circular notch specimen. Due to the geometric symmetry of the semi-circular specimen, only a quarter was modelled for the 2D FE analysis, while one eighth was modelled for 3D FE analysis. The boundary conditions were applied along the appropriate planes of symmetry. Uniformly distributed forces were applied upward on the top surface of the specimen, as shown in Figure 2. The ABAQUS [11, 12] FE software package was used in the FE analyses for the 2D and 3D specimens.

The results obtained from approximate methods and FE analysis are presented in terms of K_t*S versus elastic-plastic strain, in Figure 3, so that the material's stress-strain curve can also be included. Different thicknesses of the semi-specimen represent different strain constraints. The elastic-plastic stress and strain components along the coordinate axes were also derived for plane-stress and plane-strain conditions for comparison with the results obtained from the nonlinear FE analysis.

2.4 Discussion of results

As shown in Table 1 for different types of materials, the local elastic-plastic stress and strain are a function of geometry as specified by the stress concentrator K_t, material properties, E, n and K, and the applied nominal force, S. It was reported [2-4] that Neuber's rule, at times, overestimates the local elastic-plastic strain. The Glinka method, on the other hand, tends to underestimate the value of local elastic-plastic strain by computing local strain energy density. Referring to Table 1, the Glinka method predicts smaller stresses and strains compared to those from Neuber's rule. Further studies show that Neuber's rule is better for predicting plane-stress conditions and the Glinka method is best for plane-strain conditions [4 to 5]. Since the intermediate levels of strain constraints are between the two extremes of plane stress and plane strain conditions, the degree of constraint at the notch root is another influencing factor.

As shown in Figure 3, the results obtained in this study indicate that the solutions obtained using Neuber's method, though predicting larger local elastic-plastic strain, are closest to the FE results for plane-stress condition and the three dimensional model of

2mm thickness. Between the conditions of plane-stress and the three dimensional model of 2mm thickness, slightly larger strains are shown for the 3D model. With the increase of constraints presented in the 3D model of 8mm thickness, the $Kt*S$ versus strain curve represents an intermediate level of strain constraint, also shown in Figure 3. With even larger constraint, the FE results of plane-strain and the 3D 16mm thickness models matched well with the Glinka solutions placed between the two sets of FE results. Therefore, similar conclusions may be drawn, that the Neuber prediction is in a good agreement with plane-stress conditions, while results of the Glinka method are more comparable to those under plane-strain condition.

3 ELASTIC-PLASTIC RESPONSE OF A SIMPLIFIED SPOKED STRUCTURE

3.1 FE modelling of a simplified spoked structure

Typical aeroengine casing structures consist of shell chambers with flanges supported by spoked components and local geometrical features. The elastic-plastic behaviour of such structures depends on the material properties, geometry, load and boundary conditions. To assess the approximate methods for predicting the elastic-plastic behaviour of spoke-type structures, a simplified structure was studied. The elastic-plastic stress and strain components derived from the approximate methods, using elastic FE results, were compared with the corresponding elastic-plastic FE results.

As shown in Figure 4, the structure has a thick tube connected to a shell structure with a set of spoked ribs. A solid element (C3D8) model and a shell element (S4R) model were generated using FEAGV code [10]. The material properties used were those of a cast Aluminium at room temperature. The Young's modulus is E=71.2GPa, Poisson's ratio is ν=0.3 and the ultimate tensile stress is σ_u=216MPa. Fixed displacement constraints were applied to the ends of the two flanges; displacement constraints were also applied to the symmetric plane of the structure since half of the structure was used in the FE analyses. An axial load, up to 550kN, was applied on the right hand flange, along the z axis. The elastic and elastic-plastic analysis was conducted using ABAQUS software [11, 12].

3.2 Results and Discussion

The deformed shapes of the solid and shell models of the structure under axial force are shown in Figure 5. For the solid model, referring to Figure 5(a), the thick tube can be seen to deform in the axial direction. Subsequent to the axial displacement of the tube, localised elastic-plastic deformations occur at the corners of the ribs. Bulging deformations at the corners between the shell and ribs were observed at R1, for example, due to the pushing of the spokes, whilst indentation deformations were obtained at R2, for example, of the shell, due to pulling of the spokes. At the connection between the ribs and the tube (R3 and R4) elastic-plastic deformations are also experienced. Similar deformation patterns of the structure were observed from the results of the shell element model, as shown in Figure 5(b).

The stress states for both solid and shell models, in Figure 5, are such that the local elastic-plastic deformation zones R1 and R4 are under predominantly compressive stress, while local elastic-plastic deformation zone R2 and R3 are under predominantly tensile stress. On the other hand, the outer surface of the casing shell in the vicinity of spoke area R1 is under tension and the inner surface is under compression, while the reverse is true for the casing shell connected to spoke area R2.

Local equivalent stresses and strains in the elastic-plastic deformation zones were obtained using the approximate prediction method, Eq. (3) to (8), and by nonlinear FE analysis. Figure 6 shows $Kt*S$ verses total strain in zone R1 to R3. Within a total strain of 0.5%, reasonably good predictions, based on Neuber's rule were obtained when compared with the results from elastic-plastic FE analysis. As can be observed, Neuber's rule slightly overestimates the elastic-plastic strains. However, discrepancies occur when larger elastic-plastic strains are present at the locations of both R1 and R3. These may be attributed to factors such as the influence of stress concentration when using the approximate prediction. The constraints in the regions of the elastic-plastic deformations may also be significant. Further assessments of the approximate methods are needed in order to ascertain the ranges over which the elastic-plastic stress and strain components can be accurately determined for spoke-type structures in aeroengines.

4 CONCLUSIONS

As an alternative method to full elastic-plastic analysis of complex structures, such as aeroengine casing structures, approximate approaches can be used in combination with elastic FE solutions. For semi-circular notched specimens, the results show that Neuber's rule works better for the plane-stress condition and the Glinka method is more suitable for the condition of plane-strain. The elastic-plastic responses of a simplified spoked structure were also obtained using solid and shell element models. The equivalent stresses and strains at elastic-plastic regions were predicted reasonably accurately. When the total strain is larger than 0.5%, discrepancies between the approximate methods and the elastic-plastic FE solutions were found to get worse, indicating the need for further assessment of the approximate approaches in order for a better estimation of the elastic-plastic response of aeroengine casing structures to be achieved.

Acknowledgements

The authors would like to thank Rolls-Royce plc for supplying materials for experimental testing and the EPSRC for funding the present research.

5 REFERENCES

(1) Neuber, H., *ASME, J. Applied Mech.*, Vol. 27, 1961, pp. 544-551.

(2) Molski, K. and Glinka, G., *Mater. Science and Eng.*, Vol. 50, 1981, pp. 93-100.

(3) Glinka, G., *Eng. Fracture Mech.*, Vol. 22, 1985, pp. 839-854.

(4) Sharpe, W.N.Jr., Yang, C.H. and Tregoning, R.L., *ASME, J. Applied Mechanics*, Vol. 59, 1992, pp. S50-S56

(5) Sharpe, W.N.Jr. *ASME, J. Eng. Mat. and Tech.*, Vol. 117, 1995, pp. 1-7.

(6) Hoffmann, M. and Seeger, T., *ASME, J. Eng. Mater. and Tech.*, Vol. 107, 1985, pp. 250-254.

(7) Hoffmann, M. and Seeger, T., *ASME, J. Eng. Mater. and Tech.*, Vol. 107, 1985, pp. 255-260.

(8) Walker, E.K., *J. Testing and Evaluation*, Vol. 5, 1977, pp. 106-113.

(9) Peterson, R.E., *Stress Concentration Factors*, Wiley, New York, 1974.

(10) *FEMGV User Manual 4.1*, Femsys Engineering Software, 1996

(11) *ABAQUS User's Manual 5.7*, Hibbitt, Karlsson & Sorensen, 1997

(12) *ABAQUS Theory Manual 5.7*, Hibbitt, Karlsson & Sorensen, 1997

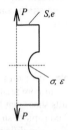

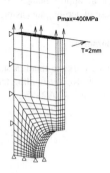

$$W_p = W_e = K_t^2 W_s$$

(a) Nominal and notch stresses and strains

(b) Strain energy densities for nominal and notch stresses

FIGURE 1 Elastic-plastic stresses and strains of semi- circularly notched specimen

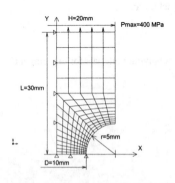

(a) Geometry and mesh of 2D FE model

(b) FE mesh of 3D FE model (2mm thickness)

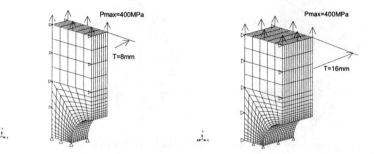

(c) FE mesh of 3D FE model (8mm thickness)   (d) FE mesh of 3D FE model (16mm thickness)

FIGURE 2 2D and 3D FE models of semi-circular by notched specimens

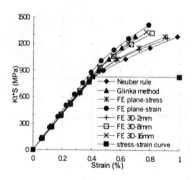

FIGURE 3 Elastic-plastic stresses/strains by Neuber's rule and
Glinka method for semi-circular specimen

467

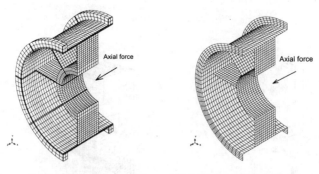

(a) Solid element (C3D8) model   (b) Shell element (S4R) model

FIGURE 4 FE meshes of simplified spoked structure

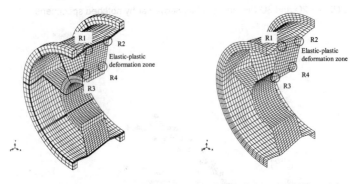

(a) Solid element (C3D8) model   (b) Shell element (S4R) model

FIGURE 5 Deformation of simplified spoked structure

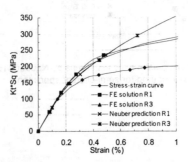

FIGURE 6 Equivalent stress and strain results using Neuber's rule
and the FE method

468

THE ELASTO-VISCOPLASTIC RESPONSE OF PLASTICINE TO INDENTATION

Z. Huang*, M. Lucas* and M.J.Adams†

This paper describes an experimental and analytical study of contact compliance data to characterise material properties of a model elasto-viscoplastic material, plasticine, from spherical and conical indentation measurements. An analytical model is employed to determine the Young's modulus and yield stress from the experimental data. The widely used procedure proposed by Oliver and Pharr and the Box-Cox transformation has been adapted in the analytical description of the data to extract the required material characteristic data and minimise the influence of the errors inherent in compliance methods. The material characteristics deduced for plasticine are shown to be consistent with the values reported in the literature for this material. In particular, the Young's modulus, yield stress and the load–depth relationship compare well with those obtained from a finite element simulation and simple compression measurements.

INTRODUCTION

The indentation hardness test, which measures the mean contact pressure when a spherical, conical or pyramidal indenter is pressed into the surface of a flat specimen, provides a simple and non-destructive means of assessing the mechanical properties of the material. Although the test is easy to perform, an interpretation in terms of the resulting stress-strain relationship is not straightforward due to the complex strain field produced by the indentation process.

The pioneering work on interpreting the results of indentation procedures was carried out by Tabor [1] who studied the indentation of a number of metals deformed by hardened spherical indenters. A similar study was subsequently undertaken by

* Department of Mechanical Engineering, University of Glasgow, Glasgow, G12 8QQ, UK
† Unilever Research Port Sunlight, Bebington, Wirral, CH63 3JW, UK

Stillwell and Tabor [2] to examine the behaviour of conical indenters. One particularly important observation from these studies concerns the shape of the hardness impression after the indenter is unloaded and the material recovers elastically. Tabor also used these results to show that the shape of the entire unloading curve and the total amount of recovered displacement can be accurately related to the elastic modulus and the size of the contact impression for both spherical and conical indenters.

The general response of an elastoplastic material to indentation is governed by the ratio of the imposed strain to the yield strain of the material, (E/Y) $tan\beta$, where β is the angle of inclination of the indenter to the sample surface, Y and E are the yield stress and Young's modulus respectively. For $2 < (E/Y)$ $tan\beta < 50$, the response is elastoplastic [3]. Plastic deformation is initiated in a small contained region beneath the centre of the indenter at a pressure $ca.$ $1.1Y$ and it expands with increasing values of (E/Y) $tan\beta$. With cylindrical or spherical indenters this expansion is brought about by an increase in load. When the mean contact pressure, p_m, has increased to about $2.85Y$, full plastic flow allows the contact radius to grow at a rate sufficient to maintain a constant value of p_m/Y, in the manner suggested by rigid-plastic theory. Viscoplastic materials appear to follow a similar pattern, although the relationship between the load and the contact radius is modified once plastic flow has fully developed. Unloading during this stage results in a permanent residual depression with a depth that depends on the maximum applied load. Tabor [1] has shown that the radius of the indent at the surface of a specimen does not change significantly during unloading.

Interest in load and displacement sensing indentation testing began in the early 1970's. For the contact compliance method, in which the reaction force of the indenter is measured as a function of an imposed displacement, the result is a set of loading and unloading curves. For an elasto-viscoplastic response, the unloading curve is entirely elastic but the loading curve contains an irreversible viscoplastic component. The relationships between the applied force and the depth of indentation as a function of the indenter geometry and the effective elastic modulus, are described in the next section as a basis for obtaining the elastic modulus from the unloading curves. Methods for independently estimating the contact area from the indenter shape function are then used to calculate the hardness or the mean pressure over the circle of contact.

For both conical and spherical indenters, the load-displacement relationships are non-linear and the contact area changes continuously during unloading. However, it is important to appreciate that the nominal applied strain is a function of the angle β rather than the penetration depth for a cone. Essentially, the strain is greater for sharp compared with blunt cones. The corresponding angle increases with depth for a sphere so that the strain also increases.

In many experimental studies of metal working processes, plasticine has been used as a favoured model plastic material [8,11,13], especially in simulating hot steel. Plasticine is an elasto-viscoplastic solid consisting of a highly concentrated dispersion of clay in a hydrocarbon liquid medium. The current paper describes the data obtained from indentation measurements using conical and spherical indenters. The simple analytical models described above have been adapted and applied to these data as a means to obtain material parameters. With the development of computer based numerical modelling techniques, such as finite element methods, it is possible to develop a more detailed understanding of the indentation process and also the capability to predict detailed material deformation history. The results of the application of such a method are also described here.

DIMENSIONAL ANALYSIS OF THE CONTACT COMPLIANCE

The general relationship for between the applied load, P, and the penetration depth, h, may be described by [12],

$$P = mh^{n} \qquad (1)$$

where the constants m and n are geometric and material property factors. The stiffness, S, is defined by the initial gradient of the unloading curve and is given by [7],

$$S = \frac{dP}{dh} = \frac{2}{\sqrt{\pi}} E_r \sqrt{A} \qquad (2)$$

where A is the projected area of elastic contact which is distinguished from the apparent area of contact corresponding to the value computed from the total depth of penetration, h_{max}. The parameter E_r is the reduced modulus which is defined by the following relationship,

$$\frac{1}{E_r} = \frac{(1-v^2)}{E} + \frac{(1-v_I^2)}{E_I} \qquad (3)$$

where E and v are the Young's modulus and Poisson's ratio for the specimen and E_I and v_I are the Young's modulus and Poisson's ratio for the indenter. By measuring the initial unloading stiffness and assuming that the contact area is equal to the measured area of the hardness impression, the modulus can thus be derived. The hardness, H, is defined as

$$H = \frac{P_{max}}{A} \qquad (4)$$

where P_{max} is the indentation load corresponding to a projected area of contact, A.

For an elasto-viscoplastic contact, the form of the unloading curve, shown in figure 1a, reflects the elastic response of both the bulk, relatively undeformed material around the region of gross indentation, and also the elastic recovery within the plastically deformed indent itself. The former component is predominant in the initial portion of the unloading curve, which is approximately linear, and the latter contribution is manifested towards the final part of the unloading curve. This latter portion is remarkably non-linear in its character. As a consequence, neither the depth of the penetration at the maximum load, h_{max}, nor the residual depth of penetration, h_r, provide directly a means of determining the area of the plastically deformed contact region. If the depth of penetration, corresponding to the elastic recovery of the bulk material around the indent, is extracted from the value of h_{max}, then the remainder, h_p, may now be used to define the geometry of the plastic indentation. In general, indentation may result in sink-in or pile-up (see figure 1b) depending on the mechanical properties of the material and the coefficient of friction at the indenter-material interface. The area of the plastically deformed contact zone may be deduced from the computed numerical value of h_p when geometry of the indenter is known or assumed (Loubet et al. [4]). Figure 1 also shows the depth zero error, h_o, which is a significant source of uncertainty in the application of the compliance method.

These equations reveal some difficulties associated with the extraction of the material properties from the experimental compliance data. Apart from the obvious effect of the accuracy of the transducers used for the measurement of P and h, other factors which have a considerable influence on the measured compliance are the accuracy of the geometry of the indenter, sink-in/ pile-up, and the ambiguity in the extrapolation procedure used to describe the linear part of unloading curve. Therefore, the actual geometry of contact and consequent changes in the $P(h)$ relationship need to be modelled more closely for an unequivocal extraction of h_p and S, and thus of the property information.

The associated errors due to the uncertainties of the zero point, the tip defect and the ambiguity of assignment of the linear extrapolation may be greatly minimised by the adoption of the Box-Cox transformation curve-fitting procedure [5] for the experimental compliance data, from which the various values of h and the slopes may be readily obtained. The general $P(h)$ relationship is then obtained as

$$P_1 = m_1(h - h_0)^{n_1} , \quad \text{for the loading curve} \tag{5a}$$

$$P_2 = m_2(h - h_r)^{n_2} , \quad \text{for the unloading curve} \tag{5b}$$

where h_0 and h_r denote the error or residual values of h in the loading and unloading curves respectively. This method and its application to the analysis of the contact compliance data has been described in detail by Briscoe and Sebastian [6], and a brief account of the method is given in the appendix. The major advantage of this method is that the computed values of m and n are independent of the magnitude of the zero error and it is possible to derive this quantity accurately.

We now consider the effects of pile-up of the surface profile on estimating the contact depth or area under load in indentation. Based on the procedure suggested by Oliver and Pharr [7] for estimating the contact depth h_p, from the initial unloading slope, an expression for h_p at the indenter displacement h_{max} can be developed as

$$h_p = h_{max} - \frac{\xi P_{max}}{S} \qquad (6)$$

where P_{max} and S are the respective load at the indenter displacement depth h_{max} and initial slope of the unloading curve. $\xi = 0.72$ for a conical indenter and $\xi = 0.75$ for the paraboloid of revolution.

Substituting for P_{max} derived from equation (5), and the slope derived from equation (5b), $n_2 m_2 (h - h_r)^{(n_2 - 1)}$, and rearranging equation (6) gives

$$h_p = (1 - 2\xi + \frac{\xi}{n_2})h_t - \frac{\xi}{n_2}h_r \qquad (7)$$

The contact radius, a, corresponding to an elastic deformation may be obtained as

$$a = \frac{2}{\pi} h_p \tan\theta, \text{ for a conical indenter;} \qquad (8a)$$

$$a = \sqrt{Rh_p}, \quad \text{for a spherical indenter,} \qquad (8b)$$

where θ is the semi-included angle for the conical indenter and R is the radius of the spherical indenter. Since the depth of indentation is large compared to the tip defect, δ, of the conical indenter for all the experiments described in this paper, the conical indenters are assumed to be perfect cones and no partial compensation for this type of tip defect is included in the computed value of h_0. The projected contact area may then be obtained as $A = \pi a^2$.

The hardness H and elastic modulus are computed using equations (4) and (2) respectively.

EXPERIMENTAL PROCEDURE

Material and indentation test

For the indentation studies, 100mm cubic blocks of plasticine were prepared and aged for 24 hours at 21°C. The sample surface was smoothed and lubricated with a thin layer of a commercial silicon grease, which has proven to be a good lubricant in the compressive deformation of plasticine (Huang et al. [8]).

The conical and spherical indenters were made from stainless steel with a polished surface. A range of included angles of 60°, 90°, 120° and 150° with a depth of 10mm were employed for conical indenters. The diameters of the spherical indenters were 4, 6, 10 and 20 mm.

The indenters were attached to a compression load cell of a mechanical testing machine (LLOYD) and then indented to a depth of 1-2mm into the plasticine specimen. The reaction force, P, and the depth of indentation, h, were recorded during loading and unloading of the sample. The indenters were loaded into the specimen with a speed of 5mm/min, and reversed at the same speed without any significant dwell time at the maximum depth of penetration. The data were subjected to the curve-fitting procedure described previously.

Indentation results

Figures 2 and 3 show the force-displacement curves obtained from the conical and spherical indentation tests respectively. Table 1 provides the parameters of the Box-Cox type of curves fitted to the data for a maximum depth of 1-2mm. The values of h_0 indicate the errors in the experimentation, in particular the location of the zero point. When the depth of indentation is large compared to the tip defect, δ, the value of h_0 is the sum of the defect length, δ, and the intrinsic zero error in the measurement of h. In the case of spheres, which have an inherently better geometrical accuracy, the value of h_0 reflects the uncertainty of the zero point sensed by the limited resolution of the experimental method.

The indices of h for the loading and unloading curves, n_1 and n_2 are generally found to be close to the expected theoretical values of 2 and 1.5 for the cones and spheres respectively [12] as described in Table 1. The efficacy of this procedure is shown in figure 4, for the computed values of hardness obtained by the various indenters, as a function of the parameters $cot\theta$ and h_p/a, which are a measure of the imposed strain (Johnson [9]). The hardness values shown in figure 4 were corrected for the tip defect and pile-up according to the procedure set out previously.

The experimental results of hardness H with spheres and cones in figure 4 for an elastoplastic material is expected that it followed a steady transition from elastic to fully plastic deformation reaching an asymptotic value [3]. Then, the hardness may be related to the yield stress of the material in simple compression, Y, by an expression based on the theory of indentation by Tabor [10], $H = 2.85Y$. On this basis, using the asymptotic value of hardness in figure 4, which represents the fully plastic case, the yield stress is given as 0.48 MPa. It shows a higher value than the reported value of 0.26 MPa for plasticine [8,11]. It may be explained by the natural of sensitivity of plasticine to the batch, colour, temperature and age.

The value of E may also be obtained by direct application of the $P(h)$ relationship, listed in Table 1, into equation 2. Figure 5 shows a plot of the Young's modulus as a function of the imposed strain calculated from the measured partial unloading data. Assuming $\nu = 0.5$, the mean value of Young's modulus is found to be 17.5 MPa, which compares favourably with the value of 16 MPa obtained from a simple compression test using smooth lubricated platens (Adams et al. [11]).

FINITE ELEMENT SIMULATION

The finite element code ABAQUS was used to model the $P(h)$ relationship during conical indentation and test the analytical procedure for the experimental compliance data described previously. The finite element model is illustrated in figure 6. The indenter is assumed to be rigid and the surface of the indenter was defined as an analytical rigid surface with half angle of 30°, which corresponds to a conical indenter. Contact between the indenter and the specimen was assumed to be frictionless. As a consequence of axisymmetric conditions, the material was modelled using a set of axisymmetric solid elements with four nodes, eight degree-of-freedom, quadrilateral cross-section. The constitutive behaviour of plasticine was treated as non-linear elasto-viscoplastic [13], with the material property parameters obtained from the results in the previous section. Due to only one indentation velocity was employed in this paper, hence it could not get flow index which was taken from [11]. The yield criterion was that of von Mises. A fine mesh in the vicinity of the indenter and a gradually coarser mesh in the far field were used to ensure a high degree of numerical accuracy and an accurate representation of a semi-infinite solid.

The loading and unloading curves were obtained directly from the output of the total reaction force in the normal direction on the rigid indenter as a function of indenter vertical displacement. A comparison of the $P(h)$ relationship obtained from the finite element simulation with the experimental results is shown in figure 7, using a conical indenter with a half angle of 30°. The results are in close agreement. The corresponding surface profile under load, shown as an insert in figure 7, demonstrates the well-known pile-up phenomenon. The results are consistent with experimental observations of plasticine. The contact depth may be obtained directly from the simulation, and is found to be 2.02 mm for a maximum indentation depth of 1.88 mm with a 60° conical indenter. Close agreement is achieved with the value of 1.91 mm obtained from the experimental initial unloading slope using the analytical procedure.

CONCLUSION

A simple analytical model has been proposed which simulates the entire loading and unloading of an elasto-viscoplastic model material, plasticine. A relationship was derived based on the Box-Cox transformation for curve fitting and the Oliver-Pharr procedure to extract the required material characteristics and minimise the influence of the error inherent in the compliance method.

In this study, the pile-up of the surface profile, caused by indentation in the model material, has been considered. The procedure proposed by Oliver and Pharr for estimating the contact depth is then evaluated systematically. By comparing the contact depth obtained directly from finite-element calculations with that obtained from the initial unloading slope using the analytical procedure, a close correlation was obtained. For the finite element simulation incorporating the material parameters extracted using the analytical procedure, a close agreement is obtained for the *P(h)* relationship and the deformed surface profile when compared with the experimental observations.

APPENDIX: APPLICATION OF THE BOX-COX TRANSFORMATION

The dependent variable in the *P(h)* relationship is transformed using the Box-Cox transformation, and is given by:

$$Z_i(\lambda) = \frac{P_i^\lambda - 1}{\lambda \hat{P}^{(\lambda-1)}}$$ (A1).

where $Z_i(\lambda)$ is the normalised transformed variable, λ is a transformation parameter and $\hat{P}$ is the geometric mean of all P_i, $P_i > 0$. The magnitude of the transformation parameter, λ, is then determined by a criterion that is normally the minimisation of the sum of the squares of the residuals, $\sum \varepsilon_i^2$. The transformed variable $Z(\lambda)$ satisfies the required statistical conditions on the error distribution and linearises the functionality of the dependent variable. A linear relationship is then used to interrelate, by least squares fitting, the transformed variable, $Z_i(\lambda)$, and the independent variable h_i, which is of the form

$$Z(\lambda) = c' + m'h$$ (A2).

Such that $\sum_i \varepsilon_i^2(\lambda) = \sum_i [Z_i^\lambda(\lambda) - (c' + m'h_i)]^2$.

Substituting this equation into equation (A1) gives

$$P = (c + mh)^n$$ (A3)

where $c = c'\lambda \hat{P}^{(\lambda-1)} + 1$, $m = m'\lambda \hat{P}^{(\lambda-1)}$ and $n = 1/\lambda$. Using the boundary conditions

$$h = h_0, \text{ at } P_1 = 0 \text{ and } h = h_r, \text{ at } P_2 = 0,$$

where h_0 and h_r denote the error or residual value of h in the loading and unloading curves respectively, equation (A3) may be written as

$$P_1 = m_1(h - h_0)^{n_1} \qquad \text{(A3a)}$$

$$P_2 = m_2(h - h_r)^{n_2} \qquad \text{(A3b)}$$

for the loading and unloading curves respectively.

REFERENCES

(1) Tabor, D., *Proc. R. Soc. A*, Vol. 192, 1948, pp. 247-274.

(2) Stillwell, N.A. and Tabor, D., *Proc. Phys. Soc. London*, Vol. 78, 1961, pp. 169-179.

(3) Johnson, K.L., *J. Mech. Phys. Solids*, Vol. 18, 1970, pp. 115-126.

(4) Loubet, J.L., Georges, J.M., Marchesini, O. and Meille, G., *Trans. ASME: J. Tribol.*, Vol. 106, 1984, pp. 43-48.

(5) Box, G.E.P. and Cox, D.R., *J. Roy. Statistical Soc.*, Vol. 26, 1964, pp. 211-243.

(6) Briscoe, B.J. and Sebastian, K.S., *Proc. R. Soc. Lond. A.*, Vol. 452, 1996, pp. 439-457.

(7) Oliver, W.C. and Pharr, G.M., *J. Mater. Res.*, Vol. 7, No. 6, 1992, 1564-1583.

(8) Huang, Z., Lucas, M. and Adams, M.J., *Proceedings of the SEM Annual Conference, Cincinnati, USA*, 1999, pp. 471-474.

(9) Johnson, K.L., *Contact Mechanics*, Cambridge University Press, 1985.

(10) Tabor, D., Hardness of Metals, Oxford University Press, 1951.

(11) Adams, M.J., Briscoe, B.J. and Sinha, S.K., *27th International SAMPE Technical Conference*, 1995, pp.877-890.

(12) Sneddon, I.N., *Int. J. Engng. Sci.*, Vol. 3, 1965, pp. 47-57.

(13) Adams, M.J., Edmondson, B., Caughey, D.G. and Yahya, R., *Journal of Non-Newtonian Fluid Mechanics*, Vol. 51, 1994, pp. 61-78.

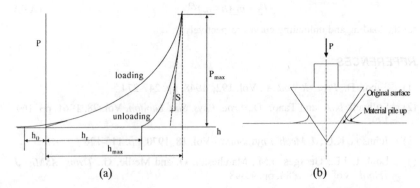

(a)   (b)

FIGURE 1   (a) Schematic representation of the load as a function depth for an indentation experiment. The quantities shown are P_{max}, the peak indentation load; h_{max}, the indenter displacement at peak load; h_f, the final depth of the contact impression after unloading; h_0, the depth zero error. (b) Indentation geometry under load.

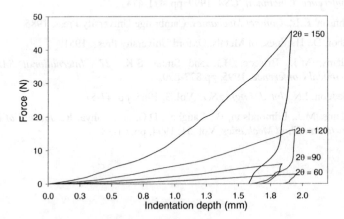

FIGURE 2 Load as a function of displacement for plasticine indented by cones of various included angles. Each set of data consists of a loading and unloading cycle.

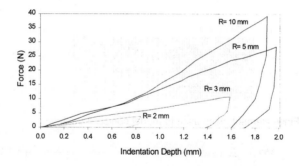

FIGURE 3 Load as a function of displacement for plasticine indented by spheres of various radii. Each set of data consists of a loading and unloading cycle.

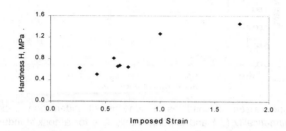

FIGURE 4 Hardness of plasticine as a function of the imposed strain. Results obtained using spherical and conical indenters.

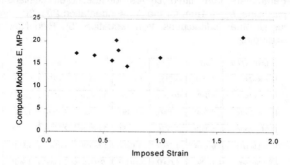

FIGURE 5 Variation of computed elastic modulus of plasticine with imposed strain. Results obtained using spherical and conical indenters.

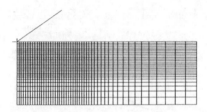

FIGURE 6 Finite element mesh used to model conical indentation.

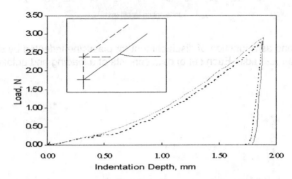

FIGURE 7 Comparison of load as a function of indentation depth obtained numericallly (...) and experimentally (—) for a conical indenter with an included semi-angle of 30°. The surface profile (insert) shows the computed pile-up.

TABLE 1 Parameters from fitted curves for the force displacement data of plasticine; $h_{max} \approx 1$mm for the cone indentation $2\theta = 30°$, and $h_{max} \approx 2$mm for all other indentations, from equation (5), P in Newtons and h in millimetres.

INDENTER	m1	n1	ho	m2	n2	hr
R=2mm	4.7446	1.0152	0.0175	14.0594	2.1978	0.7163
R=3mm	8.0402	0.9390	0.0118	14.6366	1.9231	1.3739
R=5mm	9.7994	1.1299	-0.0197	11.0202	2.5000	1.6821
R=10mm	6.0528	1.5038	-0.0151	14.9840	2.1277	1.5795
2θ= 60°	0.9208	1.7699	-0.0267	17.8554	1.8182	1.8511
2θ= 90°	1.6297	1.6000	-0.0259	9.0318	2.1739	1.6015
2θ= 120°	2.5795	1.6949	-0.0436	9.9485	2.2727	1.6567
2θ= 150°	3.8234	1.8692	-0.0644	16.2792	2.0000	1.5515

480

A GENERAL FORMULATION FOR THE STEADY-STATE CREEP DEFORMATION OF MULTI-MATERIAL COMPONENTS

T. H. Hyde*, W. Sun* and A. Tang*

Analytical solutions for steady-state creep deformations, using a Norton creep law for some two- and three-material components with simple geometries, are presented. Based on these solutions, a general formulation for the steady-state creep deformations of components consisting of a multiple number of materials is proposed. Using this general formulation, a procedure for performing steady-state parametric analyses for the creep deformation of multi-material components has been established. A parametric analysis performed for a typical thick-walled pipe weld is used to demonstrate the use of the method. The advantages of the parametric analysis method are related to the small number of analyses required and the simple and compact way in which the results can be presented.

1. INTRODUCTION

Relatively few analytical solutions can be obtained for predicting the stresses and deformations under creep conditions, within multi-material components, such as welded structures, operating at elevated temperature. Nicol [1] analysed a two-material, plane strain, cross-weld specimen using Cosserat shell theory and obtained approximate expressions for the variation in stresses and strain rates across the joint. This work was later extended to three- and four-material cross-weld geometries (Craine, Hawkes and Newman [2, 3]) and to simple axisymmetric models.

Because of the complex nature of multi-material problems, closed-form analytical solutions do not exist, except for a few structures with simple geometries, under creep conditions. Therefore, numerical methods, such as the finite element (FE) method, are commonly used to obtain solutions for specific material properties, geometries and loadings. Steady-state creep analyses have been widely used in the parametric analyses of multi-material welded components (Hyde and Sun [4, 5] and Law and Payten [6]). For example, Hyde and Sun [4, 5] used the FE method to investigate the effects of specimen size and relative material properties on the stresses and strain rates in a two-material axisymmetric model, including a stress singularity study. FE creep and continuum damage solutions have also been obtained for simple cross-weld geometries such as plates and pipes (Coleman et al [7], Hall and Hayhurst [8], Hyde and Sun [9] and Buglino et al [10]). However, obtaining (usually from FE analyses) information to allow the stresses and deformations to be determined for a systematic parametric analysis of a welded

* School of Mechanical, Materials, Manufacturing Engineering and Management
University of Nottingham, Nottingham NG7 2RD, UK

component, under creep conditions, is time-consuming, and often the presentation of the results can be unwieldy [e.g. 4-6].

Observations on the creep of multi-material components have been made using analytical solutions derived from several simple geometry structures (Hyde et al [11]). Steady-state creep solutions were derived for the stresses in some two and three material components with simple geometries, i.e. bar structures, compound beams in pure bending and compound thin and thick cylinders under internal pressure (Hyde et al [11, 12]). It was assumed that the materials obey the Norton creep law of the form:

$$\dot{\varepsilon}^c / \dot{\varepsilon}_{oi} = \left(\sigma / \sigma_{nom} \right)^{n_i} \tag{1}$$

where $\dot{\varepsilon}_{oi}$ and n_i are material constants and σ_{nom} is a conveniently chosen nominal stress. Based on the analytical solutions obtained, a general formulation for stresses in multi-material components was established using an inductive procedure [12]. At a position in material i of a component consisting of p materials, the general form of the solutions for stress, σ_i, is:

$$\sum_{j=1}^{p} \left\{ f_j(n_1, n_2, ..., n_p, [dim]_j) \left(\frac{\dot{\varepsilon}_{oi}}{\dot{\varepsilon}_{oj}} \right)^{\frac{1}{n_j}} \left(\frac{\sigma_i}{\sigma_{nom}} \right)^{\frac{n_i}{n_j}} \right\} = 1 \tag{2}$$

where $f_1, f_2, ..., f_p$ are functions of stress indices and component dimensions, *dim*. Applications of the general formulation for stress were made to multi-material cross-weld specimens and thick-walled pipe welds (Hyde et al [12-14]) to investigate the general effects of weld geometry and relative creep properties. The advantages of the parametric analysis method, based on the general formulation, are related to the small number of analyses required and the simple and compact way in which the results can be presented.

Adopting a similar approach, it is possible to obtain a general formulation for the creep deformation in multi-material components. This paper contains a brief description of the basis of the general formulation for creep deformation and an indication of how the creep deformation analysis of multi-material components can be simplified by using it. A parametric analysis of a typical thick-walled pipe weld is used to demonstrate the method.

2. GENERAL FORMULATION OF CREEP DEFORMATION

2.1 Two-material components

The steady-state solutions for a two-material bar structure, beams in bending and a thick cylinder under internal pressure are given in Appendix 1. From these solutions, it can be seen that the general form of the expressions from which the deformation rate at a position in material i, $\dot{u}_i$, can be written as

482

$$g_1(n_1, dim)\left(\frac{\dot{\varepsilon}_{oi}}{\dot{\varepsilon}_{o1}}\right)^{\frac{1}{n_1}}\left(\frac{\dot{u}_i}{\dot{u}_{nom}}\right)^{\frac{1}{n_1}} + g_2(n_2, dim)\left(\frac{\dot{\varepsilon}_{oi}}{\dot{\varepsilon}_{o2}}\right)^{\frac{1}{n_2}}\left(\frac{\dot{u}_i}{\dot{u}_{nom}}\right)^{\frac{1}{n_2}} = 1 \qquad (3)$$

where g_1 and g_2 are functions of n_1 and n_2, respectively, and the non-dimensional component dimensions, dim, and $\dot{u}_{nom}$ is a conveniently chosen nominal deformation rate.

2.2 Three-material components

The steady-state solutions for a three-material bar structure, beams in bending and a thick cylinder under internal pressure are given in Appendix 2. From these solutions, it can be seen that the general form of the expressions from which the deformation rate at a position in material i, $\dot{u}_i$, can be written as

$$g_1(n_1, dim)\left(\frac{\dot{\varepsilon}_{oi}}{\dot{\varepsilon}_{o1}}\right)^{\frac{1}{n_1}}\left(\frac{\dot{u}_i}{\dot{u}_{nom}}\right)^{\frac{1}{n_1}} + g_2(n_2, dim)\left(\frac{\dot{\varepsilon}_{oi}}{\dot{\varepsilon}_{o2}}\right)^{\frac{1}{n_2}}\left(\frac{\dot{u}_i}{\dot{u}_{nom}}\right)^{\frac{1}{n_2}} +$$

$$g_3(n_3, dim)\left(\frac{\dot{\varepsilon}_{oi}}{\dot{\varepsilon}_{o3}}\right)^{\frac{1}{n_3}}\left(\frac{\dot{u}_i}{\dot{u}_{nom}}\right)^{\frac{1}{n_3}} = 1 \qquad (4)$$

where g_1, g_2 and g_3 are functions of n_1, n_2 and n_3, respectively, and the non-dimensional component dimensions, dim.

2.3 Multi-material components

Considering the similarity of the general forms of the solutions obtained for two-material components (equation (3)) and three-material components (equation (4)), the general formulation for the deformation rate at a position in material i, $\dot{u}_i$, in a component consisting of p materials is given by

$$g_1(n_1, dim)\left(\frac{\dot{\varepsilon}_{oi}}{\dot{\varepsilon}_{o1}}\right)^{\frac{1}{n_1}}\left(\frac{\dot{u}_i}{\dot{u}_{nom}}\right)^{\frac{1}{n_1}} + g_2(n_2, dim)\left(\frac{\dot{\varepsilon}_{oi}}{\dot{\varepsilon}_{o2}}\right)^{\frac{1}{n_2}}\left(\frac{\dot{u}_i}{\dot{u}_{nom}}\right)^{\frac{1}{n_2}} +$$

$$g_3(n_3, dim)\left(\frac{\dot{\varepsilon}_{oi}}{\dot{\varepsilon}_{o3}}\right)^{\frac{1}{n_3}}\left(\frac{\dot{u}_i}{\dot{u}_{nom}}\right)^{\frac{1}{n_3}} + \ldots\ldots + g_p(n_p, dim)\left(\frac{\dot{\varepsilon}_{oi}}{\dot{\varepsilon}_{op}}\right)^{\frac{1}{n_p}}\left(\frac{\dot{u}_i}{\dot{u}_{nom}}\right)^{\frac{1}{n_p}} = 1 \qquad (5a)$$

or
$$\sum_{j=1}^{p}\left\{g_j(n_j, [dim]_j)\left(\frac{\dot{\varepsilon}_{oi}}{\dot{\varepsilon}_{oj}}\right)^{\frac{1}{n_j}}\left(\frac{\dot{u}_i}{\dot{u}_{nom}}\right)^{\frac{1}{n_j}}\right\} = 1 \qquad (5b)$$

where g_1, g_2, ..., g_p are functions of n_1, n_2, ..., n_p, respectively, and the non-dimensional component dimensions, dim.

When $n_1 = n_2 = \ldots = n_p = n$, equation (5b) reduces to

$$\sum_{j=1}^{p}\left\{g_j(n,[dim]_j)\left(\frac{\dot{\varepsilon}_{oi}}{\dot{\varepsilon}_{oj}}\right)^{\frac{1}{n}}\right\}\left(\frac{\dot{u}_i}{\dot{u}_{nom}}\right)^{\frac{1}{n}}=1 \qquad (6)$$

3. APPLICATION TO THE DEFORMATION ANALYSIS OF A PIPE WELD

For the particular case in which all of the materials have the same n-values, the g_i are simply functions of n, the common stress exponent, and *dim*, the non-dimensional functions of dimensions. For a three-material component, the formulation for the deformation rate at a position in material 3, equation (6) further reduces to

$$\left\{g_1(n,dim)\left(\frac{\dot{\varepsilon}_{o3}}{\dot{\varepsilon}_{o1}}\right)^{\frac{1}{n}}+g_2(n,dim)\left(\frac{\dot{\varepsilon}_{o3}}{\dot{\varepsilon}_{o2}}\right)^{\frac{1}{n}}+g_3(n,dim)\right\}\times\left(\frac{\dot{u}_i}{\dot{u}_{nom}}\right)^{\frac{1}{n}}=1 \qquad (7)$$

in which g_i (i = 1, 2 and 3) are the unknown functions to be determined for the geometry and stress index, n, of the component studied. Knowing the g_i values for particular n-values, the corresponding $\dot{u}_i$ values can be determined from equation (7). For a three-material component with a given geometry, the g_i values for a given n-value can be obtained by performing 3 FE calculations (analytical solutions are usually not available), each with the same n-value, but with (any) different combinations of $\dot{\varepsilon}_{oi}/\dot{\varepsilon}_{oj}$ ratios. The 3 combinations of $\dot{\varepsilon}_{oi}/\dot{\varepsilon}_{oj}$ and the corresponding 3 values of $\dot{u}_i$ can be substituted into equation (7) to give a set of 3 simultaneous equations from which the g_i can be obtained. Repeating this procedure for other n-values allows the g_i (n) functions to be determined. Then, for this position, the g_i values can be determined for any n-value and equations (7) can be solved to determine $\dot{u}_i$ for any $\dot{\varepsilon}_{oi}/\dot{\varepsilon}_{oj}$ values. Thus, a complete parametric analysis for the deformation at the position of interest in material 3, can be performed easily and quickly, for any combinations of n-values and $\dot{\varepsilon}_{oi}/\dot{\varepsilon}_{oj}$ ratios by solving equations (7) instead of performing further FE calculations. In equations (7), the $\dot{u}_{nom}$ can be chosen to be any convenient constants, without changing the behaviour of the resulting deformation.

The steady-state creep deformation rates in an axisymmetrical thick-walled main steam pipe weld are used here to illustrate the application of the general formulation. A symmetric half of the weld model is shown in Fig. 1. The pipe weld consists of three-material zones, the parent material, heat-affected zone (HAZ) and weld metal, and is subjected to an internal pressure, p_i, and a uniform axial stress, $\overline{\sigma}_{ax}$. The position chosen for the deformation is a typical position for monitoring the deformation behaviour of a pipe weld, i.e. at the weld centre on the outer surface (position A in Fig. 1).

484

The g_1, g_2 and g_3 for a range of n-values (n = 3 to 9 was chosen in this work) were obtained and shown in Table 1. By curve fitting to the data in Table 1, g_i (n) functions can be accurately determined. Using these g_i (n) functions in equation (7), the deformation rates at this particular position, for any combinations of n-values and $\dot{\varepsilon}_{o3} / \dot{\varepsilon}_{o1}$ and $\dot{\varepsilon}_{o3} / \dot{\varepsilon}_{o2}$ ratios, can be easily determined. Hence, the effects of n-value and $\dot{\varepsilon}_{oi}$ ratios on the $\dot{u}_r$ value can be assessed.

TABLE 1 g_i values for different n, obtained at position A in the three-material pipe weld

n	g_1	g_2	g_3
3	-0.1135	0.0387	1.0651
5	-0.1641	0.0402	1.1237
7	-0.1501	0.0356	1.1168
9	-0.1545	0.0376	1.1171

The normalised radial deformation rate, $\dot{u}_r / \dot{u}_o$ (where $\dot{u}_o$ is the radial deformation rate of the plain pipe (parent material) on the outer surface) is shown plotted against $\dot{\varepsilon}_{o3} / \dot{\varepsilon}_{o1}$ for a range of $\dot{\varepsilon}_{o3} / \dot{\varepsilon}_{o2}$, with n = 4, in Fig. 2. It can be seen that the $\dot{u}_r / \dot{u}_o$ value at the position increases with increasing $\dot{\varepsilon}_{o3} / \dot{\varepsilon}_{o1}$ but decreases with increasing $\dot{\varepsilon}_{o3} / \dot{\varepsilon}_{o2}$.

The normalised radial deformation rate, $\dot{u}_r / \dot{u}_o$, is shown plotted against n for a range of $\dot{\varepsilon}_{o3} / \dot{\varepsilon}_{o1}$ with $\dot{\varepsilon}_{o3} / \dot{\varepsilon}_{o2}$ = 0.1 and 10, in Figs 3(a) and 3(b), to illustrate the effect of varying n. It can be seen that, at the studied position, for the given range of $\dot{\varepsilon}_{o3} / \dot{\varepsilon}_{o1}$ and for $\dot{\varepsilon}_{o3} / \dot{\varepsilon}_{o2}$ = 0.1 and 10, the effect of n on the $\dot{u}_r / \dot{u}_o$ value is not very significant except when $\dot{\varepsilon}_{o3} / \dot{\varepsilon}_{o1}$ is large (~ 1000)   and n is small.

TABLE 2   Comparison of $\dot{u}_r / \dot{u}_o$ values at position A obtained from FE analyses and equation (7)

n	$\dot{\varepsilon}_{o3} / \dot{\varepsilon}_{o1}$	$\dot{\varepsilon}_{o3} / \dot{\varepsilon}_{o2}$	FE	Eqn. (7)
4	2.0	0.5	1.1651	1.1776
4	0.5	2.0	0.8942	0.8982
6	2.0	0.5	1.1547	1.1637
6	0.5	2.0	0.8891	0.8822

The accuracy of the deformation rates, obtained using equation (7), can be assessed by comparing the results with the corresponding solutions obtained from FE analyses, using the interpolated g_i values. The results of the $\dot{u}_r / \dot{u}_o$ values at point A, obtained for n = 4 and 6 for the pipe weld, with two $\dot{\varepsilon}_{o3} / \dot{\varepsilon}_{o1}$ and

$\dot{\varepsilon}_{o3} / \dot{\varepsilon}_{o2}$ ratios, were presented in Table 2. It can be seen that the deformation rates have been accurately predicted by using equation (7).

Parametric analyses for more general cases, where $n_1 \neq n_2 \neq n_3$, can be performed using a similar procedure [e.g. 14].

4. DISCUSSION AND CONCLUSIONS

Analytical solutions for the steady-state creep deformation rates in multi-material components (i.e. two and three-material bar structures, beams in bending and thick cylinder under internal pressure) are presented (Appendices 1 and 2). Similar solutions exist for other multi-material components, e.g. multi-material thin cylinders under internal pressure and circular cross-sectioned bars in torsion. Based on the similarity of these solutions, a general form for the solution to the creep deformation rate of multi-material components has been postulated (equations (5)). The functions g_j (j = 1 to p) in equations (5) depend on the stress indices n_j and the geometrical dimensions of the components. It should be noted that the deformation rate in equations (5) can be applied to any creep deformation parameters (displacements, strains, curvatures, twists, etc.) without changing the general form of the equations. It is interesting to see that the effects of the $\dot{\varepsilon}_{oi} / \dot{\varepsilon}_{oj}$ ratios are explicitly defined in the equations and are the same for all component types; this is particularly attractive in assessing the effects of $\dot{\varepsilon}_{oi} / \dot{\varepsilon}_{oj}$ on the deformation rate. If the functions g_j (n_j, $[dim]_j$) (j = 1 to p) in equations (5) can be obtained, the corresponding deformation rates, $\dot{u}$, can be determined by simply solving equations (5). In general, analytical solutions for g_j do not exist for multi-material components with complex geometry and loading, therefore, numerical calculations need to be performed to obtain the values of the g_j functions. For a component consisting of p materials with a given geometry, the g_j values for a given n_j value can be obtained by performing p FE calculations, each with the same n_j-value, but with different combinations of $\dot{\varepsilon}_{oi} / \dot{\varepsilon}_{oj}$ ratios. The p combinations of $\dot{\varepsilon}_{oi} / \dot{\varepsilon}_{oj}$ and the corresponding p values of $\dot{u}_i$ can be substituted into equations (5) to give a set of p simultaneous equations from which the g_j can be obtained. Repeating this procedure for other n_j-values allows the g_j (n_j) (j = 1, ..., p) functions to be determined. A parametric analysis procedure based on the general formulations of stress and deformation rate for multi-material components (equations (2) and (5)) has been established and can be applied to situations such as pipe welds containing parent, weld and heat-affected zone materials, all of which have different creep properties. Examples of the steady-state parametric creep deformation analysis of a typical thick-walled main steam pipe weld are presented to illustrate the application of the general formulation for creep deformation. However, the proposed methodology may also be applied to more complicated geometries not addressed in this paper. Accuracy of the deformation predictions was assessed.

ACKNOWLEDGEMENTS

The authors wish to acknowledge the financial support of the Engineering and Physical Science Research Council, National Power, British Energy and PowerGen through an EPSRC/ERCOS grant.

REFERENCES

(1) Nicol, D. A., *Int. J. Engng. Sci.*, Vol. 23, 1985, pp. 541-553.

(2) Craine, R. E. and Hawkes, T. D., *J. Strain Analysis*, Vol. 28, 1993, pp. 303-309.

(3) Craine, R. E. and Newman, M. G., *J. Strain Analysis*, Vol. 31, 1996, pp. 117-124.

(4) Hyde, T. H. and Sun, W., *J. Strain Analysis*, Vol. 32, No. 2, 1997, pp. 107-117.

(5) Hyde, T. H. and Sun, W., *Int. J. Mech. Sci.*, Vol. 39, No. 8, 1997, pp. 885-898.

(6) Law, M. and Payten, W., *Int. J. Pres. Ves. & Piping*, Vol. 72, 1997, pp. 45-49.

(7) Coleman, M. C., Parker, J. D. and Walters, D. J., *Int. J. Pres. Ves. & Piping*, Vol. 18, 1985, pp. 277-310.

(8) Hall, F. R. and Hayhurst, D. R., *Proc. R. Soc. London*, A443, 1991, pp. 383-403.

(9) Hyde T. H. and Sun W., *Proc. of IMechE.*, Vol. 212, Part E, *J. of Mech. Processing Eng.*, 1998. pp. 171-182.

(10) Buglino, V., Delia, M.A., Masnata, A. and Megna, G., Welded joint behaviour under conditions of creep, *Proc. of Int. Conf. on Integrity of High Temperature Welds*, November 1998, Nottingham, pp. 333-341.

(11) Hyde, T H, Yehia, K and Sun, W, *J. Strain Analysis*, Vol. 31, No. 6, 1996, pp. 441-462.

(12) Hyde, T. H., Sun, W., Tang, A. and P. J. Budden, *J. Strain Analysis*, 2000 (in print).

(13) Hyde, T. H., Tang, A. and Sun, W, Parametric analyses of stresses and deformations in a pipe with a circumferential weld under creep conditions, *Proc. of Int. Conf. on Integrity of High Temperature Welds*, Nottingham, UK, November 1998, pp. 323-332.

(14) Hyde, T. H., Sun, W. and Tang, A., A parametric analysis of stresses in a thick-walled pipe weld during steady-state creep, *Proc. of 5th Int. Colloquium on Ageing of Materials and Methods for the Assessment of Lifetimes of Engineering Plant*, Cape Town, April 1999, pp. 231-246.

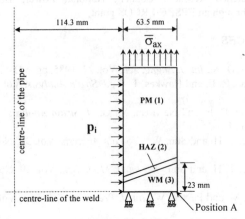

Fig. 1 Three-material thick-walled pipe weld model.

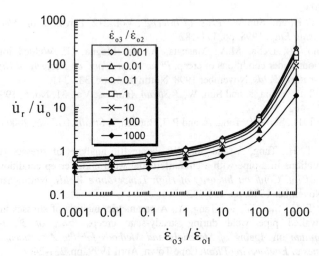

Fig. 2 Variation of $\dot{u}_r / \dot{u}_o$ with $\dot{\varepsilon}_{o3} / \dot{\varepsilon}_{o1}$ for n = 4 and a range of $\dot{\varepsilon}_{o3} / \dot{\varepsilon}_{o2}$ values.

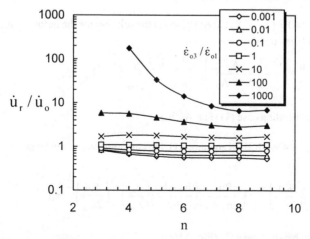

Fig. 3(a) Variation of $\dot{u}_r / \dot{u}_o$ with n for $\dot{\varepsilon}_{o3} / \dot{\varepsilon}_{o2}$ = 0.1 and a range of $\dot{\varepsilon}_{o3} / \dot{\varepsilon}_{o1}$ values.

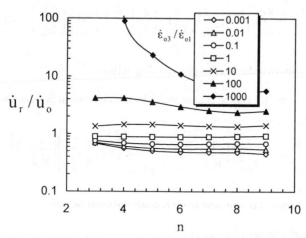

Fig. 3(b) Variation of $\dot{u}_r / \dot{u}_o$ with n for $\dot{\varepsilon}_{o3} / \dot{\varepsilon}_{o2}$ = 10 and a range of $\dot{\varepsilon}_{o3} / \dot{\varepsilon}_{o1}$ values.

Appendix 1. Analytical solutions to two-material components

(i)   Two-bar structure (Fig. A1(a))

Choosing $\sigma_{nom} = P / (A_1 + A_2)$ in equation (1) the solution for the deformation rate of the two bars, $\dot{u}$, is

$$\left(\frac{A_1}{A_1 + A_2}\right)\left(\frac{\dot{u}}{l_1 \dot{\varepsilon}_{o1}}\right)^{\frac{1}{n_1}} + \left(\frac{A_2}{A_1 + A_2}\right)\left(\frac{l_1 \dot{\varepsilon}_{o1}}{l_2 \dot{\varepsilon}_{o2}}\right)^{\frac{1}{n_2}}\left(\frac{\dot{u}}{l_1 \dot{\varepsilon}_{o1}}\right)^{\frac{1}{n_2}} = 1$$

(ii)   Beam in bending case (1) (Fig. A1(b))

Assuming $\sigma_{nom} = 4M / b_2 d^2$ in equation (1), the curvature rate of the beam, $\dot{K}$, is given by

$$\left(\frac{2n_1}{2n_1 + 1}\right)\left(\frac{b_1}{b_2}\right)\left(\frac{\dot{K}d}{2\dot{\varepsilon}_{o1}}\right)^{\frac{1}{n_1}} + \left(\frac{2n_2}{2n_2 + 1}\right)\left(\frac{b_2 - b_1}{b_2}\right)\left(\frac{\dot{\varepsilon}_{o1}}{\dot{\varepsilon}_{o2}}\right)^{\frac{1}{n_2}}\left(\frac{\dot{K}d}{2\dot{\varepsilon}_{o1}}\right)^{\frac{1}{n_2}} = 1$$

(iii)   Beam in bending case (2) (Fig. A1(c))

Assuming $\sigma_{nom} = 4M / bd_2^2$ in equation (1), the curvature rate of the beam, $\dot{K}$, is given by

$$\left(\frac{2n_1}{2n_1 + 1}\right)\left(\frac{d_1}{d_2}\right)^{2+\frac{1}{n_1}}\left(\frac{\dot{K}d_2}{2\dot{\varepsilon}_{o1}}\right)^{\frac{1}{n_1}} + \left(\frac{2n_2}{2n_2 + 1}\right)\left[1 - \left(\frac{d_1}{d_2}\right)^{2+\frac{1}{n_2}}\right]\left(\frac{\dot{\varepsilon}_{o1}}{\dot{\varepsilon}_{o2}}\right)^{\frac{1}{n_2}}\left(\frac{\dot{K}d_2}{2\dot{\varepsilon}_{o1}}\right)^{\frac{1}{n_2}} = 1$$

(iv)   Thick cylinder under internal pressure (Fig. A1(d))

Assuming $\sigma_{nom} = p_i$ in equation (1), the radial deformation rate in material two, $\dot{u}_2$, at $r = R_1$, is

$$\left(\frac{n_1}{\sqrt{3}^{1+\frac{1}{n_1}}}\right)\left[\left[\frac{R_1}{R_i}\right]^{\frac{2}{n_1}} - 1\right]\left(\frac{\dot{\varepsilon}_{o2}}{\dot{\varepsilon}_{o1}}\right)^{\frac{1}{n_1}}\left(\frac{2\dot{u}_2}{R_1 \dot{\varepsilon}_{o2}}\right)^{\frac{1}{n_1}} + \left(\frac{n_2}{\sqrt{3}^{1+\frac{1}{n_2}}}\right)\left[1 - \left[\frac{R_1}{R_o}\right]^{\frac{2}{n_2}}\right]\left(\frac{2\dot{u}_2}{R_1 \dot{\varepsilon}_{o2}}\right)^{\frac{1}{n_2}} = 1$$

Appendix 2. Analytical solutions to three-material components

(i)   Three-bar structure (Fig. A2(a))

Choosing $\sigma_{nom} = P / A_o$ in equation (1) the solution for the deformation rate of the three bars, $\dot{u}$, is

$$\left(\frac{A_1}{A_o}\right)\left(\frac{\dot{u}}{l_1\dot{\varepsilon}_{o1}}\right)^{\frac{1}{n_1}}+\left(\frac{A_2}{A_o}\right)\left(\frac{l_1\dot{\varepsilon}_{o1}}{l_2\dot{\varepsilon}_{o2}}\right)^{\frac{1}{n_2}}\left(\frac{\dot{u}}{l_1\dot{\varepsilon}_{o1}}\right)^{\frac{1}{n_2}}+\left(\frac{A_3}{A_o}\right)\left(\frac{l_1\dot{\varepsilon}_{o1}}{l_3\dot{\varepsilon}_{o3}}\right)^{\frac{1}{n_3}}\left(\frac{\dot{u}}{l_1\dot{\varepsilon}_{o1}}\right)^{\frac{1}{n_3}}=1$$

where $A_o = A_1 + A_2 + A_3$.

(ii) Beam in bending case (1) (Fig. A2(b))

Assuming $\sigma_{nom} = 4M / b_3 d^2$ in equation (1), the solution for the curvature rate of the beam, $\dot{K}$, in case (1) is

$$\left(\frac{2n_1}{2n_1+1}\right)\left(\frac{b_1}{b_3}\right)\left(\frac{\dot{K}d}{2\dot{\varepsilon}_{o1}}\right)^{\frac{1}{n_1}}+\left(\frac{2n_2}{2n_2+1}\right)\left(\frac{b_2-b_1}{b_3}\right)\left(\frac{\dot{\varepsilon}_{o1}}{\dot{\varepsilon}_{o2}}\right)^{\frac{1}{n_2}}\left(\frac{\dot{K}d}{2\dot{\varepsilon}_{o1}}\right)^{\frac{1}{n_2}}+$$

$$\left(\frac{2n_3}{2n_3+1}\right)\left(\frac{b_3-b_2}{b_3}\right)\left(\frac{\dot{\varepsilon}_{o1}}{\dot{\varepsilon}_{o3}}\right)^{\frac{1}{n_3}}\left(\frac{\dot{K}d}{2\dot{\varepsilon}_{o1}}\right)^{\frac{1}{n_3}}=1$$

(iii) Beam in bending case (2) (Fig. A2(c))

Assuming $\sigma_{nom} = 4M / bd_3^2$ in equation (1), the solution for the curvature rate of the beam, $\dot{K}$, in case (2) is

$$\left(\frac{2n_1}{2n_1+1}\right)\left(\frac{d_1}{d_3}\right)^{2+\frac{1}{n_1}}\left(\frac{\dot{K}d_3}{2\dot{\varepsilon}_{o1}}\right)^{\frac{1}{n_1}}+\left(\frac{2n_2}{2n_2+1}\right)\left[\left(\frac{d_2}{d_3}\right)^{2+\frac{1}{n_2}}-\left(\frac{d_1}{d_3}\right)^{2+\frac{1}{n_2}}\right]\left(\frac{\dot{\varepsilon}_{o1}}{\dot{\varepsilon}_{o2}}\right)^{\frac{1}{n_2}}\left(\frac{\dot{K}d_3}{2\dot{\varepsilon}_{o1}}\right)^{\frac{1}{n_2}}+$$

$$\left(\frac{2n_3}{2n_3+1}\right)\left[1-\left(\frac{d_2}{d_3}\right)^{2+\frac{1}{n_3}}\right]\left(\frac{\dot{\varepsilon}_{o1}}{\dot{\varepsilon}_{o3}}\right)^{\frac{1}{n_3}}\left(\frac{\dot{K}d_3}{2\dot{\varepsilon}_{o1}}\right)^{\frac{1}{n_3}}=1$$

(iv) Thick cylinder under internal pressure (Fig. A2(d))

Assuming $\sigma_{nom} = p_i$ in equation (1), the radial deformation rate in material three, $\dot{u}_3$, at $r = R_2$, is

$$\left(\frac{n_1}{\sqrt{3}^{1+\frac{1}{n_1}}}\right)\left(\left[\frac{R_2}{R_i}\right]^{\frac{2}{n_1}}-\left[\frac{R_2}{R_1}\right]^{\frac{2}{n_1}}\right)\left(\frac{\dot{\varepsilon}_{o3}}{\dot{\varepsilon}_{o1}}\right)^{\frac{1}{n_1}}\left(\frac{2\dot{u}_3}{R_2\dot{\varepsilon}_{o3}}\right)^{\frac{1}{n_1}}+\left(\frac{n_2}{\sqrt{3}^{1+\frac{1}{n_2}}}\right)\left(\left[\frac{R_2}{R_1}\right]^{\frac{2}{n_2}}-1\right)\left(\frac{\dot{\varepsilon}_{o3}}{\dot{\varepsilon}_{o2}}\right)^{\frac{1}{n_2}}\left(\frac{2\dot{u}_3}{R_2\dot{\varepsilon}_{o3}}\right)^{\frac{1}{n_2}}+$$

$$\left(\frac{n_3}{\sqrt{3}^{1+\frac{1}{n_3}}}\right)\left(1-\left[\frac{R_2}{R_o}\right]^{\frac{2}{n_3}}\right)\left(\frac{2\dot{u}_3}{R_2\dot{\varepsilon}_{o3}}\right)^{\frac{1}{n_3}}=1$$

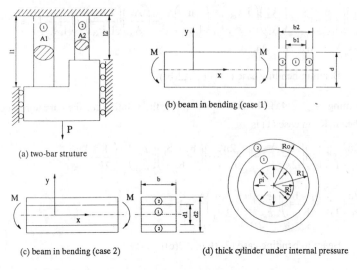

(a) two-bar struture

(b) beam in bending (case 1)

(c) beam in bending (case 2)

(d) thick cylinder under internal pressure

Fig. A1 Dimensions of the two-material components.

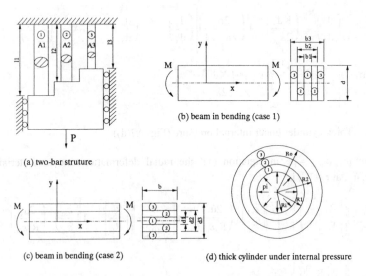

(a) two-bar struture

(b) beam in bending (case 1)

(c) beam in bending (case 2)

(d) thick cylinder under internal pressure

Fig. A2 Dimensions of the three-material components.

FINITE ELEMENT AND EXPERIMENTAL STUDIES OF THE POST-BUCKLING BEHAVIOUR OF WELDED AND RIVETED FUSELAGE PANELS

C. Lynch*, A. Gibson†, A. Murphy†, M. Price†, S. Sterling†

This paper presents the results from studies of the post-buckling behaviour of riveted and welded sheet-stringer panels subject to uniform in-plane compression. The element type and mesh density required for the prediction of the buckling mode were investigated, as were methods for modelling the interface between the skin and stringers, and the effect of these idealisations on the resulting behaviour have been highlighted. The FE results are compared with theoretical results based on conventional methods and to experimental data from the accompanying test programme. In the case of the welded panels modifications to the theoretical analysis for riveted panels are also suggested to provide simple design and analysis rules. The studies indicate that considerable care must be taken with the choice of element type and density as well as the definition of model boundary conditions. The studies also indicate the levels of idealisations and definition of imperfections necessary for non-linear Finite Element Models. The use of FEA to study the post buckling behaviour of stiffened panels allows for a consistent approach to assessing the performance of different construction techniques and offers both potential weight savings, due to more accurate analyses, and a basis for comparison where current methods cannot be directly compared.

1. INTRODUCTION

Riveting has been the predominant joining process for metal airframe structures for many years and is a mature and well researched technology. The process has become highly automated with the introduction of CNC riveting machines but it is now accepted that the potential for further improvements in this area is limited to design improvements. Furthermore, mechanical fasteners have weight penalties both in themselves and in the nature of the designs which have evolved around them. These factors have led to considerable interest being shown in joining technologies which may provide a direct alternative to conventional mechanical fasteners in primary and secondary metal airframe structures. Laser beam welding is one such technology with the potential to realise production cost and weight reductions.

The consideration of such alternative joining processes raises two important issues with respect to the design of fuselage panels:

1. Can further weight reductions be achieved in existing riveted panel structures by performing a more accurate buckling/post-buckling analysis than is presently possible.

*Body CAE, Jaguar Car Ltd., Whitley, Coventry, CVE 4LF

† School of Aeronautical Engineering, The Queen's University of Belfast, Belfast, N. Ireland, BT9 5AG

2. Can welded panels offer a weight saving over riveted panels and what analysis tools can be used in the design process.

These issues have led to interest in the use of FE techniques for the analysis of fuselage structures. This paper reports on the development of FE techniques for the analysis of conventional riveted panels subjected to in-plane compressive loading, and on the application of these techniques for the analysis of comparable welded panels. The findings are taken from two parallel research projects being performed at Queen's University Belfast. The first is aimed at developing non-linear FE analysis techniques for the design/analysis of fuselage shell structures; the other is investigating the static strength and behaviour of welded fuselage panels subject to in-plane compressive loading.

For the purposes of validating the FE techniques, flat, riveted sheet-stringer panels typical of fuselage construction were manufactured and tested in compression. These panels were 36" wide by 34" high and comprised 6 bulbed-tee stringers at a 6" pitch riveted to the skin (Figure 1). Two frame segments were also attached giving the stringers a column length of 16". These full-size panels are discussed in detail in subsequent papers. Sub-panels, representing a small section of a full-size panel, were manufactured and tested and used to validate the FE techniques in the initial stages of development. The sub-panels comprised one stringer riveted to a skin 11.24" wide by 17" high. The results for the sub-panels are presented here.

For the purposes of investigating the strength of welded compression panels, full-size test articles were also designed and manufactured. Laser beam welding (LBW) and the aluminium alloy 6013-T6 were the joining process and material of choice respectively. The design drivers for the welded test panels were the overall dimensions, the ultimate strength and the weight of the riveted panels. Testing has not been completed on the full-size welded panels and results will be published in due course. However, in the same manner as for the riveted panels, sub-panels based on full-size welded panel designs were manufactured and tested, the results of which are discussed here.

The following section highlights the issues with conventional theory and the necessary modifications for the analysis of welded panels. This is followed by details of the specimens panels used in the experimental and FE studies. The approach used in FE is then presented for both riveted and welded panels and these experimental results are then given. The paper is concluded with a discussion of the results.

2. BASIC BUCKLING THEORY

The theoretical approach is primarily based on that presented by Bruhn [1] and ESDU [2]. The traditional analysis of the buckling and post-buckling behaviour of stiffened panels employs a combination of heuristic techniques, design formula based on empirical and semi-empirical data and structural testing. The formulae used in this approach include lower bound factors which leads to over design of the structure even when boundary conditions are well defined.

In an actual fuselage panel the boundary conditions for the loaded edges would be dependent on the support offered by the frame to the skin and stringer. The boundary conditions for the unloaded edges would be dependent on the support offered by the stringer to the skin. In both cases the exact nature of these support conditions is indeterminate and hence the boundaries are conservatively assumed to be simply-supported. These two factors can result in a significant weight penalty.

2.1 Welded panel analysis

One of the objectives of the welded panel project was to determine if simple modifications could be made to existing analysis techniques in order to allow for the effects of welding on aluminium alloys. Two methods were developed to allow for the fact that, when welding aluminium alloys, there is a reduction in material strength in an area surrounding the weld bead called the Heat Affected Zone (HAZ). In the HAZ, it is assumed that strength properties are reduced by a constant factor, k_z, and that outside the HAZ, full parent properties apply. A flat, welded plate, for instance, can then be considered as consisting of two materials, parent material and HAZ material.

Both methods had the result of reducing the number of variables in the problem such that conventional procedures could be used, i.e. the variables being the HAZ material properties. To use these methods required values for HAZ widths, knowledge of HAZ material strength properties and resulting k_z factors. These were estimated for compression panel analysis based on tensile tests on flat laser welded plates, Gibson [3].

Both methods used the stringer cross-sectional area plus the cross-sectional area of a strip of "effective" skin in the analyses. The effective skin is assumed to be a width of unbuckled skin which acts with the stringer in the post-buckled range, i.e. following skin local buckling. A more comprehensive description of these analysis methods can be found in [3] and in Gibson and Sterling [4]. The design of the test specimens for both riveted welded panels will now be described.

3. SPECIMEN PANEL DESIGN

The riveted and welded test panel, on which this paper focuses, are based on a riveted panel which is representative of a section of a typical lower fuselage structure. This baseline panel is shown in Figure 1.

3.1 Riveted Panels

The rivet panels tested consisted of a 11.24" × 17.00" flat skin stiffened by a bulbed-tee stringer, as shown in Figure 2. The skin material was 2024-T3 aluminium alloy and the stringer 2024-T8511 aluminium alloy extrusion. The stringer was fastened to the skin by two rows of 5/32" diameter MS20426 countersunk rivets.

The ends of the assembled panel were potted in cerrobend low melting alloy and machined flat and parallel in a direction perpendicular to the skin. Support conditions at the unloaded edges of the skin were similar to those used by Rothwell [5] and are detailed in Figure 2. A clearance of 0.2" was provided between the cerrobend and the support bars to ensure that the compressive load would be solely carried by the skin and stringer

The panel was tested in a 25t capacity hydraulic, displacement-controlled testing machine. Relative motion between the platens was measured using two linear voltage displacement transducers located close to the edges of the panel.

3.2 Welded Panels

The full-size welded panel configuration was developed, utilising simple blade stringers. The overall dimensions and layout for this full-size design are the same as for the riveted baseline panel. Stringers were attached to the skin by welding to a pad-up (local increase in thickness) along the joint line in the skin. Welded sub-panels based on this design had the same overall dimension as the riveted sub-panel shown in Figure 2, were then developed (Figure 3). Overall FE analysis of these welded specimens was performed using the same techniques and procedures as was used for the riveted specimens. Models were assumed to consist only of sections of parent material and sections of HAZ material with appropriate uniform properties in each section. The next section describes the FE studies.

4. FINITE ELEMENT ANALYSIS

For both welded and riveted panels a Finite Element Study of buckling and post-buckling behaviour was carried out using ABAQUS and the results validated using physical tests.

The riveted panel was analysed first and was used to provide the baseline for convergence studies and choice of element type and density. The main findings are summarised in the following sections.

4.1 Riveted Panels

4.1.1 Element Choice and Mesh Density

A detailed study was undertaken to determine the most suitable combination of element type and mesh density for the accurate and effective modelling of buckling shell structures. A number of ABAQUS shell elements were used to model a simply supported flat plate subject to uniform longitudinal compression. Eigenvalue buckling analyses were performed to determine the first and second buckling modes. The performance of each element was then assessed based on convergence (with increasing mesh density) of the buckling stresses to the corresponding theoretical values, given in [1] and [2].

The result of this study indicates that S8R5 elements with approximately 4 elements (9 nodes) per buckle half-wave is the most suitable combination for modelling the panel's skin, stringer flange and stringer web structures. The study also determined that the panel's bulb may be accurately and effectively modelled using 3-noded quadrilateral beam elements B32.

The quadrilateral shell element S8R5 is a second order, 8-noded, small strain, thin-shell element with reduced integration. The quadratic beam element B32 is a Timoshenko (Shear Flexible) 3-noded beam element. A fuller description of the study to determine the most appropriate combination of element type and mesh density can be found in Lynch [6].

4.1.2 Model Idealisation

Four different FE idealisations of the skin/stringer interface were examined. These different models are outlined schematically in Figure 4. In all four cases the bulb was connected to the web and the web to the flange by rigid beams (MPC type BEAM in ABAQUS). In method (a) the panel is assumed to act as an integral structure with the skin and flange material represented with shell elements located on the structures mid-plane. The use of 2D elements to model the 3D structure causes an eccentricity between the two sets of shell elements. In order to model the structure integrally the skin and flange elements were connected with rigid beams between appropriate nodes.

The second approach, (b), also models the panel as an integral assembly but here a single layer of shells located on the combined mid-plane was used to model the skin and stringer flange. This modelling technique causes an eccentricity between the mid-surface shell elements representing the skin and stringer flange and the mid-surface shell elements representing the skin. In this case the eccentricity was accounted for via the use of "dummy layer" of low modulus material, similar to the model used by Skrna-Jakl et al [7]. Which effectively shifts the mid-plane of the skin/flange combination into line with the skin mid-surface shell elements. The layer of shells representing the skin/flange structure was then modelled as a composite section.

The remaining two approaches use rivet idealisations and allow separation of the skin and stringer flange to occur. The mesh was generated in such a way that adjacent nodes existed at the rivet locations. These nodes were connected with rigid beams in method (c). In method (d) a combination of spring elements was used to connect these nodes with one spring element representing the axial stiffness and two spring elements representing the shear stiffness of the rivet (the flexible joint element, JOINTC, was used to define the three spring elements at each rivet location). The contact conditions between the remaining nodes were represented using gap elements in both cases.

The mesh used in approaches (c) and (d) was slightly different to that used in (a) and (b) to account for the details required in modelling the rivets. However although there were local changes near the rivet locations the overall density was kept as close as possible in all models.

4.1.3 Loads and Boundary

The loading and Boundary Conditions applied to the models were the same in all four cases. The models where build to be as representative of the experimentally tests as possible.

A uniform axial displacement was applied to one end of the panel models with the displacement at the opposite end restrained in the axial displacement direction. The nodes within areas which were potted in cerrobend in the experimental tests were restrained in-plane and in the direction perpendicular to the axial displacement direction. Nodes within areas clamped with supports bars during the tests were also restrained in-plane.

4.2 Welded panels

4.2.1 Element Choice and Mesh Density

The element type used for the welded panels was the S8R5 element due to its successful applications in the riveted panels. A similar mesh density to that of the integral panel models (a) and (b) from the riveted panel study was used.

4.2.2 Model Idealisation

To accommodate the skin pad-up in these welded models, a layer of "dummy" material had to be used and a composite element created (c.f. idealisation (b) in Figure 4). The dummy material was given negligible stiffness and its sole purpose was to cause alignment of the surfaces of the skin and pad-up elements as shown.

4.2.3 Loads and Boundary Conditions

Loads and boundary conditions were applied as per the riveted panel model.

4.3 Analysis Procedure

The panels were analysed for initial buckling using a standard linear buckling analysis and the post-buckling behaviour then determined from a large-displacement analysis accounting for both material and geometric non-linearity.

Buckling loads and corresponding mode shapes for each model were determined from an eigenvalue buckling analysis. The initial geometry was then seeded with an imperfection in the shape of the first buckling mode obtained from the eigenvalue buckling analysis. The maximum magnitude of this imperfection was 10% of the skin thickness. The post-buckling analysis was performed on the imperfect model using an arc-length solution technique. These results are presented in the next section.

5. RESULTS

In this section the FE theoretical and experimental results are presented for both riveted and welded panels.

5.1 Riveted Panels

The experimental and finite element failure loads together with the percentage error based on the experimental values are presented in Table 1. The discrepancies between the test data and the FE predictions using models (a) and (b) indicate the possible errors associated with analysing a riveted structure as an integral structure. This is reinforced by the accuracy of models (c) and (d) which allow separation of the skin and stringer flange to occur.

Table 1 Experimental and FE failure loads

	P_b (lbf)	% error in P_b	P_{ult} (lbf)	% error in P_{ult}	Run Time hrs
Test	8610	----	24299	----	----
FE (a)	10493	21.9	27169	11.8	1.33
FE (b)	10504	22.0	27153	11.7	0.82
FE (c)	8840	2.7	24610	1.3	5.67
FE (d)	8068	-6.3	24109	-0.8	10.83
Theory (ff)	8920	3.7	23950	-1.4	---
Theory (ss)	6503	-24.5	18337	-24.5	---

Note : P_b is the local skin buckling load
P_{ult} is the panel collapse load.

The experimental and finite element load-deflection curves for the panel are shown in Figure 5. The significant differences between models (a) and (b) and models (c) and (d) can clearly be seen from this graph, highlighting the importance of modelling the skin/stringer interface correctly.

There are slight differences between the load-deflection characteristics of models (c) and (d) due to the increased flexibility generated by idealising the rivets using spring elements as opposed to rigid beams. The underestimation of the buckling load by model (d) indicates an error in the stiffness of the spring elements used to represent the rivets.

The stiffness of the panel in both the pre and postbuckling regimes predicted by all four FE models was higher than the experimentally observed values (see Figure 5). This was shown to be due to the support, subsequent analysis indicated that the support bars were under-designed and deflected during testing resulting in a decrease in panel stiffness. The differences between the experimental and FE end shortening at failure are a result of the corresponding stiffness discrepancies.

499

Table 1 also shows that the theoretical results for the fully fixed panel compare well to both FE and experimental results. This was expected as clamped conditions were enforced on both the model and the test specimen. As such the clamped conditions have provided a useful benchmark for these studies. However as mentioned preciously boundary conditions in real panels are not so well defined and simply supported conditions are often applied for a conservative analysis. The results for a simply supported panel are included in Table 1.

Details of the FE postbuckling solutions run times are given in Table 2. Note that solution times are based on CPU times using a Silicon Graphics Indigo workstation with 64MB of RAM. The large run-times of models (c) and (d) are due to the time consuming severe discontinuity iterations associated with contact analysis. Method (b) is clearly more efficient for the FE analysis of integral panels. Method (c) is the more accurate of the two riveted models although it is felt that, using more precise spring stiffnesses to model the rivets, method (d) may be more representative of the actual structure. However the run-time associated with method (d) is almost double that of method (c), hence the latter is clearly the most efficient modelling technique for the postbuckling analysis of riveted fuselage panels. A more detailed description of these results can be found in [6]

5.2 Welded Panels

For consistency with the riveted panels the modified theoretical analysis was developed for both supply support and fully fixed cases. The results for both hybrid and equivalent section methods were similar hence only the hybrid material results were presented in table 2. The two cases represent the upper and lower bounding conditions for skin buckling and failure using the modified conventional analysis techniques. An unaffected specimen is one for which there is no reduction in strength in the HAZ, i.e. $k_z = 1.0$. While it is reasonable to assume the Cerrobend provided fully fixed support for the loaded edges, assuming the side support bars provided fully fixed support was thought optimistic. More realistically, the support on the unloaded edges would have been between simple support and fully fixed. These support bars were strengthened in comparison to those used for the riveted specimens.

Table 2 Experimental and FE failure loads

	P_b (lbf)	% error in P_b	P_{ult} (lbf)	% error in P_{ult}
Test	10333	----	29120	----
FE	12129	17.4	30099	3.4
Theory (ff)	11424	10.6	27955	-4.0
Theory (ss)	8176	-20.9	20832	-28.5
Note : P_b is the local skin buckling load P_{ult} is the panel collapse load.				

Average test results were based on three specimens. It can be seen that skin buckling occurred at loads between the upper and lower theoretical predictions, tending towards the upper values. The ultimate test strength was underestimated even by the upper bound prediction. The experimental and finite element load-deflection curves for the panel are shown in Figure 6. Further details on the results can be found in [3].

6.0 DISCUSSION AND CONCLUSIONS

Following testing of the welded sub-panels, the validity of the modified analysis techniques was not proven conclusively. This was thought to be due to the empirical nature of conventional techniques. In addition, there was only a small (theoretical) loss in strength of a specimen due to laser welding (compared to an "unaffected" specimen) which was difficult to detect with the methods used. Generally, welded specimen strength was proven and no adverse behaviour was observed in the weld regions. These facts led to the conclusion that the full-size welded panels will, on testing, behave as expected and the predictions of strength and weight, given subsequently, are reasonably valid.

The non-conclusive results regarding the modified conventional analysis techniques led to retrospective analyses being performed on the welded sub-panels using the FE techniques being developed in the parallel project. A very simple modelling approach was taken with the aim of assessing the potential of FE techniques for this type of structure. The results of the sub-panel tests, the analytical predictions and the FE results are listed in subsequent sections.

Correlation between FE predictions and test data was shown to be very good, and with tightly controlled boundary conditions in tests providing experimental failure loads within 2.5% of the FE predictions. The use of FE techniques indicates a possible weight reduction of 5-12% over the conventional analytical techniques for riveted panels. The modified conventional analysis for welded panels showed a potential saving of up to 10% compared with a similar riveted panel[4]. The FE results for the welded panels also showed good correlation with the tests.

The studies indicate that considerable care must be taken with the choice of element type and density as well as the definition of model boundary conditions [6]. The studies also indicate the levels of idealisations and definition of imperfections necessary for non-linear Finite Element Models. In particular

1. For single stringer panels second order small strain thin shell elements were the most efficient for buckling analysis.

2. The separation of the skin and stringer flange under compression loading can result in a significant reduction of the buckling and failure loads of riveted panels. Riveted panels should therefore not be modelled as integral structures when accuracy is a prime consideration.

3. Current conventional techniques for riveted panels underestimate buckling and failure loads and the use of FE can result in weight savings of 5-12%.

4. Modifications to conventional analysis techniques can be applied to provide simple empirical formulae for welded constructions but a significant volume of test data would be required to provide reliable design factors.

5. Welded construction can provide weight savings over riveted panels of up to 10% for similar performance.

6. It is difficult to incorporate effects such as residual stress distributions and distortions accurately in the modified conventional analysis, and thus it will always be difficult to eliminate conservatism using this approach.

7. A common FE modelling strategy for element type, mesh density and boundary conditions provides a basis for direct comparison of panels with different construction techniques.

Use of FE to study the post buckling behaviour of stiffened panels allows for a consistent approach to assessing the performance of different construction techniques and offers both potential weight savings, due to more accurate analyses, and a basis for comparison where current methods cannot be directly compared.

ACKNOWLEDGEMENTS

This work has been carried out with the support of Bombardier Aerospace Shorts. In particular thanks are due to Ken Poston, Gary Moore and Rodney Steele of the Materials and Processes Engineering Department.

REFERENCES

1. Bruhn, E.F., *Analysis and Design of Flight Vehicle Structures*. Tri-State Offset Company, USA

2. ESDU: *Structures Sub-series*

3. Gibson, A., *An Investigation into the Strength and Behaviour of Welded, Sheet-Stringer Airframe Components in Compression*. PhD Thesis, The Queen's University of Belfast, School of Aeronautical Engineering, May 2000

4. Gibson, A., and Sterling, S., A Design And Test Programme Involving Welded Sheet-Stringer Compression Panels, . 21st ICAS Congress, Paper A98-31712, 1998

5. Rothwell, A., *Aeronautical J.*, An Experimental Investigation of the Post-buckled Efficiency of Z-Section Stringer-Skin Panels, , Vol.85, No.840, 1981, pp.29-33

6. Lynch, C.J., *A Finite Element Study of the Postbuckling Behaviour of a Flat Stiffened Panel.*. 21st ICAS Congress, Paper A98-31711, 1998

7. Skrna-Jakl, I., Stiftinger, M. and Rammerstorfer, F., *Numerical Investigations of an Imperfect Stringer-Stiffened Composite Wing Torsion Box - An Analysis Concept*, Composites, Vol.27B, No.1, 1996, pp.59-69

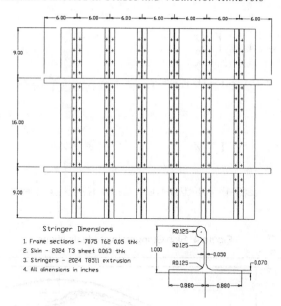

Stringer Dimensions

1. Frame sections – 7075 T62 0.05 thk
2. Skin – 2024 T3 sheet 0.063 thk
3. Stringers – 2024 T8511 extrusion
4. All dimensions in inches

Figure 1 : Riveted Base Panel Layout

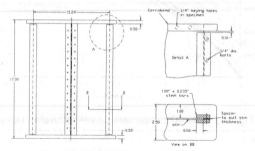

Figure 2: Riveted Sub-panel Layout

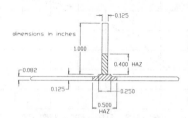

Figure 3 : Welded panel detail

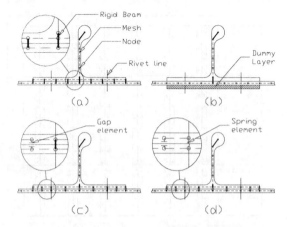

Figure 4 Skin Stringer Joint Idealisations

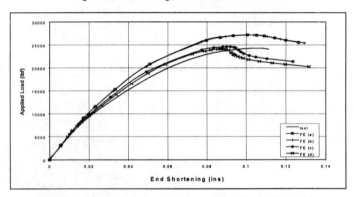

Figure 5 : Load-Displacement curves for riveted sub-panels.

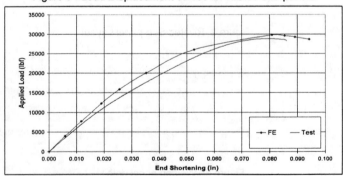

Figure 6: Load-Displacement Curves for Welded Sub-panel

REFINEMENT OF CRITICAL INTERACTION CURVES FOR RECTANGULAR PLATES BUCKLING UNDER COMBINED DIRECT COMPRESSION AND SHEAR

J.S. Munro*, J.E. Cooper* and M. Major**

This paper presents new efficient methods of determining the critical interaction curves for any rectangular plate buckling under combined loads. Example curves are obtained from the results of Finite Element Analysis predictions of plates buckling under combined direct compression and shear. These curves are then fitted by polynomials or used for interpolation so that others can be predicted for other aspect ratios. The new methods can accommodate plates of any aspect ratio or thickness and easily be extended for plates having any edge restraint or material property, including composites. Accurate estimates were obtained for a wide range of aspect ratios.

INTRODUCTION

As aircraft structural design requires greater efficiency with respect to the strength/weight ratios, a more detailed understanding of the increasingly complex elastic stability behaviour is required. One critical design criterion is the buckling of thin cross-sectional rectangular plates. In order to optimize structural efficiency, it is necessary to predict accurately the critical buckling loads of plates for the loading conditions encountered in flight.

These loading conditions usually contain more than one mode of application. For example, the bending of a wing spar will induce combinations of compression and shear within the sub-components; such as the rectangular plates that form the spar webs of each rib-bay. Both applied compressive and shearing stresses can cause a thin flat plate to fail due to buckling. Therefore the buckling behavior of thin plates under combined compression and shear is a key issue for structural designers.

This work deals with the compression and shear loads that are critical to the buckling behavior of spar webs. For a rectangular plate, uniform compression and shear loads can be applied in two modes: combined transverse compression and shear, or combined longitudinal compression and shear. When the aspect ratio (AR) is less than unity, the combined transverse compression and shear case (figure 1a) is

* Manchester School Of Engineering, University Of Manchester, Oxford Road, Manchester, M13 9PL, UK

**BAE Systems-Airbus, Chester Road, Woodford, Cheshire, SK7 1QR,UK

important, whereas when AR is greater than one, the combined longitudinal compression and shear case (figure 1b) occurs.

The *stress-ratio* method is employed to predict the buckling behaviour of plates under different ratios of combined loads. A detailed description of this method is given by Shanley and Ryder [1]. Essentially, non-dimensional stress ratios are defined where R_c = ratio of applied compressive stress to the critical buckling compressive stress and R_s = ratio of applied shear stress to critical buckling shear stress. The two ratios can be plotted against each other to determine the effect of one loading condition upon the other. An example of such an interaction curve for a plate buckling under uniform combined transverse compression and shear is given in figure 2.

A number of different ways of modelling the buckling behaviour of such plates have been used, however, the commonly used general interaction curve is only applicable to plates of aspect ratio close to unity.

This paper presents two different approaches for obtaining interaction curves for a range of plates having different geometries, materials and boundary conditions that are subject to combined loadings. Of particular note is the ability to deal with a wide range of aspect ratios. The methods are demonstrated upon a number of examples and are shown to give accurate estimates for all aspect ratios.

Analytical Methods

There are two classical theoretical methods used to predict the interaction behavior of plates acting under combined loads:

1) Exact solution of the differential equation [2,3,4]

The exact solution of the differential equation was first solved by Southwell and Skan [6] to obtain the critical load of an infinitely long plate with simply supported and fully clamped edges buckling under pure shear. This was later solved for an infinitely long flat plate with edges elastically restrained, buckling under combined shear and direct stress by Stowell and Schwartz [4]. They found that if the edge restraint provided by the stiffeners is that of simple support, then the relationship between the stress ratios R_c and R_s is governed by the following general interaction equation

$$R_c + R_s^{\,2} = 1 \tag{1}$$

The exact solution of the differential equation of equilibrium is practical only for the simple cases of infinitely long plates. The solution becomes too laborious when applied to plates of finite length. In order to obtain critical buckling loads for finite length plates the Energy Method, described next, is much simpler to apply.

2) Approximate solution using the Energy Method [2,4,5]

The Energy Method was initially investigated by Timoshenko and Gere [2]. It was first applied to the case of plates buckling under combined compression and shear by Hopkins and Rao [5]. They concluded that the general interaction equation derived by Stowell and Schwartz [4] "...is very nearly independent of the ratio a/b". This conclusion became the basis of the widely used E.S.D.U. data sheet 02.04.01 [7]. However, subsequent work, such as that of Bartdorf and Stein [3] and the findings of this paper have shown that the general interaction equation is true for only a limited range of aspect ratios (0.5 ≤ a/b ≤ 1) acting under the combined transverse compression and shear load case. For longitudinal compression and shear, equation (1) is reasonably accurate for all aspect ratios.

FINITE ELEMENT ANALYSIS

The main objective of the work described in this paper was to develop a generic method for generating interaction curves. Accurate curves could then be generated for realistic aerospace plates without relying on a multitude of design charts, such as the E.S.D.U. data sheets [7].

A series of FE models having a range of combinations of applied uni-axial compression and uniform shear stresses were generated. A Linear Buckling Prediction was calculated for each load combination and the critical buckling compressive and shearing stresses determined. These critical stresses, along with the relevant applied stresses produce the stress ratios, were used to create the critical interaction curves.

Prior to considering a range of edge restraints, the simply supported and fully clamped cases were analyzed as they give the upper and lower bounds to buckling behaviour. This paper gives the results for these extreme cases. If the actual edge restraint provided by an edge stiffener is to be considered, the FE model has to be amended in order to incorporate these effects.

The F.E. generated curves were found to be in good agreement with curves predicted by Bartdorf and Stein [3]. Figure 3a shows the F.E. generated curves for simply supported plates acting under combined shear and transverse compression, with aspect ratios of 0.1 to 1. It shows the inaccuracy of using the general interaction equation for aspect ratios less than 0.5. Figure 3b gives the FE results for the case of combined shear and longitudinal compression, aspect ratios of 1 to 10. These curves are very similar to the general interaction curve. Figure 4 shows the curves for the case of fully clamped plates under combined shear and transverse compression.

CURVE FITTING THE FE RESULTS

Although it would be possible to use FE to solve every case, this is not feasible when there are a large number of cases to consider. The aim of this work was to use a number of FE calculations and then to fit these results in order to obtain the interaction curves. Three methods of fitting the F.E. generated data are considered in this paper. The methods were tested for the case of 5mm thick Aluminium rectangular plates, having all four edges restrained as either simply supported or fully clamped. Only the combined shear and transverse compression load case was considered as plates buckling under longitudinal compression and shear were proven to have interaction curves that are accurately predicted by the general interaction curve.

Least Squares Curve Fitting, Using A Coefficient Representing Aspect Ratio

The general interaction curve of equation (1) is inaccurate for rectangular plates with aspect ratios less than approx. 0.5, buckling under combined shear and transverse compression. The approach taken here was to modify equation (1) as some form of polynomial including the effects of aspect ratio and to curve-fit the FE data to find the values of the polynomial coefficients. The resulting interaction curves then become more accurate.

By examining the F.E. generated interaction curves shown in figure 3a the following boundary conditions of the system are found

1)   when $R_s = 0$, $R_c = 1$

2)   when $\dfrac{dR_c}{dR_s} = 0$, $R_s = 0$

3)   when $R_c = 0$, $R_s = 1$

Substituting these boundary conditions into a general polynomial of the nth order gives:

$$R_c = 1 - R_s^2 + A_3(R_s^3 - R_s^2) + A_4(R_s^4 - R_s^2) + ... + A_n(R_s^n - R_s^2) \qquad (2)$$

Several orders of polynomial were tested, but it was found that any order greater than the third gave rise to unacceptably high non-linearity in the relationship between the coefficients A_n and aspect ratio. A 3rd order polynomial produced the modified general interaction equation

$$R_c = 1 - R_s^2 + A(R_s^3 - R_s^2) \qquad (3)$$

which has only a single unknown coefficient A. By curvefitting the R_c and R_s values for a given aspect ratio, the A coefficient was found using a Least Squares curvefit. The A values were plotted against aspect ratio and a 6th order least squares polynomial fit was used to give accurate values of A for any aspect ratio within the range of the known data (AR = 0.1→1). Figure 5 shows how the 6th order polynomial models the relationship between A and aspect ratio.

Interaction curves could then be found for any plates buckling under combined transverse compression and shear, with aspect ratios in the range of 0.1 to 1. The value of coefficient A for the desired aspect ratio was taken from figure 5 and substituted into equation (3). A range of values of R_s between 0 and 1 were chosen and the corresponding R_c values estimated for the coefficient A using equation 3.

The method was tested for aspect ratios of 0.5 and 0.1 and the resulting interaction curves can be compared with the F.E. generated curves in figure 6. The percentage difference between curves generated by the F.E. method and this curve fitting method was found by using the expression.

$$\text{percentage difference} = \frac{\text{FE value - Estimated value}}{\text{FE value}} \qquad (4)$$

At most the differences between the two curves were ± 6% for the range $0<R_s<0.5$ and ± 30% for $0.5<R_s<1$. These results are substantially better than using the general interaction curve.

Least Squares Curve Fitting Considering Buckling Mode Shapes

Although the above curve fitting method gave more accurate curves than the general interaction equation, it was felt that the method could be improved upon. Close inspection of the curve for AR = 0.1 in figure 6 shows that there is a discontinuity around $R_s = 0.6$. In fact there are a number of these discontinuities. These result from changes in critical buckling mode shape of the deformed plate around this aspect ratio. An example of changing critical mode shape is illustrated in figure 7. It shows that a plate of aspect ratio 0.25 has three critical buckling mode shapes for the range of combinations of applied loads.

Upon examining the buckling mode shapes of all the F.E. modeled aspect ratios it became apparent that the number of changes between mode shapes increases as the aspect ratios approach zero for the case of combined transverse compression and shear. For combined longitudinal compression and shear it was found that the change in mode shape had no significant effect on the shape of the interaction curves, so the general interaction equation still holds true for any aspect ratio. Again, this is in agreement with the findings of Bartdorf and Stein [3].

Each individual buckling mode shape can be accurately modeled with a relatively low order polynomial. Consequently, the critical interaction curve could then be constructed by knowing the curves of each mode shape and the intersection points where changes between modes occur. A series of low order polynomials can thus predict the number of changes and the load combination at which these changes occur, for any aspect ratio in the F.E. examined range.

A buckling mode shape is defined as the number of deflected sinusoidal ½-waves in the x and y directions. It is possible to obtain the mode shape by post-processing F.E. results visually. However, this process was automated and incorporated into the post-processor developed for this work. The F.E. results were used to produce interaction curves for each buckling mode shape. The curves of each mode shape were fitted by a 3rd order polynomial having the form of equation (3).

A database was created containing all coefficients and positions of change in mode shape. For the full range of shear stress ratios of 0 to 1, each position of change in mode shape was plotted against aspect ratio, as shown in figure 8. There is no change in mode shape for plates of aspect ratio greater than 0.5 as expected from the work of Timoshenko and Gere [2].

The post-processor referenced the database and predicted the position and number of changes in critical mode shape for any aspect ratio in the range of 0.1 to 1. Thus it was possible to decide which of the coefficients to be used in the third order polynomial, so creating the correct interaction curve for that critical mode shape.

A selection of predicted curves are compared with F.E. generated curves for aspect ratios of 0.1 to 0.45, in increments of 0.05. The curves are in very good agreement with F.E. and the percentage difference (calculated using equation 4) between the two methods is found to be at most ± 2% for $0 < R_s < 0.7$, and ± 10% for $0.7 < R_s < 1$.

Two Dimensional Surface Interpolation

The third method examined in this paper uses 2D surface interpolation to predict critical interaction curves. The interaction data produced by the FE analysis can be arranged and plotted with aspect ratio as a third axis, added to the two axes (R_s and R_c) of a normal interaction curve. An example 2D surface plot showing critical interaction behavior for simply supported plates under combined transverse compression and shear is given in figure 9.

It is possible to predict curves for aspect ratios not modeled by FE by interpolating between the interaction curves of known aspect ratio. There are many established methods of performing 2D surface interpolation between known points. A Delauny Triangulation method was used for interpolating between scattered data points.

A limitation of this method is that it is not capable of predicting the buckling mode shapes of the non-modeled aspect ratio, but this may not be of significance for preliminary design studies of buckling structures. This method provides the most accurate means of predicting interaction curves, with percentage differences between the curves of this method and F.E. being at most ± 2% for $0 < R_s < 1$.

510

CONCLUSIONS

A Finite Element Analysis based method has been developed that accurately predicts the interaction curves of plates buckling under combined load cases. Having obtained a database of interaction curves using the FE analysis, three curve-fitting methods were used to obtain general models that include the effect of aspect ratio. The fitted models can then be used to determine the interaction curves for any aspect ratio.

All of the methods obtained vastly superior results compared to the conventional general interaction curve. It was found that the approach based upon a surface fit gave the best results. The method could easily be extended to consider plates with more complicated geometries or boundary conditions.

SYMBOLS

a	length of plate
b	height of plate
a/b	aspect ratio of plate
R_c	compressive stress ratio
R_s	shear stress ratio
A	arbitrary coefficient

REFERENCES

(1) Shanley, F. R., and Ryder, E. I, *Aviation*, Vol. 36, No. 6, 1937, pp. 28-70.

(2) Timoshenko, S. P., and Gere, J. M., *Theory Of Elastic Stability*, McGraw-Hill, Singapore, 1931, ISBN 0-07-Y85821-7

(3) Bartdorf, S. B., and Stein, M., Critical Combinations Of Shear And Direct Stress For Simply Supported Rectangular Flat Plates, *NACA Technical Note 1223*, 1947.

(4) Stowell, E. Z., and Schwartz, E. B., Critical Stress For An Infinitely long Flat Plate With Elastically Restrained Edges Under Combined Shear And Direct Stress, *NACA ARR 3k13*, 1943

(5) Hopkins, H. G., and Rao, B. A., The Initial Buckling Of Flat Rectangular Panels Under Combined Shear And Compression, *Aeronautical Research Council's Reports And Memoranda*, No. 1965, Vol. 2, March 1943, pp. 1-8.

(6) Southwell, R. V., and Skan, S. W., On The Stability Under Shearing Forces Of A Flat Elastic Strip, *Proceedings Of the Royal Society.*, No. 133:582, Vol. 105, May 1924, pp. 582-607.

(7) E.S.D.U. Data Sheet 02.04.01., Buckling Stress Ratios For Plates Under Uniform Compression And Shear, *Engineering Sciences Data Unit Ltd.*, 1976.

FIGURE 1   Examples of rectangular plates under the two modes of loading application; uniform combined compression and shear.

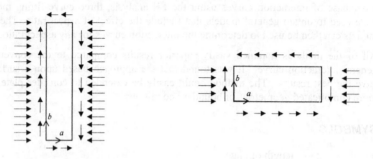

a) Transverse compression and shear
$a < 1, b = 1$

b) Longitudinal compression and shear
$a > 1, b = 1$

FIGURE 2   The *general interaction curve* relating R_c to R_s, where the relationship is defined by the *general interaction equation* of equation 1.

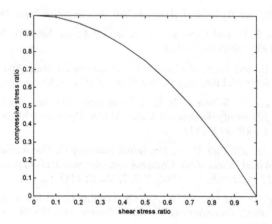

FIGURE 3   F.E. generated critical interaction curves for simply supported plates buckling under combined compression and shear.

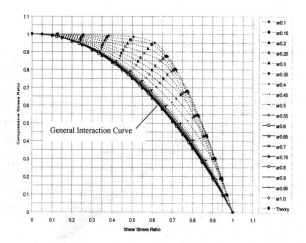

a) Transverse compression and shear

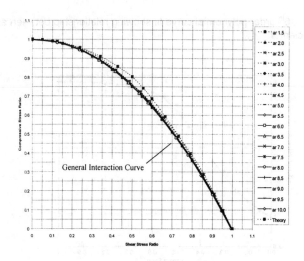

b) Longitudinal compression and shear

FIGURE 4   F.E. generated critical interaction curves for fully clamped plates
buckling under combined transverse compression and shear.

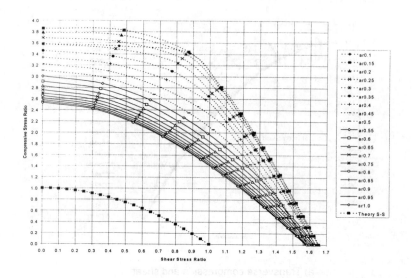

FIGURE 5   6th order polynomial curve fit showing relationship between aspect
ratio and coefficient A.

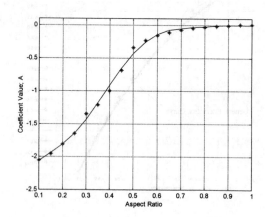

FIGURE 6   Interaction curves generated by Finite Element Analysis and Least Squares Curve Fitting, using a coefficient representing aspect ratio.

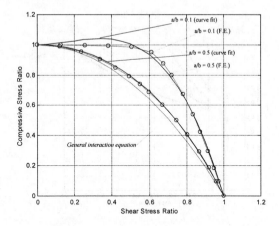

FIGURE 7   Interaction curves of individual buckling mode shapes that form the critical interaction curve for simply supported plate of aspect ratio 0.25

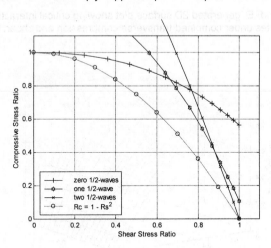

515

FIGURE 8 R_s values of changes in critical mode shape for simply supported plates buckling under combined transverse compression and shear.

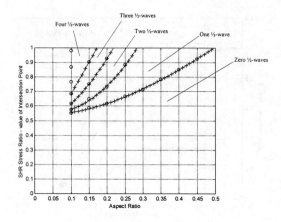

FIGURE 9   F.E. generated 2D surface plot showing critical interaction behaviour of plates under combined transverse compression and shear.

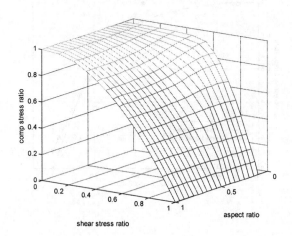

AUTHOR INDEX

517